Algebra and Trigonometry

Second Edition

Algebra and Trigonometry

Second Edition

Margaret L. Lial / Charles D. Miller

American River College

Scott, Foresman and Company   **Glenview, Illinois**

Dallas, Tex.   Oakland, N.J.   Palo Alto, Cal.   Tucker, Ga.   London, England

Paper sculpture by Joyce Culkin.

Library of Congress Cataloging in Publishing Data

Lial, Margaret L.
  Algebra and trigonometry
  Includes index.
  1. Algebra. 2. Trigonometry. I. Miller, Charles David, 1942−
joint author. II. Title
QA154.2.L49   1980   512′.13   80−26

ISBN 0-673-15272-3

Certain portions of this book were previously published in *College Algebra, 2nd ed,* Copyright © 1977 Scott, Foresman and Company, and *Trigonometry,* Copyright © 1977 Scott, Foresman and Company.

1 2 3 4 5 6-KPF-84 83 82 81 80

Preface

The Second Edition of *Algebra and Trigonometry* prepares students for further work in mathematics. In particular, this book offers a thorough and complete preparation for calculus. The only prerequisite we have assumed is a previous course in algebra. Nevertheless, the book offers a brief review of high-school algebra, followed by a solid introduction to those ideas needed in later courses.

The following features are found in *Algebra and Trigonometry:*

- The text is rigorous yet accessible. We avoid making statements that need to be "corrected" in later courses. At the same time, we realize that mathematical accuracy does no good if a student cannot read it.

- We take a fresh approach to the topics of high-school algebra. We try to maintain students' interest by doing things in a way they haven't seen.

- This book has one of the best treatments of word problems. Methods of solving word problems are presented using techniques of *How to Solve It* by George Polya. Word problems are then presented in exercise sections throughout the text.

- Calculator exercises carefully integrate the advantages of the calculator.

- Each chapter ends with a large number of review exercises which review and expand on the ideas of the chapter.

- Most review-exercise sets end with a selection of exercises from standard calculus texts. These exercises show the topics of the chapter as used in calculus.

- Trigonometry is presented carefully through a unit-circle approach. The analytic aspects are emphasized.

- Numerical applications of trigonometry are grouped in a separate chapter.

- The Instructor's Manual features answers to even-numbered exercises, a large group of additional exercises which may be used for test preparation or additional student practice, and solutions to a large number of exercises in the text.

Many people helped in the preparation of this book. In particular, help far beyond that normally provided by a reviewer came from Douglas Hall, Michigan State University, and Marc Hale, University of Florida. Editors Michael Timins and Pamela Carlson worked long and hard to make this book useable by instructors and students alike.

Margaret L. Lial

Charles D. Miller

Contents

◉ Introduction on Calculators

Throughout this book you will find exercises designed for use with a calculator. These exercises are identified by the symbol ◉. Some instructors will assign these exercises; others may not. Even if these exercises are not assigned, you should still work on them. We are now in the calculator age, and ability to use calculators will be assumed when you get to more advanced classes or when you get a job.

You don't really need a scientific calculator for the great bulk of our calculator exercises—for the most part, a calculator with a square-root key will be sufficient. However, if you do plan to do much further work in mathematics you may want to consider the purchase of a scientific calculator. The price of the basic models of these calculators is not much more than the price of this textbook. Scientific calculators offer the advantage of doing away with most tables; it is not necessary to look up logarithms or antilogarithms, for example. This can save a lot of time, especially in the trigonometry portion of the course. However, a basic calculator together with the tables in this book is really all you need for most of the exercises in this book.

How sophisticated a calculator do you want to buy? It is a waste of money to buy one with more features than you will ever need. On the other hand, you should try to get those features that you expect to use in the future. Here are some features to consider when looking at calculators.

Memory.   A memory is an electronic scratch pad. You can store intermediate calculations in the memory and then recall them later. This feature is very helpful and usually adds only a few dollars to the cost of a calculator.

Automatic Constant.   The formula for the circumference of a circle is $C = 2\pi r$. To find the circumference of a circle, you would have to enter r and then multiply by 2 times π. If you had to do this for a great many circles, you could save time by finding 2 times π and then activating the automatic constant key. In this way, for every circle you need to do calculations for, you need enter only r and then push the multiplication key in order to get $2\pi r$ displayed. For each value of r you enter, the answer would be displayed automatically.

Scientific Notation.   Machines with this feature usually have a key labeled EE. Using this key, numbers can be entered into the machine in scientific notation, so that numbers from 1×10^{-99} to $9.999999999 \times 10^{99}$ may be used. Very large and very small numbers such as these occur often in science.

Logarithms.   Logarithms, both common logarithms and natural logarithms (which we study in detail in Chapter 5), occur again and again in mathematics. You will very likely use this key enough to make its purchase worthwhile.

Trigonometric Functions.   Again, these keys will come in very handy in this course as well as in further work in mathematics, physics, or engineering.

Powers and Roots.   These functions are used often in mathematical work.

Statistical Functions.   Some machines do factorials, mean, standard deviation, and linear regression. Will you need these?

There are two types of logic in common use on calculators today. Both algebraic and Reverse Polish Notation (RPN) have advantages and disadvantages. Algebraic logic is the easiest to learn. For example, the problem $8 + 17$ is entered into an algebraic machine by pressing

$$8 + 17 = .$$

On a machine with Reverse Polish Notation, this same problem would be entered as

$$8 \text{ ENTER } 17 + .$$

Some people claim that Reverse Polish machines work advanced problems more easily than algebraic machines. Others claim that algebraic machines are easier to use for the great bulk of ordinary, common problems. It's up to you to decide which to buy. Our recommendation: one of us has a Reverse Polish machine and the other has an algebraic machine.

A common mistake when working with calculators is to give the answer to more accuracy than is warranted by the original data. Almost all numbers encountered in real-world problems are approximations.

If we measure a wall to the nearest meter and say that it is 18 meters long, then we are really saying that the wall has a length between the range of 17.5 meters and 18.5 meters. If we measure the wall more accurately and say that it is 18.3 meters long, then we know that its length is really between the range 18.25 meters and 18.35 meters. A measurement of 18.00 meters would indicate that the wall's length is between the range 17.995 and 18.005 meters. The measurement 18 meters is said to have 2 significant digits of accuracy; 18.3 has 3 significant digits and 18.00 has 4.

In general, to find the number of **significant digits** in a measurement, count from left to right, starting at the first nonzero digit and counting to the right to the last digit.

The following chart shows some numbers, the number of significant digits in each number, and the range represented by each number.

Number	Number of significant digits	Range represented by number
29.6	3	29.55 to 29.65
1.39	3	1.385 to 1.395
.000096	2	.0000955 to .0000965
.03	1	.025 to .035
100.2	4	100.15 to 100.25

There is one possible place for trouble when finding significant digits. We know that the measurement 19.00 meters is a measurement to the nearest hundredth meter. What about the measurement 93,000 meters? Does it represent a measurement to the nearest meter? the nearest ten meters? hundred meters?

thousand meters? We cannot tell by the way the number is written. To get around this problem, we write the number in **scientific notation,** the product of a number between 1 and 10 and a power of 10. Depending on what we know about the accuracy of the measurement, we could write 93,000 using scientific notation as follows.

Measurement to nearest . . .	Scientific notation	Number of significant digits
Meter	9.3000×10^4	5
Ten meters	9.300×10^4	4
Hundred meters	9.30×10^4	3
Thousand meters	9.3×10^4	2

When calculating with approximate data, use the following rules:

1. For *adding and subtracting,* add or subtract normally, and then round the answer so that the last digit you keep is in the right-most column in which all the numbers have significant digits.

2. When *multiplying or dividing,* round your answers to the *least* number of significant digits found in any of the given numbers.

3. For *powers and roots,* round the answer so that it has the same number of significant digits as the number whose power or root you are finding.

Exercises *The following numbers represent approximate measurements. State the range represented by each of the measures.*

1. 5 pounds
2. 8 feet
3. 9.6 tons
4. 7.8 quarts
5. 8.95 meters
6. 2.37 kilometers
7. 19.7 liters
8. 32 centimeters
9. 253.741 meters
10. 47.358 ounces

11. When the area around Mt. Everest was first surveyed, the surveyors obtained a height of 29,000 feet to the nearest foot. State the range represented by this number. (The surveyors felt that no one would believe a measurement of 29,000 feet, so they reported it as 29,002.)

12. At Denny's, a chain of restaurants, the Low-Cal Special is said to have "approximately 472 calories." What is the range of calories represented by this number? By claiming "approximately 472 calories," they are probably claiming more accuracy than is possible. In your opinion, what might be a better claim?

Give the number of significant digits in each of the following.

13. 21.8
14. 37
15. 42.08
16. 600.9
17. 31.00
18. 20,000
19. 3.9×10^7
20. 5.43×10^3
21. 2.7100×10^4
22. 3.7000×10^3

Round each of the following numbers to three significant digits. Then refer to the original numbers and round each to two significant digits.

23. 768.7   **26.** 28.17   **29.** 7.125   **31.** 11.55

24. 921.3   **27.** 9.003   **30.** 9.375   **32.** 9.155

25. 12.53   **28.** 1.700

Use a calculator to work the following problems to the correct number of significant digits.

33. $(8.742)^2$

34. $(.98352)^2$

35. $\dfrac{.746}{.092}$

36. $\dfrac{.375}{.005792}$

37. $(.425)(89.3)(746,000)$

38. $\dfrac{1.0000}{897.62}$

39. $\dfrac{3.0000}{521.84}$

40. $\dfrac{2.000}{(74.83)(.0251)}$

41. $\dfrac{1.000}{(.0900)^2 + (3.21)^2}$

42. $\dfrac{(6.93)^2 + (21.74)^2}{(38.76)^2 - 29.4}$

43. $\dfrac{8.92}{[(3.14)^2 + 2.79]^2}$

44. $\dfrac{4.63 - (2.158)^2}{[(5.728)^2 - 33.9142]}$

45. $\sqrt{74.689}$

46. $\sqrt{215.89}$

47. $\sqrt{89,000,000}$

48. $\sqrt{253,000}$

49. $\dfrac{1.00}{\sqrt{28.6} + \sqrt{49.3}}$

50. $\dfrac{4.00}{\sqrt{59.7} - \sqrt{74.6}}$

51. $\dfrac{-5.000(2.143)}{\sqrt{.009826}}$

52. $\dfrac{78.9(258.6)}{\sqrt{.05382}}$

53. $6.0(7.4896) + 58\sqrt{79.42} - 38(489.7)$

54. $128.9(3.02) + 97.6(.0589) - \sqrt{700.9}$

55. $\left[\dfrac{89^2(25.8) + (314.2)(5.098) - \sqrt{910.593}}{258(.0972) - \sqrt{104.38} + (65.923)^2}\right]^2$

56. $\left[\dfrac{(.00900)(74)}{1.0 - (.0382)\sqrt{741.6} + \sqrt{98.32}}\right]^2$

Chapter 1

Fundamentals
of Algebra

Why study algebra and trigonometry? For many students, the answer is "It's required." Today, this course is required for students in a great variety of fields, ranging from accounting, through engineering and physical science, to zoology. This course is also needed as preparation for calculus, itself required for many majors. The reason that all these fields require mathematics is that mathematics is *useful* in them. Equations, graphs, functions, and the other topics we study occur again and again in many different areas.

To begin, we review the basics of algebra in this first chapter.

1.1 The Real Numbers

Numbers are the foundation of mathematics. The most common numbers in mathematics are the **real numbers,** which are all the numbers that can be written as a decimal, either repeating, such as

$$\frac{1}{3} = .33333 \ldots$$

$$\frac{3}{4} = .75000 \ldots$$

$$2\frac{4}{7} = 2.571428571428 \ldots$$

or nonrepeating, such as

$$\sqrt{2} = 1.4142135 \ldots$$

$$\pi = 3.14159 \ldots .$$

There are four fundamental operations on real numbers: addition, subtraction, multiplication, and division. Addition is indicated with the symbol $+$. Subtraction is written with the symbol $-$, as in $8 - 2 = 6$. Multiplication is written in a variety of ways. All the symbols 2×8, $2 \cdot 8$, $2(8)$, and $(2)(8)$ represent the product of 2 and 8, or 16. When writing products involving variables (letters used to represent numbers), no operation symbols may be necessary: $2x$ represents the product of 2 and x, while xy indicates the product of x and y. Division of real numbers a and b is written $a \div b$, or more commonly a/b.

The set of real numbers, together with the relation of equality and the operations of addition and multiplication, forms the **real number system**. This system is an example of a mathematical system called a **field**.

The key properties of the real numbers that we shall need are as follows.

Properties of the Real Numbers

For all real numbers a, b, and c,

closure properties	$a + b$ is a real number.
	ab is a real number.
commutative properties	$a + b = b + a$.
	$ab = ba$.
associative properties	$(a + b) + c = a + (b + c)$.
	$(ab)c = a(bc)$.
identity properties	There exists a unique real number 0 such that

$$a + 0 = a \quad \text{and} \quad 0 + a = a.$$

There exists a unique real number 1 such that

$$a \cdot 1 = a \quad \text{and} \quad 1 \cdot a = a.$$

inverse properties   There exists a unique real number $-a$ such that

$$a + (-a) = 0 \quad \text{and} \quad (-a) + a = 0.$$

If $a \neq 0$, there exists a unique real number $1/a$ such that

$$a \cdot \frac{1}{a} = 1 \quad \text{and} \quad \frac{1}{a} \cdot a = 1.$$

distributive property $a(b + c) = ab + ac$.

Example 1   By the closure properties, the sum or product of two real numbers is a real number. Thus,

(a) $4 + 5$ is a real number, 9.

(b) $-9(-4)$ is a real number, 36.

(c) $8 \cdot 0$ is a real number, 0.

(d) $\sqrt{5} + \sqrt{3}$ is a real number.

(e) $\sqrt{2} \cdot \sqrt{11}$ is a real number.   ▌

Example 2   The following statements are examples of the commutative property. Notice that the order of the numbers changes from one side of the equal sign to the other.

(a) $6 + x = x + 6$

(b) $(6 + x) + 9 = (x + 6) + 9$

(c) $(6 + x) + 9 = 9 + (6 + x)$

(d) $5 \cdot (9 \cdot 8) = (9 \cdot 8) \cdot 5$

(e) $5 \cdot (9 \cdot 8) = 5 \cdot (8 \cdot 9)$. ▌

The associative properties are used when we have three numbers to add or multiply. For example, the associative property for addition says that to find the sum

$$a + b + c$$

of the real numbers a, b, and c, we can associate a and b, adding as follows

$$(a + b) + c;$$

or we may associate b and c,

$$a + (b + c).$$

Either method by the associative property gives the same result.

Example 3 The following statements are examples of the associative properties. Here the order of the numbers does not change, but the placement of the parentheses does change.

(a) $4 + (9 + 8) = (4 + 9) + 8$

(b) $3(9x) = (3 \cdot 9)x$

(c) $(\sqrt{3} + \sqrt{7}) + 2\sqrt{6} = \sqrt{3} + (\sqrt{7} + 2\sqrt{6})$. ▌

The identity properties show the special properties of the numbers 0 and 1. If we find the sum of 0 and any real number a, we get the number a for an answer. Thus, 0 preserves the identity of a number under addition. For this reason, 0 is the **identity element for addition.** In the same way, 1 preserves the identity of a real number a under multiplication. Thus, 1 is the **identity element for multiplication.**

Example 4 By the identity properties,

(a) $-8 + 0 = -8$

(b) $(-9)1 = -9$. ▌

According to the inverse properties, if we start with any real number a, we will be able to find a real number, written $-a$, such that the sum of these two numbers is 0, or $a + (-a) = 0$. The number $-a$ is called the **additive inverse** or **negative** of a.

Don't confuse the *negative of a number* with a *negative number*. Since a is a variable, it can represent a positive or a negative number (as well as zero). The negative of a, written $-a$, can also be either a negative or a positive number (or zero). Don't make the common mistake of thinking that $-a$ *must* be a negative number. For example, if a is -3, then $-a$ is $-(-3)$ or 3.

For each real number a (except 0) there is a real number $1/a$ such that the product of a and $1/a$ is 1, or

$$a \cdot \frac{1}{a} = 1 \qquad (a \neq 0).$$

The number $1/a$ is called the **multiplicative inverse** or **reciprocal** of the number a. Every real number except 0 has a reciprocal.

Example 5 By the inverse properties,

(a) $9 + (-9) = 0$

(b) $-15 + 15 = 0$

(c) $6 \cdot \dfrac{1}{6} = 1$

(d) $-8 \cdot \left(\dfrac{1}{-8}\right) = 1$

(e) $\dfrac{1}{\sqrt{5}} \cdot \sqrt{5} = 1$

(f) There is no real number x such that $0 \cdot x = 1$, so that 0 has no inverse for multiplication. ▍

One of the most important properties, and the only one that involves both addition and multiplication, is the distributive property. The next example shows how this property is applied.

Example 6 By the distributive property,

(a) $9(6 + 4) = 9 \cdot 6 + 9 \cdot 4$

(b) $3(x + y) = 3x + 3y$

(c) $-\sqrt{5}(m + 2) = -\sqrt{5}m - 2\sqrt{5}.$ ▍

The distributive property can be extended to include more than two numbers in the sum, as follows.

$$a(b + c + d + e + \ldots + n) = ab + ac + ad + ae + \ldots + an.$$

This form is called the *extended distributive property.*

Another key property is called the **substitution property:**

If $a = b$, then a may replace b in any expression without affecting the truth or falsity of the statement.

Many further properties of the real numbers can be proved directly from those given above. Two of the most important of these properties will be used in the next chapter, when we solve equations. For real numbers a, b, and c,

$$\boxed{\begin{array}{l} \text{If } a = b, \text{ then } a + c = b + c \\ \text{If } a = b, \text{ then } ac = bc. \end{array}}$$

In words, these properties say that the same number may be added or multiplied on both sides of an equation.

Further properties that come from the rules above include the following: For all real numbers a and b,

$$a \cdot 0 = 0$$
$$\text{If } ab = 0, \text{ then } a = 0 \text{ or } b = 0$$
$$-(-a) = a$$
$$-a(b) = -(ab)$$
$$a(-b) = -(ab)$$
$$(-a)(-b) = ab$$

The proofs of many of these properties are included in Exercises 61–66 below.

Example 7 If a is a real number, prove that

$$-(-a) = a.$$

We shall prove that both $-(-a)$ and a are additive inverses of $-a$. Since a real number has only one additive inverse, this will show that $-(-a)$ and a are equal. First,

$$-a + [-(-a)] = 0$$

since $-(-a)$ is the additive inverse of $-a$. Also,

$$a + (-a) = 0$$

since $-a$ is the additive inverse of a. Since both $-(-a)$ and a are additive inverses of $-a$, and since $-a$ has only one additive inverse, we must have

$$-(-a) = a. \quad \blacksquare$$

The properties above apply to addition or multiplication. Two other common operations for the real numbers are subtraction and division. These two operations are defined in terms of the operations of addition and multiplication, respectively.

Subtraction is defined by saying that the difference of the numbers a and b, written $a - b$, is

$$a - b = a + (-b).$$

That is, to subtract b from a, add a and the additive inverse of b.

Example 8 (a) $7 - 2 = 7 + (-2) = 5$

(b) $-8 - (-3) = -8 + (+3) = -5$

(c) $6 - (-15) = 6 + (+15) = 21$

(d) $-\dfrac{1}{2} - \left(-\dfrac{2}{3}\right) = -\dfrac{1}{2} + \left(+\dfrac{2}{3}\right) = \dfrac{1}{6} \quad \blacksquare$

Division of a real number a by a nonzero real number b is defined as follows.

$$\frac{a}{b} = a \cdot \frac{1}{b}$$

That is, to divide a by b, multiply a by the reciprocal of b.

Example 9 (a) $\dfrac{6}{3} = 6 \cdot \dfrac{1}{3} = 2$

(b) $\dfrac{-8}{4} = -8 \cdot \dfrac{1}{4} = -2$

(c) $\dfrac{-9}{0}$ is meaningless since there is no reciprocal for 0;

also, $\dfrac{0}{0}$ is meaningless. ▮

To avoid possible ambiguity when working problems, use the following **order of operations,** which has been generally agreed upon. (By the way, this order of operations is used by computers and many calculators.)

1. First, do any work inside parentheses or brackets.
2. Perform any multiplications or divisions, in order, from left to right.
3. Do any additions or subtractions, in order, from left to right.
4. If the problem involves a fraction bar, treat the numerator and the denominator separately.

Example 10 Use the order of operations given above to simplify the following.

(a) $6 \div 3 + 2 \cdot 4 = 2 + 2 \cdot 4 = 2 + 8 = 10$

(b) $\dfrac{-9(-3) + (-5)}{2(-8) - 5(3)} = \dfrac{27 + (-5)}{-16 - 15}$

$= \dfrac{22}{-31}$

$= -\dfrac{22}{31}$ ▮

The set of real numbers is perhaps the most useful single set of numbers that we shall use. Several subsets* of the set of real numbers come up so often that they are given special names.

whole numbers	$\{0, 1, 2, 3, 4, 5, \ldots\}$
integers	$\{\ldots, -3, -2, -1, 0, 1, 2, 3, \ldots\}$
rational numbers	$\{$all numbers of the form p/q, where p and q are integers, with $q \neq 0\}$, or $\{$all repeating decimals$\}$
irrational numbers	$\{$all nonrepeating decimals$\}$

Example 11 If $A = \{-8, -6, -3/4, 0, 3/8, 1/2, 1, \sqrt{2}, \sqrt{5}, 6, 21/3, \sqrt{-1}\}$, then

(a) the whole numbers in set A are 0, 1, 6, 21/3 (or 7).
(b) the integers are $-8, -6, 0, 1, 6, 21/3$ (or 7).
(c) the rational numbers are $-8, -6, -3/4, 0, 3/8, 1/2, 1, 6, 21/3$ (or 7).

---

*Set A is a **subset** of set B if every element of set A is also an element of set B.

(d) the irrational numbers are $\sqrt{2}$ and $\sqrt{5}$. (It can be shown that these numbers do not have repeating or terminating decimal expansions).

(e) all elements of A are real numbers except $\sqrt{-1}$. Square roots of negative numbers are discussed in Chapter 10. ▌

1.1 Exercises   *Identify the properties which are illustrated in each of the following. Some will require more than one property. Assume all variables represent real numbers.*

1. $8 \cdot 9 = 9 \cdot 8$

2. $3 + (-3) = 0$

3. $3 + (-3) = (-3) + 3$

4. $0 + (-7) = (-7) + 0$

5. $-7 + 0 = -7$

6. $8 + (12 + 6) = (8 + 12) + 6$

7. $[9(-3)] \cdot 2 = 9[(-3) \cdot 2]$

8. $8(m + 4) = 8m + 8 \cdot 4$

9. If x is a real number, then $x + 2$ is a real number.

10. $(7 - y) + 0 = 7 - y$

11. $8(4 + 2) = (2 + 4)8$

12. $x \cdot \dfrac{1}{x} + x \cdot \dfrac{1}{x} = x\left(\dfrac{1}{x} + \dfrac{1}{x}\right)$ (if $x \neq 0$)

For Exercises 13–22, tell if the statement is true or false. If it is false, tell why.

13. By the identity property, $8 \cdot 0 = 0$.

14. By the identity property, $8 + 1 = 9$.

15. The sum of two whole numbers is always a whole number.

16. The quotient of two whole numbers is always a whole number.

17. The quotient of two rational numbers is always a rational number.

18. The difference of two real numbers is always a real number.

19. The set $\{0, 1\}$ is closed with respect to subtraction.

20. The set $\{0, 1\}$ is closed with respect to multiplication.

21. The set $\{1, -1\}$ is closed with respect to division.

22. The set of irrational numbers contains an identity element for multiplication.

Is each of the following sets closed with respect to the indicated operations?

23. rationals, subtraction

24. rationals, division

25. irrationals, addition

26. reals, subtraction

27. irrationals, multiplication

28. irrationals, division

29. $\{0\}$, addition

30. $\{0\}$, multiplication

31. $\{1\}$, addition

32. $\{1\}$, multiplication

Simplify each of the following expressions, using the order of operations given in the text.

33. $9 \div 3 \cdot 4 \cdot 2$

34. $18 \cdot 3 \div 9 \div 2$

35. $8 + 7 \cdot 2 + (-5)$

36. $-9 + 6 \cdot 5 + (-8)$

37. $(-9 + 4 \cdot 3)(-7)$

38. $-15(-8 - 4 \div 2)$

39. $\dfrac{-8 + (-4)(-6) \div 12}{4 - (-3)}$

40. $\dfrac{15 \div 5 \cdot 4 \div 6 - 8}{-6 - (-5) - 8 \div 2}$

41. $\dfrac{17 \div (3 \cdot 5 + 2) \div 8}{-6 \cdot 5 - 3 - 3(-11)}$

42. $\dfrac{-12(-3) + (-8)(-5) + (-6)}{17(-3) + 4 \cdot 8 + (-7)(-2) - (-5)}$

◉ **43.** $\dfrac{-9.23(5.87) + 6.993}{1.225(-8.601) - 148(.0723)}$

44. $\dfrac{189.4(3.221) - 9.447(-8.772)}{4.889[3.177 - 8.291(3.427)]}$

Choose all words from the following list which apply to the expressions given in Exercises 45 – 56.

(a) whole number

(b) integer

(c) rational number

(d) irrational number

(e) real number

(f) meaningless

45. 12

46. 0

47. $-5/9$

48. 11/3

49. $\sqrt{8}$

50. $-\sqrt{2}$

51. $\sqrt{25}$

52. $-\sqrt{36}$

53. 8/0

54. $-9/(0 - 0)$

55. 0/6

56. $0/(3 + 3)$

57. We know that $a(b + c) = ab + ac$. This property is the distributive property of multiplication over addition. Is there a distributive property of addition over multiplication? That is, does

$$a + (b \cdot c) = (a + b)(a + c)$$

for all real numbers a, b, and c? To find out, try various sample values of a, b, and c.

Give a reason for each step in the following.

Example   Prove that $0 - a = -a$.

$0 - a = 0 + (-a)$	definition of subtraction
$0 + (-a) = -a$	identity property
$0 - a = -a$	substitution

58. Prove: $a - a = 0$.

$a - a = a + (-a)$ _____

$a + (-a) = 0$ _____

$a - a = 0$ _____

59. Prove: $(a + b)c = ac + bc$.

$(a + b)c = c(a + b)$ _____

$c(a + b) = ca + cb$ _____

$(a + b)c = ca + cb$ _____

$ca + cb = ac + bc$ _____

$(a + b)c = ac + bc$ _____

60. Prove: $(a + b) + (-a) = b$.

$(a + b) + (-a) = a + [b + (-a)]$ _____

$a + [b + (-a)] = a + [-a + b]$ _____

$a + [-a + b] = [a + (-a)] + b$ _____

$[a + (-a)] + b = 0 + b$ _____

$0 + b = b$ _____

$(a + b) + (-a) = b$ _____

Prove each of the following statements about real numbers a, b, and c.

61. $-a(b) = -(ab)$

62. $(-a)(-b) = ab$

63. $a \cdot 0 = 0$

64. If $a = b$, then $a + c = b + c$.

65. If $a = b$, then $ac = bc$.

66. If $ab = 0$, then $a = 0$ or $b = 0$.

1.2   The Number Line and Absolute Value

Number lines are useful when discussing real numbers. A **number line** sets up a correspondence between the set of real numbers and the set of points on a line. Draw a line and choose any point on the line to represent 0. Then choose any point to the right of 0 and label it 1. The distance from 0 to 1 sets up a unit measure which can be used to locate other points to the right of 1, which are labeled 2, 3, 4, 5, and so on, and points to the left of 0, labeled $-1, -2, -3, -4$, and so on.

   Points representing rational numbers, such as 2/3, 16/9, $-11/7$, and so on, can be found by dividing the intervals between integers. For example, 16/9 $\left(\text{or } 1\frac{7}{9} \right)$ could be found by dividing the interval from 1 to 2 into 9 equal parts (using methods given in geometry), and then choosing the correct point. Numbers such as $\sqrt{2}, \sqrt{3}, \sqrt{5}$, and so on, can be located by other geometric constructions. A point corresponding to other irrational numbers can be found to any desired degree of accuracy by using decimal approximations of the numbers.

Example 1   Locate the elements of each of the following sets on a number line.

   (a) $\{-3, -1, 0, 1, 3, 5\}$. The elements of this set are located on the number line of Figure 1.1.

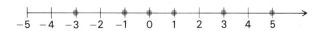

Figure 1.1

(b) $\{-2/3, 0, \sqrt{2}, \sqrt{5}, \pi, 4\}$. We know that π is an irrational number, with $\pi \approx 3.14159$ ($\approx$ means "approximately equal to"). From the square root table in the back of this book or from a calculator, we can find that $\sqrt{2} \approx 1.414$ and $\sqrt{5} \approx 2.236$. Using this information, we get the points on the number line shown in Figure 1.2. ▌

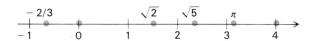

Figure 1.2

The number that corresponds to a point on a number line is called the **coordinate** of the point. For example, in Figure 1.2, $-2/3$ is the coordinate of the leftmost marked point, while 4 is the coordinate of the rightmost point. From now on, the phrase "the point on a number line corresponding to the real number x" will be abbreviated as "the point having coordinate x" or just "the point x."

If a number a is to the left of a number b on a number line, then a **is less than** b, written

$$a < b.$$

If a is less than b, then b **is greater than** a, written

$$b > a.$$

To prove statements involving order, use the following alternate forms of the definitions of the previous paragraph.

$a < b$ means $b - a$ is positive
$b > a$ means $a < b$.

In Figure 1.2 above, 0 is to the left of 1, so that $0 < 1$. Also, $1 > 0$. Since $\sqrt{5}$ is to the left of π, we have $\sqrt{5} < \pi$, or $\pi > \sqrt{5}$.

Example 2   Decide whether or not the following statements are correct.

(a) $6 < 10$
 Since $10 - 6 = 4$ is positive, the statement is correct.
(b) $8 < 3$
 Here, $3 - 8 = -5$, which is negative. Thus $8 < 3$ is false.
(c) $-15 > -20$
 Since $-20 < -15$, the statement $-15 > -20$ is correct. ▌

The following variations on $<$ and $>$ are often used:

Symbol	Meaning
≤	less than or equal to
≥	greater than or equal to
≮	not less than
≯	not greater than

Statements involving these symbols are called **inequalities.**

Example 3   (a) $8 \leq 10$,   (since $8 < 10$)
(b) $8 \leq 8$ (since $8 = 8$)
(c) $-9 \geq -14$ (since $-9 > -14$)
(d) $-8 \not> -2$ (since $-8 < -2$)
(e) $4 \not< 2$ (since $4 > 2$) ▮

The distance on the number line from a number to 0 is called the **absolute value** of that number. The absolute value of the number x is written $|x|$. For example, the distance on the number line from 0 to 9 is 9, as is the distance from 0 to -9. (See Figure 1.3.) Therefore,

$$|9| = 9 \quad \text{and} \quad |-9| = 9.$$

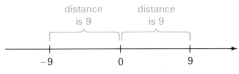

Figure 1.3

Example 4   (a) $|-4| = 4$
(b) $|2\pi| = 2\pi$
(c) $\left|-\dfrac{5}{8}\right| = \dfrac{5}{8}$
(d) $-|8| = -(8) = -8$
(e) $-|-2| = -(2) = -2.$ ▮

The definition of absolute value can be stated formally as follows:

$$|a| = \begin{cases} a & \text{if } a \geq 0 \\ -a & \text{if } a < 0. \end{cases}$$

The second part of this definition requires some thought. If a is a negative number, that is, if $a < 0$, then $-a$ is positive. Thus, for a *negative a*,

$$|a| = -a.$$

For example, if $a = -5$, then $|a| = |-5| = -(-5) = 5.$

Example 5   Write each of the following without absolute value bars.

(a) $|-8 + 2|$. Since $-8 + 2 = -6$,

$$|-8 + 2| = |-6| = 6.$$

(b) $|\sqrt{5} - 2|$. Since $\sqrt{5} > 2$ (see Figure 1.2), $\sqrt{5} - 2 > 0$, and

$$|\sqrt{5} - 2| = \sqrt{5} - 2.$$

(c) $|\pi - 4|$. We know $\pi < 4$, so $\pi - 4 < 0$; therefore

$$|\pi - 4| = -(\pi - 4)$$
$$= -\pi + 4$$
$$= 4 - \pi.$$

(d) $|m - 2|$ if $m < 2$. If $m < 2$, then $m - 2 < 0$, so $|m - 2| = -(m - 2) = 2 - m.$

The definition of absolute value can be used to prove the following properties of absolute value. (See the exercises below.) For all real numbers a and b,

(a) $|a| \geq 0$

(b) $|-a| = |a|$

(c) $|a - b| = |b - a|$

(d) $|a| \cdot |b| = |ab|$

(e) $\left|\dfrac{a}{b}\right| = \dfrac{|a|}{|b|}$ $(b \neq 0)$

(f) $-|a| \leq a \leq |a|$

(g) $|a + b| \leq |a| + |b|$ (the *triangle inequality*)

Let us prove part (a) as a sample. If $a \geq 0$, then by the definition of absolute value, $|a| = a$, which is assumed to be greater than or equal to 0. Thus, if $a \geq 0$, then $|a| \geq 0$.

If $a < 0$, then $|a| = -a$, which is positive. If either $a \geq 0$ or $a < 0$, we have $|a| \geq 0$, so that $|a| \geq 0$ for every real number a.

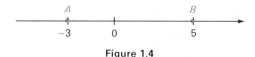

Figure 1.4

The number line of Figure 1.4 shows the point A, with coordinate -3, and the point B, with coordinate 5. The distance between points A and B can be found by subtracting the smaller coordinate from the larger. If $d(A, B)$ represents the distance between points A and B, then

$$d(A, B) = 5 - (-3) = 8.$$

To avoid worrying about which coordinate is smaller, use absolute value as in the following definition.

Suppose points A and B have coordinates a and b respectively. The *distance* between A and B, written $d(A, B)$, is

$$d(A, B) = |a - b|.$$

Example 6   (a) $d(5, -2) = |5 - (-2)| = 7$
(b) $d(-6, -9) = |-6 - (-9)| = 3$
(c) $d(12, 12) = |12 - 12| = 0.$ ▮

This definition, along with the properties of absolute value given above, can be used to prove the following.

Let point A have coordinate a, B have coordinate b, and 0 have coordinate 0. Then

$$d(A, B) = d(B, A)$$
$$d(A, B) \geq 0$$
$$d(A, 0) = |a|$$
$$d(A, A) = 0.$$

1.2 Exercises   *Write the following numbers in numerical order, from smallest to largest.*

1. $-9, -2, 3, -4, 8$
2. $7, -6, 0, -2, -3$
3. $|-8|, -|9|, -|-6|$
4. $-|-9|, -|7|, -|-2|$

5. $\sqrt{8}, -4, -\sqrt{3}, -2, -5, \sqrt{6}, 3$
6. $\sqrt{2}, -1, 4, 3, \sqrt{8}, -\sqrt{6}, \sqrt{7}$
7. $3/4, \sqrt{2}, 7/5, 8/5, 22/15$
8. $-9/8, -3, -\sqrt{3}, -\sqrt{5}, -9/5, -8/5$

Let $x = -4$ and $y = 2$. Evaluate each of the following.

9. $|2x|$
10. $|-3y|$
11. $|x - y|$

12. $|2x + 5y|$
13. $|3x + 4y|$
14. $|-5y + x|$

15. $|-4x + y| - |y|$
16. $|-8y + x| - |x|$

Write each of the following without absolute value bars.

17. $|-6|$
18. $-|-2|$
19. $-|-8| + |-2|$
20. $3 - |-4|$
21. $|8 - \sqrt{50}|$
22. $|2 - \sqrt{3}|$
23. $|\sqrt{7} - 5|$
24. $|\sqrt{2} - 3|$

25. $|\pi - 3|$
26. $|\pi - 5|$
27. $|x - 4|,$ if $x > 4$
28. $|y - 3|,$ if $y < 3$
29. $|2k - 8|,$ if $k < 4$
30. $|3r - 15|,$ if $r > 5$
31. $|7m - 56|,$ if $m < 4$
32. $|2k - 7|,$ if $k > 4$

33. $|-8 - 4m|,$ if $m > -2$
34. $|6 - 5r|,$ if $r < -2$
35. $|x - y|,$ if $x < y$
36. $|x - y|,$ if $x > y$
37. $|3 + x^2|$
38. $|x^2 + 4|$

In the following exercises, the coordinates of four points are given. Find (a) $d(A, B)$; (b) $d(B, C)$; (c) $d(B, D)$; (d) $d(D, A)$; (e) $d(A, B) + d(B, C)$.

39. $A, -4; B, -3; C, -2; D, 10$

40. $A, -8; B, -7, C, 11; D, 5$

41. $A, -3; B, -5; C, -12; D, -3$

42. $A, 0; B, 6; C, 9; D, -1$

Under what conditions are the following true?

43. $|x| = |y|$

44. $|x + y| = |x| + |y|$

45. $|x + y| = |x| - |y|$

46. $\left||x + y|\right| = |x + y|$

Prove each of the following properties.

47. $|-a| = |a|$

48. $|a - b| = |b - a|$

49. $|a| \cdot |b| = |ab|$

50. $\left|\dfrac{a}{b}\right| = \dfrac{|a|}{|b|}$, if $b \neq 0$

51. $-|a| \leq a \leq |a|$

52. $|a + b| \leq |a| + |b|$

53. $d(A, B) = d(B, A)$

54. $d(A, B) \geq 0$

55. $d(A, 0) = |a|$

56. $d(A, A) = 0$

Evaluate each of the following if x is a nonzero real number.

57. $\dfrac{|x|}{x}$

58. $\left|\dfrac{|x|}{x}\right|$

1.3 Integer Exponents

Exponents are used to write repeated products. If n is any positive integer and a is any real number, then the symbol a^n is defined as

$$a^n = a \cdot a \cdot a \cdots a,$$

where a appears in the product n times. Here n is called the **exponent,** a is called the **base,** and the expression a^n is called an **exponential.** (Read a^n as "a to the nth power.") Thus,

$$(-6)^2 = (-6)(-6) = 36, \qquad 4^3 = 4 \cdot 4 \cdot 4 = 64, \qquad \text{and} \qquad \left(\frac{2}{3}\right)^4 = \frac{16}{81}.$$

Work with exponents can be simplified with various **properties of exponents.** By definition, a^m (where m is a positive integer and a is a real number) means a appears in the product m times. In the same way, a^n (where n is a positive integer) means that a appears in the product n times. Thus, in the product $a^m \cdot a^n$, a appears $m + n$ times. Therefore, for any positive integers m and n and any real number a,

$$a^m \cdot a^n = a^{m+n}$$

Similar arguments can be given for the other properties of exponents given in the following theorem.

Theorem 1.1   For any positive integers m and n, and for any real numbers a and b,

$$\text{(a) } a^m \cdot a^n = a^{m+n}$$

$$\text{(b) } \frac{a^m}{a^n} = \begin{cases} a^{m-n} \text{ if } m > n \\ 1 \text{ if } m = n \quad (a \neq 0) \\ \dfrac{1}{a^{n-m}} \text{ if } m < n \end{cases}$$

$$\text{(c) } (a^m)^n = a^{mn}$$

$$\text{(d) } (ab)^m = a^m b^m$$

$$\text{(e) } \left(\frac{a}{b}\right)^m = \frac{a^m}{b^m} \quad (b \neq 0).$$

Complete proofs of the various parts of Theorem 1.1 require the method of mathematical induction, discussed in Chapter 12 of this book. Parts (a) and (d) of the theorem can be generalized further; for example

$$a^m \cdot a^n \cdot a^p = a^{m+n+p} \quad \text{and} \quad (abc)^n = a^n \cdot b^n \cdot c^n$$

and so on.

Example 1   Each of the following examples is justified by one or more parts of Theorem 1.1 and by the properties of multiplication.

(a) $(4x^3)(-3x^5) = (4)(-3)x^3 \cdot x^5 = -12x^8$

(b) $-3^4(-3)^5 = -(3)^4 \cdot [-(3)^5] = 3^9$

(c) $-3^5(-3)^4 = -(3)^5(3)^4 = -3^9$

(d) $\dfrac{m^4 n^2}{m^3 n^5} = \dfrac{m^4}{m^3} \cdot \dfrac{n^2}{n^5} = m \cdot \dfrac{1}{n^3} = \dfrac{m}{n^3} \quad (m \neq 0, \, n \neq 0)$

(e) $\left(\dfrac{2x^5}{5}\right)^3 = \dfrac{2^3(x^5)^3}{5^3} = \dfrac{8x^{15}}{125}$

(f) $(2z^{2r})(z^{r+1}) = (2)z^{2r} \cdot z^{r+1} = 2z^{2r+(r+1)} = 2z^{3r+1}$

(g) $\dfrac{k^{r+1}}{k^r} = k^{(r+1)-r} = k, \quad$ for any positive integer r and any real number k not equal to 0. $\quad$ ▌

By part (a) of Theorem 1.1, we have $a^m \cdot a^n = a^{m+n}$. Suppose we try to extend this general formula to zero exponents. If $n = 0$,

$$a^m \cdot a^n = a^{m+n} \text{ becomes } a^m \cdot a^0 = a^{m+0} = a^m.$$

The only way that $a^m \cdot a^0$ can equal a^m is if $a^0 = 1$. Therefore, we make the following definition. If a is a nonzero real number, then

$$\boxed{a^0 = 1.}$$

We make no attempt to define 0^0.

Example 2   (a) $3^0 = 1$ (d) $(-\sqrt{11})^0 = 1$

(b) $(-4)^0 = 1$ (e) $-4^0 = -1$

(c) $\left(\dfrac{1}{7}\right)^0 = 1$ (f) $-(-4)^0 = -1$ ▮

All the work above can be generalized to include *all* integer exponents, not just positive integer and zero exponents. We would like to define negative integer exponents in such a way that the various properties of Theorem 1.1 are still valid. For example, for positive integers m and n and any nonzero real number a,

$$\frac{a^m}{a^n} = a^{m-n} \qquad \text{if } m > n.$$

To generalize this result, we remove the restriction that the integers be positive. Let $m = 0$ to get

$$\frac{a^0}{a^n} = a^{0-n} = a^{-n}$$

Since $a^0 = 1$ for nonzero a,

$$\frac{a^0}{a^n} = \frac{1}{a^n},$$

and

$$a^{-n} = \frac{1}{a^n}.$$

Thus, it is reasonable to define a^{-n} as follows, for all integers n and all nonzero real numbers a,

$$\boxed{a^{-n} = \frac{1}{a^n}}$$

Example 3   (a) $3^{-1} = \dfrac{1}{3}$

(b) $2^{-3} = \dfrac{1}{2^3} = \dfrac{1}{8}$

(c) $\left(\dfrac{1}{2}\right)^{-2} = \dfrac{1}{\left(\dfrac{1}{2}\right)^2} = \dfrac{1}{\dfrac{1}{4}} = 4$

(d) $\left(-\dfrac{2}{3}\right)^{-3} = -\dfrac{27}{8}$

(e) $-4^{-2} = -\dfrac{1}{4^2} = -\dfrac{1}{16}$ ▮

It can be shown that all properties of exponents from Theorem 1.1 are true for all integer exponents and not just for positive integer exponents. We shall now restate Theorem 1.1 in its more general version.

Theorem 1.1
(restated)

For any integers m and n and for all nonzero real numbers a and b,

(a) $a^m \cdot a^n = a^{m+n}$ (d) $(ab)^m = a^m \cdot b^m$

(b) $\dfrac{a^m}{a^n} = a^{m-n}$ (e) $\left(\dfrac{a}{b}\right)^n = \dfrac{a^n}{b^n}$ $(b \neq 0)$.

(c) $(a^m)^n = a^{mn}$

Example 4

(a) $2^{-4} \cdot 2^5 = 2^{-4+5} = 2^1 = 2$

(b) $3x^{-2}(4^{-1}x^{-5})^2 = 3x^{-2}(4^{-2}x^{-10})$

$$= 3 \cdot 4^{-2}x^{-12}$$

$$= \frac{3}{16x^{12}}$$

(c) $\left(\dfrac{3}{4}\right)^{-3} = \dfrac{3^{-3}}{4^{-3}} = \dfrac{1}{3^3} \div \dfrac{1}{4^3} = \dfrac{1}{3^3} \cdot \dfrac{4^3}{1} = \dfrac{4^3}{3^3}$ ▮

Example 5

Simplify and write with only positive exponents.

$$\frac{(3x^2)^{-1}(3x^5)^{-2}}{(3^{-1}x^{-2})^3}$$

Begin by using part (c) of the theorem. Then use (a) and (b).

$$\frac{(3x^2)^{-1}(3x^5)^{-2}}{(3^{-1}x^{-2})^3} = \frac{(3^{-1})(x^{-2})(3^{-2})(x^{-10})}{(3^{-3})(x^{-6})}$$

$$= \frac{(3^{-3})(x^{-12})}{(3^{-3})(x^{-6})}$$

$$= \frac{x^{-12}}{x^{-6}}$$

$$= x^{-12-(-6)}$$

$$= x^{-6}$$

$$= \frac{1}{x^6}$$ ▮

In science, numbers often come up which are either very large or very small. To avoid working with many zeros, scientists often express such numbers in **scientific notation.** In scientific notation, a number is written as the product of a number whose absolute value is at least 1, but less than 10, and a power of 10. For example,

$$125{,}000 = 1.25 \times 10^5$$
$$7900 = 7.9 \times 10^3$$
$$.008 = 8 \times 10^{-3}$$
$$.0000056 = 5.6 \times 10^{-6}.$$

With scientific notation, it is customary to use the symbol $\times$ to indicate multiplication.

Example 6   Find each of the following.

(a) $(28,000,000)(.000012)$
Write each number in scientific notation.

$$(28,000,000)(.000012) = (2.8 \times 10^7)(1.2 \times 10^{-5})$$
$$= (2.8 \times 1.2) \times 10^{7+(-5)}$$
$$= 3.36 \times 10^2$$
$$= 336$$

(b) $\dfrac{.082}{.0000097} = \dfrac{8.2 \times 10^{-2}}{9.7 \times 10^{-6}}$

$$= \dfrac{8.2}{9.7} \times 10^{-2-(-6)}$$
$$= .85 \times 10^4$$
$$= 8500 \quad \blacksquare$$

Here, we rounded the quotient 8.2/9.7 to two significant digits.

1.3 Exercises

Simplify each of the following. Write all answers without exponents.

1. 15^3

2. 21^4

3. 2^{-3}

4. 3^{-2}

5. $4^{-1} + 3^{-3}$

6. $5^{-2} - 2^{-1}$

7. $(-4)^{-3}$

8. $(-5)^{-2}$

9. $\left(\dfrac{1}{2}\right)^{-3}$

10. $\left(\dfrac{2}{7}\right)^{-2}$

⦿ 11. $(9.864)^{-3}$

12. $(14.259)^{-2}$

Simplify each of the following by writing each with only positive exponents. Assume that all variables represent nonzero real numbers.

13. $(3m)^2(-2m)^3$

14. $(-2a^4b^7)(3b^2)$

15. $(6^{-2})(6^{-5})(6^3)$

16. $(4^8)(4^{-10})(4^2)$

17. $(5^3)(5^{-5})(5^{-2})$

18. $(m^{10})(m^{-4})(m^{-5})$

19. $\dfrac{(3^5)(3^{-2})}{3^{-4}}$

20. $\dfrac{(2^2)(2^{-5})}{2^7}$

21. $\dfrac{(d^{-1})(d^{-2})}{(d^8)(d^{-3})}$

22. $\dfrac{(t^5)(t^{-3})}{(t^4)(t^{-7})}$

23. $\dfrac{2^{-1}x^3y^{-3}}{xy^{-2}}$

24. $\dfrac{5^{-2}m^2y^{-2}}{5^2m^{-1}y^{-2}}$

25. $\dfrac{(4+s)^3(4+s)^{-2}}{(4+s)^{-5}}$

26. $\dfrac{(m+n)^4(m+n)^{-2}}{(m+n)^{-5}}$

27. $[(m^2n)^{-1}]^4$

28. $(x^5t^{-2})^{-2}$

29. $\left(\dfrac{a^{-1}}{b^2}\right)^{-3}$

30. $\left(\dfrac{2c^2}{d^3}\right)^{-2}$

31. $(-2x^{-3}y^2)^{-2}$

32. $(-3p^2q^{-2}s^{-1})^7$

33. $\dfrac{(3^{-1}m^{-2}n^2)^{-2}}{(mn)^{-1}}$

34. $\dfrac{(-4x^3y^{-2})^{-2}}{(4x^5y^4)^{-1}}$

35. $\dfrac{(r^2s^3t^4)^{-2}(r^3s^2t)^{-1}}{(rst)^{-3}(r^2st^2)^3}$

36. $\dfrac{(ab^2c)^{-3}(a^2bc)^{-2}}{(abc^2)^4}$

37. $\dfrac{[k^2(p+q)^4]^{-1}}{k^{-4}(p+q)^3}$

38. $\dfrac{t^4(x+y)^4t^{-8}}{(x+y)^{-2}t^{-5}}$

Express each of the following numbers in scientific notation.

39. 69300

41. 6,000,000,000

43. .00792

40. 5000

42. .0001

44. .054

Express each of the following numbers without exponents.

45. 8.2×10^5

47. 1.7×10^8

49. 6.15×10^{-3}

46. 3.7×10^3

48. 3.61×10^{-2}

50. 9.3×10^{-6}

Use scientific notation to evaluate each of the following.

51. $(4600)(.00092)$

55. $\dfrac{.000034}{.017}$

57. $\dfrac{28}{.0004}$

52. $(.87)(.0004)$

53. $(.00002)(.00009)$

56. $\dfrac{.0000042}{.0006}$

58. $\dfrac{50}{.0000025}$

54. $(.0004)(.0000015)$

◉ *Calculators with scientific notation capability display a number such as 1.46×10^{12} as*

$$1.46 \qquad 12.$$

Use a calculator to evaluate each of the following. Write all answers in scientific notation with three significant digits.

59. $(1.66 \times 10^4)(2.93 \times 10^3)$

64. $\dfrac{(1.392 \times 10^{10})(5.746 \times 10^{-8})}{4.93 \times 10^{-15}}$

60. $(6.92 \times 10^7)(8.14 \times 10^5)$

61. $(4.08 \times 10^{-9})(3.172 \times 10^4)$

65. $\dfrac{-3.9801 \times 10^{-6}}{(7.4993 \times 10^{-8})(2.117 \times 10^{-4})}$

62. $(9.113 \times 10^{12})(8.72 \times 10^{-11})$

66. $\dfrac{-5.421 \times 10^{-7}}{(4.2803 \times 10^{-4})(9.982 \times 10^{-8})}$

63. $\dfrac{(-4.389 \times 10^4)(2.421 \times 10^{-2})}{1.76 \times 10^{-9}}$

Find each of the following products or quotients. Assume all variables appearing as exponents represent integers.

67. $(2k^m)(k^{1-m})$

71. $\dfrac{(b^2)^y}{(2b^y)^3}$

73. $\dfrac{(2m^n)^2(-4m^{2+n})}{8m^{4n}}$

68. $(y^m)(y^{1+m})$

69. $\dfrac{x^{2r}}{x^r}$

72. $\left(\dfrac{3p^a}{2m^b}\right)^c$

74. $\dfrac{(3-y)^k(3-y)^{2k}}{(3-y)^2}$

70. $\dfrac{4a^{m+2}}{2a^{m-1}}$

1.4 Polynomials

A **variable** is a letter used to represent a number. An **algebraic expression** is any expression of variables or constants obtained by performing the basic operations of addition, subtraction, multiplication, division (except by 0), or extraction of roots. The simplest algebraic expression is a polynomial, which we discuss in this section.

First, any product of a constant (called the **coefficient**) and one or more variables raised to powers is called a **term**. A finite sum of terms with nonnegative integer exponents on the variables (such as $-2x^2 + 4x^2 - 5$, or $2m^3n^2y - 3$, or 3, or $3p$) is called a **polynomial**. If every term in a polynomial contains only one variable, such as x, the polynomial is called a **polynomial in x**.

The general form of a polynomial in x is

$$a_n x^n + a_{n-1} x^{n-1} + \ldots + a_1 x + a_0,$$

where a_n (read "a-sub-n"), $a_{n-1}, \ldots a_1$, and a_0 are real numbers. If $a_n \neq 0$, then n is the **degree** of the polynomial. A nonzero constant is said to have degree zero. By the definition above, $3x^4 - 5x^2 + 2x + 3$ is a polynomial of degree 4.

A term containing more than one variable is said to have degree equal to the sum of all exponents appearing on the variables in the term. For example, $-3x^4y^3z^5$ is of degree $4 + 3 + 5 = 12$.

The degree of a polynomial in more than one variable is equal to the highest degree of any term appearing in the polynomial. Thus,

$$2x^4y^3 - 3x^5y + x^6y^2$$

is of degree 8, because of the x^6y^2 term.

A polynomial containing exactly three terms is called a **trinomial;** one containing exactly two terms is a **binomial;** and a single-term polynomial is called a **monomial**. Thus, $7x^9 - \sqrt{2}x^4 + 1$ is a trinomial of degree 9.

Sums and differences of polynomials can be found by using the rules and properties for the real numbers. Thus,

$$3m^5 - 8m^5 = (3 - 8)m^5$$
$$= -5m^5.$$

Example 1 (a) $(2y^4 - 3y^2 + y) + (4y^4 + 7y^2 + 6y) = (2 + 4)y^4 + (-3 + 7)y^2 + (1 + 6)y$
$$= 6y^4 + 4y^2 + 7y$$

(b) $(6r^4 + 2r^2) + (3r^3 + 9r) = 6r^4 + 3r^3 + 2r^2 + 9r$ ▮

The distributive property can be used to find the product of two polynomials when one or both of them is not a monomial. For example, if we treat $3x - 4$ as a single quantity, we can use the distributive property as follows.

$$(3x - 4)(ex^2 - 3x + 5) = (3x - 4)(2x^2) + (3x - 4)(-3x) + (3x - 4)(5).$$

If we use the distributive property again, we have

$$(3x - 4)(2x^2 - 3x + 5) = (3x)(2x^2) - 4(2x^2) + (3x)(-3x) - 4(-3x) + (3x)5$$
$$- 4(5)$$
$$= 6x^3 - 8x^2 - 9x^2 + 12x + 15x - 20$$
$$= 6x^3 - 17x^2 + 27x - 20.$$

It is sometimes more convenient to write such a product as

$$
\begin{array}{r}
2x^2 - \ 3x + \ 5 \\
3x - \ 4 \\
\hline
- \ \ 8x^2 + 12x - 20 \\
6x^3 - \ 9x^2 + 15x \\
\hline
6x^3 - 17x^2 + 27x - 20.
\end{array}
$$

Example 2

$$(6m + 1)(4m - 3) = (6m)(4m) + (6m)(-3) + 1(4m) + 1(-3)$$
$$= 24m^2 - 14m - 3 \quad \blacksquare$$

Example 3

$$(2k^n - 5)(k^n + 3) = 2k^{2n} - 5k^n + 6k^n - 15$$
$$= 2k^{2n} + k^n - 15 \quad \blacksquare$$

Example 4

$$(2x + 7)(2x - 7) = 4x^2 - 14x + 14x - 49$$
$$= 4x^2 - 49 \quad \blacksquare$$

Example 4 shows a special product which reduces to two terms instead of the expected three. In general, for any real numbers x and y,

$$\boxed{(x + y)(x - y) = x^2 - y^2.}$$

This product is called the **difference of two squares.**

Example 5   (a) $(3p + 11)(3p - 11) = (3p)^2 - 11^2 = 9p^2 - 121$

(b) $(5m^3 - 3)(5m^3 + 3) = (5m^3)^2 - 3^2$
$$= 25m^6 - 9$$

(c) $(9k - 11r^3)(9k + 11r^3) = (9k)^2 - (11r^3)^2 = 81k^2 - 121r^6 \quad \blacksquare$

The **square of a binomial** is another special product, in which, for real numbers x and y,

$$\boxed{(x + y)^2 = x^2 + 2xy + y^2.}$$

Example 6   (a) $(2m - 5)^2 = (2m)^2 + 2(2m)(-5) + (-5)^2$
$$= 4m^2 - 20m + 25$$

(b) $(3z - 7y^4)^2 = (3z)^2 + 2(3z)(-7y^4) + (-7y^4)^2$
$$= 9z^2 - 42zy^4 + 49y^8 \quad \blacksquare$$

One last special product shows how to find the **cube of a binomial;** for all real numbers x and y,

$$\boxed{(x + y)^3 = x^3 + 3x^2y + 3xy^2 + y^3}$$

Example 7 (a) $(m - 4n)^3 = m^3 + 3m^2(-4n) + 3m(-4n)^2 + (-4n)^3$
$$= m^3 - 12m^2n + 48mn^2 - 64n^3$$

(b) $(5k - 2z^5)^3 = (5k)^3 + 3(5k)^2(-2z^5) + 3(5k)(-2z^5)^2 + (-2z^5)^3$
$$= 125k^3 - 150k^2z^5 + 60kz^{10} - 8z^{15}$$ ▌

It is useful to memorize and be able to apply these three special products.
   To divide a polynomial by a monomial, divide each term of the polynomial by the monomial.

Example 8 (a) $\dfrac{2m^5 - 6m^3}{2m^3} = \dfrac{2m^5}{2m^3} - \dfrac{6m^3}{2m^3} = m^2 - 3$

The polynomial $m^2 - 3$ is called the **quotient** of $2m^5 - 6m^3$ and $2m^3$.

(b) $\dfrac{3y^6x^3 - 6y^3x^6 + 8y^5x}{3y^3x^3} = \dfrac{3y^6x^3}{3y^3x^3} - \dfrac{6y^3x^6}{3y^3x^3} + \dfrac{8y^5x}{3y^3x^3}$

$$= y^3 - 2x^3 + \dfrac{8y^2}{3x^2}$$ ▌

In this example, the quotient is not a polynomial.

1.4 Exercises *Find each of the following.*

1. $(3x^2 - 4x + 5) + (-2x^2 + 3x - 2)$

2. $(4m^3 - 3m^2 + 5) + (-3m^3 - m^2 + 5)$

3. $(x^2 + 4x) + (3x^3 - 4x^2 + 2x + 2)$

4. $(r^5 - r^3 + r) + (3r^5 - 4r^4 + r^3 + 2r)$

5. $(12y^2 - 8y + 6) - (3y^2 - 4y + 2)$

6. $(8p^2 - 5p) - (3p^2 - 2p + 4)$

7. $(p^3 - 4p^2 + p) - (3p^2 + 2p + 7)$

8. $(4y^2 - 2y + 7) - (6y - 9)$

9. $(3a^2 - 2a) + (4a^2 + 3a + 1) - (a^2 + 2)$

10. $(6m^4 - 3m^2 + m) - (2m^3 + 5m^2 + 4m) + (m^2 - m)$

11. $(5b^2 - 4b + 3) - (2b^2 + b) - (3b + 4)$

12. $-(8x^3 + x - 3) + (2x^3 + x^2) - (4x^2 + 3x - 1)$

13. $-3(4q^2 - 3q + 2) + 2(-q^2 + q - 4)$

14. $2(3r^2 + 4r + 2) - 3(-r^2 + 4r - 5)$

15. $(4r - 1)(7r + 2)$

16. $(5m - 6)(3m + 4)$

17. $(6p + 5q)(3p - 7q)$

18. $(2z + y)(3z - 4y)$

19. $\left(3x - \dfrac{2}{3}\right)\left(5x + \dfrac{1}{3}\right)$

20. $\left(2m - \dfrac{1}{4}\right)\left(3m + \dfrac{1}{2}\right)$

21. $\left(\dfrac{2}{5}y + \dfrac{1}{8}z\right)\left(\dfrac{3}{5}y + \dfrac{1}{2}z\right)$

22. $\left(\dfrac{3}{4}r - \dfrac{2}{3}s\right)\left(\dfrac{5}{4}r + \dfrac{1}{3}s\right)$

23. $(5r + 2)(5r - 2)$

24. $(6z + 5)(6z - 5)$

25. $(4x + 3y)(4x - 3y)$

26. $(7m + 2n)(7m - 2n)$

27. $(6k - 3)^2$

28. $(3p + 5)^2$

29. $(4m + 2n)^2$

30. $(a - 6b)^2$

31. $(2z - 1)^3$

32. $(3m + 2)^3$

33. $4x^2(3x^3 + 2x^2 - 5x + 1)$

34. $2b^3(b^2 - 4b + 3)$

35. $5m(3m^3 - 2m^2 + m - 1)$

36. $4y^3(y^3 + 2y^2 - 6y + 3)$

37. $(2z - 1)(-z^2 + 3z - 4)$

38. $(x - 1)(x^2 - 1)$

39. $(3p - 1)(9p^2 + 3p + 1)$

40. $(2p - 1)(3p^2 - 4p + 5)$

41. $(2m + 1)(4m^2 - 2m + 1)$

42. $(k + 2)(12k^3 - 3k^2 + k + 1)$

43. $(m - n + k)(m + 2n - 3k)$

44. $(r - 3s + t)(2r - s + t)$

45. $(a - b + 2c)^2$

46. $(k - y + 3m)^2$

Perform each of the following divisions. Assume that all variables appearing in de-nominators represent nonzero real numbers.

47. $\dfrac{4m^3 - 8m^2 + 16m}{2m}$

48. $\dfrac{30k^5 - 12k^3 + 18k^2}{6k^2}$

49. $\dfrac{15x^4 + 30x^3 + 12x^2 - 9}{3x}$

50. $\dfrac{16a^6 + 24a^5 - 48a^4 + 12a}{8a^2}$

51. $\dfrac{25x^2y^4 - 15x^3y^3 + 40x^4y^2}{5x^2y^2}$

52. $\dfrac{-8r^3s - 12r^2s^2 + 20rs^3}{4rs}$

Find each of the following products.

53. $(k^m + 2)(k^m - 2)$

54. $(y^x - 4)(y^x + 4)$

55. $(b^r + 3)(b^r - 2)$

56. $(q^y + 4)(q^y + 3)$

57. $(3p^x + 1)(p^x - 2)$

58. $(2^a + 5)(2^a + 3)$

59. $(m^x - 2)^2$

60. $(z^r + 5)^2$

61. $(3k^a - 2)^3$

62. $(r^x - 4)^3$

1.5   Factoring

The process of finding polynomials whose product equals a given polynomial is called **factoring**. Each polynomial in the product is called a **factor**. For example, since $3x(x - 8) = 3x^2 - 24x$, both $3x$ and $x - 8$ are factors of $3x^2 - 24x$.

One way to factor a polynomial is to use the distributive property. For example, to factor $6x^2y^3 + 9xy^4 + 18y^5$, we look for a monomial which is the **greatest common factor** of each term. (The largest factor which will divide into each term.) Here, $3y^3$ is the greatest common factor. By the distributive property,

$$6x^2y^3 + 9xy^4 + 18y^5 = (3y^3)(2x^2) + (3y^3)(3xy) + (3y^3)(6y^2)$$
$$= 3y^3(2x^2 + 3xy + 6y^2)$$

Example 1   Factor $6x^2t + 8xt + 12t$.

Factor out the greatest common factor, $2t$.

$$6x^2t + 8xt + 12t = 2t(3x^2 + 4x + 6) \quad \blacksquare$$

In the previous section, we mentioned two special products that should be memorized. Those products can be easily factored from the memorized form. The following theorem lists those two and other special products which are useful in factoring.

Theorem 1.2   For all real numbers a, b, c, d and for all variables x and y:

(a) $x^2 + 2xy + y^2 = (x + y)^2$
(*Perfect Square Trinomial*)
(b) $x^2 - y^2 = (x + y)(x - y)$
(*Difference of Two Squares*)
(c) $x^2 + (a + b)x + ab = (x + a)(x + b)$
(d) $acx^2 + (ad + bc)x + bd = (ax + b)(cx + d)$.

This theorem can be proved by the methods of multiplication of polynomials presented in the previous section. The following examples illustrate the use of Theorem 1.2 in factoring.

Example 2   (a) Factor $4m^2 - 9$.

First, recognize that $4m^2 - 9$ is the difference of two squares. We can use Theorem 1.2(b) by letting $2m$ replace x and 3 replace y.

$$4m^2 - 9 = (2m)^2 - 3^2$$
$$= (2m + 3)(2m - 3)$$

(b) $x^2 - \dfrac{1}{16} = \left(x + \dfrac{1}{4}\right)\left(x - \dfrac{1}{4}\right)$ ∎

Example 3   We might be tempted to factor $x^2 - 5$ as

$$x^2 - 5 = (x - \sqrt{5})(x + \sqrt{5})$$ ∎

However, in this book a polynomial with only integer coefficients will always be factored with only integer coefficients. For this reason, we say that $x^2 - 5$ cannot be factored, or is a **prime polynomial.**

Example 4   Factor each of the following:

(a) $m^2 + 2m - 24$

We need to find two real numbers a and b such that

$$(m + a)(m + b) = m^2 + (a + b)m + ab$$
$$= m^2 + 2m - 24.$$

We can see from this that $a + b = 2$ and $ab = -24$. That is, we need two factors of -24 whose sum is 2. Since -4 and 6 satisfy these requirements,

$$m^2 + 2m - 24 = (m - 4)(m + 6).$$

(b) $p^2 + 6p + 7$

There are no integers whose product is 7 and whose sum is 6, so that $p^2 + 6p + 7$ cannot be factored. This polynomial is prime.   ∎

Example 5   Factor.

(a) $6p^2 - 7p - 5$

We use Theorem 1.2(d). We need real numbers a, b, c, and d such that $ac = 6$, $ad + bc = -7$, and $bd = -5$. To find these integers, we try various possibilities. Since $ac = 6$, we might let $a = 2$ and $c = 3$. Since $bd = -5$, we might let $b = -5$ and $d = 1$, giving

$$(2p - 5)(3p + 1) = 6p^2 - 13p - 5 \qquad \text{(wrong)}.$$

We need to make another attempt; we'll try

$$(3p - 5)(2p + 1) = 6p^2 - 7p - 5 \qquad \text{(correct)}.$$

Thus, $6p^2 - 7p - 5$ factors as $(3p - 5)(2p + 1)$.

(b) $4x^3 + 6x^2r - 10xr^2$

There is a common factor of $2x$.

$$4x^3 + 6x^2r - 10xr^2 = 2x(2x^2 + 3xr - 5r^2).$$

To factor $2x^2 + 3xr - 5r^2$, we need the factors of $2x^2$ and of $-5r^2$ that will yield the correct middle term of $3xr$. By inspection, we end up with

$$4x^3 + 6x^2r - 10xr^2 = 2x(2x + 5r)(x - r). \quad \blacksquare$$

Two other special methods of factoring are given in Theorem 1.3.

Theorem 1.3   For all variables x and y

(a) $x^3 + y^3 = (x + y)(x^2 - xy + y^2)$
    (Sum of Two Cubes)
(b) $x^3 - y^3 = (x - y)(x^2 + xy + y^2)$
    (Difference of Two Cubes)

Example 6   Factor $m^3 - 64n^3$.

Here, we have a difference of two cubes. Using Theorem 1.3(b), we replace x with m and y with $4n$.

$$m^3 - 64n^3 = m^3 - (4n)^3$$
$$= (m - 4n)[m^2 + m(4n) + (4n)^2]$$
$$= (m - 4n)(m^2 + 4mn + 16n^2). \quad \blacksquare$$

Example 7   Factor the sum of two cubes $8 + r^3$.

Since $8 = 2^3$, by Theorem 1.3(a),

$$2^3 + r^3 = (2 + r)(4 - 2r + r^2). \quad \blacksquare$$

Example 8   Factor $(a - 1)^3 + 1$.

We can use Theorem 1.3(a) with $x = a - 1$ and $y = 1$.

$$(a - 1)^3 + 1 = [(a - 1) + 1][(a - 1)^2 - (a - 1) + 1]$$
$$= a(a^2 - 2a + 1 - a + 1 + 1)$$
$$= a(a^2 - 3a + 3). \quad \blacksquare$$

Example 9 (a) Factor $p^6 - q^6$, as a difference of two cubes.

Use Theorem 1.3(b) with $x = p^2$ and $y = q^2$.

$$p^6 - q^6 = (p^2)^3 - (q^2)^3 = (p^2 - q^2)(p^4 + p^2q^2 + q^4)$$

Since $p^2 - q^2$ can be factored as $(p + q)(p - q)$, the result is

$$p^6 - q^6 = (p + q)(p - q)(p^4 + p^2q^2 + q^4).$$

(b) Factor $p^6 - q^6$ as a difference of two squares, using Theorem 1.2(b).

$$\begin{aligned} p^6 - q^6 &= (p^3)^2 - (q^3)^2 \\ &= (p^3 - q^3)(p^3 + q^3) \\ &= (p - q)(p^2 + pq + q^2)(p + q)(p^2 - pq + q^2). \end{aligned}$$ ▌

From this result, we see that we did not factor completely in part (a) above. For this reason, the approach of part (b) is better for this type of problem.

When a polynomial has more than three terms, it can often be factored by a method called **factoring by grouping.** For example, to factor

$$ax + ay + 6x + 6y,$$

collect the terms into two groups:

$$ax + ay + 6x + 6y = (ax + ay) + (6x + 6y)$$

Then factor each group:

$$= a(x + y) + 6(x + y)$$

The quantity $(x + y)$ is now a common factor, which can be factored out:

$$= (x + y)(a + 6)$$

It's not always obvious as to which terms should be grouped. Experience, plus trial and error, is the best teacher for techniques of factoring.

Example 10 Factor $x^2 + 4x + 4 - y^2$ by grouping.

Here, it will be advantageous to group the first three terms, which form a perfect square trinomial.

$$\begin{aligned} x^2 + 4x + 4 - y^2 &= (x^2 + 4x + 4) - y^2 \\ &= (x + 2)^2 - y^2 \end{aligned}$$

Now factor as a difference of two squares.

$$= (x + 2 + y)(x + 2 - y)$$ ▌

1.5 Exercises   *Factor as completely as possible.*

1. $12mn - 8m$

2. $3pq - 18pqr$

3. $12r^3 + 6r^2 - 3r$

4. $-5k^2g - 25kg - 30kg^2$

5. $6px^2 - 8px^3 - 12px$

6. $9m^2n^3 - 18m^3n^2 + 27m^2n^4$

7. $2(a + b) + 4m(a + b)$

8. $4(y - 2)^2 + 3(y - 2)$

9. $x^2 - 11x + 24$

10. $y^2 - 2y - 35$

11. $4p^2 + 3p - 1$

12. $6x^2 + 7x - 3$

13. $2z^2 + 7z - 30$

14. $4m^2 + m - 3$

15. $12r^2 + 24r - 15$

16. $12p^2 + p - 20$

17. $18r^2 - 3rs - 10s^2$

18. $12m^2 + 16mn - 35n^2$

19. $15x^2 - 14xy - 8y^2$

20. $12t^2 - 25tv + 12v^2$

21. $9x^2 - 6x^3 + x^4$

22. $30a + am - am^2$

23. $2r^2z - rz - 3z$

24. $3m^4 + 7m^3 + 2m^2$

25. $4m^2 - 25$

26. $25a^2 - 16$

27. $81 - x^2$

28. $49 - 64y^2$

29. $144r^2 - 81s^2$

30. $81m^2 - 16n^2$

31. $121p^4 - 9q^4$

32. $4z^4 - w^8$

33. $a^3 + b^3$

34. $m^3 - n^3$

35. $8m^3 - 27n^3$

36. $125x^3 - 1$

37. $64 - x^6$

38. $m^6 - 1$

39. $4x + 4y + mx + my$

40. $x^2 + xy + 5x + 5y$

41. $q^2 + 6q + 9 - p^2$

42. $4b^2 + 4bc + c^2 - 16$

43. $a^2 + 2ab + b^2 - x^2 - 2xy - y^2$

44. $d^2 - 10d + 25 - c^2 + 4c - 4$

45. $x^2 - (x - y)^2$

46. $16m^2 - 25(m - n)^2$

47. $8y^3 + 27(x - y)^3$

48. $64p^6 - 27(p^2 - q)^3$

49. $(x + y)^2 + 2(x + y)z - 15z^2$

50. $(m + n)^2 + 3(m + n)p - 10p^2$

51. $6(a + b)^2 + (a + b)c - 40c^2$

52. $12(g + h)^2 - 5(g + h)j - 25j^2$

53. $(p + q)^2 - (p - q)^2$

54. $(p - q)^2 - (p + q)^2$

55. $m^{2n} - 16$

56. $p^{4n} - 49$

57. $x^{3n} - y^{6n}$

58. $a^{4p} - b^{12p}$

59. $2x^{2n} - 23x^n y^n - 39y^{2n}$

60. $3a^{2x} + 7a^x b^x + 2b^{2x}$

● *Factor a common factor (a decimal) from each of the following.*

61. $9.44x^3 + 48.144x^2 - 30.208x + 37.76$

62. $12.915m^2 + 2.05m - 23.575m^3 + 20.5$

63. $64.616z^4 - 23.64z^2 + 7.88z + 114.26$

64. $1.47y^5 - 8.526y^3 + 69.384y^2 - 36.75$

1.6   Rational Expressions

An expression which is the quotient of two algebraic expressions (with denominator not 0) is called a **fractional expression.** The most common fractional expressions are those which are the quotients of two polynomials; these are called

rational expressions. Since a rational expression is similar to a rational number (which is a quotient of integers) many of the results given earlier for rational numbers generalize to rational expressions. These results are summarized as follows. For all polynomials P, $Q \neq 0$, R, and $S \neq 0$:

(a) $\dfrac{P}{Q} = \dfrac{R}{S}$ if and only if $P \cdot S = Q \cdot R$

(b) $\dfrac{P}{Q} = \dfrac{P \cdot S}{Q \cdot S}$

(*Fundamental Property of Rational Expressions*)

(c) $\dfrac{P}{Q} \cdot \dfrac{R}{S} = \dfrac{P \cdot R}{Q \cdot S}$

(*Multiplication of Rational Expressions*)

(d) $\dfrac{P}{Q} + \dfrac{R}{Q} = \dfrac{P + R}{Q}$

(*Addition of Rational Expressions*)

(e) $\dfrac{P}{Q} - \dfrac{R}{Q} = \dfrac{P - R}{Q}$

(*Subtraction of Rational Expressions*)

(f) $\dfrac{P}{Q} \div \dfrac{R}{S} = \dfrac{P \cdot S}{Q \cdot R}$ $(R \neq 0).$

(*Division of Rational Expressions*)

In the statement of these rules, when we say, for example, that $Q \neq 0$, we don't mean that Q is not the polynomial 0. Rather, $Q \neq 0$ says to exclude from consideration those values of x for which $Q = 0$.

The set of values for which a rational expression is defined is called the **domain** of the rational expression. For example, -2 is not in the domain of the rational expression

$$\frac{x + 6}{x + 2}$$

since -2 makes the denominator equal 0 when substituted for x. The domain of this rational expression can be written $x \neq -2$. In the same way, the domain of

$$\frac{(x + 6)(x + 4)}{(x + 2)(x + 4)}$$

can be written $x \neq -2$ and $x \neq -4$. Although, by part (b) of the theorem,

$$\frac{x + 6}{x + 2} = \frac{(x + 6)(x + 4)}{(x + 2)(x + 4)},$$

we should remember that this holds only when

$$x \neq -2 \quad \text{and} \quad x \neq -4.$$

When multiplying or dividing rational expressions, it is best to factor (if possible) all numerators and denominators first. Then reduce to lowest terms by the fundamental property. The answer is usually left in factored form.

Example 1

$$\frac{3m^2 - 2m - 8}{3m^2 + 14m + 8} \cdot \frac{3m + 2}{3m + 4} = \frac{(m - 2)(3m + 4)}{(m + 4)(3m + 2)} \cdot \frac{3m + 2}{3m + 4}$$

$$= \frac{(m - 2)(3m + 4)(3m + 2)}{(m + 4)(3m + 2)(3m + 4)}$$

$$= \frac{m - 2}{m + 4}$$

for all $m \neq -4$, $m \neq -\frac{2}{3}$, $m \neq -\frac{4}{3}$ ∎

From now on, we will not state (unless specifically required) all restrictions on the variable. But keep in mind that no statement involving rational expressions is meaningful for values of the variable which make any denominator zero.

Example 2

$$\frac{6p^2 - 7pq - 20q^2}{6p^2 - 25pq + 25q^2} \div \frac{6p^2 + 11pq + 4q^2}{2p^2 + 9pq + 4q^2}$$

$$= \frac{(2p - 5q)(3p + 4q)}{(2p - 5q)(3p - 5q)} \div \frac{(2p + q)(3p + 4q)}{(2p + q)(p + 4q)}$$

$$= \frac{(2p - 5q)(3p + 4q)(2p + q)(p + 4q)}{(2p - 5q)(3p - 5q)(2p + q)(3p + 4q)}$$

$$= \frac{p + 4q}{3p - 5q}$$ ∎

Before two rational expressions can be added, they must have the same denominator. Therefore, the first step in adding rational expressions is to find a common denominator. Then change both fractions to fractions with that denominator (using the fundamental property). Finally, add by adding numerators and putting the result over the common denominator.

Example 3

$$\frac{y + 2}{y - 1} + \frac{y}{y + 1} = \frac{(y + 2)(y + 1)}{(y - 1)(y + 1)} + \frac{y(y - 1)}{(y - 1)(y + 1)}$$

Here we use the fact that $(y - 1)(y + 1)$ is the common denominator.

$$= \frac{y^2 + 3y + 2}{(y - 1)(y + 1)} + \frac{y^2 - y}{(y - 1)(y + 1)}$$

$$= \frac{y^2 + 3y + 2 + y^2 - y}{(y - 1)(y + 1)}$$

$$= \frac{2y^2 + 2y + 2}{(y - 1)(y + 1)}$$

$$= \frac{2(y^2 + y + 1)}{(y - 1)(y + 1)}$$ ∎

The next two examples show how negative exponents can lead to problems involving rational expressions.

Example 4 Simplify $\dfrac{(x + y)^{-1}}{x^{-1} + y^{-1}}$. Write the result with only positive exponents.

Use the definition of negative integer exponent.

$$\frac{(x + y)^{-1}}{x^{-1} + y^{-1}} = \frac{\dfrac{1}{x + y}}{\dfrac{1}{x} + \dfrac{1}{y}}$$

$$= \frac{\dfrac{1}{x + y}}{\dfrac{x + y}{xy}}$$

$$= \frac{1}{x + y} \cdot \frac{xy}{x + y}$$

$$= \frac{xy}{(x + y)^2} \quad \blacksquare$$

Example 5 Simplify $x^{-1}(x^{-1} - y^{-1})^{-1}$.

We have

$$x^{-1}(x^{-1} - y^{-1})^{-1} = \frac{x^{-1}}{x^{-1} - y^{-1}}$$

$$= \frac{\dfrac{1}{x}}{\dfrac{1}{x} - \dfrac{1}{y}}$$

$$= \frac{\dfrac{1}{x}}{\dfrac{y - x}{xy}}$$

$$= \frac{1}{x} \cdot \frac{xy}{y - x}$$

$$= \frac{y}{y - x} \quad \blacksquare$$

Any quotient of two rational expressions in fractional form is called a **complex fraction**. Complex fractions can be simplified in either of two ways, as shown in the next example.

Example 6 Simplify

$$\frac{\dfrac{a}{a + 1} + \dfrac{1}{a}}{\dfrac{1}{a} + \dfrac{1}{a + 1}}.$$

First simplify numerator and denominator respectively.

$$\frac{\dfrac{a}{a+1}+\dfrac{1}{a}}{\dfrac{1}{a}+\dfrac{1}{a+1}}=\frac{\dfrac{a^2+1(a+1)}{a(a+1)}}{\dfrac{1(a+1)+1(a)}{a(a+1)}}$$

$$=\frac{\dfrac{a^2+a+1}{a(a+1)}}{\dfrac{2a+1}{a(a+1)}}$$

Now perform the division.

$$=\frac{a^2+a+1}{a(a+1)}\cdot\frac{a(a+1)}{2a+1}$$

$$=\frac{a^2+a+1}{2a+1}$$

We can also simplify the complex fraction by multiplying both numerator and denominator by the common denominator of all the fractions, in this case $a(a+1)$.

$$\frac{\dfrac{a}{a+1}+\dfrac{1}{a}}{\dfrac{1}{a}+\dfrac{1}{a+1}}=\frac{\left(\dfrac{a}{a+1}+\dfrac{1}{a}\right)a(a+1)}{\left(\dfrac{1}{a}+\dfrac{1}{a+1}\right)a(a+1)}$$

$$=\frac{a^2+(a+1)}{(a+1)+a}$$

$$=\frac{a^2+a+1}{2a+1}\quad\blacksquare$$

1.6 Exercises   *Give the domain of each of the following.*

1. $\dfrac{2x}{5x-3}$ 2. $\dfrac{6x}{2x-8}$ 3. $\dfrac{-8}{x^2+1}$ 4. $\dfrac{3x}{2x^2+3}$

Find each of the following.

5. $\dfrac{x+y}{5}\cdot\dfrac{3}{x+y}$

6. $\dfrac{7(a+b)}{12}\cdot\dfrac{4}{a+b}$

7. $\dfrac{x(y+2)}{4}\div\dfrac{x}{2}$

8. $\dfrac{mn}{m+n}\div\dfrac{p}{m+n}$

9. $\dfrac{x^2+x}{5}\cdot\dfrac{25}{xy+y}$

10. $\dfrac{3m+6}{5m+5}\cdot\dfrac{5m+20}{6m+12}$

11. $\dfrac{a^2-a-6}{a+2}\div\dfrac{a-3}{a+2}$

12. $\dfrac{m^2+11m+30}{m+6}\div\dfrac{m+5}{m+6}$

13. $\dfrac{p^2-p-12}{p^2-2p-15}\cdot\dfrac{p^2-9p+20}{p^2-8p+16}$

14. $\dfrac{x^2 + 2x - 15}{x^2 + 11x + 30} \cdot \dfrac{x^2 + 2x - 24}{x^2 - 8x + 15}$

15. $\left(1 + \dfrac{1}{x}\right)\left(1 - \dfrac{1}{x}\right)$

16. $\left(3 + \dfrac{2}{y}\right)\left(3 - \dfrac{2}{y}\right)$

17. $\dfrac{x^3 + y^3}{x^2 - y^2} \cdot \dfrac{x + y}{x^2 - xy + y^2}$

18. $\dfrac{8y^3 - 125}{4y^2 - 20y + 25} \cdot \dfrac{2y - 5}{y}$

19. $\dfrac{x^3 + y^3}{x^3 - y^3} \cdot \dfrac{x^2 - y^2}{x^2 + 2xy + y^2}$

20. $\dfrac{x^2 - y^2}{(x - y)^2} \cdot \dfrac{x^2 - xy + y^2}{x^2 - 2xy + y^2} \div \dfrac{x^3 + y^3}{(x - y)^4}$

21. $\dfrac{m}{m + n} + \dfrac{n}{m + n}$

22. $\dfrac{3}{y} + \dfrac{4}{y}$

23. $\dfrac{1}{y} + \dfrac{1}{y + 1}$

24. $\dfrac{2}{(3x - 1)} + \dfrac{1}{4(x - 1)}$

25. $\dfrac{2}{a + b} - \dfrac{1}{2(a + b)}$

26. $\dfrac{3}{m} - \dfrac{1}{m - 1}$

27. $\dfrac{m + 1}{m - 1} + \dfrac{m - 1}{m + 1}$

28. $\dfrac{2}{x - 1} + \dfrac{1}{1 - x}$

29. $\dfrac{3}{a - 2} - \dfrac{1}{2 - a}$

30. $\dfrac{q}{p - q} - \dfrac{q}{q - p}$

31. $\dfrac{x + y}{2x - y} - \dfrac{2x}{y - 2x}$

32. $\dfrac{m - 4}{3m - 4} + \dfrac{3m + 2}{4 - 3m}$

33. $\dfrac{r}{r^2 + 5r + 6} + \dfrac{5r}{r^2 + 2r - 3}$

34. $\dfrac{5}{t^2 - 1} - \dfrac{8}{t^2 + 2t + 1}$

35. $\dfrac{1}{a^2 - 5a + 6} - \dfrac{1}{a^2 - 4}$

36. $\dfrac{-3}{m^2 - m - 2} - \dfrac{1}{m^2 + 3m + 2}$

37. $\left(\dfrac{3}{p - 1} - \dfrac{2}{p + 1}\right)\left(\dfrac{p - 1}{p}\right)$

38. $\left(\dfrac{y}{y^2 - 1} - \dfrac{y}{y^2 - 2y + 1}\right)\left(\dfrac{y - 1}{y + 1}\right)$

39. $\dfrac{3a}{a^2 + 5a - 6} - \dfrac{2a}{a^2 + 7a + 6}$

40. $\dfrac{2k}{k^2 + 4k + 3} + \dfrac{3k}{k^2 + 5k + 6}$

41. $\dfrac{4x - 1}{x^2 + 3x - 10} + \dfrac{2x + 3}{x^2 + 4x - 5}$

42. $\dfrac{3y + 5}{y^2 - 9y + 20} + \dfrac{2y - 7}{y^2 - 2y - 8}$

43. $\dfrac{\dfrac{1}{x + h} - \dfrac{1}{x}}{h}$

44. $\dfrac{1}{h}\left(\dfrac{1}{(x + h)^2 + 9} - \dfrac{1}{x^2 + 9}\right)$

Perform all indicated operations. Write all answers with positive integer exponents. Assume that all variables represent nonzero real numbers.

45. $\dfrac{a^{-1} + b^{-1}}{(ab)^{-1}}$

46. $\dfrac{p^{-1} - q^{-1}}{(pq)^{-1}}$

47. $\dfrac{r^{-1} + q^{-1}}{r^{-1} - a^{-1}} \cdot \dfrac{r - q}{r + q}$

48. $\dfrac{xy^{-1} + yx^{-1}}{x^2 + y^2}$

49. $(a + b)^{-1}(a^{-1} + b^{-1})$

50. $(m^{-1} + n^{-1})^{-1}$

51. $(x - 9y^{-1})[(x - 3y^{-1})(x + 3y^{-1})]^{-1}$

52. $(m + n)^{-1}(m^{-2} - n^{-2})^{-1}$

Perform the indicated operations.

53. $\dfrac{1+\dfrac{1}{x}}{1-\dfrac{1}{x}}$

55. $\dfrac{1+\dfrac{1}{1-b}}{1-\dfrac{1}{1+b}}$

57. $1+\dfrac{1}{1+\dfrac{1}{x}}$

54. $\dfrac{2-\dfrac{2}{y}}{2+\dfrac{2}{y}}$

56. $m-\dfrac{m}{m+\dfrac{1}{2}}$

58. $1-\dfrac{1}{1-\dfrac{1}{x}}$

1.7 Radicals

Given any positive real number b, there is a positive real number a such that $b = a^2$. The number a is the **square root** of b, written $a = \sqrt{b}$. The symbol $\sqrt{}$ is a **radical,** and b is the **radicand.**

If a is a square root of b, then $-a$ is also a square root of b, since $(-a)^2 = a^2 = b$. The symbol $\sqrt{b}$ is always reserved for the *positive* square root of b. In fact, the positive square root of b is called the **principal** square root of b.

In the same way, if b is *any* real number, $\sqrt[3]{b}$ represents the **cube root** of b:

$$\sqrt[3]{b} = a \qquad \text{means that} \qquad a^3 = b.$$

Example 1 (a) $\sqrt{64} = 8$ since $8 > 0$ and $8^2 = 64$

(b) $-\sqrt{100} = -10$

(c) $\sqrt{-4}$ is not a real number, since there is no real number whose square is -4

(d) $\sqrt[3]{8} = 2$ since $2^3 = 8$

(e) $\sqrt[3]{-1000} = -10$ since $(-10)^3 = -1000$ ▍

If $b > 0$, then both $\sqrt{b}$ and $\sqrt[3]{b}$ are positive. If $b < 0$, then $\sqrt{b}$ is not a real number, while $\sqrt[3]{b} < 0$.

In general, if a and b are nonnegative real numbers, and n is a positive integer, or if both a and b are negative and n is an odd positive integer, then

$$\boxed{\sqrt[n]{b} = a \qquad \text{means} \qquad a^n = b.}$$

We call $\sqrt[n]{b}$ the **principal nth root** of b (often abbreviated as just the **nth root** of b); n is the **index** of the **radical expression** $\sqrt[n]{b}$. The number b is the *radicand.*

Example 2 (a) $\sqrt[5]{32} = 2$ since $2^5 = 32$

(b) $\sqrt[4]{256} = 4$, since $4^4 = 256$

(c) $\sqrt[7]{-128} = -2$, since $(-2)^7 = -128$

(d) $\sqrt[6]{-64}$ is not a real number   ▍

The basic properties of nth roots are summarized in the following theorem.

Theorem 1.4   For any real numbers a and b and for any positive integers m and n, for which the following are real numbers,

(a) $(\sqrt[n]{a})^n = a$

(b) If n is even, $\sqrt[n]{a^n} = |a|$;
    if n is odd, $\sqrt[n]{a^n} = a$

(c) $\sqrt[n]{a} \cdot \sqrt[n]{b} = \sqrt[n]{ab}$

(d) $\dfrac{\sqrt[n]{a}}{\sqrt[n]{b}} = \sqrt[n]{\dfrac{a}{b}}$ $(b \neq 0)$

(e) $\sqrt[m]{\sqrt[n]{a}} = \sqrt[mn]{a}$.

We prove only part of this result, with the remainder left as exercises. To prove (a), let $x = \sqrt[n]{a}$. Then, by the definition of nth root, $x^n = a$. By substitution, $(\sqrt[n]{a})^n = x^n = a$, which is what we wanted to show.

To verify (c), let $x = \sqrt[n]{a}$, and $y = \sqrt[n]{b}$. Then, by the definition of nth root, $x^n = a$ and $y^n = b$. Hence, $x^n \cdot y^n = ab$. However, by our previous work with exponents, $x^n \cdot y^n = (xy)^n$, giving

$$(xy)^n = ab.$$

Thus, xy is an nth root of ab, or

$$xy = \sqrt[n]{ab}.$$

Substituting the original values of x and y gives

$$\sqrt[n]{a} \cdot \sqrt[n]{b} = \sqrt[n]{ab}.$$

Example 3   Find each of the following. Assume that all variables represent nonnegative real numbers.

(a) $\sqrt{3^2} = |3| = 3$, by part (b) of the theorem

(b) $\sqrt{(-7)^2} = |-7| = 7$, by part (b)

(c) $\sqrt[3]{(-6)^3} = -6$ by part (b)

(d) $(\sqrt[4]{3})^4 = 3$, by part (a)

(e) $(\sqrt[6]{-64})^6$ is not a real number, since $\sqrt[6]{-64}$ is not a real number

(f) $\sqrt{6} \cdot \sqrt{54} = \sqrt{6 \cdot 54} = \sqrt{324} = 18$, by part (c)

(g) $\sqrt[4]{\sqrt{x}} = \sqrt[8]{x}$, by part (e)

(h) $\sqrt[7]{\sqrt[3]{2y}} = \sqrt[21]{2y}$ ▌

The results of the theorem can also be used to simplify radical expressions. An expression containing a radical is **simplified** when all the following conditions are satisfied.

1. All possible factors have been removed from under the radical sign.

2. The index on the radical is as small as possible.

3. All radicals are removed from any denominators (a process called **rationalizing** the denominator).

4. All indicated operations have been performed if possible.

Example 4   Simplify each of the following. Assume that all variables represent nonnegative real numbers.

(a) $\sqrt{75} = \sqrt{25 \cdot 3} = \sqrt{25} \cdot \sqrt{3} = 5\sqrt{3}$

(b) $\sqrt[3]{81x^5y^7z^6} = \sqrt[3]{27 \cdot 3 \cdot x^3 \cdot x^2 \cdot y^6 \cdot y \cdot z^6}$

$\qquad = \sqrt[3]{(27x^3y^6z^6)(3x^2y)}$

$\qquad = 3xy^2z^2\sqrt[3]{3x^2y}$

(c) Simplify $\sqrt{98x^3y} + 3x\sqrt{32xy}$.

First remove all perfect square factors from under the radical. Then use the distributive property.

$$\sqrt{98x^3y} + 3x\sqrt{32xy} = \sqrt{49 \cdot 2 \cdot x^2 \cdot x \cdot y} + 3x\sqrt{16 \cdot 2 \cdot x \cdot y}$$

$$= 7x\sqrt{2xy} + (3x)(4)\sqrt{2xy}$$

$$= 7x\sqrt{2xy} + 12x\sqrt{2xy}$$

$$= 19x\sqrt{2xy}$$

(d) $\sqrt[3]{64m^4n^5} \quad \sqrt[3]{-27m^{10}n^{14}} = \sqrt[3]{(64m^3n^3)(mn^2)} - \sqrt[3]{(-27m^9n^{12})(mn^2)}$

$\qquad = 4mn\sqrt[3]{mn^2} - (-3)m^3n^4\sqrt[3]{mn^2}$

$\qquad = 4mn\sqrt[3]{mn^2} + 3m^3n^4\sqrt[3]{mn^2}$

$\qquad = (4 + 3m^2n^3)mn\sqrt[3]{mn^2}$ ▌

Multiplying radical expressions is just like multiplying polynomials.

Example 5 $(\sqrt{2} + 3)(\sqrt{8} - 5) = \sqrt{2}(\sqrt{8}) + \sqrt{2}(-5) + 3\sqrt{8} + 3(-5)$

$\qquad = 4 - 5\sqrt{2} + 6\sqrt{2} - 15$

$\qquad = -11 + \sqrt{2}$ ▌

Example 6   Simplify.

(a) $\dfrac{4}{\sqrt{3}}$

To rationalize the denominator, multiply by $\sqrt{3}/\sqrt{3}$ (or 1) so that the denominator of the product is a rational number.

$$\frac{4}{\sqrt{3}} \cdot \frac{\sqrt{3}}{\sqrt{3}} = \frac{4\sqrt{3}}{3}$$

(b) $\sqrt[4]{\dfrac{3}{5}}$

Start by writing the radical of a quotient as the quotient of radicals:

$$\sqrt[4]{\frac{3}{5}} = \frac{\sqrt[4]{3}}{\sqrt[4]{5}}$$

To rationalize the denominator, multiply numerator and denominator by $\sqrt[4]{5^3}$. We use this number so that the denominator will be a rational number.

$$\frac{\sqrt[4]{3}}{\sqrt[4]{5}} = \frac{\sqrt[4]{3} \cdot \sqrt[4]{5^3}}{\sqrt[4]{5} \cdot \sqrt[4]{5^3}} = \frac{\sqrt[4]{3 \cdot 5^3}}{\sqrt[4]{5^4}} = \frac{\sqrt[4]{375}}{5}$$ ▌

Example 7 Rationalize the denominator of $\dfrac{1}{1 - \sqrt{2}}$.

The best approach here is to multiply both numerator and denominator by the **conjugate*** of the denominator, in this case $1 + \sqrt{2}$.

$$\frac{1}{1 - \sqrt{2}} = \frac{1(1 + \sqrt{2})}{(1 - \sqrt{2})(1 + \sqrt{2})} = \frac{1 + \sqrt{2}}{1 - 2} = -1 - \sqrt{2}. \quad \blacksquare$$

1.7 Exercises *Simplify each of the following. Assume that all variables represent nonnegative real numbers, and that no denominators are zero.*

1. $\sqrt{50}$

2. $\sqrt{12}$

3. $\sqrt[3]{81}$

4. $\sqrt[3]{16}$

5. $\sqrt[3]{250}$

6. $\sqrt[3]{128}$

7. $-\sqrt{\dfrac{9}{5}}$

8. $\sqrt{\dfrac{3}{8}}$

9. $\sqrt{\dfrac{5}{12}}$

10. $\sqrt{\dfrac{49}{5}}$

11. $\sqrt{5} + \sqrt{20}$

12. $\sqrt{6} + \sqrt{54}$

13. $4\sqrt{3} - 5\sqrt{12} + 3\sqrt{75}$

14. $2\sqrt{5} - 3\sqrt{20} + 2\sqrt{45}$

15. $-\sqrt[3]{\dfrac{3}{2}}$

16. $-\sqrt[3]{\dfrac{4}{5}}$

17. $\sqrt[4]{\dfrac{3}{2}}$

18. $\sqrt[4]{\dfrac{32}{81}}$

19. $3\sqrt[3]{16} - 4\sqrt[3]{2}$

20. $\sqrt[3]{2} - \sqrt[3]{16} + 2\sqrt[3]{54}$

21. $\dfrac{1}{\sqrt{3}} - \dfrac{2}{\sqrt{12}} + 2\sqrt{3}$

22. $\dfrac{1}{\sqrt{2}} + \dfrac{3}{\sqrt{8}} + \dfrac{1}{\sqrt{32}}$

23. $\sqrt{2x^3y^2z^4}$

24. $\sqrt{98r^3s^4t^{10}}$

25. $\sqrt[3]{16z^5x^8y^4}$

26. $\sqrt[3]{81p^5x^2y^6}$

27. $\sqrt[4]{m^2n^6p^8}$

28. $\sqrt[4]{x^8y^6z^{10}}$

29. $\sqrt{a^3b^5} - 2\sqrt{a^7b^3} + \sqrt{a^3b^9}$

30. $\sqrt{p^7q^3} - \sqrt{p^5q^9} + \sqrt{p^9q}$

31. $(\sqrt{2} + 3)(\sqrt{2} - 3)$

32. $(\sqrt{5} + \sqrt{2})(\sqrt{5} - \sqrt{2})$

33. $(\sqrt[3]{11} - 1)(\sqrt[3]{11^2} + \sqrt[3]{11} + 1)$

34. $(\sqrt[3]{7} + 3)(\sqrt[3]{7^2} - 3\sqrt[3]{7} + 9)$

35. $(\sqrt{3} + \sqrt{8})^2$

36. $(\sqrt{2} - 1)^2$

37. $(3\sqrt{2} + \sqrt{3})(2\sqrt{3} - \sqrt{2})$

38. $(4\sqrt{5} - 1)(3\sqrt{5} + 2)$

39. $(2\sqrt[3]{3} + 1)(\sqrt[3]{3} - 4)$

40. $(\sqrt[3]{4} + 3)(5\sqrt{4} + 1)$

41. $\sqrt{\dfrac{2}{3x}}$

42. $\sqrt{\dfrac{5}{3p}}$

43. $\sqrt{\dfrac{x^5y^3}{z^2}}$

44. $\sqrt{\dfrac{g^3h^5}{r^3}}$

45. $\sqrt[3]{\dfrac{8}{x^2}}$

46. $\sqrt[3]{\dfrac{9}{16p^4}}$

47. $-\sqrt[3]{\dfrac{k^5m^3r^2}{r^8}}$

48. $-\sqrt[3]{\dfrac{9x^5y^6}{z^5w^2}}$

49. $\sqrt[4]{\dfrac{g^3h^5}{9r^6}}$

50. $\sqrt[4]{\dfrac{32x^6}{y^5}}$

51. $\dfrac{\sqrt[3]{mn} \cdot \sqrt[3]{m^2}}{\sqrt[3]{n^2}}$

52. $\dfrac{\sqrt[3]{8m^2n^3} \cdot \sqrt[3]{2m^2}}{\sqrt[3]{32m^4n^3}}$

53. $\dfrac{\sqrt[4]{32x^5y} \cdot \sqrt[4]{2xy^4}}{\sqrt[4]{4x^3y^2}}$

54. $\dfrac{\sqrt[4]{rs^2t^3} \cdot \sqrt[4]{r^3s^2t}}{\sqrt[4]{r^2t^3}}$

55. $\sqrt[3]{\sqrt{4}}$

56. $\sqrt[4]{\sqrt[3]{2}}$

57. $\sqrt[6]{\sqrt[3]{x}}$

58. $\sqrt[8]{\sqrt[4]{y}}$

59. $\dfrac{3}{1 - \sqrt{2}}$

60. $\dfrac{2}{1 + \sqrt{5}}$

*The **conjugate** of $a + b\sqrt{m}$ is $a - b\sqrt{m}$, for any real numbers a, b, and positive real number m.

61. $\dfrac{\sqrt{3}}{4 + \sqrt{3}}$

62. $\dfrac{2\sqrt{7}}{3 - \sqrt{7}}$

63. $\dfrac{\sqrt{x} + \sqrt{x+1}}{\sqrt{x} - \sqrt{x+1}}$

64. $\dfrac{\sqrt{p} + \sqrt{p^2 - 1}}{\sqrt{p} - \sqrt{p^2 - 1}}$

65. $\dfrac{5}{\sqrt[3]{a} + \sqrt[3]{b}}$

66. $\dfrac{1}{\sqrt[3]{m} - \sqrt[3]{n}}$

In advanced mathematics it is sometimes useful to write a radical expression with a rational numerator. The procedure is similar to rationalizing the denominator. Rationalize the numerator of each of the following.

67. $\dfrac{\sqrt{3}}{2}$

68. $\dfrac{\sqrt{6}}{5}$

69. $\dfrac{1 + \sqrt{2}}{2}$

70. $\dfrac{1 - \sqrt{3}}{3}$

71. $\dfrac{\sqrt{x}}{1 + \sqrt{x}}$

72. $\dfrac{\sqrt{p}}{1 - \sqrt{p}}$

73. $\dfrac{\sqrt{x} + \sqrt{x+1}}{\sqrt{x} - \sqrt{x+1}}$

74. $\dfrac{\sqrt{p} + \sqrt{p^2 - 1}}{\sqrt{p} - \sqrt{p^2 - 1}}$

⊙ *Evaluate each of the following. Write all answers in scientific notation with three significant digits. For fourth roots, use the square root key twice.*

75. $\sqrt{2.876 \times 10^7}$

76. $\sqrt{5.432 \times 10^9}$

77. $\sqrt[4]{3.87 \times 10^{-4}}$

78. $\sqrt[4]{5.913 \times 10^{-8}}$

79. $\dfrac{2.04 \times 10^{-3}}{\sqrt{5.97 \times 10^{-5}}}$

80. $\dfrac{3.86 \times 10^{-5}}{\sqrt{4.82 \times 10^{-5}}}$

81. $\sqrt{(4.721)^2 + (8.963)^2 - 2(4.721)(8.963)(.0468)}$

82. $\sqrt{(157.3)^2 + (184.7)^2 - 2(157.3)(184.7)(.9082)}$

Prove each of the following (for all real numbers a *and* b *and for any positive integers* m *and* n *for which all the following are real numbers).*

83. If n is even, $\sqrt[n]{a^n} = |a|$.

84. If n is odd, $\sqrt[n]{a^n} = a$.

85. $\dfrac{\sqrt[n]{a}}{\sqrt[n]{b}} = \sqrt[n]{\dfrac{a}{b}}$ $(b \neq 0)$

86. $\sqrt[m]{\sqrt[n]{a}} = \sqrt[mn]{a}$

⊙ **87.** Use a calculator to find an approximate value for $\sqrt{5 + 2\sqrt{6}}$.

88. Show that $\sqrt{5 + 2\sqrt{6}} = \sqrt{2} + \sqrt{3}$.

1.8 Rational Exponents

We have now defined a^n for all integer values of n. In this section we wish to extend this definition to give meaning to a^n for *rational* (and not just integer) values of the exponent.

To start, let us define $a^{1/n}$ for positive integers n. Any definition of $a^{1/n}$ that we give should be consistent with past rules of exponents. In particular, we want the rule $(b^m)^n = b^{mn}$ to be still valid. If we replace b^m with $a^{1/n}$, then

$$(a^{1/n})^n = a^{n/n} = a^1 = a.$$

Thus, $a^{1/n}$ must be an nth root of a, or, as a definition,

If a is a real number, n is a positive integer, and $\sqrt[n]{a}$ is a real number, then

$$a^{1/n} = \sqrt[n]{a}.$$

Example 1   (a) $16^{1/2} = \sqrt{16} = 4$

(b) $(-32)^{1/5} = \sqrt[5]{-32} = -2$ ▌

What about rational exponents in general? We want to define $a^{m/n}$ so that all the rules for integer exponents still hold. For the rule $(b^m)^n = b^{mn}$ to hold, we must have $(a^{1/n})^m = a^{m/n}$. Therefore, $a^{m/n}$ is defined as follows:

For all integers m and all positive integers n and all real numbers a for which $\sqrt[n]{a}$ is a real number,

$$a^{m/n} = (\sqrt[n]{a})^m.$$

(a) $125^{2/3} = (\sqrt[3]{125})^2 = 5^2 = 25$

(b) $x^{5/2} = (\sqrt{x})^5$ $(x \geq 0)$

(c) $(16m)^{3/4} = (\sqrt[4]{16m})^3 = (2\sqrt[4]{m})^3 = 8(\sqrt[4]{m})^3$ $(m \geq 0)$ ▌

We shall now show that $(a^{1/n})^m = (a^m)^{1/n}$, so that $a^{m/n}$ is also equal to $\sqrt[n]{a^m}$.

Theorem 1.5   For all integers m and positive integers n, and all real numbers for which $\sqrt[n]{a^m}$ exists,

$$a^{m/n} = \sqrt[n]{a^m}.$$

To prove this, we use some of the results of this chapter.

$$[(a^{1/n})^m]^n = (a^{1/n})^{mn} = [(a^{1/n})^n]^m = a^m$$

Hence, $(a^{1/n})^m$ is an nth root of a^m, so that

$$(a^{1/n})^m = (a^m)^{1/n}.$$

Since $a^{m/n} = (a^{1/n})^m$ by definition, then

$$a^{m/n} = (a^{1/n})^m = (a^m)^{1/n}.$$

In radical form,

$$a^{m/n} = (\sqrt[n]{a})^m = \sqrt[n]{a^m}.$$

Although either $(\sqrt[n]{a})^m$ or $\sqrt[n]{a^m}$ can be used to evaluate $a^{m/n}$, in practice the definition $(\sqrt[n]{a})^m$ is usually easier to calculate.

It can be shown that all the earlier results concerning integer exponents also apply to rational exponents. We will not prove this, but will assume it from now on.

Example 3   Evaluate each of the following.

(a) $(27)^{4/3} = ((27)^{1/3})^4 = (3)^4 = 81$

(b) $(27)^{4/3} = ((27)^4)^{1/3} = (531,441)^{1/3} = 81$

(c) $4^{5/2} = (4^{1/2})^5 = 2^5 = 32$ ▌

Example 4   (a) $81^{5/4} \cdot 4^{-3/2} = (3^4)^{5/4}(2^2)^{-3/2} = 3^5 \cdot 2^{-3} = \dfrac{3^5}{8}$

(b) $\left(\dfrac{3m^{5/6}}{y^{3/4}}\right)^2 \cdot \left(\dfrac{8y^3}{m^6}\right)^{2/3} = \dfrac{9m^{5/3}}{y^{3/2}} \cdot \dfrac{4y^2}{m^4} = \dfrac{36y^{1/2}}{m^{7/3}}$ ▌

Example 5   (a) $\dfrac{\sqrt[4]{9}}{\sqrt{3}} = \dfrac{9^{1/4}}{3^{1/2}} = \dfrac{(3^2)^{1/4}}{3^{1/2}} = \dfrac{3^{1/2}}{3^{1/2}} = 1$

(b) $\dfrac{\sqrt[3]{m^8}}{\sqrt{m^5}} = \dfrac{m^{8/3}}{m^{5/2}} = m^{8/3-5/2} = m^{1/6} = \sqrt[6]{m}$

(c) $\sqrt{a^3b^5} \ \sqrt[3]{a^4b^2} = (a^3b^5)^{1/2}(a^4b^2)^{1/3}$

$\qquad = (a^{3/2}b^{5/2})(a^{4/3}b^{2/3})$

$\qquad = (a^{3/2+4/3})(b^{5/2+2/3})$

$\qquad = a^{17/6}b^{19/6}$

$\qquad = a^2 \cdot a^{5/6} \cdot b^3 \cdot b^{1/6}$

$\qquad = a^2b^3 \ \sqrt[6]{a^5b}$ ▌

1.8   Exercises

Simplify each of the following. Assume all variables represent nonnegative real numbers.

1. $4^{1/2}$

2. $25^{1/2}$

3. $8^{2/3}$

4. $81^{3/4}$

5. $27^{-2/3}$

6. $32^{-4/5}$

7. $\left(\dfrac{4}{9}\right)^{-3/2}$

8. $\left(\dfrac{1}{8}\right)^{-5/3}$

9. $(16p^4)^{1/2}$

10. $(36r^6)^{1/2}$

11. $(27x^6)^{2/3}$

12. $(64a^{12})^{5/6}$

Write each of the following using rational exponents instead of radical signs. Assume that all variables represent positive real numbers.

13. $\sqrt[3]{x^2}$

14. $\sqrt[3]{y^4}$

15. $\sqrt[3]{z^5}$

16. $p\sqrt[3]{p^4}$

17. $y^3\sqrt{y^6}$

18. $p^2\sqrt[3]{\sqrt[4]{p^8}}$

19. $m^{-2/3}\sqrt[4]{m^6}$

20. $y^{-3/2}\sqrt[4]{\sqrt{y^6}}$

Rewrite each of the following, using only positive exponents. Assume that all variables represent positive real numbers and that variables used as exponents represent rational numbers.

21. $(m^{2/3})(m^{5/3})$

22. $(x^{4/5})(x^{2/5})$

23. $(1 + n)^{1/2}(1 + n)^{3/4}$

24. $(m + 7)^{-1/6}(m + 7)^{-2/3}$

25. $(2y^{3/4}z)(3y^{1/4}z^{-1/3})$

26. $(4a^{-1/2}b^{2/3})(a^{3/2}b^{-1/3})$

27. $(r^{5/7}s^{3/5})(r^{-1/2}s^{-1/4})$

28. $(t^{3/2}w^{3/5})(t^{-1/3}w^{-1/5})$

29. $\dfrac{a^{4/3} \cdot b^{1/2}}{a^{2/3} \cdot b^{-3/2}}$

30. $\dfrac{x^{1/3} \cdot y^{2/3} \cdot z^{1/4}}{x^{5/3} \cdot y^{-1/3} \cdot z^{3/4}}$

31. $\dfrac{k^{-3/5} \cdot h^{-1/3} \cdot t^{2/5}}{k^{-1/5} \cdot h^{-2/3} \cdot t^{1/5}}$

32. $\dfrac{m^{7/3} \cdot n^{-2/5} \cdot p^{3/8}}{m^{-2/3} \cdot n^{3/5} \cdot p^{-5/8}}$

33. $\dfrac{k^{3/2} \cdot k^{-1/2}}{k^{1/4} \cdot k^{3/4}}$

34. $\dfrac{m^{2/5} \cdot m^{3/5} \cdot m^{-4/5}}{m^{1/5} \cdot m^{-6/5}}$

35. $\dfrac{x^{-2/3} \cdot x^{4/3}}{x^{1/2} \cdot x^{-3/4}}$

36. $\dfrac{-4a^{1/2} \cdot a^{2/3}}{a^{-5/6}}$

37. $\dfrac{8y^{2/3}y^{-1}}{2^{-1}y^{3/4} \cdot y^{-1/6}}$

38. $\dfrac{9 \cdot k^{1/3} \cdot k^{-1/2} \cdot k^{-1/6}}{k^{-2/3}}$

39. $\left(\dfrac{x^4 y^3 z}{16x^{-6}yz^5}\right)^{-1/2}$

40. $\left(\dfrac{p^3 r^9}{27p^{-3}r^{-6}}\right)^{-1/3}$

41. $(r^{3/p})^{2p}(r^{1/p})p^2$

42. $(m^{2/x})^{x/3}(m^{x/4})^{2/x}$

43. $\dfrac{m^{1-a} \cdot m^a}{m^{-1/2}}$

44. $\dfrac{(y^{3-b})(y^{2b-1})}{y^{1/2}}$

45. $\dfrac{(p^{1/n})(p^{1/m})}{p^{-m/n}}$

46. $\dfrac{(q^{2r/3})(q^r)^{-1/3}}{(q^{4/3})^{1/r}}$

47. $(r^{1/2} - r^{-1/2})^2$

48. $(p^{1/2} - p^{-1/2})(p^{1/2} + p^{-1/2})$

49. $[(x^{1/2} - x^{-1/2})^2 + 4]^{1/2}$

50. $[(x^{1/2} + x^{-1/2})^2 - 4]^{1/2}$

Write each of the following as a single radical. Assume all variables represent nonnegative real numbers.

51. $\sqrt{r^3} \cdot \sqrt[3]{r}$

52. $\sqrt[6]{y^3} \cdot \sqrt[4]{y^3}$

53. $\sqrt[10]{p^8} \cdot \sqrt{p}$

54. $\sqrt[8]{y^6} \cdot \sqrt[3]{y}$

55. $\sqrt[4]{p^2 q^8} \cdot \sqrt[3]{p^5}$

56. $\sqrt[6]{q^4 r^{18}} \cdot \sqrt[3]{r^5}$

57. $\sqrt{m^2 n} \cdot \sqrt[3]{m^4 n^2}$

58. $\sqrt[4]{y^2 r^3} \cdot \sqrt[3]{y^6}$

59. $\sqrt[5]{m^3 n^6} \cdot \sqrt[3]{m^4 n^5}$

60. $\sqrt[6]{r^8 s^5} \cdot \sqrt[3]{r^3 s^7}$

One important application of mathematics to business and management concerns supply and demand. Usually, as the price of an item increases, the supply increases and the demand decreases. By studying past records of supply and demand at different prices, economists can construct an equation which describes (approximately) supply and demand for a given item. The next two exercises show examples of this.

61. The price of a certain type of solar heater is approximated by p, where

$$p = 2x^{1/2} + 3x^{2/3}$$

and x is the number of units supplied. Find the price when the supply is 64 units.

62. The demand for a certain commodity and the price are related by the equation

$$p = 1000 - 200x^{-2/3} \qquad (x > 0),$$

where x is the number of units of the product demanded. Find the price when the demand is 27.

In our system of government, the president is elected by the electoral college and not by individual voters. Because of this, smaller states have a greater voice in the selection of a president than they would otherwise. Two political scientists have studied the problems of campaigning for president under the current system and have concluded that candidates should allot their money according to the formula:

$$\text{amount for large state} = \left(\dfrac{E_{\text{large}}}{E_{\text{small}}}\right)^{3/2} \times \text{amount for small state.}$$

Here E_{large} represents the electoral vote of the large state, and E_{small} represents the electoral vote of the small state. Find the amount that should be spent in each of the following larger states if $1,000,000 is spent in the small state and the following statements are true.

63. The large state has 48 electoral votes, and the small state has 3.

64. The large state has 36 electoral votes, and the small state has 4.

⦿ **65.** Six votes in a small state; 28 in a large.

66. Nine votes in a small state; 32 in a large.

A Delta Airlines map gives a formula for calculating the visible distance from a jet plane to the horizon. On a clear day, this distance is approximated by

$$D = 1.22x^{1/2},$$

where x is altitude in feet, and D is distance to the horizon in miles. Find D for an altitude of

⦿ **67.** 5000 feet

68. 10,000 feet

69. 30,000 feet

70. 40,000 feet.

The Galápagos Islands are a chain of islands ranging in size from 2 to 2249 square miles. A biologist has shown that the number of different land-plant species on an island in this chain is related to the size of the island by

$$S = 28.6A^{0.32},$$

where A is the area of an island in square miles and S is the number of different plant species on that island. Estimate S (rounding to the nearest whole number) for islands of area

⦿ **71.** 1 square mile

72. 25 square miles

73. 300 square miles

74. 2000 square miles.

Chapter 1 Review Exercises

Identify the property which tells why the following are true.

1. $6 \cdot 4 = 4 \cdot 6$

2. $8(5 + 9) = (5 + 9)8$

3. $3 + (-3) = 0$

4. If $x \neq 0$, then $x \cdot \dfrac{1}{x} = 1$

5. $4 \cdot 6 + 4 \cdot 12 = 4(6 + 12)$

6. $3(4 \cdot 2) = (3 \cdot 4)2$

7. Is the set of rational numbers closed for division?

8. Is the set of irrationals closed for division?

Simplify each of the following.

9. $(4 + 2 \cdot 8) \div 3$

10. $-7 + (-6)(-2) - 8$

11. $\dfrac{-9 + (2)(-8) + 7}{3(-4) - (-1 - 3)}$

Answer true *or* false *for the following.*

12. $-6 + 10$ is an integer

13. $-\sqrt{8}$ is a rational number

Write the following numbers in numerical order, from smallest to largest.

14. $\dfrac{5}{6}, \dfrac{1}{2}, -\dfrac{2}{3}, -\dfrac{5}{4}, -\dfrac{3}{8}$

15. $|6 - 4|, -|-2|, |8 + 1|, -|3 - (-2)|$

16. $\sqrt{7}, -\sqrt{8}, -|\sqrt{16}|, |-\sqrt{12}|$

Write without absolute value bars.

17. $|3 - \sqrt{7}|$

18. $|\sqrt{8} - 3|$

19. $|m - 3|$, if $m > 3$

20. $|-6 - x^2|$

In each of the following exercises, the coordinates of three points are given. Find (a) $d(A, B)$ *(b)* $d(A, B) + d(B, C)$.

21. $A, -2; B, -1; C, 10$

22. $A, -8; B, -12; C, -15$

Under what conditions are the following statements true?

23. $|x| = x$

24. $|a + b| = -a - b$

25. $|x + y| = -|x| - |y|$

26. $|x| \leq 0$

27. $d(A, B) = 0$

28. $d(A, B) + d(B, C) = d(A, C)$

Evaluate each of the following.

29. $(-6x^2 - 4x + 11) + (-2x^2 - 11x + 5)$

30. $(3x^3 - 9x^2 - 5) - (-4x^3 + 6x^2) + (2x^3 - 9)$

31. $(8k - 7)(3k + 2)$

32. $(3r - 2)(r^2 + 4r - 8)$

33. $\dfrac{2x^5 t^2 \cdot 4x^3 t}{16x^2 t^3}$

34. $\dfrac{(2k^2)^2 (3k^3)}{(4k^4)^2}$

35. $(r^z - 8)(r^z + 8)$

Factor as completely as possible.

36. $2x^2 - 8x + 6$

37. $(x - 1)^2 - 4$

38. $a^3 - 27b^3$

39. $3x(x - 2) + 9x^2(x - 2) - 12x^3(x - 2)$

40. $2bx - b + 6x - 3$

41. $z^{6n} - 100$

Perform the indicated operation.

42. $\dfrac{3m - 9}{8m} \cdot \dfrac{16m + 24}{15}$

43. $\dfrac{5x^2 y}{x + y} \cdot \dfrac{3x + 3y}{30xy^2}$

44. $\dfrac{1}{4y} + \dfrac{8}{5y}$

45. $\dfrac{m}{4 - m} + \dfrac{3m}{m - 4}$

46. $\left(1 - \dfrac{3}{p}\right)\left(1 + \dfrac{3}{p}\right)$

47. $\dfrac{3}{x^2 - 4x + 3} - \dfrac{2}{x^2 - 1}$

48. $\dfrac{x^2 + x - 2}{x^2 + 5x + 6} \div \dfrac{x^2 + 3x - 4}{x^2 + 4x + 3}$

49. $\dfrac{\dfrac{1}{p} + \dfrac{1}{q}}{1 - \dfrac{1}{pq}}$

50. $\left(\dfrac{1}{(x + h)^2 + 16} - \dfrac{1}{x^2 + 16}\right) \div h$

51. $1 + \dfrac{1}{1 + \dfrac{1}{1 + x}}$

Simplify each of the following. Assume all variables represent nonzero real numbers.

52. $\dfrac{(p^4)(p^{-2})}{p^{-6}}$

53. $(-6x^2 y^{-3} z^2)^{-2}$

54. $\dfrac{6^{-1} r^3 s^{-2}}{6r^4 s^{-3}}$

55. $\dfrac{(3m^{-2})^{-2}(m^2 n^{-4})^3}{9m^{-3} n^{-5}}$

56. $\dfrac{(2x^{-3})^2 (3x^2)^{-2}}{6(x^2 y^3)}$

57. $\dfrac{m^{-1} - (2n)^{-1}}{(2mn)^{-1}}$

Simplify. Assume that all variables represent nonnegative numbers.

58. $\sqrt{200}$

59. $\sqrt{\dfrac{7}{3r}}$

60. $\sqrt{\dfrac{2^7 y^8}{m^3}}$

61. $-\sqrt[3]{\dfrac{r^6 m^5}{z^2}}$

62. $\sqrt[4]{\sqrt[3]{m}}$

63. $\dfrac{\sqrt[4]{8p^2 q^5} \cdot \sqrt[4]{2p^3 q}}{\sqrt[4]{p^5 q^2}}$

64. $\sqrt{18m^3} - 3m\sqrt{32m} + 5\sqrt{m^3}$

65. $\dfrac{z}{\sqrt{z - 1}}$

66. $\dfrac{6}{3 - \sqrt{2}}$

67. $\dfrac{1}{\sqrt{5} + 2}$

68. $\dfrac{\sqrt{x} - \sqrt{x - 2}}{\sqrt{x} + \sqrt{x - 2}}$

Simplify each of the following. Assume that all variables represent nonnegative real numbers.

69. $36^{-3/2}$

70. $(125m^6)^{-2/3}$

71. $(8r^{3/4} s^{2/3})(2r^{3/2} s^{5/3})$

72. $\dfrac{p^{-3/4} \cdot p^{5/4} \cdot p^{-1/4}}{p \cdot p^{3/4}}$

73. $\left(\dfrac{y^6 x^3 z^{-2}}{16x^5 z^4}\right)^{-1/2}$

74. $\dfrac{m^{2+p} \cdot m^{-2}}{m^{3p}}$

75. $(x^{1/2} - x^{-1/2})^2$

The following exercises are taken with permission from a standard calculus book.

Simplify each of the following.

76. $(|a| + a)(|a| - a)$

77. $\sqrt{[2a^4 + (b^2 - a^2)^2 - (a^2 - b^2)^2][a^6 - (-a^2)^3]}$

Suppose a value of the number a has been given. Let $b = a + 1$ and $c = \sqrt{a + b}$. Show that

78. $b(a - c)^2 + a(b + c)^2 = c^2(ab + c^2)$

79. $b(a - c)^2 + ab(1 + c)^2 = b^2(c^2 + a)$

80. If $x + |x| = x - |x|$, what is x?

81. Prove that if $(x + 1)^2 = (|x| + 1)^2$, then $x \geq 0$.

Suppose $0 < a < 1$ and $a + b = 1$. Are the following less than, equal to, or greater than 1?

82. $a^2 + b^2$

83. $\sqrt{a} + \sqrt{b}$

What are the order relations among $1, a, a^2, \sqrt{a}, \dfrac{1}{a}, b, b^2, \sqrt{b}, \dfrac{1}{b}$ if

84. $\sqrt{b} < a < b$

85. $b < a < \sqrt{b}$

86. If $a > 0$, show that $a + 1/a \geq 2$.

87. If $a > 0$, show that

$$4a + 1 < (\sqrt{a} + \sqrt{a + 1})^2 < 4a + 2$$

Chapter 2

Equations and Inequalities

For many people, the study of algebra is really the study of equations. Many applications of mathematics require the solution of one or more equations. More recently, the study of inequalities has also become important as more and more applications utilize inequalities.

An **equation** is a statement that two expressions are equal. Examples of equations include,

$$x + 2 = 9 \qquad 11y = 5y + 6y \qquad x^2 - 2x - 1 = 0,$$

and so on. In this chapter we discuss the solution of several different kinds of equations and inequalities.

2.1 Linear Equations

To *solve* an equation means to find the number or numbers which make the equation a true statement. A number which is a solution of an equation is said to **satisfy** the equation. An equation which is satisfied by every number in the domain of the variable is called an **identity.** Examples of identities are

$$3x + 4x = 7x, \quad \frac{2m + 3}{2} = m + \frac{3}{2}, \text{ and } x^2 - 3x + 2 = (x - 2)(x - 1).$$

Most equations are satisfied by some numbers, but not satisfied by others. These are called **conditional equations.** Some conditional equations are

$$2m + 3 = 7, \, x^2 - 4x + 2 = 3x - 1, \text{ and } \frac{5r}{r - 1} = 7.$$

Any two equations with the same domain and the same solutions are called **equivalent equations.** For example, $x + 1 = 5$ and $6x + 3 = 27$ are equivalent equations since they both have the same solution, 4. On the other hand, the equations

$$x + 1 = 5 \quad \text{and} \quad (x - 4)(x + 2) = 0$$

are not equivalent. The number 4 is a solution of both equations, but the equation $(x - 4)(x + 2) = 0$ also has a solution of -2.

As a generalization, equations are solved by beginning with the given equation and writing a chain of simpler and simpler equivalent equations. A key way to get these simpler equivalent equations is to use the properties of Chapter 1 which say that we may add the same number to both sides of an equation or that we may multiply both sides of an equation by the same nonzero number. We can expand those properties to include not just numbers that are added or multiplied but algebraic expressions.

In this section, we see how to solve **linear equations,** which are equations equivalent to one of the form $ax + b = 0$, where a and b are real numbers with $a \neq 0$. This equation can be solved by writing the following equivalent equations.

$$ax + b = 0 \qquad \text{given equation}$$

$$ax + b + (-b) = 0 + (-b) \qquad \text{add } -b \text{ on both sides}$$

$$ax = -b$$

$$\frac{1}{a} \cdot ax = \frac{1}{a} \cdot (-b) \qquad \text{multiply by } 1/a \text{ on both sides}$$

$$x = -\frac{b}{a}$$

Example 1   Solve $3(2x - 4) = 7 - (x + 5)$.

By using the distributive property and then collecting like terms, we can get a simpler equivalent equation as follows.

$$3(2x - 4) = 7 - (x + 5)$$
$$6x - 12 = 7 - x - 5$$
$$6x - 12 = 2 - x$$

We now add similar quantities to both sides of the equation.

$$x + 6x - 12 = 2 - x + x$$
$$7x - 12 = 2$$
$$7x - 12 + 12 = 2 + 12$$
$$7x = 14$$

Finally, we multiply both sides by the same quantity.

$$\frac{1}{7} \cdot 7x = \frac{1}{7} \cdot 14$$
$$x = 2 \quad \blacksquare$$

Since each step above is reversible, we need to check the answer only to guard against algebraic or arithmetic errors. Check by substituting 2 for x in the original equation.

Example 2   Solve $\dfrac{3p - 1}{3} - \dfrac{2p}{p - 1} = p$.

We first obtain a simpler equivalent equation by multiplying both sides by $3(p - 1)$, where we must assume $p \neq 1$. (Why?)

$$3(p-1)\left(\frac{3p-1}{3}\right) - 3(p-1)\left(\frac{2p}{p-1}\right) = 3(p-1)p$$

$$(p-1)(3p-1) - 3(2p) = 3p(p-1)$$

$$3p^2 - 4p + 1 - 6p = 3p^2 - 3p$$

We can obtain an even simpler equivalent equation by combining terms and adding $-3p^2$ to both sides.

$$-10p + 1 = -3p$$

We now add $10p$ to both sides.

$$1 = 7p.$$

Multiplying both sides by 1/7 gives

$$1/7 = p.$$

Verify that the solution of the given equation is 1/7. ▌

Example 3 Solve $\dfrac{x}{x-2} = \dfrac{2}{x-2} + 2.$

Multiply both sides of the equation by $x - 2$, assuming that $x - 2 \neq 0$.

$$x = 2 + 2x - 4$$

$$x = 2$$

We had to assume $x - 2 \neq 0$ in order to multiply both sides of the equation by $x - 2$. Our proposed solution of 2, however, makes $x - 2 = 0$. Because of this, the given equation has no solution. (To see that 2 is not a solution, substitute 2 for x in the given equation.) ▌

Sometimes we need to solve an equation with more than one letter in which one letter represents a variable and the others represent constants. As a general rule, the first letters of the alphabet, a, b, c, and so on, are used to represent constants, but letters such as x, y, and z are used for variables.

Example 4 Solve for x.

$$3(2x - 5a) + 4b = 4x - 2.$$

Use the distributive property.

$$6x - 15a + 4b = 4x - 2$$

Get all terms with x on one side of the equation, and all terms without x on the other side.

$$6x - 4x = 15a - 4b - 2$$

$$2x = 15a - 4b - 2$$

$$x = \frac{15a - 4b - 2}{2} \quad ▌$$

2.1 Exercises

Decide which of the following pairs of equations are equivalent.

1. $3x - 5 = 7$
$-6x + 10 = 14$

2. $-x = 2x + 3$
$-3x = 3$

3. $\dfrac{3x}{x-1} = \dfrac{2}{x-1}$
$3x = 2$

4. $\dfrac{x+1}{12} = \dfrac{5}{12}$
$x + 1 = 5$

5. $\dfrac{x}{x-2} = \dfrac{2}{x-2}$
$x = 2$

6. $\dfrac{x+3}{x+1} = \dfrac{2}{x+1}$
$x = -1$

7. $x = 4$
$x^2 = 16$

8. $z^2 = 9$
$z = 3$

Decide whether each of the following equations is an identity or a conditional equation.

9. $x^2 + 5x = x(x + 5)$

10. $3y + 4 = 5(y - 2)$

11. $2(x - 7) = 5x + 3 - x$

12. $2x - 4 = 2(x - 2)$

13. $\dfrac{m+3}{m} = 1 + \dfrac{3}{m}$

14. $\dfrac{p}{2-p} = \dfrac{2}{p} - 1$

15. $4q^2 - 25 = (2q + 5)(2q - 5)$

16. $3(k + 2) - 5(k + 2) = -2k - 4$

Solve each of the following equations.

17. $4x - 1 = 15$

18. $-3y + 2 = 5$

19. $.2m - .5 = .1m + .7$

20. $.01p + 3.1 = 2.03p - 2.96$

21. $\dfrac{5}{6}k - 2k + \dfrac{1}{3} = \dfrac{2}{3}$

22. $\dfrac{3}{4} + \dfrac{1}{5}r - \dfrac{1}{2} = \dfrac{4}{5}r$

23. $2[m - (4 + 2m) + 3] = 2m + 2$

24. $4[2p - (3 - p) + 5] = -7p - 2$

25. $\dfrac{3x-2}{7} = \dfrac{x+2}{5}$

26. $\dfrac{2p+5}{5} = \dfrac{p+2}{3}$

27. $\dfrac{3k-1}{4} = \dfrac{5k+2}{8}$

28. $\dfrac{9x-1}{6} = \dfrac{2x+7}{3}$

29. $\dfrac{1}{4p} + \dfrac{2}{p} = 3$

30. $\dfrac{2}{t} + 6 = \dfrac{5}{2t}$

31. $\dfrac{m}{2} - \dfrac{1}{m} = \dfrac{6m+5}{12}$

32. $\dfrac{-3k}{2} + \dfrac{9k-5}{6} = \dfrac{11k+8}{k}$

33. $\dfrac{2r}{r-1} = 5 + \dfrac{2}{r-1}$

34. $\dfrac{3x}{x+2} = \dfrac{1}{x+2} - 4$

35. $\dfrac{5}{2a+3} + \dfrac{1}{a-6} = 0$

36. $\dfrac{2}{x+1} = \dfrac{3}{2x-5}$

37. $\dfrac{4}{x-3} - \dfrac{8}{2x+5} + \dfrac{3}{x-3} = 0$

38. $\dfrac{5}{2p+3} - \dfrac{3}{p-2} = \dfrac{4}{2p+3}$

39. $\dfrac{3}{2m+4} = \dfrac{1}{m+2} - 2$

40. $\dfrac{8}{3k-9} - \dfrac{5}{k-3} = 4$

41. $2(m + 1)(m - 1) = (2m + 3)(m - 2)$

42. $(2y - 1)(3y + 2) = 6(y + 2)^2$

Solve each of the following equations for x.

43. $2(x - a) + b = 3x + a$

44. $5x - (2a + c) = a(x + 1)$

45. $ax + b = 3(x - a)$

46. $4a - ax = 3b + bx$

47. $\dfrac{x}{a - 1} = ax + 3$

48. $\dfrac{2a}{x - 1} = a - b$

49. $a^2x + 3x = 2a^2$

50. $ax + b^2 = bx - a^2$

51. Find the error in the following.

$$x^2 + 2x - 15 = x^2 - 3x$$
$$(x + 5)(x - 3) = x(x - 3)$$
$$x + 5 = x$$
$$5 = 0$$

Find a value of k so that the following equations are equivalent to x = 2.

52. $9x - 7 = k$

53. $-5x + 11x - 2 = k + 4$

54. $\dfrac{8}{k + x} = 1$

55. $\sqrt{x + k} = 0$

56. $\sqrt{3x - 2k} = 4$

⊙ *Solve each of the following equations. Round solutions to the nearest hundredth.*

57. $9.06x + 3.59(8x - 5) = 12.07x + .5612$

58. $-5.74(3.1 - 2.7p) = 1.09p + 5.2588$

59. $\dfrac{2.5x - 7.8}{3.2} + \dfrac{1.2x + 11.5}{5.8} = 6$

60. $\dfrac{4.19x + 2.42}{.05} - \dfrac{5.03x - 9.74}{.02} = 1$

61. $\dfrac{2.63r - 8.99}{1.25} - \dfrac{3.90r - 1.77}{2.45} = r$

62. $\dfrac{8.19m + 2.55}{4.34} - \dfrac{8.17m - 9.94}{1.04} = 4m$

2.2 Formulas and Applications

Mathematics is an important problem-solving tool. Many times the solution of a problem depends on the use of a formula which expresses a relationship among several variables. For example, the formula

$$A = \frac{24f}{b(p + 1)}$$

gives the approximate true annual interest rate for a consumer loan paid off with monthly payments. Here f is the finance charge on the loan, p is the number of payments, and b is the original amount of the loan.

Suppose we need to find the number of payments, p, when the other quantities are known. To do this, solve the equation for p, by treating p as the variable and the other letters as constants. Begin by multiplying both sides of $A = \dfrac{24f}{b(p+1)}$ by $p + 1$.

$$A \cdot (p + 1) = \frac{24f}{b(p+1)}(p+1)$$

$$A(p + 1) = \frac{24f}{b}$$

Multiply both sides by $1/A$. (Here we must assume $A \neq 0$. Why is this a very safe assumption?)

$$\frac{1}{A} \cdot A(p + 1) = \frac{1}{A} \cdot \frac{24f}{b}$$

$$p + 1 = \frac{24f}{Ab}$$

Finally, add -1 to both sides to get

$$p = \frac{24f}{Ab} - 1.$$

Example 1 Solve $J\left(\dfrac{x}{k} + a\right) = x$ for x.

We want to get all terms with x on one side of the equation and all terms without x on the other. To do this, first use the distributive property.

$$J\left(\frac{x}{k}\right) + Ja = x$$

Now multiply both sides by k.

$$kJ\left(\frac{x}{k}\right) + kJa = kx$$

$$Jx + kJa = kx$$

Then add $-Jx$ to both sides.

$$kJa = kx - Jx$$

$$kJa = x(k - J)$$

If we assume $k \neq J$, we can multiply both sides by $1/(k - J)$ to find x.

$$x = \frac{kJa}{k - J}. \quad \blacksquare$$

For many students, learning how to apply mathematical skills to applications or word problems is the most difficult task they face. When trying to solve word problems, you should find the following steps to be helpful. They are from *How to Solve It*, by George Polya, published by Princeton University Press. This book is a modern classic among mathematics books.

Understanding the problem

What is the unknown? What are the data? What is the condition? Is it possible to satisfy the condition? Is the condition sufficient to determine the unknown? Or is it insufficient? Or redundant? Or contradictory?

Draw a figure. Introduce suitable notation.

Separate the various parts of the condition. Can you write them down?

First.
You have to *understand* the problem.

Devising a plan

Have you seen it before? Or have you seen the same problem in a slightly different form?

Do you know a related problem? Do you know a theorem that could be useful?

Look at the unknown! And try to think of a familiar problem having the same or a similar unknown.

Here is a problem related to yours and solved before. Could you use it? Could you use its result? Could you use its method? Should you introduce some auxiliary element in order to make its use possible?

Could you restate the problem? Could you restate it still differently? Go back to definitions.

If you cannot solve the proposed problem try to solve first some related problem. Could you imagine a more accessible related problem? A more general problem? A more special problem? An analogous problem? Could you solve a part of the problem? Keep only a part of the condition, drop the other part; how far is the unknown then determined, how can it vary? Could you derive something useful from the data? Could you think of other data appropriate to determine the unknown? Could you change the unknown or the data, or both if necessary, so that the new unknown and the new data are nearer to each other?

Did you use all the data? Did you use the whole condition? Have you taken into account all essential notions involved in the problem?

Second.
Find the connection between the data and the unknown. You may be obliged to consider auxiliary problems if an immediate connection cannot be found. You should obtain eventually a *plan* of the solution.

Carrying out the plan

Carrying out your plan of the solution, *check each step.* Can you see clearly that the step is correct? Can you prove that it is correct?

Third.
Carry out your plan.

From G. Polya, *How to Solve It: A New Aspect of Mathematical Method* (copyright 1945 © 1973 by Princeton University Press, also copyright © 1957 by G. Polya; Princeton Paperback, 1971), pp. xvi-xvii. Reprinted by permission of Princeton University Press.

Looking back

Fourth.

Examine the solution obtained.

Can you *check the result?* Can you check the argument? Can you derive the result differently? Can you see it at a glance?

Can you use the result, or the method, for some other problem?

Example 2   If the side of a square is increased by 3 cm, the new perimeter is 40 cm larger than twice the side of the original square. Find the dimensions of the original square.

First, what should the variable represent? We want to find the side of the original square, so let the variable represent that.

$$x = \text{length of side of the original square.}$$

The side of the new square is 3 cm longer than the side of the old square. Write a variable expression for that.

$$x + 3 = \text{the side of the new square.}$$

Now write a variable expression for the new perimeter.

$$4(x + 3) = \text{the perimeter of the new square.}$$

We are now ready to write an equation. The new perimeter is 40 more than twice the side of the original square, so the equation is

the new perimeter	is	40	more than	twice the side of the original square
$4(x + 3)$	$=$	40	$+$	$2x$

Now solve the equation. The result should be checked by using the wording of the stated problem.

$$4(x + 3) = 40 + 2x$$
$$4x + 12 = 40 + 2x$$
$$2x = 28$$
$$x = 14.$$

A side of the new square would be $14 + 3 = 17$; its perimeter would be $4(17) = 68$. Twice the side of the original square is $2(14) = 28$. Since $40 + 28 = 68$, the solution satisfies the problem.

Example 3   Chuck and Mary both traveled from San Francisco to Chicago for a convention. Chuck drove his car at an average speed of 50 mph, while Mary took a plane. Her trip required 4 hours, his, 40 hours. What was the average speed of Mary's plane?

To solve constant velocity problems of this kind, we need the formula $d = rt$, where d is distance traveled in t hours at a constant rate of speed r. We can use a chart to organize the information given in the problem and the variable expressions we need to write. We know the two times and Chuck's speed or rate. We also know that the distance traveled by each person is the same. Let's use x to represent the plane's (or Mary's) rate. This information goes in the columns headed t and r. Now we use the distance formula to fill in the distance column.

For Chuck, $d = (50)(40) = 2000$.

For Mary, $d = x \cdot 4 = 4x$.

	d	r	t
Chuck	2000	50	40
Mary	$4x$	x	4

Since both traveled the same distance, the equation is

$$2000 = 4x$$
$$x = 500.$$

The average speed of Mary's plane was 500 mph.

Example 4   Rick and Joann are refinishing an antique table. Working alone, Rick would need 8 days to finish the table, though Joann would require 10. If they work together, how long will it take them to complete the project?

Let x represent the number of days it will take Rick and Joann working together to finish the table. Then, in one day, they will together complete $1/x$ of the job.

In one day, Rick will do 1/8 of the task, while Joann will do 1/10. The amount of the job done by each in one day must equal the amount done working together in one day, or

$$\frac{1}{8} + \frac{1}{10} = \frac{1}{x}.$$

Multiply both sides of this equation by $40x$, getting

$$5x + 4x = 40$$
$$9x = 40$$
$$x = 40/9 \left(\text{or } 4\frac{4}{9} \right)$$

Hence, working together they can finish the table in $4\frac{4}{9}$ days.

Example 5   A homeowner opens a valve to fill her swimming pool. The pool would normally fill in 10 hours. However, after 3 hours, a mistake is made and the drain is also opened. The drain can empty a full pool in 15 hours. How long does it now take to fill the pool?

Let us first find the time it would take to fill the pool if the inlet pipe and the drain were open *from the beginning*. Let t represent this time. In one hour, the inlet will fill 1/10 of the pool, while the outlet would empty 1/15 of the pool. With both open, $1/t$ of the pool would be filled in one hour, so that

$$\frac{1}{10} - \frac{1}{15} = \frac{1}{t}$$

(Why did we use a − sign?) To solve this equation, start by multiplying both sides by $30t$.

$$30t\left(\frac{1}{10} - \frac{1}{15}\right) = 30t\left(\frac{1}{t}\right)$$

$$30t\left(\frac{1}{10}\right) - 30t\left(\frac{1}{15}\right) = 30$$

$$3t - 2t = 30$$

$$t = 30$$

It would take 30 hours to fill the pool if both the inlet and drain were open from the beginning. However, we were told in the problem that only the inlet was open for the initial 3 hours. In 3 hours, the inlet would fill 3/10 of the pool, leaving 7/10 unfilled. When the drain was opened, 7/10 of the pool remained to be filled; this would take

$$\frac{7}{10}(30) = 21 \text{ hours.} \quad \blacksquare$$

Example 6   Elizabeth Thornton is a chemist. One day, she needed a 20% solution of potassium permanganate. She had a 15% solution on hand as well as a 30% solution. How many liters of the 15% solution should she add to 3 liters of the 30% solution to get her 20% solution?

Let x be the number of liters of 15% solutions to be added. Arrange the information of the problem in a table.

strength	liters of solution	liters of pure potassium permanganate
15%	x	$.15x$
30%	3	$.30(3)$
20%	$3 + x$	$.20(3 + x)$

Since the number of liters of potassium permanganate in the 15% solution plus the number of liters in the 30% solution must equal the number of liters in the final 20% solution, we have

liters in 15%   liters in 30%   liters in 20%

$$.15x \quad + \quad .30(3) \quad = \quad .20(3 + x).$$

Solve this equation.

$$.15x + .90 = .60 + .20x$$

$$.30 = .05x$$

$$6 = x$$

Thus, 6 liters of the 15% solution should be mixed with 3 liters of the 30% solution. The result will be $6 + 3 = 9$ liters of 20% solution. $\quad \blacksquare$

Example 7   Richard Jones receives a $14,000 bonus from his company. He invests part of the money in 6% tax-free bonds, and the remainder at 8%. He earns $950 per year in interest from the investments. Find the amount he has invested at each rate.

Let x represent the amount Jones invests at 6%, so that $14,000 - x$ is the amount invested at 8%. Since interest is given by the product of principal, rate, and time ($i = prt$), we have

$$\text{interest at } 6\% = x \cdot 6\% \cdot 1 = .06x \quad (1 \text{ year})$$
$$\text{interest at } 8\% = (14,000 - x)(8\%)(1) = .08(14,000 - x)$$

Since the total interest is $950, we have

$$.06x + .08(14,000 - x) = 950.$$

Solve this equation.

$$.06x + .08(14,000) - .08x = 950$$
$$-.02x + 1120 = 950$$
$$-.02x = -170$$
$$x = 8500.$$

Thus, $8500 was invested at 6%, and $14,000 - \$8500 = \$5500$ at 8%.

2.2 Exercises   *Solve each of the following for the letter indicated. Assume all denominators are nonzero.*

1. $PV = k$ for V

2. $F = whA$ for h

3. $V = lwh$ for l

4. $i = prt$ for p

5. $V = V_0 + gt$ for g

6. $s = s_0 + gt^2 + k$ for g

7. $s = \dfrac{1}{2}gt^2$ for g

8. $A = \dfrac{1}{2}(B + b)h$ for h

9. $A = \dfrac{1}{2}(B + b)h$ for B

10. $C = \dfrac{5}{9}(F - 32)$ for F

11. $S = 2\pi(r_1 + r_2)h$ for r_1

12. $A = P\left(1 + \dfrac{i}{m}\right)$ for m

13. $g = \dfrac{4\pi^2 l}{t^2}$ for l

14. $P = \dfrac{E^2 R}{r + R}$ for R

15. $S = 2\pi rh + 2\pi r^2$ for h

16. $u = f \cdot \dfrac{k(k + 1)}{n(n + 1)}$ for f

17. $A = \dfrac{24f}{b(p + 1)}$ for f

18. $A = \dfrac{24f}{b(p + 1)}$ for b

19. $\dfrac{1}{R} = \dfrac{1}{r_1} + \dfrac{1}{r_2}$ for R

20. $m = \dfrac{Ft}{v_1 - v_2}$ for v_2

Solve each of the following.

21. An accountant has determined that the sales of a company last year were 1000 more than 50 times the number of years the company has been in business. The sales last year were 2300. How many years has the company been in business?

22. The demand for gasoline depends on the price. At a certain gas station the demand, in gallons, is 725 gallons less five times the price. Find the price, in cents, when the demand is 100 gallons.

23. While taking inventory, music store employees found that they had three times as many electric guitars as folk guitars and five more than twice as many classical guitars as folk guitars. If they had 53 guitars in stock, how many of each kind did they have?

24. Ms. Harris has an allergy which requires that she take two drugs, which come in two different capsules, orange and white. She takes five less than twice as many orange capsules as white each week. If she takes a total of 22 capsules per week, how many are white?

25. A triangle has a perimeter of 30 cm. Two sides of the triangle are both twice as long as the shortest side. Find the length of the short side.

26. The length of a rectangle is three inches less than twice the width. The perimeter is 54 inches. Find the width.

27. A clock-radio is on sale for $49. If the sale price is 15% less than the regular price, what was the regular price?

28. A shopkeeper prices his items 20% over their wholesale price. If a lamp is marked $74, what was its wholesale price?

29. Ms. Prullage invests $20,000 received from an insurance settlement in two ways, some at $6\frac{1}{2}$% and some at 8%. Altogether, she makes $1420 per year interest. How much is invested at each rate?

30. Bruce Hallett received $52,000 profit from the sale of some land. He invested part at $7\frac{1}{2}$% interest and the rest at $9\frac{1}{2}$% interest. He earned a total of $4520 interest per year. How much did he invest at each rate?

31. John Raton won $100,000 in a state lottery. He first paid income tax of 40% on the winnings. Of the rest, he invested some at $8\frac{1}{2}$% and some at 16%, making $5550 interest per year. How much is invested at each rate?

32. Mary Collins earned $48,000 from royalties on her cookbook. She paid a 40% income tax on these royalties. The balance was invested in two ways, at $7\frac{1}{2}$% and at $10\frac{1}{2}$%. The investments produced $2550 interest income per year. Find the amount invested at each rate.

33. Susan Futterman bought two plots of land for a total of $120,000. On the first plot, she made a profit of 15%. On the second, she lost 10%. Her total profit was $5500. How much did she pay for each piece of land?

34. Suppose $10,000 is invested at 6%. How much additional money must be invested at 8% to produce a yield on the entire amount invested of 7.2%?

35. Mario Nunez earns take-home pay of $198 a week. If his deductions for retirement, union dues, medical plan, and so on amount to 26% of his wages, what is his weekly pay before deductions?

36. Janet gives 10% of her net income to the church. This amounts to $80 a month. In addition, her paycheck deductions are 24% of her gross monthly income. What is her gross monthly income?

37. A pharmacist wishes to strengthen a mixture which is 10% alcohol to one which is 30% alcohol. How much pure alcohol should be added to 7 liters of the 10% mixture?

38. A student needs some 10% hydrochloric acid for a chemistry experiment. How much 5% acid should be mixed with 60 ml of 20% acid to get a 10% solution?

39. The Old Time Goodies Store sells mixed nuts. Cashews sell for $4 per quarter kilogram, hazelnuts for $3 per quarter kilogram, and peanuts for $1 per quarter kilogram. How many kilograms of peanuts should be added to 10 kilograms of cashews and 8 kilograms of hazelnuts to make a mixture which will sell for $2.50 per quarter kilogram?

40. The Old Time Goodies Store also sells candy. They want to prepare 200 kilograms of a mixture for a special Halloween promotion to sell at $4.84 per kilogram. How much $4-per-kilogram candy should be mixed with $5.20-per-kilogram candy for the required mix?

41. On a vacation trip, Toni Tyson averaged 50 mph traveling from Amarillo to Flagstaff. Returning by a different route that covered the same number of miles, she averaged 55 mph. What is the distance between the two cities if her total traveling time was 32 hours?

42. Cindy left by plane to visit her mother in Hartford, 420 kilometers away. Fifteen minutes later, her mother left to meet her at the airport. She drove the 20 kilometers to the airport at 40 kph and arrived just as the plane taxied in. What was the speed of the plane?

43. Russ and Janet are running in the Apple Hill Fun Run. Russ runs at 7 mph, Janet at 5 mph. If they start at the same time, how long will it be before they are 1/2 mile apart?

44. If the run in Exercise 43 has a staggered start with Janet starting first and Russ starting 10 minutes later, how long will it be before he catches up with her?

45. Joann took 20 minutes to drive her boat upstream to water-ski at her favorite spot. Coming back later in the day, at the same boat speed, took her 15 minutes. If the current in that part of the river is 5 kph, what was her boat speed?

46. Joe traveled against the wind in a small plane at 180 mph for 3 hours. The return trip at the same speed took 2.8 hours. What was the wind speed?

47. Mark can clean the house in 9 hours and Wendy in 6. How long will it take them if they work together to clean it?

48. Helen can paint a room in 5 hours. Jay can paint the same room in 4 hours. (He does a sloppier job.) How long will it take them to paint the room together?

49. Two chemical plants are polluting a river. If plant A produces a predetermined maximum amount of pollution twice as fast as plant B, and together they produce the maximum pollution in 26 hours, how long will it take plant B alone?

50. A sewage treatment plant has two inlet pipes to its settling pond. One can fill the pond in 10 hours, the other in 12 hours. If the first pipe is open for 5 hours, and then the second pipe is opened, how long will it take to fill the pond?

51. An inlet pipe can fill Dominic's pool in 5 hours, while an outlet pipe can empty it in 8 hours. In his haste to watch television, Dominic left both pipes open. How long would it then take to fill the pool?

52. Suppose Dominic discovered his error (see Exercise 51) after an hour-long program. If he then closed the outlet pipe, how much longer would be needed to fill the pool?

53. A sink will fill in 1/2 hour if both faucets are on and the drain is closed. The sink will empty in 2/3 hour. If both faucets are on and the drain is open, how long will it take before the sink overflows?

54. A cashier has some $5 bills and some $10 bills. The total number of bills is n, and the total value of the money is t. Find the number of each kind of bill that the cashier has.

55. Let $0 < a < b < c < 100$. How many liters of $a\%$ solution should be mixed with m liters of $c\%$ solution to make a $b\%$ mixture?

56. One way that biologists estimate the number of individuals of a species in an area is as follows. First, 100 animals of the species are caught and marked. A period of time is permitted to elapse, and then b animals are caught. If c of these ($c \leq b$) are marked, find the number of individuals in the area.

57. Suppose B dollars are invested, some at $m\%$ and the rest at $n\%$. If a total of I dollars in interest is earned per year, find the amount invested at each rate.

2.3 Quadratic Equations

A **quadratic equation** is an equation of the form

$$ax^2 + bx + c = 0,$$

where a, b, and c are real numbers, with $a \neq 0$. (Why is the restriction $a \neq 0$ necessary?) The simplest method of solving quadratic equations, but one that is not always easily applied, is by factoring. This method depends on the following property mentioned in Chapter 1:

If a and b are real numbers, with $ab = 0$,
then $a = 0$ or $b = 0$.

Example 1 Solve $6r^2 + 7r = 3$.
First get the equation equal to 0.

$$6r^2 + 7r - 3 = 0.$$

Now factor $6r^2 + 7r - 3$ to get

$$(3r - 1)(2r + 3) = 0.$$

By the property above, $(3r - 1)(2r + 3)$ can equal 0 only if

$$3r - 1 = 0 \quad \text{or} \quad 2r + 3 = 0.$$

Solve each of these equations separately to find that the solutions of the original equation are 1/3 and −3/2. Check these solutions by substituting them back in the original equation. ▮

We can use factoring to solve a quadratic equation of the form $x^2 = k$, where $k \geq 0$. Work as follows.

$$x^2 = k$$
$$x^2 - k = 0$$
$$(x - \sqrt{k})(x + \sqrt{k}) = 0$$
$$x - \sqrt{k} = 0 \quad \text{or} \quad x + \sqrt{k} = 0$$
$$x = \sqrt{k} \quad \text{or} \quad x = -\sqrt{k}$$

This proves the following result.

Theorem 2.1 The solutions of $x^2 = k$, where $k \geq 0$, are $\pm\sqrt{k}$.

Example 2 The solutions of $z^2 = 17$ are $\pm\sqrt{17}$. ∎

Example 3 Solve $(y - 4)^2 = 12$.

Use a generalization of Theorem 2.1.

$$(y - 4)^2 = 12$$
$$y - 4 = \pm\sqrt{12}$$
$$y = 4 \pm \sqrt{12}$$
$$y = 4 \pm 2\sqrt{3}$$ ∎

As suggested by Example 3, any quadratic equation can be solved using Theorem 2.1 if it can be written in the form $(x + n)^2 = k$, for suitable real numbers n and k, where $k \geq 0$. The next example shows how to write a quadratic equation in this form.

Example 4 Solve $9z^2 - 12z - 1 = 0$.

We need to find constants n and k so that the given equation can be written in the form $(z + n)^2 = k$. If we expand $(z + n)^2$, we get $z^2 + 2zn + n^2$, where z^2 has a coefficient of 1. To get a coefficient of 1 in our given equation, multiply both sides by 1/9, giving

$$z^2 - \frac{4}{3}z - \frac{1}{9} = 0.$$

We need to change $-1/9$ into a number that will make the left side a perfect square. To find this number, first add 1/9 on both sides.

$$z^2 - \frac{4}{3}z = \frac{1}{9}$$

The term $-4z/3$ is twice the product of z and n, the number we need to make the left side a perfect square. That is, n satisfies the equation

$$2zn = -\frac{4}{3}z$$

or

$$n = -\frac{2}{3}.$$

If $n = -2/3$, then $n^2 = 4/9$, which we add to both sides.

$$z^2 - \frac{4}{3}z + \frac{4}{9} = \frac{1}{9} + \frac{4}{9}$$

Factor on the left to get

$$\left(z - \frac{2}{3}\right)^2 = \frac{5}{9}$$

Now use Theorem 2.1.

$$z - \frac{2}{3} = \pm\sqrt{\frac{5}{9}}$$

$$z - \frac{2}{3} = \pm\frac{\sqrt{5}}{3}$$

$$z = \frac{2}{3} \pm \frac{\sqrt{5}}{3} \quad \blacksquare$$

This process of changing $9z^2 - 12z - 1 = 0$ into the equivalent equation $(z - 2/3)^2 = 5/9$ is called **completing the square.**

We shall now use the method of completing the square on the general quadratic equation,

$$ax^2 + bx + c = 0 \qquad (a \neq 0),$$

in order to convert it to one whose solution can be found by Theorem 2.1. We can thus find a general method of solving any quadratic equation. First multiply both sides by $1/a$ (here we use the fact that $a \neq 0$) to get

$$x^2 + \frac{b}{a}x + \frac{c}{a} = 0.$$

Then add $-c/a$ to both sides,

$$x^2 + \frac{b}{a}x = -\frac{c}{a}.$$

Now take half of b/a, square the result, and add the square to both sides.

$$x^2 + \frac{b}{a}x + \frac{b^2}{4a^2} = \frac{b^2}{4a^2} - \frac{c}{a}$$

We can now write the expression on the left-hand side as the square of a binomial, while the expression on the right can be simplified.

$$\left(x + \frac{b}{2a}\right)^2 = \frac{b^2 - 4ac}{4a^2}$$

This last statement leads to

$$x + \frac{b}{2a} = \sqrt{\frac{b^2 - 4ac}{4a^2}} \qquad \text{or} \qquad x + \frac{b}{2a} = -\sqrt{\frac{b^2 - 4ac}{4a^2}},$$

which we can also write as

$$x = \frac{-b + \sqrt{b^2 - 4ac}}{2a} \qquad \text{or} \qquad x = \frac{-b - \sqrt{b^2 - 4ac}}{2a}.$$

A simplified form of this result is given in Theorem 2.2.

Theorem 2.2   (*Quadratic Formula*)   The solutions of the quadratic equation $ax^2 + bx + c = 0$ ($a \neq 0$) are given by

$$x = \frac{-b \pm \sqrt{b^2 - 4ac}}{2a}$$

Example 5   Solve $x^2 - 4x + 1 = 0$.
Here $a = 1$, $b = -4$, and $c = 1$. Use the quadratic formula.

$$x = \frac{-b \pm \sqrt{b^2 - 4ac}}{2a}$$

$$x = \frac{4 \pm \sqrt{16 - 4}}{2}$$

$$x = \frac{4 \pm 2\sqrt{3}}{2}$$

$$x = \frac{2(2 \pm \sqrt{3})}{2}$$

$$x = 2 \pm \sqrt{3}.$$

The solutions are $2 + \sqrt{3}$ and $2 - \sqrt{3}$.   █

The quantity under the radical in the quadratic formula, $b^2 - 4ac$, is called the **discriminant.** From the sign of the discriminant, when a, b, and c are integers, we can determine whether the solutions will be rational, irrational, or not real numbers at all. If the discriminant is 0, there will be only one solution. (Why?)

Example 6   Use the discriminant to determine whether the solutions of $5x^2 + 2x - 4 = 0$ are rational, irrational, or not real numbers.
The discriminant is

$$b^2 - 4ac = (2)^2 - (4)(5)(-4) = 84.$$

Since the discriminant is positive, there are two real number solutions. Since 84 is not a perfect square, the solutions will be irrational numbers.   █

In general, the discriminant indicates the following information about the solutions.

Discriminant	Number of solutions	Kind of solutions
positive, perfect square	two	rational
positive, not a perfect square	two	irrational
zero	one	rational
negative	no real solutions	

Example 7   Michael wants to make an exposed aggregate border of uniform width around a rectangular pool in his garden. The pool is 10 feet by 6 feet. He has enough material to cover 36 square feet. How wide will the border be?

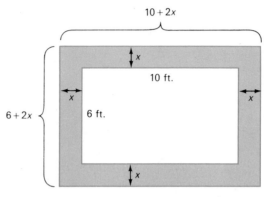

Figure 2.1

A sketch of the pool with border is shown in Figure 2.1. Let x represent the width of the border. Then the width of the large rectangle is $6 + 2x$ and its length is $10 + 2x$. The area of the large rectangle is $(6 + 2x)(10 + 2x)$. The area of the pool is $6 \cdot 10 = 60$. The area of the border is found by subtracting the area of the pool from the area of the large rectangle. This difference should be 36 square feet.

$$(6 + 2x)(10 + 2x) - 60 = 36$$
$$60 + 32x + 4x^2 - 60 = 36$$
$$4x^2 + 32x - 36 = 0$$
$$x^2 + 8x - 9 = 0$$
$$(x + 9)(x - 1) = 0$$

The solutions are -9 and 1. We cannot use -9 as the width of the border, so the solution is to make the border one foot wide. ▌

2.3 Exercises   *Solve the following equations.*

1. $p^2 = 16$

2. $k^2 = 25$

3. $x^2 = 27$

4. $y^2 = 24$

5. $(m - 3)^2 = 5$

6. $(p + 2)^2 = 7$

7. $(3k - 1)^2 = 12$

8. $(4t + 1)^2 = 20$

9. $(x - 2)(x + 3) = 0$

10. $(2m - 1)(3m + 2) = 0$

11. $p^2 - 5p + 6 = 0$

12. $q^2 + 2q - 8 = 0$

13. $6z^2 - 5z - 50 = 0$

14. $6r^2 + 7r = 3$

15. $m^2 - m - 1 = 0$

16. $y^2 - 3y - 2 = 0$

17. $3a^2 + 7a - 2 = 0$

18. $4z^2 - 4z = 1$

19. $x^2 - 6x + 7 = 0$

20. $11p^2 - 7p + 1 = 0$

21. $2r^2 + 7r = -1$

22. $r^2 + 8r + 25 = 0$

23. $9g^2 = 12g + 13$

24. $k^2 + 2k + 3 = 0$

25. $x^2 = 8x$

26. $16y^2 - 12y = 0$

27. $4 - \dfrac{11}{x} - \dfrac{3}{x^2} = 0$ **29.** $2 - \dfrac{5}{r} + \dfrac{3}{r^2} = 0$ **30.** $2 + \dfrac{2}{k^2} = \dfrac{5}{k}$

28. $3 - \dfrac{4}{p} = \dfrac{2}{p^2}$

Use a calculator to give the solutions of the following equations to the nearest thousandth.

31. $5n^2 - 4 = 3n$ **33.** $x^2 - 2 = 3x$ **35.** $5z^2 - 3z = 1$

32. $9p^2 = 30p + 25$ **34.** $3k^2 - 2 = 4k$ **36.** $a^2 - a - 3 = 0$

Identify the values of a, b, and c for each of the following. Then evaluate the discriminant and use it to predict the type of solutions. Do not solve the equations.

37. $x^2 + 8x + 16 = 0$ **39.** $4p^2 = 6p + 3$ **41.** $9k^2 + 11k + 4 = 0$

38. $x^2 - 5x + 4 = 0$ **40.** $2r^2 - 4r + 1 = 0$ **42.** $3z^2 = 4z - 5$

Solve each of the following for the indicated variable. Assume all denominators are non-zero.

43. $s = \dfrac{1}{2}gt^2$ for t **47.** $s = s_0 + gt^2 + k$ for t

44. $A = \pi r^2$ for r **48.** $g = \dfrac{4\pi^2}{t^2}$ for t

45. $L = \dfrac{d^4k}{h^2}$ for h **49.** $P = \dfrac{E^2 R}{(r + R)^2}$ for R

46. $F = \dfrac{kMv^2}{r}$ for v **50.** $S = 2\pi rh + 2\pi r^2$ for r

Solve the following problems.

51. Find two consecutive even integers whose product is 288.

52. The sum of the squares of two consecutive integers is 481. Find the integers.

53. Two integers have a sum of 10. The sum of the squares of the integers is 148. Find the integers.

54. A shopping center has a rectangular area of 40,000 square yards enclosed on three sides for a parking lot. The length is 200 yards more than twice the width. What are the dimensions of the lot?

55. An ecology center wants to set up an experimental garden. It has 300 meters of fencing to enclose a rectangular area of 5000 square meters. Find the dimensions of the rectangle.

56. Fred went into a frame-it-yourself shop. He wanted a frame 3 decimeters longer than wide. The frame he chose extends 1.5 decimeters beyond the picture on each side. Find the outside dimensions of the frame if the area of the unframed picture is 70 square decimeters.

57. Joan wants to buy a rug for a room that is 12 feet by 15 feet. She wants to leave a uniform strip of floor around the rug. She can afford 108 square feet of carpeting. What dimensions should the rug have?

58. It takes Pablo 10 hours to write a term report for his history class. His girlfriend, Maria, completes her report in 3 hours. How long would it take them to write a report if they could work together?

59. Donna can write a term report for a history class in 2-1/3 hours less time than her boyfriend, Wayne. If they work together, they can write the report in 4 hours. How long would it take Wayne working alone?

60. Max can clean the garage in 9 hours less time than his brother Paul. Working together, they can do the job in 20 hours. How long would it take each one to do the job alone?

61. Dolores drives 10 mph faster than Steve. Both start at the same time for Atlanta from Chattanooga, a distance of about 100 miles. It takes Steve 1/3 of an hour longer than Dolores to make the trip. What is Steve's average speed?

62. Amy walks 1 mph faster than her friend Lisa. In a walk for charity, both walked the full distance of 24 miles. Lisa took 2 hours longer than Amy. What was Lisa's average speed?

◉ *Find the solution for each of the following. Round to the nearest hundredth.*

63. One leg of a right triangle is four centimeters larger than the other leg. The hypotenuse (longest side) is ten centimeters larger than the shorter leg. Find each of the three sides of the triangle.

64. A rectangle has a diagonal 16 m long. The width of the rectangle is 3.2 cm shorter than the length. Find the length and width of the rectangle.

Find all values of k for which the following equations have exactly one solution.

65. $9x^2 + kx + 4 = 0$

66. $25m^2 - 10m + k = 0$

67. $y^2 + 11y + k = 0$

68. $z^2 - 5z + k = 0$

69. $kr^2 + (2k + 6)r + 16 = 0$

70. $ky^2 + 2(k + 4)y + 25 = 0$

Let r_1 and r_2 be the solutions of the quadratic equation $ax^2 + bx + c = 0$. Show that

71. $r_1 + r_2 = -\dfrac{b}{a}$

72. $r_1 r_2 = \dfrac{c}{a}$

73. Let m, n, and k be real numbers. Find the solutions of the equation $(x - m)(x - n) = k^2$ and show that they are real.

74. Suppose one solution of the equation $km^2 + 10m = 8$ is -4. Find the value of k, and the other solution.

For each of the following equations, (a) solve for x, (b) solve for y.

75. $4x^2 - 2xy + 3y^2 = 2$

76. $3y^2 + 4xy - 9x^2 = -1$

2.4 Other Types of Equations

Sometimes we can use the methods for solving quadratic equations on equations which are not quadratic by first making a substitution.

Example 1 Solve $12m^4 - 11m^2 + 2 = 0$.

This equation can be converted into a quadratic by letting $x = m^2$. That is, the equation is quadratic in m^2. Doing this gives

$$12x^2 - 11x + 2 = 0,$$

which can be solved by factoring.

$$(3x - 2)(4x - 1) = 0$$
$$x = 2/3 \quad \text{or} \quad x = 1/4$$

Since $x = m^2$, we have

$$m^2 = 2/3 \quad \text{or} \quad m^2 = 1/4$$
$$m = \pm \sqrt{\frac{2}{3}} \qquad m = \pm \sqrt{\frac{1}{4}}$$
$$m = \pm \frac{\sqrt{2}}{\sqrt{3}}$$
$$m = \frac{\pm \sqrt{6}}{3} \qquad m = \pm \frac{1}{2}$$

The four solutions of the given equation are $\sqrt{6}/3, -\sqrt{6}/3, 1/2, -1/2$. ▌

To solve an equation containing radicals or fractional exponents, such as $x = \sqrt{15 - 2x}$ or $x^{1/3} = 3x + 4$, we need the following theorem.

Theorem 2.3 If P and Q are algebraic expressions in x, then all solutions of the equation $P = Q$ are also solutions of the equation $(P)^n = (Q)^n$, for any positive integer n.

This theorem says only that each solution of the original equation is also a solution of the new equation. The new equation may have more solutions or **roots** than the original equation. For example, the only solution for $x = -2$ is -2. If we square both sides, we get $x^2 = 4$, which has *two* solutions, 2 and -2. Because of this, it is essential to check all proposed roots back in the original equation.

Example 2 Solve $x = \sqrt{15 - 2x}$.

By Theorem 2.3, the equation $x = \sqrt{15 - 2x}$ can be solved by squaring both sides.

$$x^2 = (\sqrt{15 - 2x})^2$$
$$x^2 = 15 - 2x$$
$$x^2 + 2x - 15 = 0$$
$$(x + 5)(x - 3) = 0$$
$$x = -5 \quad \text{or} \quad x = 3.$$

Now check the proposed roots in the original equation,

$$x = \sqrt{15 - 2x}.$$

If $x = -5$, does $x = \sqrt{15 - 2x}$?   If $x = 3$, does $x = \sqrt{15 - 2x}$?

$$-5 = \sqrt{15 + 10}$$ $$3 = \sqrt{15 - 6}$$

$$-5 = 5 \quad \text{(false)}$$ $$3 = 3 \quad \text{(true)}$$

As this check shows, only 3 is a root. ▌

Example 3 Solve $(a - 2)^{2/3} + (a - 2)^{1/3} - 2 = 0$.

Here we can let $x = (a - 2)^{1/3}$. By substitution, we have

$$x^2 + x - 2 = 0,$$

which can be factored as follows.

$$(x + 2)(x - 1) = 0$$

$$x = -2 \quad \text{or} \quad x = 1$$

Since $x = (a - 2)^{1/3}$,

$$(a - 2)^{1/3} = -2 \quad \text{or} \quad (a - 2)^{1/3} = 1$$

$$a - 2 = -8 \qquad\qquad a - 2 = 1$$

$$a = -6 \qquad\qquad\quad a = 3.$$

These solutions can be verified by substituting in the original equation. ▌

Example 4 Solve $\sqrt{2x + 3} - \sqrt{x + 1} = 1$.

Write the equation as

$$\sqrt{2x + 3} = 1 + \sqrt{x + 1}.$$

Now square both sides.

$$2x + 3 = 1 + 2\sqrt{x + 1} + x + 1$$

$$x + 1 = 2\sqrt{x + 1}$$

One side of the equation still contains a radical, and to eliminate it, we need to square both sides again.

$$x^2 + 2x + 1 = 4(x + 1)$$

$$x^2 - 2x - 3 = 0$$

$$(x - 3)(x + 1) = 0$$

$$x = 3 \quad \text{or} \quad x = -1$$

Check these proposed roots in the original equation.

If $x = 3$, does $\sqrt{2x + 3} - \sqrt{x + 1} = 1$?

$$\sqrt{9} - \sqrt{4} = 1$$

$$3 - 2 = 1 \quad \text{(true)}$$

If $x = -1$, does $\sqrt{2x + 3} - \sqrt{x + 1} = 1$?

$$\sqrt{1} - \sqrt{0} = 1$$

$$1 - 0 = 1 \quad \text{(true)}$$

Here both the proposed solutions 3 and -1 are solutions of the given equation.

2.4 Exercises   *Solve the following equations by first rewriting in quadratic form.*

1. $m^4 - 13m^2 + 36 = 0$

2. $p^4 - 17p^2 + 16 = 0$

3. $2r^4 - 7r^2 + 5 = 0$

4. $4x^4 - 8x^2 + 3 = 0$

5. $(g - 2)^2 - 6(g - 2) + 8 = 0$

6. $(p + 2)^2 - 2(p + 2) - 15 = 0$

7. $6(k + 2)^4 - 11(k + 2)^2 + 4 = 0$

8. $8(m - 4)^4 - 10(m - 4)^2 + 3 = 0$

9. $7p^{-2} + 19p^{-1} = 6$

10. $5k^{-2} - 43k^{-1} = 18$

11. $(r - 1)^{2/3} + (r - 1)^{1/3} = 12$

12. $(y + 3)^{2/3} - 2(y + 3)^{1/3} - 3 = 0$

Solve the following equations.

13. $\sqrt{r} + 1 = 2$

14. $\sqrt{z} - 3 = 5$

15. $\sqrt{t + 8} = 2$

16. $\sqrt{y - 3} = 5$

17. $\sqrt{2m + 1} = 2\sqrt{m}$

18. $3\sqrt{p} = \sqrt{8p + 16}$

19. $\sqrt{3z + 7} = 3z + 5$

20. $\sqrt{4r + 13} = 2r - 1$

21. $\sqrt{4k + 5} - 2 = 2k - 7$

22. $\sqrt{6m + 7} - 1 = m + 1$

23. $\sqrt{4x} - x + 3 = 0$

24. $\sqrt{2t} - t + 4 = 0$

25. $\sqrt{y} = \sqrt{y - 5} + 1$

26. $\sqrt{2m} = \sqrt{m + 7} - 1$

27. $\sqrt{r + 5} - 2 = \sqrt{r - 1}$

28. $\sqrt{m + 7} + 3 = \sqrt{m - 4}$

29. $\sqrt{y + 2} = \sqrt{2y + 5} - 1$

30. $\sqrt{4x + 1} = \sqrt{x - 1} + 2$

31. $\sqrt[3]{4n + 3} = \sqrt[3]{2n - 1}$

32. $\sqrt[3]{2z} = \sqrt[3]{5z + 2}$

33. $\sqrt[3]{t^2 + 2t - 1} = \sqrt[3]{t^2 + 3}$

34. $\sqrt[3]{2x^2 - 5x + 4} = \sqrt[3]{2x^2}$

35. $(2r + 5)^{1/3} = (6r - 1)^{1/3}$

36. $(3m + 7)^{1/3} = (4m + 2)^{1/3}$

37. $\sqrt[4]{q - 15} = 2$

38. $\sqrt[4]{3x + 1} = 1$

39. $\sqrt[4]{y^2 + 2y} = \sqrt[4]{3}$

40. $\sqrt[4]{k^2 + 6k} = 2$

41. $(2r - 1)^{2/3} = r^{1/3}$

42. $(z - 3)^{2/5} = (4z)^{1/5}$

43. $k^{2/3} = 2k^{1/3}$

44. $3m^{3/4} = m^{1/2}$

⦿ *Find all solutions for each of the following, rounded to the nearest thousandth.*

45. $6p^4 - 41p^2 + 63 = 0$

46. $20z^4 - 67z^2 + 56 = 0$

47. $3k^2 - \sqrt{4k^2 + 3} = 0$

48. $2r^2 - \sqrt{r^2 + 1} = 0$

Solve the following equations for the specified variable. Assume all denominators are nonzero.

49. $d = k\sqrt{h}$ for h

50. $v = \dfrac{k}{\sqrt{d}}$ for d

51. $P = 2\sqrt{\dfrac{L}{g}}$ for L

52. $c = \sqrt{a^2 + b^2}$ for a

53. $x^{2/3} + y^{2/3} = a^{2/3}$ for y

54. $m^{3/4} + n^{3/4} = 1$ for m

2.5 Inequalities

A **linear inequality** is an expression which can be simplified to a form such as $ax < b$ or $ax > b$. To solve a linear inequality use the following properties of inequalities:

> For real numbers a, b, and c,
>
> (a) if $a < b$, then $a + c < b + c$.
>
> (b) if $a < b$, and if $c > 0$, then $ac < bc$.
>
> (c) if $a < b$, and if $c < 0$, then $bc < ac$.

To prove these properties, recall that $a < b$ means that $b - a$ is positive. Also, recall that the sum or product of two positive numbers is positive.

To prove part (a), use the fact that $a < b$ to see that $b - a$ is positive. Rewrite $b - a$ as

$$b - a = (b + c) - (a + c).$$

Since $b - a$ is positive, $(b + c) - (a + c)$ must also be positive, and

$$a + c < b + c.$$

To prove part (b), again use the assumption $a < b$ to see that $b - a$ is positive. Since c is assumed positive, the product $(b - a)c$ is positive. By the distributive property,

$$(b - a)c = bc - ac,$$

and $bc - ac$ must be positive, giving

$$ac < bc.$$

For part (c), again we are given $a < b$, so that $b - a$ is positive. We are also told that $c < 0$. Since c is less than 0, we must have $0 - c$, or $-c$, as positive. Thus,

$$(b - a)(-c) = -bc + ac = ac - bc$$

is positive. If $ac - bc$ is positive, we have

$$bc < ac.$$

Similar proofs could be given if we replaced $<$ with $>$, $\leq$, or $\geq$.

To use these properties to solve the inequality $3x - 5 < 7$, write the following series of inequalities.

$$3x - 5 < 7$$
$$3x - 5 + 5 < 7 + 5$$
$$3x < 12$$
$$x < 4$$

Thus, all solutions of $3x - 5 < 7$ are in the interval $x < 4$, as shown in Figure 2.2. The parenthesis is used to show that 4 itself is not a solution.

Figure 2.2

The interval $x < 4$ is an example of an **open interval.** This interval can also be expressed in **interval notation** as $(-\infty, 4)$. Some examples of other intervals and the corresponding interval notation follow.

Type of interval	Inequality	Interval notation	Graph
open interval	$a < x$	(a, ∞)	
	$a < x < b$	(a, b)	
	$x < b$	$(-\infty, b)$	
half-open interval	$a \leq x$	$[a, \infty)$	
	$a < x \leq b$	$(a, b]$	
	$a \leq x < b$	$[a, b)$	
	$x \leq b$	$(-\infty, b]$	
closed interval	$a \leq x \leq b$	$[a, b]$	

Example 1 Solve $4 - 3y \leq 7 + 2y$. Graph the solution on a number line.
Write the following series of inequalities.

$$4 - 3y \leq 7 + 2y$$
$$-4 - 2y + 4 - 3y \leq -4 - 2y + 7 + 2y$$
$$-5y \leq 3$$
$$(-1/5)(-5y) \geq (-1/5)(3)$$
$$y \geq -3/5$$

In interval notation, the solution is $[-3/5, \infty)$. See Figure 2.3 for the graph. The square bracket is used to show that $-3/5$ itself is part of the solution.

Figure 2.3

Example 2   Solve $-2 < 5 + 3m < 20$.

A number can be a solution of $-2 < 5 + 3m < 20$ if and only if it is a solution of both

$$-2 < 5 + 3m \qquad \text{and} \qquad 5 + 3m < 20.$$

Solve each of these inequalities separately.

$$-2 + (-5) < 5 + 3m + (-5) \qquad 5 + 3m + (-5) < 20 + (-5)$$
$$-7 < 3m \qquad\qquad\qquad 3m < 15$$
$$-\frac{7}{3} < m \qquad\qquad\qquad\qquad m < 5$$

Finally, m can satisfy the original inequality if and only if m satisfies

$$-\frac{7}{3} < m \qquad \text{and} \qquad m < 5$$

or

$$-\frac{7}{3} < m < 5.$$

The solution, graphed in Figure 2.4, can be written in interval notation as $(-7/3, 5)$.

The inequality $-2 < 5 + 3m < 20$ can be solved more quickly as follows.

$$-2 < 5 + 3m < 20$$
$$-2 + (-5) < 5 + 3m + (-5) < 20 + (-5)$$
$$-7 < 3m < 15$$
$$-\frac{7}{3} < m < 5 \quad \blacksquare$$

$-\dfrac{7}{3}$	5

Figure 2.4

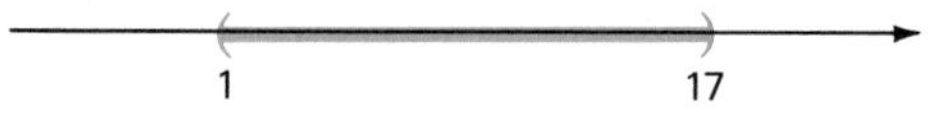

	1	17

Figure 2.5

The next two examples show how to solve compound inequalities. A **compound inequality** involves two inequalities connected with *and* or *or*.

Example 3   Solve $2x + 3 > 5$ and $7 - x > -10$.

Solve each part separately.

$$2x + 3 > 5 \qquad \text{and} \qquad 7 - x > -10$$
$$2x > 2 \qquad\qquad\qquad -x > -17$$
$$x > 1 \qquad\qquad\qquad x < 17$$

The original inequality is solved by all real numbers which are both greater than 1 and less than 17 *at the same time*. The numbers satisfying this condition are those between 1 and 17, or the numbers x such that $1 < x < 17$. In interval notation, the solution is $(1, 17)$. A graph of the solution is shown in Figure 2.5. $\quad \blacksquare$

Example 4 Solve $r - 1 > 5$ or $-3r + 7 < 1$.

Here we need to find all real numbers that make either inequality true. Solve each inequality separately.

$$r - 1 > 5 \quad \text{or} \quad -3r + 7 < 1$$
$$r > 6 \qquad\qquad r > 2$$

The result $r > 6$ or $r > 2$ is satisfied by all real numbers which are *either* greater than 6 *or* greater than 2. This solution is thus $r > 2$, or, in interval notation, $(2, \infty)$. This solution is shown in Figure 2.6. ▌

Figure 2.6

To solve the quadratic inequality $x^2 - x - 12 < 0$, begin by finding the values of x which satisfy $x^2 - x - 12 = 0$.

$$x^2 - x - 12 = 0$$
$$(x + 3)(x - 4) = 0$$
$$x = -3 \quad \text{or} \quad x = 4$$

Figure 2.7

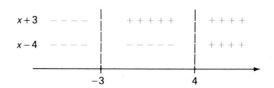

Figure 2.8

These two points divide the number line into the three regions shown in Figure 2.7. If a point in region A, for example, makes the polynomial $x^2 - x - 12$ negative, then all points in region A will make that polynomial negative. To find which regions make $x^2 - x - 12$ negative, we make the **sign graph** shown in Figure 2.8. First we decide on the sign of the factor $x + 3$ in each of the three regions. Then we do the same for the factor $x - 4$. Now we consider the sign of the product of the two factors in each region. As the sign graph shows, both factors are negative in the interval $(-\infty, -3)$, so that their product is positive. For the interval $(-3, 4)$, one factor is positive while the other is negative. This means that the product will be negative. In the last region, $(4, \infty)$, both factors are positive, so their product is positive. The polynomial $x^2 - x - 12$ is negative (what our original problem calls for) when the product of its factors is negative, that is, for $(-3, 4)$. The graph of this solution is shown in Figure 2.9.

Figure 2.9

Example 5 Solve the inequality $2x^2 + 5x - 12 \geq 0$.

We begin by finding the values of x which satisfy $2x^2 + 5x - 12 = 0$.

$$2x^2 + 5x - 12 = 0$$
$$(2x - 3)(x + 4) = 0$$
$$x = 3/2 \quad \text{or} \quad x = -4$$

These two points divide the number line into the three regions shown in the sign graph of Figure 2.10. Since both factors are negative in the first region, their product, and hence $2x^2 + 5x - 12$, is positive there. In the second region, the factors have opposite signs, therefore their product is negative. Both factors are positive in the third region, and so their product is also positive there. Thus, the polynomial $2x^2 + 5x - 12$ is positive or zero in the interval $(-\infty, -4]$ or $[3/2, \infty)$. The graph of the solution set is shown in Figure 2.11.

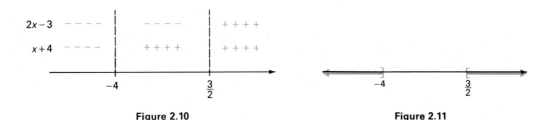

Figure 2.10   Figure 2.11

Example 6 Solve the inequality $\dfrac{5}{x + 4} \geq 1$.

We could begin by multiplying both sides of the inequality by $x + 4$, but we would then have to consider whether $x + 4$ is positive or negative. Instead, subtract 1 from both sides of the inequality.

$$\frac{5}{x + 4} - 1 \geq 0$$

Now write the left side as a single fraction.

$$\frac{5 - (x + 4)}{x + 4} \geq 0$$

$$\frac{1 - x}{x + 4} \geq 0$$

Set the numerator and denominator each equal to 0 and solve to get the numbers which determine the regions for a sign graph.

$$1 - x = 0 \quad \text{or} \quad x + 4 = 0$$
$$x = 1 \qquad\qquad x = -4$$

Make a sign graph as before. This time we consider the sign of the quotient of the two quantities rather than their product. See Figure 2.12.

We know that the quotient of two numbers is positive if both numbers are positive or if both numbers are negative. On the other hand, the quotient is negative if the two numbers have opposite signs. From the sign graph, since we want a positive quotient, we see that the interval $(-4, 1)$ is part of the solution. When we have a quotient, we must consider the endpoints separately. Here -4 leads to a zero denominator, whereas 1 satisfies the given inequality. Thus, the solution is the interval $(-4, 1]$. ▌

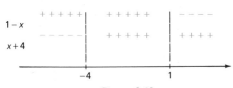

Figure 2.12

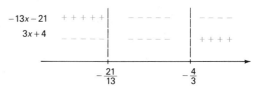

Figure 2.13

Example 7   Solve $\dfrac{2x - 1}{3x + 4} < 5$.

Begin by subtracting 5 on both sides and combining the terms on the left into a single fraction.

$$\frac{2x - 1}{3x + 4} < 5$$

$$\frac{2x - 1}{3x + 4} - 5 < 0$$

$$\frac{2x - 1 - (15x + 20)}{3x + 4} < 0$$

$$\frac{-13x - 21}{3x + 4} < 0$$

Set the numerator and denominator equal to zero.

$$-13x - 21 = 0 \quad \text{or} \quad 3x + 4 = 0$$

$$x = \frac{-21}{13} \qquad\qquad x = \frac{-4}{3}$$

Use the numbers $-21/13$ and $-4/3$ to divide the number line into three regions. Now complete a sign graph and find the regions where the quotient is negative. See Figure 2.13.

From the sign graph, we see that values of x in the two intervals $(-\infty, -21/13)$ and $(-4/3, \infty)$ make the quotient negative, as required. Neither endpoint satisfies the strict inequality, so the solution is $(-\infty, -21/13)$ or $(-4/3, \infty)$. ▌

2.5 Exercises   *Solve the following inequalities. Write the solutions in interval notation. Graph each solution for Exercises 1–22.*

1. $2x + 1 \le 9$

2. $3y - 2 \le 10$

3. $-3p - 2 \le 1$

4. $-5r + 3 \ge -2$

5. $2(m + 5) - 3m + 1 \ge 5$

6. $6m - (2m + 3) \ge 4m - 5$

7. $8k - 3k + 2 < 2(k + 7)$

8. $2 - 4x + 5(x - 1) < -6(x - 2)$

9. $2 \le y + 1 \le 5$

10. $-3 \le 2t \le 6$

11. $-10 > 3r + 2 > -16$

12. $4 > 6a + 5 > -1$

13. $x + 2 \le 8$ and $x \ge 3$

14. $y - 1 > 0$ and $y < 0$

15. $8 - 5b < 3$ and $12 + 2b < 16$

16. $2h + 3 \le 4h$ and $h - 5 \le 6$

17. $4c + 1 < 9$ or $-c < -8$

18. $3r + 2 < -11$ or $2r - 5 > 15$

19. $k + 3 > 12$ or $2k - 15 > 10$

20. $5y - 10 \ge -15$ or $3y + 9 \le 12$

21. $x > 3$ and $\dfrac{4x + 7}{-3} \le 2x + 5$

22. $z > -1$ or $\dfrac{2z - 5}{-8} \le 1 - z$

23. $x^2 \le 9$

24. $p^2 > 16$

25. $y^2 - 10y + 25 < 25$

26. $m^2 + 6m + 9 < 9$

27. $x^2 - x \le 6$

28. $r^2 + r < 12$

29. $2k^2 - 9k > -4$

30. $3n^2 < -10 - 13n$

31. $x^2 + 5x - 2 < 0$

32. $4x^2 + 3x + 1 \le 0$

33. $x^3 - 4x \le 0$

34. $r^3 - 9r \ge 0$

35. $4m^3 + 7m^2 - 2m > 0$

36. $6p^3 - 11p^2 + 3p > 0$

37. $\dfrac{5c + 2}{c} > 3$

38. $\dfrac{6 - 8m}{m} > -5$

39. $\dfrac{3}{x - 6} \le 2$

40. $\dfrac{1}{k - 2} < \dfrac{1}{3}$

41. $\dfrac{1}{m - 1} < \dfrac{5}{4}$

42. $\dfrac{6}{5 - 3x} \le 2$

43. $\dfrac{10}{3 + 2x} \le 5$

44. $\dfrac{x + 1}{x + 2} \ge 3$

45. $\dfrac{7}{k + 2} \ge \dfrac{1}{k + 2}$

46. $\dfrac{5}{p + 1} > \dfrac{12}{p + 1}$

47. $\dfrac{3}{2r - 1} > \dfrac{-4}{r}$

48. $\dfrac{-5}{3h + 2} \ge \dfrac{5}{h}$

49. $\dfrac{4}{y - 2} \le \dfrac{3}{y - 1}$

50. $\dfrac{4}{n + 1} < \dfrac{2}{n + 3}$

51. $\dfrac{2x - 3}{x^2 + 1} \ge 0$

52. $\dfrac{9x - 8}{4x^2 + 25} < 0$

53. $(x - 2)^2(x - 4) < 0$

54. $(x + 1)^2(x - 3) \ge 0$

55. $\dfrac{(3x - 5)^2}{(2x - 5)^3} > 0$

56. $\dfrac{(5x - 3)^3}{(8x - 25)^2} \le 0$

57. $\dfrac{(2x - 3)(3x + 8)}{(x - 6)^3} \geq 0$

58. $\dfrac{(9x - 11)(2x + 7)}{(3x - 8)^3} > 0$

59. Rick has 420 points so far in his math class. He must have at least 80% of a total of 700 points to get a B in the class. If the final is worth 200 points, what is the lowest score he can get on the final to get a B in the class?

60. On a trip to the market, Kevin bought twice as many apples as oranges. If he bought at least a dozen pieces of fruit, what is the smallest number of oranges he bought?

A product will break-even or produce a profit only if the revenue from selling the product at least equals the cost of producing it. Find all intervals when the following products will at least break-even.

61. The cost to produce x units of wire is $C = 50x + 5000$, while the revenue is $R = 60x$.

62. The cost to produce x units of squash is $C = 100x + 6000$, while the revenue is $R = 500x$.

63. $C = 85x + 900$; $R = 105x$.

64. $C = 150x + 6000$; $R = 250x$.

65. $C = 70x + 500$; $R = 60x$.

66. $C = 1000x + 5000$; $R = 900x$.

67. The commodity market is very unstable; money can be made or lost quickly when investing in soybeans, wheat, and so on. Suppose that an investor kept track of her total profit, P, at time t, measured in months, after she began investing, and found that

$$P = 4t^2 - 29t + 30.$$

Find the time intervals where she has been ahead. (Hint: $t > 0$ in this case.)

68. Suppose the velocity of an object is given by

$$v = 2t^2 - 5t - 12,$$

where t is time in seconds. (Here, t can be positive or negative.) Find the intervals where the velocity is negative.

69. An analyst has found that his company's profits, in hundred thousands of dollars, are given by

$$P = 3x^2 - 35x + 50,$$

where x is the amount, in hundreds, spent on advertising. For what values of x does the company make a profit?

70. The manager of a large apartment complex has found that the amount of profit he makes is given by

$$P = -x^2 + 250x - 15,000,$$

where x is the number of units rented. For what values of x does the complex produce a profit?

71. The formula for converting from Celsius to Fahrenheit temperature is $F = 9/5(C) + 32$. What temperature range in °F corresponds to 0°C to 30°C?

72. If $a > b > 0$, show that $1/a < 1/b$.

73. If $a > b$, is it always true that $1/a < 1/b$?

74. Suppose $a > b > 0$. Show that $a^2 > b^2$.

75. Let $b > 0$. When is $b^2 > b$?

76. If $a < b$ and $c < d$, show that $a + c < b + d$.

77. Solve $\dfrac{(m-1)(m-2)}{(m-3)(m-4)} \geq 0$

78. Solve $\dfrac{(a+2)(a+3)}{(a+4)(a-5)} \leq 0$.

2.6 Absolute Value Equations and Inequalities

Recall from Chapter 1 the definition of absolute value:

$$|a| = \begin{cases} a & \text{if } a \geq 0 \\ -a & \text{if } a < 0. \end{cases}$$

We use this definition to solve absolute value equations and inequalities.

Example 1   Solve $|x| = 3$.

Since either $|3| = 3$ or $|-3| = 3$, the solutions are 3 and -3.   █

Example 2   Solve $|p - 4| = 2$.

Again we have two cases. In the definition, if we let $a = p - 4$, then

$$\begin{array}{lll} p - 4 = 2 & \text{or} & -(p - 4) = 2 \\ p = 6 & & -p + 4 = 2 \\ & & p = 2. \end{array}$$

Thus, the solutions are 6 and 2.   █

Example 3   Solve $|4m - 3| = |m + 6|$.

The quantities in absolute value bars must either be equal or be negatives of one another to satisfy the equation. Therefore,

$$\begin{array}{lll} 4m - 3 = m + 6 & \text{or} & 4m - 3 = -(m + 6) \\ 3m = 9 & & 4m - 3 = -m - 6 \\ m = 3 & & 5m = -3 \\ & & m = -3/5. \end{array}$$

The two solutions of the equation are 3 and $-3/5$.   █

Example 4   Solve $|x| < 5$.

Since absolute value gives the distance from a number to 0, the inequality $|x| < 5$ will be solved by all real numbers whose distance from 0 is less than 5. This includes all numbers from -5 to 5, or $-5 < x < 5$. In interval notation, the solution is written as the open interval $(-5, 5)$. A graph of the solution is shown in Figure 2.14.   █

Figure 2.14   Figure 2.15

In a similar way, the solution of $|x| > 5$ is made up of all real numbers whose distance from 0 is greater than 5. This includes all numbers greater than 5, or less than -5, or

$$x < -5 \quad \text{or} \quad x > 5.$$

In interval notation, the solution is written $(-\infty, -5)$ or $(5, \infty)$. A graph of the solution is shown in Figure 2.15.

Generalizing from these examples, we have the following result.

Theorem 2.4   For all real numbers a and b, with $b > 0$:

(a) $|a| < b$ if and only if $-b < a < b$;

(b) $|a| > b$ if and only if $a < -b$ or $a > b$.

Example 5   Solve $|x| \geq 3$.

We need all real numbers whose distance from 0 is 3 or more. By Theorem 2.4(b), if $|x| \geq 3$, then $x \leq -3$ or $x \geq 3$, as shown on the number line of Figure 2.16. Using intervals, the solution can be written $(-\infty, -3]$ or $[3, \infty)$.   █

Figure 2.16   Figure 2.17

Example 6   Solve $|x - 2| < 5$.

Here we need to find all real numbers whose distance from 2 is less than 5. (See Figure 2.17).

From Theorem 2.4(a), letting $a = x - 2$ and $b = 5$, $|x - 2| < 5$ becomes

$$-5 < x - 2 < 5$$
$$-3 < x < 7.$$

In interval notation, the solution is $(-3, 7)$.   █

Example 7   Solve $|x - 8| \geq 1$.

We need to find the numbers whose distance from 8 is greater than or equal to 1, as shown in Figure 2.18 on the next page. Use Theorem 2.4(b), with $a = x - 8$ and $b = 1$.

$$|x - 8| \geq 1 \quad \text{becomes}$$
$$x - 8 \leq -1 \quad \text{or} \quad x - 8 \geq 1$$
$$x \leq 7 \quad \text{or} \quad x \geq 9.$$

In interval notation, the solution is $(-\infty, 7]$ or $[9, \infty)$.   █

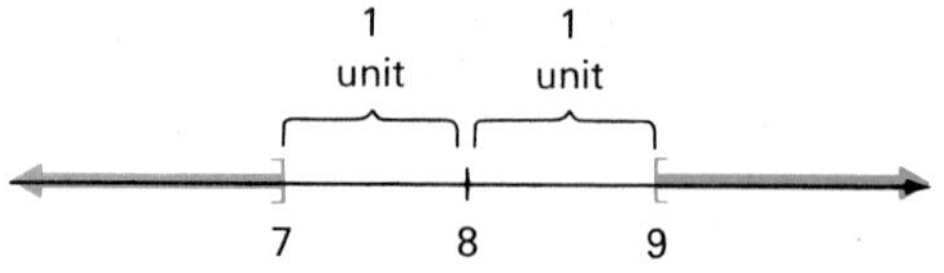

Figure 2.18

Example 8 Solve $|2 - 7m| - 1 > 4$.

To use Theorem 2.4(b), first add 1 to both sides of the inequality.

$$|2 - 7m| - 1 > 4$$
$$|2 - 7m| > 5$$

$$2 - 7m < -5 \quad \text{or} \quad 2 - 7m > 5$$
$$m > 1 \qquad\qquad m < -3/7$$

The interval solution is $(-\infty, -3/7)$ or $(1, \infty)$. █

Example 9 Solve $|2 - 5x| \geq -4$.

The absolute value of a number is always nonnegative. Thus $|2 - 5x| \geq -4$ is always true, so that the solution includes all real numbers. In interval notation, the solution is $(-\infty, \infty)$. █

Now let us see how to solve absolute value inequalities with variable denominators. The following examples show a method for solving this kind of inequality.

Example 10 Solve $\left|\dfrac{3k + 1}{k - 1}\right| < 2$.

We begin by using Theorem 2.4(a) to write

$$-2 < \frac{3k + 1}{k - 1} < 2.$$

Next, separate the inequality into its two parts using the connective *and*. Then solve each inequality separately as shown in Section 2.5.

$$-2 < \frac{3k + 1}{k - 1} \qquad \text{and} \qquad \frac{3k + 1}{k - 1} < 2$$

$$\frac{3k + 1}{k - 1} > -2 \qquad\qquad \frac{3k + 1}{k - 1} - 2 < 0$$

$$\frac{3k + 1}{k - 1} + 2 > 0 \qquad\qquad \frac{3k + 1 - 2(k - 1)}{k - 1} < 0$$

$$\frac{3k + 1 + 2(k - 1)}{k - 1} > 0 \qquad\qquad \frac{k + 3}{k - 1} < 0$$

$$\frac{5k - 1}{k - 1} > 0$$

The solutions are

$$k < \frac{1}{5} \text{ or } k > 1 \quad \text{and} \quad -3 < k < 1$$

The solution for each of the separate inequalities is graphed in Figure 2.19(a) and (b).

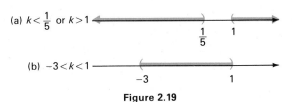

(a) $k < \frac{1}{5}$ or $k > 1$

$\frac{1}{5}$ 1

(b) $-3 < k < 1$

-3 1

Figure 2.19

In the first step of the solution, we used the word *and* when we separated the inequalities, so to find the original solution, we must take all numbers that belong to *both* the separate inequalities. We can graph the final solution by graphing the numbers that belong to both graphs (a) and (b). This gives the graph in Figure 2.20. From this graph we read the solution, $-3 < k < \frac{1}{5}$, or, in interval notation, $(-3, 1/5)$. ▌

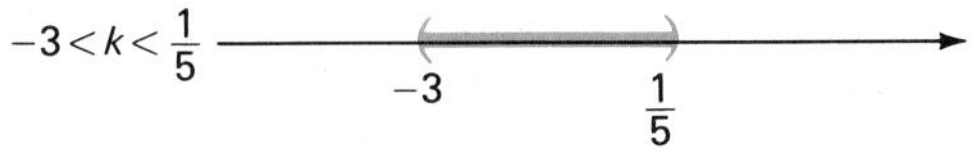

$-3 < k < \frac{1}{5}$

-3 $\frac{1}{5}$

Figure 2.20

Example 11 Solve $\left|\dfrac{y}{2y + 1}\right| > 3.$

This time we use Theorem 2.4(b), which gives

$$\frac{y}{2y + 1} > 3 \quad \text{or} \quad \frac{y}{2y + 1} < -3.$$

Again, we solve each inequality separately.

$$\frac{y}{2y + 1} - 3 > 0 \quad \text{or} \quad \frac{y}{2y + 1} + 3 < 0$$

$$\frac{y - 3(2y + 1)}{2y + 1} > 0 \qquad \frac{y + 3(2y + 1)}{2y + 1} < 0$$

$$\frac{-5y - 3}{2y + 1} > 0 \qquad \frac{7y + 3}{2y + 1} < 0$$

Solutions: $-\dfrac{3}{5} < y < -\dfrac{1}{2} \quad \text{or} \quad -\dfrac{1}{2} < y < -\dfrac{3}{7}$

The solution of each inequality is graphed in Figure 2.21(a) and (b).

In the first step of this solution, we used the word *or* when we separated the inequalities, so to find the original solution, we must take all the numbers that belong to *either* of the separate inequalities. The final solution is thus

$$-\frac{3}{5} < y < -\frac{1}{2} \quad \text{or} \quad -\frac{1}{2} < y < -\frac{3}{7}.$$

In interval notation, the solution is $(-3/5, -1/2)$ or $(-1/2, -3/7)$. The solution is graphed in Figure 2.22. ▌

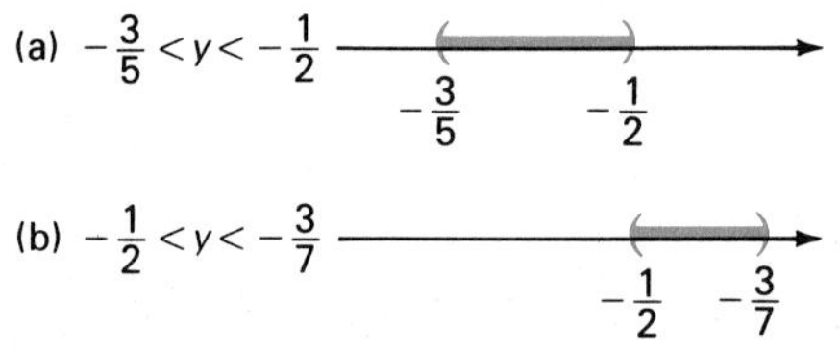

(a) $-\frac{3}{5} < y < -\frac{1}{2}$

$-\frac{3}{5} < y < -\frac{1}{2}$ or $-\frac{1}{2} < y < -\frac{3}{7}$

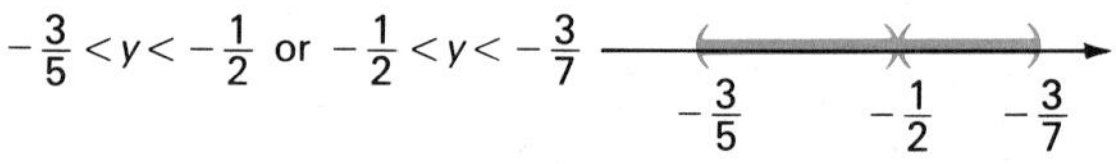

Figure 2.22

(b) $-\frac{1}{2} < y < -\frac{3}{7}$

Figure 2.21

Example 12   Solve $|m + 2| \le |4m - 1|$.

We can put this into the form of a fraction by dividing both sides by $|4m - 1|$. (We assume $|4m - 1| \ne 0$.) Since $|4m - 1|$ is positive, this gives

$$\frac{|m + 2|}{|4m - 1|} \le 1,$$

which is the same as

$$\left|\frac{m + 2}{4m - 1}\right| \le 1.$$

Now we can proceed as shown above.

$$-1 \le \frac{m + 2}{4m - 1} \qquad \text{and} \qquad \frac{m + 2}{4m - 1} \le 1$$

$$0 \le \frac{m + 2}{4m - 1} + 1 \qquad\qquad \frac{m + 2}{4m - 1} - 1 \le 0$$

$$0 \le \frac{5m + 1}{4m - 1} \qquad\qquad \frac{-3m + 3}{4m - 1} \le 0$$

The solutions are

$$m \le -\frac{1}{5} \text{ or } m > \frac{1}{4} \qquad \text{and} \qquad m < \frac{1}{4} \text{ or } m \ge 1$$

Figure 2.23 shows the two solutions.

To get the final solution, take the overlap of the intervals of Figure 2.23. The solution is

$$m \le -\frac{1}{5} \text{ or } m \ge 1$$

or, in interval notation, $(-\infty, -1/5)$ or $[1, \infty)$. The graph of the solution is shown in Figure 2.24.

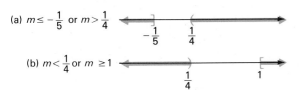

(a) $m \le -\frac{1}{5}$ or $m > \frac{1}{4}$

(b) $m < \frac{1}{4}$ or $m \ge 1$

Figure 2.23

$m \le -\frac{1}{5}$ or $m \ge 1$

Figure 2.24

2.6 Exercises   *Solve each of the following equations.*

1. $|3m - 1| = 2$

2. $|4p + 2| = 5$

3. $|5 - 3x| = 3$

4. $|-2 + 5a| = 3$

5. $\left|\dfrac{a - 4}{2}\right| = 5$

6. $\left|\dfrac{2}{m + 2}\right| = 7$

7. $\left|\dfrac{5}{r - 3}\right| = 10$

8. $\left|\dfrac{2h - 1}{5h}\right| = 4$

9. $|2k - 3| = |5k + 4|$

10. $|p + 1| = |3p - 1|$

11. $|4 - 3y| = |7 + 2y|$

12. $|2 + 5a| = |4 - 6a|$

13. $|x + 2| = |x - 1|$

14. $|y - 5| = |y + 3|$

Solve each of the following inequalities. Write the solutions in internal notation.

15. $|x| \le 3$

16. $|y| \le 10$

17. $|m| > 1$

18. $|z| > 5$

19. $|x| - 3 \le 7$

20. $|r| + 3 \le 10$

21. $|3m - 2| > 4$

22. $|6 - 4x| > 10$

23. $|4z + 6| \ge 7$

24. $|8b + 5| \ge 7$

25. $|2m - 5| + 2 > 3$

26. $|4 - 3k| - 3 > 2$

27. $|5x + 1/2| - 2 < 5$

28. $|x + 2/3| + 1 < 4$

29. $\left|\dfrac{2x + 3}{x}\right| < 1$

30. $\left|\dfrac{7 - 4y}{y}\right| < 3$

31. $\left|\dfrac{6 + 2y}{y - 5}\right| > 2$

32. $\left|\dfrac{3 - 3p}{p + 4}\right| > 5$

33. $\left|\dfrac{2}{q - 2}\right| \le 4$

34. $\left|\dfrac{5}{t - 1}\right| \le 3$

35. $\left|\dfrac{x - 1}{x - 2}\right| \ge 3$

36. $\left|\dfrac{2r + 1}{r}\right| \ge 5$

37. $|z + 1| < |2z + 5|$

38. $|3x - 1| < |4x + 2|$

39. $|6y - 5/2| > |2y - 1|$

40. $|2x + 7| \ge |x - 1/2|$

41. $|3x + 1| \le 2|x - 1|$

42. $|4x + 2| < 5|3 - x|$

Write each of the following, using absolute value statements.

43. x is within 4 units of 2

44. m is no more than 8 units from 9

45. z is no less than 2 units from 12

46. p is at least 5 units from 9

47. k is 6 units from 1

48. r is 5 units from 3

49. If x is within .0004 units of 2, then y is within .00001 units of 7.

50. y is within 10^{-6} units of 10 whenever x is within 2×10^{-4} units of 5.

51. If $|x - 2| < 3$, find the values of m and n such that $m < 3x + 5 < n$.

52. If $|x + 8| < 16$, find the values of p and q so that $p < 2x - 1 < q$.

Chapter 2   Review Exercises

Solve each of the following equations.

1. $5y - 2(y + 4) = 3(2y + 1)$

2. $\dfrac{x - 3}{2} = \dfrac{2x + 1}{3}$

3. $\dfrac{p}{2} - \dfrac{3p}{4} = 8 + \dfrac{p}{3}$

4. $\dfrac{5k}{8} + \dfrac{k - 2}{6} = -13$

5. $5(x - 3)(2x + 1) = 10(x + 2)(x - 4)$

6. $(3x + 1)^2 = 6x^2 + 3(x - 1)^2$

7. $(k + 7)^2 = 5$

8. $(3y - 2)^2 = 8$

9. $2a^2 + a - 15 = 0$

10. $12x^2 = 8x - 1$

11. $2 - \dfrac{5}{x} = \dfrac{3}{x^2}$

12. $\dfrac{4}{x^2} = 2 + \dfrac{7}{x}$

13. $4m^2 + 3m^2 + 1 = 0$

14. $2x^4 - x^2 = 0$

15. $(r + 1)^2 - 3(r + 1) = 4$

16. $4(y - 2)^2 - 9(y - 2) + 2 = 0$

17. $(2z + 3)^{2/3} + (2z + 3)^{1/3} = 6$

18. $5\sqrt{m} = \sqrt{3m + 2}$

19. $\sqrt{4x - 2} = \sqrt{3x + 1}$

20. $\sqrt{2x + 3} = x + 2$

21. $\sqrt{p + 2} = 2 + p$

22. $\sqrt{k} = \sqrt{k + 3} - 1$

23. $\sqrt{x^2 + 3x - 2} = 0$

24. $\sqrt[3]{2r} = \sqrt[3]{3r + 2}$

25. $|4x - 2| = 10$

26. $\left|\dfrac{y}{2y + 1}\right| = 5$

27. $|3m + 2| = |8m - 1|$

Solve each of the following for the indicated variable.

28. $2a + ay = 4y - 4a$ for y

29. $\dfrac{3m}{m - x} = 2m + x$ for x

30. $F = \dfrac{9}{5}C + 32$ for C

31. $A = P + Pi$ for P

32. $A = I\left(1 - \dfrac{j}{n}\right)$ for j

33. $A = \dfrac{24f}{b(p + 1)}$ for f

34. $\dfrac{1}{k} = \dfrac{1}{r_1} + \dfrac{1}{r_2}$ for r_1

35. $m = \dfrac{Ft}{\sqrt{I} - \sqrt{2}}$ for I

36. $V = \pi r^2 L$ for r

37. $P = \dfrac{E^2 R}{(r + R)^2}$ for E

38. $P = 2\pi\sqrt{\dfrac{L}{g}}$ for g

39. $c = \sqrt{a^2 + b^2}$ for b

Solve each of the following inequalities. Write solutions in interval notation.

40. $3r - 4 + r > 2(r - 1)$

41. $5 \le 2x - 3 \le 7$

42. $2x - 1 \le 3$ and $x > 4$

43. $y + 5 < 10$ or $3y > 12 - y$

44. $|2t| \le 10$

45. $|4x - 3| > 7$

46. $\left|x + \dfrac{2}{3}\right| - 1 < 4$

47. $x^2 + 3x - 10 > 0$

48. $m^2 - 4m \leq 0$

49. $\dfrac{3a - 2}{a} > 4$

50. $\dfrac{x + 1}{x} < \dfrac{x - 1}{2x}$

51. $\left|\dfrac{2p - 1}{p + 2}\right| \leq 1$

52. $|3p - 4| > |2p + 1|$

Solve each of the following problems.

53. A stereo is on sale for 15% off. The sale price is $425. What was the original price?

54. To make a special mix for Valentine's Day, the owner of a candy store wants to combine chocolate hearts which sell for $1 a pound with candy kisses which sell for $.70 a pound. How many pounds of each kind should he use to get 30 pounds of the mix, if he wants to sell the mix at $.90 a pound?

55. Ed and Camille are stuffing envelopes for a political campaign. Working together, they can stuff 5000 envelopes in 4 hours. When Camille worked at the job alone, it took her 6 hours to stuff 5000 envelopes. How long would it take Ed working alone to stuff 5000 envelopes?

56. Alison can ride her bike to the university in 20 minutes. The trip home, which is all uphill, takes her 1/2 hour. If her rate is 8 mph slower on the return trip, how far does she live from school?

57. Calvin wants to fence off a rectangular playground beside an apartment building. The building forms one boundary, so he needs to fence only the other three sides. The area of the playground is to be 11,250 square meters, and he has enough material to build 325 meters of fence. Find the dimensions of the playground.

58. Steve and Paula sell pies. It takes Paula one hour longer than Steve to bake a day's supply of pies. Working together, it takes them $1\dfrac{1}{5}$ hours to bake the pies. How long would it take Steve working alone?

The following exercises are taken from a standard calculus book.

59. If $y = 2x + |2 - x|$, express x in terms of y.

60. Show that the expression

$$M(a, b) = \frac{(a + b)}{2} + \frac{|a - b|}{2}$$

is equal to a when $a \geq b$ and is equal to b when $b \geq a$. In other words, $M(a, b)$ gives the larger of the two numbers a and b. Find a similar expression, $m(a, b)$, which gives the smaller of the two numbers.

George B. Thomas, Jr./Ross L. Finney, *Calculus and Analytic Geometry*, 5/E, © 1979, Addison-Wesley, Reading, Massachusetts. (P. 57.) Reprinted with permission.

Chapter 3

Functions and Graphs

Functions are a central idea of modern mathematics since they show how one variable is related to another. In fact, much of the rest of this text is devoted to a discussion of some of the most important types of functions. In this chapter, we introduce some of the basic ideas of functions.

3.1 A Two-Dimensional Coordinate System

We have used number lines to graph points; the idea behind a one-dimensional coordinate system can be extended to the two dimensions of a plane. To graph in two dimensions, we need *two* number lines, which meet at right angles. To locate a point in two dimensions, we need two numbers, one for each number line.

These two numbers are written as an ordered pair. An **ordered pair** of numbers consists of two numbers, written in parentheses, in which the sequence of numbers is important. For example, (2, 4) and (4, 2) are not the same ordered pair, since the order of the numbers is not the same. In fact, ordered pairs (a, b) and (c, d) are equal if and only if $a = c$ and $b = d$.

A symbol such as (3, 4) has now been used for two purposes—as an interval on the number line and as an ordered pair. In virtually every case, it is easy to tell which use is intended from the context of the discussion.

The number lines cross at their respective 0 points, with positive numbers measured to the right on the horizontal number line, or **x-axis,** and up along the vertical number line, or **y-axis.** Thus, in Figure 3.1, A represents the point having **coordinates** (3, 4), B represents (−5, 6), C represents (−2, −4), D represents (4, −3), and E represents (−3, 0).

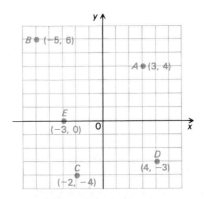

Figure 3.1

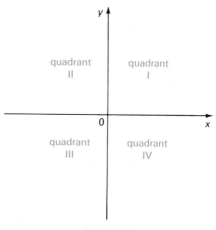

Figure 3.2

The x-axis and y-axis set up a **rectangular coordinate system,** or **Cartesian coordinate system** (named for its inventor, René Descartes.) The plane into which the coordinate system is introduced is the **coordinate plane,** or **xy-plane.** The x-axis and y-axis divide the coordinate plane into four portions, or **quadrants,** which are labeled as in Figure 3.2. The points of the x-axis and y-axis themselves belong to no quadrant.

In later work, it is often necessary to find the distance between two points on a plane. To do this, we need the distance formula. Suppose first that we have two points on a horizontal line (Figure 3.3(a)). Use the symbol $P(x_1, y_1)$ to represent point P, having coordinates (x_1, y_1). The distance between the points $P(x_1, y_1)$ and $Q(x_2, y_1)$ can be found by subtracting the x-coordinates (we use absolute value to make sure that the distance is not negative): distance between P and $Q = |x_1 - x_2|$. If we use $d(P, Q)$ to represent the distance between P and Q, then

$$d(P, Q) = |x_1 - x_2|.$$

Figure 3.3(b) shows points $Q(x_2, y_1)$ and $R(x_2, y_2)$, which are on a vertical line. To find the distance between Q and R, subtract the y-coordinates:

$$d(Q, R) = |y_1 - y_2|.$$

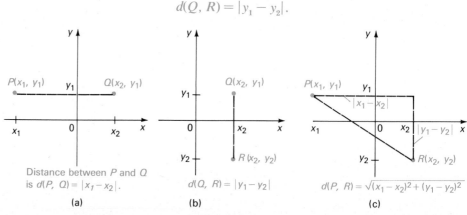

Figure 3.3

Finally, Figure 3.3(c) shows two points, $P(x_1, y_1)$ and $R(x_2, y_2)$, which are *not* on a horizontal or vertical line. To find $d(P, R)$, construct the right triangle shown in the figure. One side of this triangle is horizontal and has length $|x_1 - x_2|$. The other side is vertical and has length $|y_1 - y_2|$. By the Pythagorean theorem of geometry,

$$[d(P, R)]^2 = |x_1 - x_2|^2 + |y_1 - y_2|^2.$$

Since $d(P, R)$ must be nonnegative, and since $|x_1 - x_2|^2 = (x_1 - x_2)^2$, and $|y_1 - y_2|^2 = (y_1 - y_2)^2$, we have the result given in Theorem 3.1.

Theorem 3.1 (*The Distance Formula*) Suppose $P(x_1, y_1)$ and $R(x_2, y_2)$ are two points in a coordinate plane. Then the distance between P and R, written $d(P, R)$, is

$$d(P, R) = \sqrt{(x_1 - x_2)^2 + (y_1 - y_2)^2}.$$

Though the proof of Theorem 3.1 assumes that P and R are not on a horizontal or vertical line, the result is true for *any* choice of two points.

Example 1 Find the distance between the following pairs of points.

(a) $P(-8, 4)$ and $Q(3, -2)$
Use the distance formula.

$$\begin{aligned}
d(P, Q) &= \sqrt{(-8 - 3)^2 + [4 - (-2)]^2} \\
&= \sqrt{(-11)^2 + 6^2} \\
&= \sqrt{121 + 36} \\
&= \sqrt{157}
\end{aligned}$$

By using a calculator, $\sqrt{157} \approx 12.530$ ($\approx$ means "approximately equal to").

(b) $M(5, -11)$ and $N(-2, 13)$

$$\begin{aligned}
d(M, N) &= \sqrt{[5 - (-2)]^2 + (-11 - 13)^2} \\
&= \sqrt{7^2 + (-24)^2} \\
&= \sqrt{49 + 576} \\
&= \sqrt{625} \\
&= 25 \quad \blacksquare
\end{aligned}$$

Example 2 Are the points $M(-2, 5)$, $N(12, 3)$ and $Q(10, -11)$ the vertices of a right triangle?

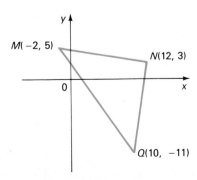

Figure 3.4

A triangle with these three points as vertices is shown in Figure 3.4. This triangle will be a right triangle if we can show the square of the length of the longest side (the hypotenuse) equals the sum of the squares of the lengths of the other two sides. Using the distance formula, we get

$$d(M, N) = \sqrt{(-2 - 12)^2 + (5 - 3)^2} = \sqrt{196 + 4} = \sqrt{200}$$
$$d(M, Q) = \sqrt{(-2 - 10)^2 + [5 - (-11)]^2} = \sqrt{144 + 256} = \sqrt{400} = 20$$
$$d(N, Q) = \sqrt{(12 - 10)^2 + [3 - (-11)^2]} = \sqrt{4 + 196} = \sqrt{200}$$

By these results,

$$[d(M, Q)]^2 = [d(M, N)]^2 + [d(N, Q)]^2,$$

proving the triangle is a right triangle with hypotenuse connecting M and Q.

The distance formula is used to find the distance between any two points in a plane. The *midpoint formula* is used to find the coordinates of the midpoint of a line segment.

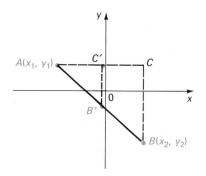

Figure 3.5

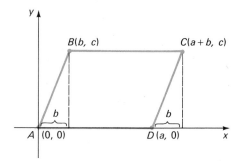

Figure 3.6

To find this formula, let $A(x_1, y_1)$ and $B(x_2, y_2)$ be two different points in a plane. (See Figure 3.5.) Assume that A and B are not on a horizontal or vertical line. Let B' (read "B-prime") be the midpoint of segment AB. Draw right triangles with right angles at C and C'. Triangles $AB'C'$ and ABC are similar, so that

$$\frac{AB'}{AB} = \frac{AC'}{AC},$$

where AB' is an abbreviation for the length of the segment with endpoints at A and B'.

Since B' is the midpoint of AB,

$$\frac{AB'}{AB} = \frac{1}{2}.$$

Thus,

$$\frac{AC'}{AC} = \frac{1}{2},$$

or

$$AC' = \frac{1}{2} AC.$$

From Figure 3.5, $AC = x_2 - x_1$. The x-coordinate of points C' and B' is thus

$$x_1 + \frac{1}{2} AC = x_1 + \frac{1}{2}(x_2 - x_1) = \frac{1}{2}(x_1 + x_2).$$

In the same way, the y-coordinate of point B is $\frac{1}{2}(y_1 + y_2)$, which proves the following result.

Theorem 3.2   (*The Midpoint Formula*) The midpoint of the segment with endpoints (x_1, y_1) and (x_2, y_2) is

$$\left(\frac{x_1 + x_2}{2}, \frac{y_1 + y_2}{2}\right).$$

Example 3   Find the midpoint of the segment with endpoints $(8, -4)$ and $(-9, 6)$.
 Use Theorem 3.2. The midpoint has coordinates

$$\left(\frac{8 + (-9)}{2}, \frac{-4 + 6}{2}\right) = \left(-\frac{1}{2}, 1\right). \quad \blacksquare$$

Example 4   A line segment has an endpoint at $(2, -8)$ and midpoint at $(-1, -3)$. Find the other endpoint of the segment.
 The formula for the x-coordinate of the midpoint is $(x_1 + x_2)/2$. Here the x-coordinate of the midpoint is -1. We can let $x_1 = 2$.

$$-1 = \frac{2 + x_2}{2}$$

$$-2 = 2 + x_2$$

$$-4 = x_2$$

In the same way, $y_2 = 2$ and the endpoint is $(-4, 2)$. $\blacksquare$

The two formulas that we have derived in this section can be used to prove various properties from geometry.

Example 5   Prove that the diagonals of a parallelogram bisect each other.
 Figure 3.6 shows parallelogram $ABCD$ placed on a coordinate system with A at the origin and side AD along the x-axis. We assign coordinates (b, c) to B and $(a, 0)$ to D. Since DC is parallel to AB and the same length as AB, we can use results from congruent triangles in geometry and write the coordinates of C as $(a + b, c)$. To show that the diagonals bisect each other, we show that they have the same midpoint. By the midpoint formula,

$$\text{midpoint of } AC = \left(\frac{a + b + 0}{2}, \frac{c + 0}{2}\right) = \left(\frac{a + b}{2}, \frac{c}{2}\right)$$

$$\text{midpoint of } BD = \left(\frac{a + b}{2}, \frac{c + 0}{2}\right) = \left(\frac{a + b}{2}, \frac{c}{2}\right).$$

Thus, AC and BD bisect each other. $\blacksquare$

3.1 Exercises   *Plot the following points in the xy-plane. Identify the quadrant for each.*

1. $A(6, -5)$ 4. $D(-9, -8)$

2. $B(8, 3)$ 5. $E(0, -5)$

3. $C(-4, 7)$ 6. $F(-8, 0)$

Graph the set of all points satisfying the following conditions for ordered pairs (x, y).

7. $x = y$ 13. $|x| = 4, y \geq 2$

8. $x > 0$ 14. $|y| = 3, x \geq 4$

9. $y \leq 0$ 15. $|y| < 2, x > 1$

10. $x \neq y$ 16. $|x| < 3, y < -2$

11. $xy < 0$ 17. $2 \leq |x| \leq 3, y \geq 2$

12. $\frac{x}{y} > 0$ 18. $1 \leq |y| \leq 4, x < 3$

Find the distance $d(P, Q)$ and the midpoint of segment PQ.

19. $P(5, 7), Q(13, -1)$ 22. $P(-6, -10), Q(6, 5)$

20. $P(-2, 5), Q(4, -3)$ 23. $P(\sqrt{2}, -\sqrt{5}), Q(3\sqrt{2}, 4\sqrt{5})$

21. $P(-8, -2), Q(-3, -5)$ 24. $P(5\sqrt{7}, -\sqrt{3}), Q(-\sqrt{7}, 8\sqrt{3})$

⊙ *Give the distance between the following points rounded to the nearest thousandth.*

25. $(5, 7), (2, 14)$ 27. $(3, -7), (-5, 19)$

26. $(-4, 6), (8, -5)$ 28. $(-9, -2), (-1, -15)$

Find the other endpoint of the segments having endpoints and midpoints as given.

29. endpoint $(-3, 6)$, midpoint $(5, 8)$ 31. endpoint $(6, -1)$, midpoint $(-2, 5)$

30. endpoint $(2, -8)$, midpoint $(3, -5)$ 32. endpoint $(-5, 3)$, midpoint $(-7, 6)$

Decide whether or not the following points are the vertices of a right triangle.

33. $(-2, 5), (1, 5), (1, 9)$

34. $(-9, -2), (-1, -2), (-9, 11)$

35. $(-4, 0), (1, 3), (-6, -2)$

36. $(-8, 2), (5, -7), (3, -9)$

37. $(\sqrt{3}, 2\sqrt{3} + 3), (\sqrt{3} + 4, -\sqrt{3} + 3), (2\sqrt{3}, 2\sqrt{3} + 4)$

38. $(4 - \sqrt{3}, -2\sqrt{3}), (2 - \sqrt{3}, -\sqrt{3}), (3 - \sqrt{3}, -2\sqrt{3})$

Find all values of x or y such that the distance between the given points is as indicated.

39. $(x, 7)$ and $(2, 3)$ is 5   42. $(x, 11)$ and $(5, -4)$ is 17

40. $(5, y)$ and $(8, -1)$ is 5   43. (x, x) and $(2x, 0)$ is 4

41. $(3, y)$ and $(-2, 9)$ is 12   44. (y, y) and $(0, 4y)$ is 6

45. Show that the points $(-2, 2), (13, 10), (21, -5)$, and $(6, -13)$ are the vertices of a square.

46. Are the points $A(1, 1), B(5, 2), C(3, 4), D(-1, 3)$ the vertices of a parallelogram? Of a rhombus (all sides equal in length)?

47. Use the distance formula to write an equation for all points that are 5 units from $(0, 0)$. Sketch a graph showing these points.

48. Write an equation for all points 3 units from $(-5, 6)$. Sketch a graph showing these points.

49. Find all points (x, y) with $x = y$ that are 4 units from $(1, 3)$.

50. Find all points with $x = -y$ that are 8 units from $(-2, 3)$.

51. Let point A be $(-3, 0)$ and point B be $(3, 0)$. Write an expression for all points (x, y) such that the sum of the distances from A to (x, y) and from (x, y) to B is 8. Simplify the result so that no radicals are involved.

Use the midpoint formula and distance formula, as necessary, to prove each of the following.

52. The midpoint of the hypotenuse of a right triangle is equally distant from all three vertices.

53. The diagonals of a rectangle are equal in length.

54. The line segment connecting the midpoints of two adjacent sides of any quadrilateral is the same length as the line segment connecting the midpoints of the other two sides.

55. The diagonals of an isosceles trapezoid are equal.

56. If the diagonals of a parallelogram are equal in length, then the parallelogram is a rectangle.

3.2 Graphs

For any set of ordered pairs, there is a corresponding set of points on a coordinate plane. If (x, y) is one of the ordered pairs in the set, then the corresponding point (x, y) can be located on the coordinate plane. This set of points is called the **graph** of the set of ordered pairs. For now, we shall find graphs by first identifying a reasonable number of ordered pairs. We then locate the points corresponding to these ordered pairs on a coordinate plane, and then try to decide on the shape of the complete graph. Later, we develop more useful methods of identifying particular graphs.

Example 1   Graph $y = -4x + 3$.

As we have just said, the only way we now have of sketching this graph is by identifying ordered pairs that can be obtained from the equation $y = -4x + 3$.

To find such ordered pairs, select a number of values for x (or y) and then find the corresponding values for the other variable. For example, if $x = -3$, then $y = -4(-3) + 3 = 15$, producing the ordered pair $(-3, 15)$. Typical such ordered pairs are given in the following table.

x	-3	-2	-1	0	1	2	3
y	15	11	7	3	-1	-5	-9
ordered pair	$(-3, 15)$	$(-2, 11)$	$(-1, 7)$	$(0, 3)$	$(1, -1)$	$(2, -5)$	$(3, -9)$

The ordered pairs from this table lead to the points that were plotted in Figure 3.7. From the points plotted, it appears that the complete graph is a straight line, which is also shown in Figure 3.7. ▌

There is a danger in the method we used here—we might choose a few values for x, find the corresponding values of y, graph the resulting points, and then make a completely wrong guess as to the actual shape of the graph. But this danger is remote in the basic graphs of this section, and when we work with more complicated graphs later, we shall develop more accurate methods of working with them.

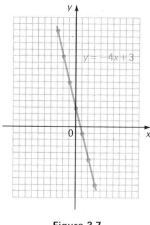

Figure 3.7

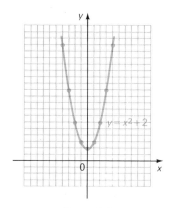

Figure 3.8

Example 2   Graph $y = x^2 + 2$.

Again, choose several values of x and find the corresponding values of y.

x	-4	-3	-2	-1	0	1	2	3	4
y	18	11	6	3	2	3	6	11	18

These points were located in Figure 3.8, and a smooth curve was drawn through them. This graph is called a **parabola.** The point $(0, 2)$ is the lowest point of this parabola; it is called the **vertex** of the parabola.

In $y = x^2 + 2$, we may choose any value at all for x. However, for any real value of x, we have $x^2 \geq 0$, so that $x^2 + 2 \geq 2$. Hence, $y \geq 2$. ▌

Example 3   Graph $x = y^2$.

Since y is squared, it is probably easier to choose values of y. If we choose the value 2 for y, we get $x = 2^2 = 4$. If we choose -2 for y, we get $x = (-2)^2 = 4$. The following table shows the results from choosing various values of y.

y	0	1	-1	2	-2	3	-3
x	0	1	1	4	4	9	9

The ordered pairs obtained from this table were used to get the points plotted in Figure 3.9. (Don't forget that x always goes first in the ordered pair.) A smooth curve was then drawn through them. This curve is a parabola with vertex (0, 0), opening to the right.

Here, y can take on any value. Since $x = y^2$, we have $x \geq 0$. ▌

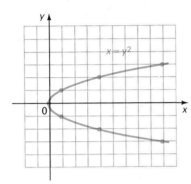

Figure 3.9

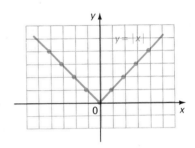

Figure 3.10

Example 4   Graph $y = |x|$.

Start with a table.

x	-4	-3	-2	-1	0	1	2	3	4
y	4	3	2	1	0	1	2	3	4

Use this table to get the points of Figure 3.10. The graph here is made up of portions of two straight lines. Here x may represent any real number while $y \geq 0$. ▌

Example 5   Graph $xy = -4$.

Make a table of values. Since this graph is more complicated than the ones above, it is a good idea to use more points.

x	-8	-4	-2	-1	$-\dfrac{1}{2}$	$-\dfrac{1}{4}$	$-\dfrac{1}{16}$	$-\dfrac{1}{64}$
y	$\dfrac{1}{2}$	1	2	4	8	16	64	256

x	$\dfrac{1}{64}$	$\dfrac{1}{16}$	$\dfrac{1}{4}$	$\dfrac{1}{2}$	1	2	4	8
y	-256	-64	-16	-8	-4	-2	-1	$-\dfrac{1}{2}$

As x approaches 0 from the left, y gets larger and larger. As x approaches 0 from the right, y gets more and more negative. If $x = 0$, there is no value of y, therefore the graph cannot cross the y-axis. Also, if $y = 0$, there is no value of x, so the graph cannot cross the x-axis either. The variables x and y can thus take on any values except 0: here $x \neq 0$ and $y \neq 0$. The table was used to get the points shown in Figure 3.11; a smooth curve was then drawn through them. ▮

Example 6   Graph $y = x^3$.

A table of values and the graph is shown in Figure 3.12. The variables x and y can take on any values at all. ▮

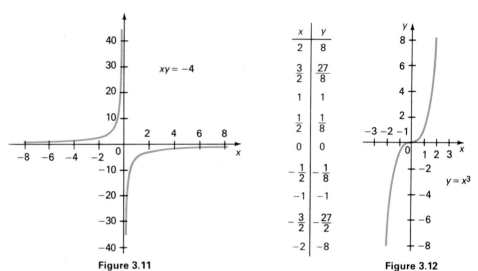

x	y
2	8
$\frac{3}{2}$	$\frac{27}{8}$
1	1
$\frac{1}{2}$	$\frac{1}{8}$
0	0
$-\frac{1}{2}$	$-\frac{1}{8}$
-1	-1
$-\frac{3}{2}$	$-\frac{27}{2}$
-2	-8

Figure 3.11   Figure 3.12

In the rest of this section we shall obtain a general equation for a circle. A **circle** is the set of points in a plane a fixed distance from a fixed point. The fixed distance is called the **radius** and the fixed point is the **center.**

Example 7   Find an equation for the circle having radius 6 and center at $(-3, 4)$.

This circle is shown in Figure 3.13. Its equation can be found by using the distance formula. Let (x, y) be any point on the circle. The distance from (x, y) to $(-3, 4)$ is given by

$$\sqrt{[x - (-3)]^2 + (y - 4)^2} = \sqrt{(x + 3)^2 + (y - 4)^2}.$$

Also, this same distance is given by the radius, 6. Therefore,

$$\sqrt{(x + 3)^2 + (y - 4)^2} = 6$$

or

$$(x + 3)^2 + (y - 4)^2 = 36. \quad ▮$$

By studying the graph of Figure 3.13, the possible values of x are seen to be $-9 \leq x \leq 3$ while the possible values of y are $-2 \leq y \leq 10$.

In general, the circle with center at (h, k) and radius r has equation

$$\boxed{(x - h)^2 + (y - k)^2 = r^2.}$$

As a special case, a circle of radius r with center at the origin has equation

$$x^2 + y^2 = r^2.$$

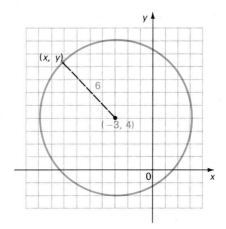

Figure 3.13

3.2 Exercises   *Graph each of the following.*

1. $y = 8x - 3$

2. $y = 2x + 7$

3. $y = 3x$

4. $y = -2x$

5. $3y + 4x = 12$

6. $5y - 3x = 15$

7. $y = 3x^2$

8. $y = 5x^2$

9. $y = -x^2$

10. $y = -2x^2$

11. $y = x^2 - 8$

12. $y = x^2 + 6$

13. $y = 4 - x^2$

14. $y = -2 - x^2$

15. $xy = -9$

16. $xy = 25$

17. $4x = y^2$

18. $9x = y^2$

19. $16y^2 = -x$

20. $4y^2 = -x$

21. $y^2 = x + 2$

22. $y^2 = -5 + x$

23. $y = x^3 - 3$

24. $y = x^3 + 4$

25. $y = 1 - x^3$

26. $y = -5 - x^3$

27. $2y = x^4$

28. $y = -x^4$

29. $y = \sqrt{x}$

30. $y = \sqrt{-x}$

31. $y = \sqrt{x + 5}$

32. $y = \sqrt{3 + x}$

33. $y = |x| + 4$

34. $y = |x| - 2$

35. $y = 8 - |x|$

36. $y = -3 - |x|$

37. $x^2 + y^2 = 36$

38. $x^2 + y^2 = 100$

39. $(x + 1)^2 + (y - 2)^2 = 25$

40. $(x - 3)^2 + (y + 7)^2 = 49$

41. $(x + 4)^2 + y^2 = 36$

42. $x^2 + (y - 2)^2 = 9$

Find equations for each of the following circles.

43. center (1, 4), radius 3

44. center (−2, 5), radius 4

45. center (−8, 6), radius 5

46. center (3, −2), radius 2

47. center (−1, 2), passing through (2, 6)

48. center (2, −7), passing through (−2, −4)

49. center (−3, −2), tangent to the x axis

50. center (5, −1), tangent to the y-axis

3.3   Symmetry and Translations as Aids to Graphing

In this section we shall study certain methods that are sometimes helpful when drawing graphs.

Symmetry.   If the graph of Figure 3.14(a) were folded in half along the *x*-axis, the portion at the top would exactly match the portion at the bottom. This graph is **symmetric with respect to the *x*-axis.** As the graph shows, symmetry with respect to the *x*-axis means that the point $(x, -y)$ must be on the graph whenever the point (x, y) is on the graph.

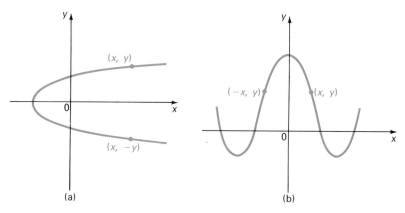

(a)   (b)

Figure 3.14

Figure 3.14(b) shows a graph which is **symmetric with respect to the *y*-axis.** For a graph to be symmetric with respect to the *y*-axis, the point $(-x, y)$ must be on the graph whenever (x, y) is on the graph.

The following test tells when a graph is symmetric to the *x*-axis or *y*-axis.

Symmetry with respect to an axis.

A graph is symmetric with respect to the *x*-axis if the replacement of *y* with −*y* results in an equivalent equation.

A graph is symmetric with respect to the *y*-axis if the replacement of *x* with −*x* results in an equivalent equation.

Example 1   Test for symmetry with respect to the *x*-axis or *y*-axis.

(a) $y = x^2 + 4$
Replace *x* with −*x*:

$$y = x^2 + 4 \text{ becomes } y = (-x)^2 + 4 = x^2 + 4.$$

The result is the same as the original equation so that the graph shown in Figure 3.15 is symmetric with respect to the *y*-axis. Check that the graph is *not* symmetric to the *x*-axis.

(b) $x = y^2 - 3$
Replace *y* with −*y*, to get $x = (-y)^2 - 3 = y^2 - 3$, the same as the original equation. The graph is symmetric to the *x*-axis, as shown in Figure 3.16. Is the graph symmetric to the *y*-axis?

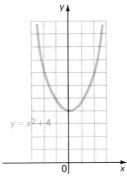

Figure 3.15

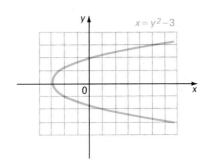

Figure 3.16

(c) $x^2 + y^2 = 16$

This graph, a circle of radius 4 with center at the origin, is symmetric to both the x-axis and y-axis.

(d) $2x + y = 4$

Replace x with $-x$ and y with $-y$; in neither case does an equivalent equation result. This graph is symmetric neither with respect to the x-axis nor the y-axis.

Another kind of symmetry is found when it is possible to rotate a graph 180° about the origin and have it coincide with the original graph. Such symmetry is called **symmetry with respect to the origin.** Figures 3.17(a) and (b) show graphs which are symmetric to the origin; Figure 3.17(c) shows a graph which is not.

A graph is symmetric with respect to the origin if the point $(-x, -y)$ is on the graph whenever (x, y) is. In summary:

> *Symmetry with respect to the origin.*
> A graph is symmetric with respect to the origin if the replacement of both x with $-x$ and y with $-y$ results in an equivalent equation.

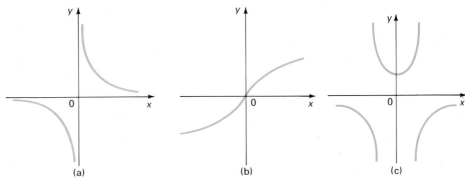

(a)   (b)   (c)

Figure 3.17

Example 2   Are the following graphs symmetric with respect to the origin?

(a) $x^2 + y^2 = 16$

Replace x with $-x$ and y with $-y$ to get

$$(-x)^2 + (-y)^2 = 16 \quad \text{or} \quad x^2 + y^2 = 16,$$

an equivalent equation. This graph, shown in Figure 3.18 is symmetric with respect to the origin.

(b) $y = x^3$

Replace x with $-x$ and y with $-y$ to get

$$-y = (-x)^3, \quad \text{or} \quad -y = -x^3, \quad \text{or} \quad y = x^3,$$

an equivalent equation. The graph, symmetric with respect to the origin, is shown in Figure 3.19.

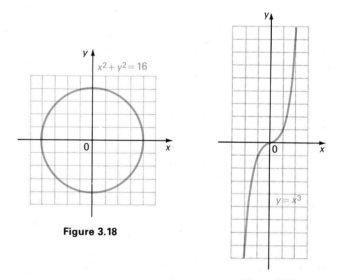

Figure 3.18

Figure 3.19

One final type of symmetry is **symmetry with respect to the line $y = x$**. Figure 3.20(a) shows a graph that is symmetric to this 45° line; Figure 3.20(b) shows one that is not. To test for such symmetry, use the following.

> *Symmetry with respect to $y = x$.*
> A graph is symmetric with respect to the line $y = x$ if the exchange of x and y results in an equivalent equation.

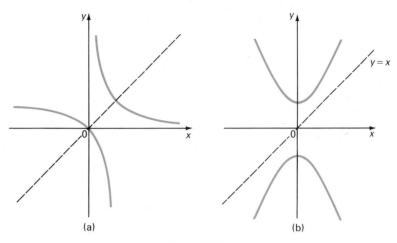

Figure 3.20

Example 3   Are the following graphs symmetric with respect to $y = x$?

(a) $x^2 + y^2 = 100$
   Exchange x and y to get

$$y^2 + x^2 = 100,$$

an equation equivalent to the original. This graph is symmetric to $y = x$ as shown in Figure 3.21.

(b) $y = x^2$
   Exchange x and y to get $x = y^2$, which is not equivalent to the original equation. As shown in Figure 3.22, this graph is not symmetric to $y = x$.

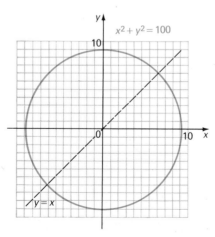

Figure 3.21

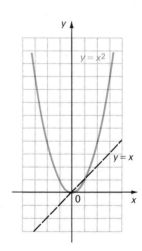

Figure 3.22

We can now summarize our tests for symmetry.

Symmetric with respect to	Example	Test
x-axis		replace y with $-y$
y-axis		replace x with $-x$
origin		replace x with $-x$ *and* replace y with $-y$
line $y = x$		exchange x and y

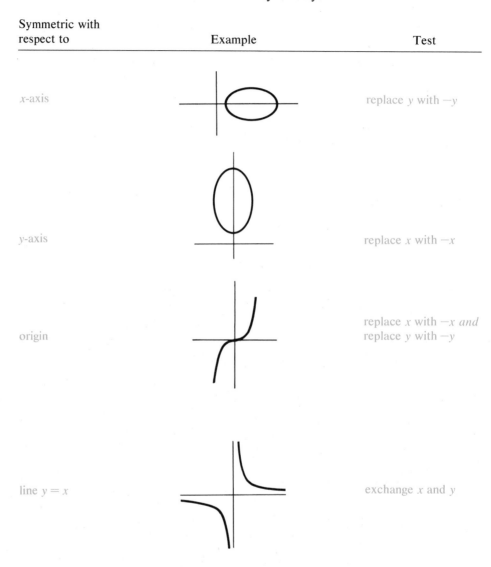

Translations.   Figure 3.23 shows the graphs of $y = x^2$ and $y = x^2 - 4$. The only difference between the two graphs is that the second one has been shifted 4 units downward. Such a vertical shift is called a **vertical translation.** Figure 3.24 shows $y = x^2$ and $y = (x - 3)^2$; the difference here is a **horizontal translation.**

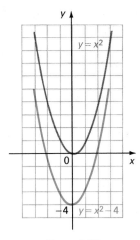

Figure 3.23

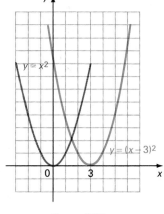

Figure 3.24

In summary:

> *Translations.*
> Replacing y in an equation by $y - b$ produces a vertical translation of $|b|$ units; the translation is up if b is positive and down if b is negative. Replacing x in an equation by $x - b$ produces a horizontal shift of b units; the shift is to the right if b is positive and to the left if b is negative.

Example 4   Graph each of the following.

(a) $y = |x - 4|$.

Here x was replaced by $x - 4$ in the equation $y = |x|$. This results in a shift of 4 units to the right as shown in Figure 3.25.

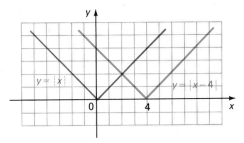

Figure 3.25

(b) $y = |x| - 5$

This equation can be written as the equivalent equation $y + 5 = |x|$. Here y was replaced with $y + 5$ in the equation $y = |x|$. Since $y + 5 = y - (-5)$, we have a shift of 5 units downward. See Figure 3.26.

(c) $y = |x + 3| + 2$

This graph is shifted 3 units to the left and 2 units upward. See Figure 3.27. ▌

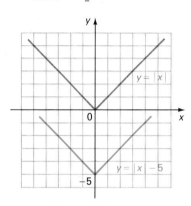

Figure 3.26   Figure 3.27

3.3 Exercises   *Plot the following points, and then plot the points that are symmetric to the given point with respect to the (a) x-axis, (b) y-axis, (c) origin.*

1. (5, −3)   **3.** (−4, −2)   **5.** (−8, 0)

2. (−6, 1)   **4.** (−8, 3)   **6.** (0, −3)

Use symmetry, point plotting, and translation to help you graph each of the following.

7. $x^2 + 2y^2 = 10$ **13.** $|y| = 2x$ **18.** $y^6 = x^3$

8. $y^2 + x^2 = 5$ **14.** $-3|y| = 4x$ **19.** $xy = 4$

9. $3x^2 - y^2 = 8$ **15.** $|y| = |x + 2|$ **20.** $\dfrac{x}{y} = 6$

10. $5y^2 - x^2 = 6$ **16.** $|x| = |y - 1|$

11. $y = 3|x|$ **17.** $x^4 = y^3$ **21.** $x^2 + xy + y^2 = 10$

12. $y = -2|x|$ **22.** $-x^2 - 4xy + y^2 = -1$

A graph of $y = x^2$ is shown in the figure. Explain how each of the following graphs could be obtained from the graph shown. Sketch each graph.

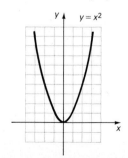

23. $y = x^2 + 2$

24. $y = x^2 - 7$

25. $y = -x^2$

26. $y = -x^2 + 8$

27. $y = -(x - 4)^2$

28. $y = -(x + 5)^2$

29. $y = (x - 2)^2 - 3$

30. $y = (x + 1)^2 + 5$

31. $y = -(x + 4)^2 + 2$

32. $y = -(x - 3)^2 - 1$

33. Suppose the equation $y = f(x)$ is changed to $y = -f(x)$. What is the effect on the graph of $y = f(x)$?

34. Suppose the equation $y = f(x)$ is changed to $y = c \cdot f(x)$, for some constant c. What is the effect on the graph of $y = f(x)$? Discuss the effect depending on whether $c > 0$ or $c < 0$, and $|c| > 1$ or $|c| < 1$.

Decide which of the following are symmetric to the line $y = x$.

35. $xy = 2$

36. $xy = -5$

37. $\dfrac{x}{y} = 8$

38. $\dfrac{y}{x} = 2$

39. $x^2 + 2y^2 = 40$

40. $3x^2 + 2y^2 = 25$

41. $(xy)^2 + 4xy = 5$

42. $(8xy - 7)^2 = xy$

43. $3x(2 + y) = 1$

44. $-9y(8 - x) = 3$

Sketch examples of graphs which are

45. symmetric to the x-axis but not the y-axis

46. symmetric to the origin but to neither the x-axis nor the y-axis

47. symmetric to the line $y = x$ but not the origin

48. symmetric to the origin but not to the line $y = x$

3.4 Functions

Suppose X is the set of all students studying this course every Monday evening at the local pizza parlor. Let Y be the set of integers between 0 and 100. To each student in set X we can associate a number from Y which represents the weight of the student to the nearest kilogram. Typical associations between students in set X and weights in set Y are shown in Figure 3.28.

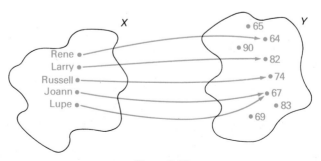

Figure 3.28

A correspondence such as the one shown in Figure 3.28 is called a **function** or a *mapping* if for each element in X there exists a single corresponding element in Y. Set X is the **domain** of the function.

Three things should be noticed about the function shown in Figure 3.28 above.

(a) There is a single weight associated with each student. That is, each element in X corresponds to exactly one element in Y.

(b) The same weight may correspond to more than one student. In the example above, two students (Joann and Lupe) have a weight of 67 kilograms.

(c) Not every element of Y need be used; for example, none of the students weighs 83 kilograms or 65 kilograms.

While the sets X and Y above were different, in many cases X and Y have many elements in common. In fact, it is not unusual at all for X and Y to be equal.

Example 1   Decide whether or not the following diagrams represent functions.

(a)

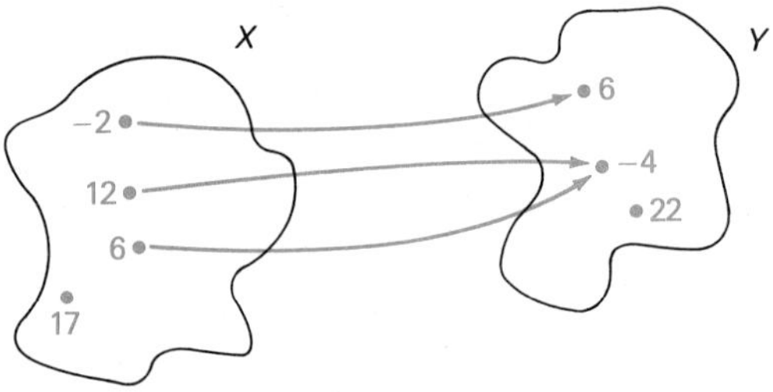

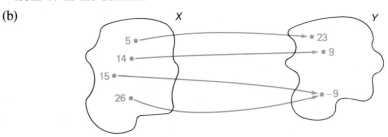

Figure 3.29

This diagram does not represent a function since there is no arrow leading from 17 in the domain.

(b)

Figure 3.30

This diagram does represent a function.   ▌

It is common to use the letters f, g, and h to represent functions. If f is a function and x is an element of the domain X, then $f(x)$ represents the element of Y that corresponds to x. For example, in the diagram of Example 1(b) above, if we use f to name that function, we have

$$f(15) = -9, \quad f(26) = -9, \quad f(5) = 23, \quad \text{and} \quad f(14) = 9.$$

For a given element x, $f(x)$ is called the **value** of f at x. Also, $f(x)$ is called the *image* of x. The set of all possible values of $f(x)$ makes up the **range** of the function.

Functions are often expressed by simply giving an equation that shows how a given value of x is used to find the corresponding element of the range. For example, if f is the function where a value of x is squared to find the corresponding value in the range, f could be expressed as

$$f(x) = x^2.$$

Throughout this book, if the domain for a function is not given, it will be assumed to be the largest possible set of real numbers for which the function is meaningful. For example, suppose

$$f(x) = \frac{-4x}{2x - 3}.$$

Here any real number can be used for x except $x = 3/2$, which makes the denominator equal 0. Thus, the domain of this function will be assumed to be $\{x \mid x \neq 3/2\}$.

Example 2 Find the domain and range for each of the following functions.

(a) $f(x) = x^2$

Any number may be squared, therefore the domain is the set of all real numbers. Since $x^2 \geq 0$ for every value of x, the range is the set $\{y \mid y \geq 0\}$.

(b) $f(x) = \sqrt{6 - x}$

Here x can take on any value less than or equal to 6, so that the domain is $\{x \mid x \leq 6\}$. The range is $\{y \mid y \geq 0\}$. ▌

For most of the functions that we use, the domain can be found with the methods we have available. The range, however, often must be found by using calculus, very complicated algebra, or graphing.

Based on the definition of a function, functions f and g are *equal* if and only if f and g have exactly the same domains and if $f(x) = g(x)$ for every value of x in the domain.

Suppose a function f is given by $f(x) = -3x + 2$. To emphasize that this statement is used to find values in the range of f, it is common to write

$$y = -3x + 2.$$

When a function is written in the form $y = f(x)$, x is called the **independent variable**, and y is the **dependent variable.**

Example 3 Let $g(x) = 3\sqrt{x}$ and $h(x) = 1 + 4x$. Find each of the following.

(a) $g(16) = 3\sqrt{16} = 12$

(b) $h(-3) = 1 + 4(-3) = -11$

(c) $g(-4)$ does not exist; -4 is not in the domain of g

(d) $h(\pi) = 1 + 4\pi$

(e) $g(m) = 3\sqrt{m}$, if m represents a nonnegative real number

(f) $g[h(3)] = g(1 + 4 \cdot 3) = g(13) = 3\sqrt{13}$ ▌

Example 4   Let $f(x) = 2x^2 - 3x$. Find each of the following, which are important in calculus.

(a) $f(x + h) = 2(x + h)^2 - 3(x + h)$
$$= 2(x^2 + 2xh + h^2) - 3(x + h)$$
$$= 2x^2 + 4xh + 2h^2 - 3x - 3h$$

(b) $f(x + h) - f(x) = (2x^2 + 4xh + 2h^2 - 3x - 3h) - (2x^2 - 3x)$
$$= 2x^2 + 4xh + 2h^2 - 3x - 3h - 2x^2 + 3x$$
$$= 4xh + 2h^2 - 3h$$

(c) $\dfrac{f(x + h) - f(x)}{h} = \dfrac{4xh + 2h^2 - 3h}{h}$
$$= \dfrac{h(4x + 2h - 3)}{h}$$
$$= 4x + 2h - 3 \quad \blacksquare$$

We have been finding the graphs of sets of ordered pairs throughout this chapter. A function can be thought of as a set of ordered pairs; in fact, a function f produces the set of ordered pairs $\{(x, f(x)) | x$ is in the domain of $f\}$. By the definition of a function, for each x which appears in the first position of an ordered pair, there will be exactly one value of $f(x)$ in the second position.

In addition, if we have a set of ordered pairs in which any two ordered pairs that have equivalent values of x in the first position also have equivalent values in the second position, we must have a function. Using these facts, we can give the following *alternate definition of a function:*

> A *function* is a set of ordered pairs where two ordered pairs cannot have the same first component and different second components.

Now that we see how a function can be used to get a set of ordered pairs, we can graph functions. There is a quick way to tell if a given graph is the graph of a function or not. Figure 3.31 shows two graphs. In the graph of part (a), for any value of x that we might choose there would be only one value of $f(x)$ or y.

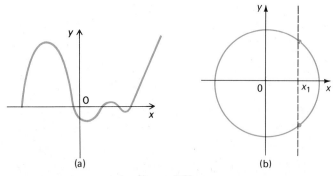

(a)   (b)

Figure 3.31

Thus, this graph is the graph of a function. On the other hand, the graph in part (b) is not the graph of a function. If we choose the x-value x_1, the vertical line shows that there are two values of y.

We summarize this as the **vertical line test** for a function:

> **If a vertical line can cut a graph in more than one point, the graph is not the graph of a function.**

Intuitively, we consider a function **increasing** if its graph moves up and to the right as we move along the x-axis from left to right. The functions graphed in Figure 3.32(a) and (b) are increasing functions. On the other hand, a function is **decreasing** if its graph goes down and to the right as we move from left to right along the x-axis. The function graphed in Figure 3.32(c) is a decreasing function.

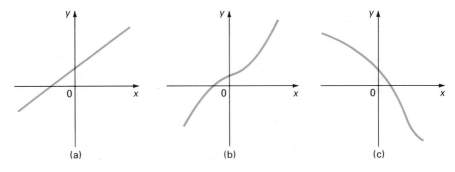

Figure 3.32

The function of Figure 3.33 is neither an increasing nor a decreasing function. However, this function is increasing if we look only at the interval $(-\infty, -2]$ or the interval $[4, \infty)$; yet f is decreasing if we look only at the interval $[-2, 4]$.

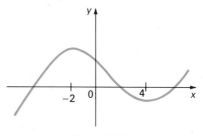

Figure 3.33

It is common to give a formal definition of *increasing* and *decreasing* in terms of intervals.

Let f be a function, with the interval $[a, b]$ in the domain of f. Let x_1 and x_2 be in $[a, b]$.

f is *increasing* on $[a, b]$ in case $f(x_1) < f(x_2)$, whenever $x_1 < x_2$

f is *decreasing* on $[a, b]$ in case $f(x_1) > f(x_2)$, whenever $x_1 < x_2$

Example 5   Find the intervals where the following functions are increasing or decreasing.

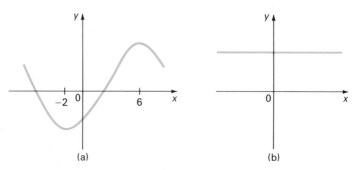

Figure 3.34

(a) The function graphed in Figure 3.34(a) is increasing on the interval $[-2, 6]$. It is decreasing on $(-\infty, -2]$ and $[6, \infty]$.

(b) The function graphed in Figure 3.34(b) is never increasing or decreasing. This function is an example of a **constant function.**   ▌

3.4 Exercises   *Give the domain of each of the following.*

1. $f(x) = 2x$

2. $f(x) = x + 2$

3. $f(x) = x^4$

4. $f(x) = (x - 2)^2$

5. $f(x) = \sqrt{16 - x^2}$

6. $f(x) = |x - 1|$

7. $f(x) = (x - 3)^{1/2}$

8. $f(x) = (3x + 5)^{1/2}$

9. $f(x) = \dfrac{2}{x^2 - 4}$

10. $f(x) = \dfrac{-8}{x^2 - 36}$

11. $f(x) = \sqrt{\dfrac{3}{x^2 + 25}}$

12. $f(x) = \sqrt{\dfrac{6}{x^2 + 121}}$

13. $f(x) = -\sqrt{\dfrac{2}{x^2 + 9}}$

14. $f(x) = -\sqrt{\dfrac{5}{x^2 + 36}}$

15. $f(x) = \sqrt{x^2 - 4x - 5}$

16. $f(x) = \sqrt{x^2 + 7x + 10}$

17. $f(x) = -\sqrt{6x^2 + 7x - 5}$

18. $f(x) = \sqrt{15x^2 + x - 2}$

Let $f(x) = 3x - 1$ and $g(x) = x^2$. Find each of the following.

19. $f(0)$

20. $f(-1)$

21. $g(2)$

22. $g(0)$

23. $f(a)$

24. $g(b)$

25. $f[f(1)]$ **29.** $g(5p - 2)$

26. $g[g(-2)]$ **30.** $g(-6k + 1)$

27. $f(5a - 2)$ **31.** $f[g(m)]$

28. $f(3 + 2k)$ **32.** $g[f(2r)]$

⊙ *Let* $f(x) = -4.6x^2 - 8.9x + 1.3$. *Find each of the following.*

33. $f(3)$ **35.** $f(-4.2)$

34. $f(-5)$ **36.** $f(-1.8)$

For all positive integers x, let $f(x) = 2^x$. *Find each of the following.*

37. $f(1)$ **42.** $f(-5r)$

38. $f(2)$

⊙ **43.** $f\left(\dfrac{1}{2}\right)$

39. $f(-2)$

40. $f(-4)$ **44.** $f\left(\dfrac{1}{4}\right)$

41. $f(m)$

For each of the following, find: (a) $f(x + h)$*; (b)* $f(x + h) - f(x)$*; (c)* $\dfrac{f(x + h) - f(x)}{h}$.

45. $f(x) = x^2 - 4$ **48.** $f(x) = 4x - 11$

46. $f(x) = 8 - 3x^2$ **49.** $f(x) = 2x^3 + x^2$

47. $f(x) = 6x + 2$ **50.** $f(x) = -4x^3 - 8x$

Find all intervals when the following functions are increasing or decreasing.

51.

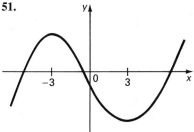

53.

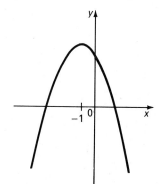

52.

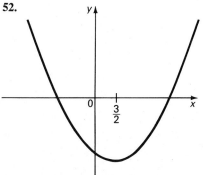

54.

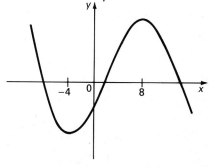

55.

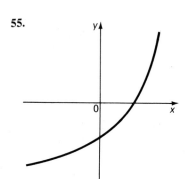

56.

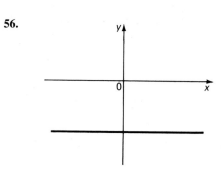

57. $y = -4x + 2$

58. $y = 5x - 1$

59. $y = x^2 + 4$

60. $y = -x^2 - 3$

61. $y = -|x + 2|$

62. $y = |3 - x|$

63. $y = x + |x|$

64. $y = |x| - x$

*A function f with the property that $f(-x) = f(x)$ for every value of x in its domain is called an **even function**. A function f with the property that $f(-x) = -f(x)$ for every x in its domain is called an **odd function**. Decide whether the following functions are even, odd, or neither.*

65. $f(x) = x^2$

66. $f(x) = x^3$

67. $f(x) = x^4 + x^2 + 5$

68. $f(x) = x^3 - x + 1$

69. $f(x) = 2x + 3$

70. $f(x) = |x|$

71. $f(x) = \dfrac{2}{x - 6}$

72. $f(x) = \dfrac{8}{x}$

73. $f(x) = \sqrt{2x^2 + 5}$

74. $f(x) = \sqrt{9 - x^2}$

75. Prove that an even function has a graph which is symmetric to the y-axis.

76. Prove that an odd function has a graph which is symmetric to the x-axis.

*The **greatest integer function**, written $y = [x]$, is defined by saying that $[x]$ represents the greatest integer less than or equal to x. Thus, $[8.4] = 8$, $[-5] = -5$, $[\pi] = 3$, $[-3.4] = -4$, and so on.*

77. Find $[0]$, $[.2]$, $[.6]$, $[1]$, $[1.8]$, $[2]$.

78. Graph $y = [x]$.

79. Give the domain and range of $y = [x]$.

Suppose a function is increasing for the interval $(-\infty, \infty)$.

80. Could the graph of the function be symmetric with respect to the x-axis?

81. The y-axis?

82. The origin?

3.5   Algebra of Functions

It is often necessary to use two functions f and g to obtain a third function. For example, the *sum* of functions f and g is written $(f + g)(x)$, and defined as

$$(f + g)(x) = f(x) + g(x)$$

for all values of x where both $f(x)$ and $g(x)$ exist. Similar definitions could be given for the *difference, product* and *quotient* of functions. (What would be acceptable values of x in the quotient?)

Example 1   Let $f(x) = 8x - 9$ and $g(x) = \sqrt{2x - 1}$.

(a) $(f + g)(x) = f(x) + g(x) = 8x - 9 + \sqrt{2x - 1}$

(b) $(f - g)(x) = f(x) - g(x) = 8x - 9 - \sqrt{2x - 1}$

(c) $(f \cdot g)(x) = f(x) \cdot g(x) = (8x - 9)\sqrt{2x - 1}$

(d) $\left(\dfrac{f}{g}\right)(x) = \dfrac{f(x)}{g(x)} = \dfrac{8x - 9}{\sqrt{2x - 1}}$ ▌

In this example, the domain of $f(x)$ contains all real numbers, while the domain of $g(x) = \sqrt{2x - 1}$ is made up of the numbers in the interval $\left[\dfrac{1}{2}, \infty\right)$. The domain of $(f + g)(x)$, $(f - g)(x)$, and $(f \cdot g)(x)$ is thus $\left[\dfrac{1}{2}, \infty\right)$, while the domain of $\left(\dfrac{f}{g}\right)(x)$ is $\left(\dfrac{1}{2}, \infty\right)$.

Suppose that f and g are functions such that at least one element of the range of g is in the domain of f. Then the **composition** of f and g, written as $f \circ g$, is defined as

$$(f \circ g)(x) = f[g(x)].$$

The domain of $f \circ g$ is made up of all the elements x from the domain of g for which $g(x)$ is in the domain of f.

Example 2   Let $f(x) = 4x + 1$ and $g(x) = 2x^2 + 5x$.
Find $(a)\ (f \circ g)(x)$ and $(b)\ (g \circ f)(x)$.

(a) $(f \circ g)(x) = f[g(x)]$
$\qquad\qquad = f[2x^2 + 5x]$

Substitute $2x^2 + 5x$ for x wherever x appears in $f(x)$.
$\qquad\qquad = 4(2x^2 + 5x) + 1$
$\qquad\qquad = 8x^2 + 20x + 1$

(b) $(g \circ f)(x) = g[f(x)]$

$$= g[4x + 1]$$
$$= 2(4x + 1)^2 + 5(4x + 1)$$
$$= 2(16x^2 + 8x + 1) + 20x + 5$$
$$= 32x^2 + 16x + 2 + 20x + 5$$
$$= 32x^2 + 36x + 7 \quad \blacksquare$$

Note that $(f \circ g)(x) \neq (g \circ f)(x)$. Here the domain of both of these composite functions is the set of all real numbers.

Example 3 Let $f(x) = \dfrac{1}{x}$ and let $g(x) = \sqrt{3 - x}$.

Find (a) $(f \circ g)(x)$ and (b) $(g \circ f)(x)$. Find the domain of each.

(a) $(f \circ g)(x) = f[g(x)]$

$$= f(\sqrt{3 - x})$$
$$= \frac{1}{\sqrt{3 - x}}$$

The domain of $(f \circ g)(x)$ is the set of all real numbers less than 3. (Why not $x \leq 3$?)

(b) $(g \circ f)(x) = g[f(x)]$

$$= g\left[\frac{1}{x}\right]$$
$$= \sqrt{3 - \frac{1}{x}}$$

The domain here is the set of all nonzero real numbers satisfying

$$3 - \frac{1}{x} \geq 0,$$

or

$$-\frac{1}{x} \geq -3,$$

or

$$\frac{1}{x} \leq 3.$$

By methods given in Chapter 2, the solution of this inequality is $x < 0$ or $x \geq \dfrac{1}{3}$.

$\blacksquare$

3.5 Exercises *For each of the following functions, find $(f + g)(x)$, $(f - g)(x)$, $(f \cdot g)(x)$, and $\left(\dfrac{f}{g}\right)(x)$. Give the domain of each.*

1. $f(x) = 4x - 1$, $g(x) = 6x + 3$
2. $f(x) = 9 - 2x$, $g(x) = -5x + 2$
3. $f(x) = 3x^2 - 2x$, $g(x) = x^2 - 2x + 1$
4. $f(x) = 6x^2 - 11x$, $g(x) = x^2 - 4x - 5$
5. $f(x) = \sqrt{2x + 5}$, $g(x) = \sqrt{4x - 9}$
6. $f(x) = \sqrt{11x - 3}$, $g(x) = \sqrt{2x - 15}$
7. $f(x) = 4x^2 - 11x + 2$, $g(x) = x^2 + 5$
8. $f(x) = 15x^2 - 2x + 1$, $g(x) = 16 + x^2$

Let $f(x) = 4x^2 - 2x$ and let $g(x) = 8x + 1$. Find each of the following values.

9. $(f + g)(3)$

10. $(f + g)(-5)$

11. $(f \cdot g)(4)$

12. $(f \cdot g)(-3)$

13. $\left(\dfrac{f}{g}\right)(-1)$

14. $\left(\dfrac{f}{g}\right)(4)$

15. $(f + g)(m)$

16. $(f - g)(2k)$

17. $(f \circ g)(2)$

18. $(f \circ g)(-5)$

19. $(g \circ f)(2)$

20. $(g \circ f)(-5)$

21. $(f \circ g)(k)$

22. $(g \circ f)(5z)$

Find $(f \circ g)(x)$ and $(g \circ f)(x)$ for each of the following.

23. $f(x) = 8x + 12, \ g(x) = 3x - 1$

24. $f(x) = -6x + 9, \ g(x) = 5x + 7$

25. $f(x) = 5x + 3, \ g(x) = -x^2 + 4x + 3$

26. $f(x) = 4x^2 + 2x + 8, \ g(x) = x + 5$

27. $f(x) = -x^3 + 2, \ g(x) = 4x$

28. $f(x) = 2x, \ g(x) = 6x^2 - x^3$

29. $f(x) = \dfrac{1}{x}, \ g(x) = x^2$

30. $f(x) = 2/x^4, \ g(x) = 2 - x$

31. $f(x) = \sqrt{x + 2}, \ g(x) = 8x^2 - 6$

32. $f(x) = 9x^2 - 11x, \ g(x) = 2\sqrt{x + 2}$

33. $f(x) = \dfrac{1}{x - 5}, \ g(x) = \dfrac{2}{x}$

34. $f(x) = \dfrac{8}{x - 6}, \ g(x) = \dfrac{4}{3x}$

35. $f(x) = \sqrt{x + 1}, \ g(x) = \dfrac{-1}{x}$

36. $f(x) = \dfrac{8}{x}, \ g(x) = \sqrt{3 - x}$

For each of the following, show that $(f \circ g)(x) = x$ and $(g \circ f)(x) = x$.

37. $f(x) = 8x, \ g(x) = \dfrac{1}{8}x$

38. $f(x) = \dfrac{3}{4}x, \ g(x) = \dfrac{4}{3}x$

39. $f(x) = 8x - 11, \ g(x) = \dfrac{x + 11}{8}$

40. $f(x) = \dfrac{x - 3}{4}, \ g(x) = 4x + 3$

41. $f(x) = x^3 + 6, \ g(x) = \sqrt[3]{x - 6}$

42. $f(x) = \sqrt[5]{x - 9}, \ g(x) = x^5 + 9$

For each of the following, a function h is given. Find functions f and g such that $h(x) = (f \circ g)(x)$. Many such pairs of functions exist.

43. $h(x) = (6x - 2)^2$

44. $h(x) = (11x^2 + 12x)^2$

45. $h(x) = \sqrt{x^2 - 1}$

46. $h(x) = \dfrac{1}{x^2 + 2}$

47. $h(x) = \dfrac{8x + 2}{4x - 3}$

48. $h(x) = (x + 2)^3 - 3(x + 2)^2$

49. Suppose the population P of a certain species of fish depends on the number x of a smaller kind of fish which serves as its food supply, so that

$$P(x) = 2x^2 + 1.$$

Suppose, also, that the number x of the smaller species of fish depends upon the amount a of its food supply, a kind of plankton. Suppose

$$x = f(a) = 3a + 2.$$

Find $[P \circ f](a)$, the relationship between the population P of the large fish and the amount a of plankton available.

50. Suppose the demand for a certain brand of vacuum cleaner is given by

$$D(p) = \frac{-p^2}{100} + 500.$$

where p is the price in dollars. If the price, in terms of the cost, c, is expressed as

$$p(c) = 2c - 10,$$

find the demand in terms of the cost.

51. An oil well off the Gulf Coast is leaking, with the leak spreading oil over the surface as a circle. At any time t, in minutes, after the beginning of the leak, the radius of the circular oil slick on the surface is $r(t) = 4t$ feet. Let $A(r) = \pi r^2$ represent the area of a circle of radius r. Find and interpret $(A \circ r)(t)$.

52. When a thermal inversion layer is over a city (such as happens often in Los Angeles), pollutants cannot rise vertically but are trapped below the layer and must disperse horizontally. Assume that a factory smokestack begins emitting a pollutant at 8 A.M. Assume that the pollutant disperses horizontally, forming a circle. If t represents the time, in hours, since the factory began emitting pollutants ($t = 0$ represents 8 A.M.), assume that the radius of the circle of pollution is $r(t) = 2t$ miles. Let $A(r) = \pi r^2$ represent the area of a circle of radius r. Find and interpret $(A \circ r)(t)$.

Recall that we defined odd and even functions in the exercises for the previous section.

53. Let f be any function. Prove that the function

$$g(x) = \frac{1}{2}[f(x) + f(-x)]$$

is even.

54. Let f be any function. Prove that the function

$$g(x) = \frac{1}{2}[f(x) - f(-x)]$$

is odd.

55. Use the results of the two previous exercises to show that any function may be expressed as the sum of an odd function and an even function.

Prove each of the following.

56. The sum of two even functions is even.

57. The product of two even functions is even.

58. The sum of two odd functions is even.

59. The product of two odd functions is even.

60. The product of an odd function and an even function is odd.

61. What can you say about the sum of an odd and an even function? Give examples.

3.6   Inverse Functions

For the function $y = 5x - 8$, two different values of x produce two different values of y. On the other hand, for the function $y = x^2$, two different values of x can lead to the *same* value of y; for example, both $x = 4$ and $x = -4$ give $y = 4^2 = (-4)^2 = 16$. Two different values of x here lead to the same value of y.

A function, such as $y = 5x - 8$, where different x-values lead to different y-values is called a one-to-one function:

> Suppose a and b are two values from the domain of a function f. Then f is a *one-to-one function* if $a \neq b$ implies $f(a) \neq f(b)$.

Example 1   Decide whether or not the following functions are one-to-one.

(a) $f(x) = -4x + 12$
Suppose that $a \neq b$. Then $-4a \neq -4b$, and $-4a + 12 \neq -4b + 12$. Thus, the fact that $a \neq b$ implies that $f(a) \neq f(b)$, so that f is one-to-one.

(b) $f(x) = \sqrt{25 - x^2}$
As an example, if $x = 3$, then $f(3) = \sqrt{25 - 3^2} = \sqrt{16} = 4$. For $x = -3$, we have $f(-3) = \sqrt{25 - (-3)^2} = \sqrt{16} = 4$. Two x-values, 3 and -3, lead to the same y-value, 4, so that f is not one-to-one. ▌

There is a useful graphical test which tells whether or not a function is one-to-one. Figure 3.35(a) shows the graph of a function cut by a horizontal line. Each point where the horizontal line cuts the graph has the same y-value, but a different x-value. Here, three different values of x lead to the same value of y, so that the function is not one-to-one. On the other hand, the graph of Figure 3.35(b) can be cut by any horizontal line in no more than one point, so that it is the graph of a one-to-one function.

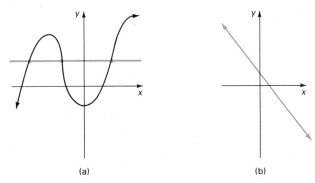

(a)   (b)

Figure 3.35

In summary, we have the **horizontal line test** for one-to-one functions:

> If any horizontal line cuts the graph of a function in no more than one point, then the function is one-to-one.

Suppose that f is a one-to-one function with domain X and range Y. Suppose we choose a value x in X. The function f will then produce exactly one value $f(x)$ in Y. Since f is one-to-one, a different value of x in X would produce a different value of $f(x)$ in Y.

Thus, there is a one-to-one pairing of values of x in X and values of $f(x)$ in Y. Because of this pairing, we could define a new function g that would start with a value of $f(x)$ in Y and produce the value x in X. That is,

$$\text{if } f(x) = y, \quad \text{then} \quad g(y) = x.$$

See the sketch in Figure 3.36.

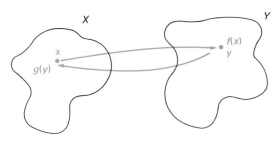

Figure 3.36

If $f(x) = y$, then $g(y) = x$; or

$$(g \circ f)(x) = g(f(x)) = x \qquad \text{for every } x \text{ in } X.$$
$$\text{Also, } (f \circ g)(y) = f(g(y)) = y \qquad \text{for every } y \text{ in } Y.$$

Since it is customary to use x for the domain element of a function, we replace y with x to change this last statement to

$$(f \circ g)(x) = f(g(x)) = x \qquad \text{for every } x \text{ in } Y.$$

Our two functions f and g have a very special property:

$$(f \circ g)(x) = x \qquad \text{and} \qquad (g \circ f)(x) = x.$$

In summary, we can make the following definition:

Let f be a one-to-one function. Let the domain of f be the set X. Let the range of f be the set Y. Let g be a function with domain Y and range X. Then g is the **inverse function** of f if

$$(f \circ g)(x) = x \qquad \text{for every } x \text{ in } Y$$
$$\text{and } (g \circ f)(x) = x \qquad \text{for every } x \text{ in } X.$$

Example 2   Let $f(x) = x^3 - 1$, and let $g(x) = \sqrt[3]{x + 1}$. Is g the inverse function of f?
Use the definition:

$$(f \circ g)(x) = f(g(x)) = (\sqrt[3]{x + 1})^3 - 1 = x + 1 - 1 = x$$
$$(g \circ f)(x) = g[f(x)] = \sqrt[3]{(x^3 - 1) + 1} = \sqrt[3]{x^3} = x.$$

Thus, g is the inverse function of f. Also, f is the inverse function of g. ∎

A special notation is often used for inverse functions: If g is the inverse function of f, then g can be written as f^{-1} (read "f-inverse"). In Example 2,

$$f^{-1}(x) = \sqrt[3]{x+1}.$$

Do not confuse the -1 in f^{-1} with a negative exponent. The symbol $f^{-1}(x)$ does not represent $1/f(x)$; it represents the inverse function of $f(x)$.

Keep in mind that a function f can have an inverse function f^{-1} if and only if f is one-to-one. Since increasing and decreasing functions are one-to-one, they must have inverse functions.

Given a one-to-one function f and a value x in the domain of f, we can find the corresponding value in the range of f by means of the equation $y = f(x)$. By the inverse function f^{-1}, we can take y and produce x: $x = f^{-1}(y)$. Therefore, to find the equation for f^{-1}, it is only necessary to solve $y = f(x)$ for x.

For example, let $f(x) = 7x - 2$. Then $y = 7x - 2$. This function is one-to-one, so that f^{-1} exists. Solve the equation for x:

$$y = 7x - 2$$
$$7x = y + 2$$
$$x = \frac{y+2}{7}$$

or

$$f^{-1}(y) = \frac{y+2}{7}$$

For a given value of x in X, the domain of f, the equation $y = 7x - 2$ produces a value of $f(x)$ in Y, the range of f. The function $f^{-1}(y) = (y+2)/7$ takes a value of y in Y and produces a value x in X. As we said, it is customary to use x for the domain element of a function, so we replace y with x in f^{-1} to get

$$f^{-1}(x) = \frac{x+2}{7}.$$

Check that $(f \circ f^{-1})(x) = (x)$ and $(f^{-1} \circ f)(x) = x$, so that our function f^{-1} is indeed the inverse of f.

In summary,

(a) Let f be a one-to-one function.

(b) Let $y = f(x)$.

(c) To find an equation for f^{-1}, interchange x and y to get $x = f(y)$, and then solve this equation for y.

Example 3   For each of the following functions, find an equation of its inverse function where possible.

(a) $f(x) = \dfrac{4x+6}{5}$

This function is one-to-one and thus has an inverse. Let $f(x) = y$ and then exchange x and y. Finally, solve for y.

$$y = \frac{4x + 6}{5} \qquad \text{Let } y = f(x).$$

$$x = \frac{4y + 6}{5} \qquad \text{Exchange } x \text{ and } y.$$

$$5x = 4y + 6$$

$$\frac{5x - 6}{4} = y \qquad \text{Solve for } y.$$

Thus, $f^{-1}(x) = \dfrac{5x - 6}{4}$.

(b) $f(x) = x^3 - 1$

This function is one-to-one and thus has an inverse. We begin with the equation $y = x^3 - 1$ and exchange x and y. We get $x = y^3 - 1$. Solving for y, we get $\sqrt[3]{x + 1} = y$.

(c) $f(x) = x^2$

This function is not one-to-one, so it has no inverse function.

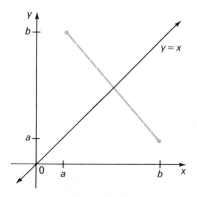

Figure 3.37

Suppose f and f^{-1} are inverse functions of each other. By the definition of inverse function, if the ordered pair (a, b) belongs to the graph of f, then (b, a) will belong to the graph of f^{-1}. As shown in Figure 3.37, the points (a, b) and (b, a) are symmetric with respect to the 45° line $y = x$. Thus, the graph of f^{-1} can be obtained from the graph of f by reflecting the graph of f about the line $y = x$.

For example, Figure 3.38 shows the graph of $f(x) = x^3 - 1$ as a solid line, with the graph of $f^{-1}(x) = \sqrt[3]{x + 1}$ as a dashed line. These graphs are symmetric with respect to the line $y = x$.

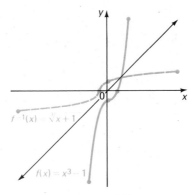

Figure 3.38

Example 4 Let $f(x) = \sqrt{x + 5}$, with domain $[-5, \infty)$. Find $f^{-1}(x)$.

   Function f is increasing and thus is one-to-one and has an inverse function. To find this inverse function, start with

$$y = \sqrt{x + 5}$$

and exchange x and y to get

$$x = \sqrt{y + 5},$$

or

$$x^2 = y + 5,$$

or

$$y = x^2 - 5.$$

   In the definition of f above, the domain was given as $[-5, \infty)$. The range of f can be shown to be $[0, \infty)$. The *range* of f becomes the *domain* of f^{-1}, so that we must give f^{-1} as

$$f^{-1}(x) = x^2 - 5, \qquad \text{domain } [0, \infty).$$

A graph of f and f^{-1} is shown in Figure 3.39.

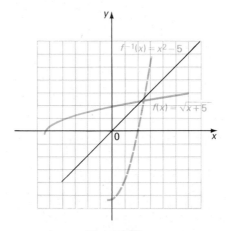

Figure 3.39

3.6 Exercises   *Which of the following functions are one-to-one?*

1.

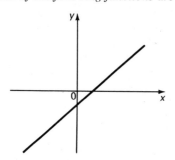

2.

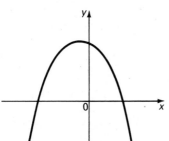

3.

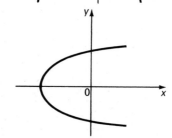

4. $y = 3x - 4$

5. $y = 4x - 5$

6. $y = -x^2$

7. $y = (x - 2)^2$

8. $y = -(x + 3)^2 - 8$

9. $y = \sqrt{36 - x^2}$

10. $y = -\sqrt{100 - x^2}$

11. $y = |25 - x^2|$

12. $y = -|16 - x^2|$

13. $y = x^3 - 1$

14. $y = -\sqrt[3]{x + 5}$

15. $y = \dfrac{1}{x + 2}$

16. $y = \dfrac{-4}{x - 8}$

17. $y = 9$

18. $y = -4$

Which of the following pairs of functions are inverses of each other?

19.

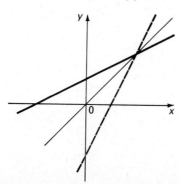

20.

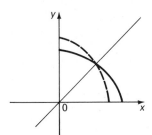

21.

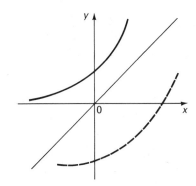

22. $f(x) = -8x$ and $g(x) = -\dfrac{1}{8}x$

23. $f(x) = 2x + 4$ and $g(x) = \dfrac{1}{2}x - 2$

24. $f(x) = \dfrac{1}{x+1}$ and $g(x) = \dfrac{x-9}{12}$

25. $f(x) = \dfrac{1}{x+1}$ and $g(x) = \dfrac{1-x}{x}$

26. $f(x) = \dfrac{2}{x+6}$ and $g(x) = \dfrac{6x+2}{x}$

27. $f(x) = \dfrac{1}{x}$ and $g(x) = \dfrac{1}{x}$

28. $f(x) = 4x$ and $y = -\dfrac{1}{4}x$

29. $f(x) = \sqrt{x+8}$, domain $[-8, \infty)$, and $g(x) = x^2 - 8$, domain $[0, \infty)$.

30. $f(x) = x^2 + 3$, domain $[0, \infty)$, and $g(x) = \sqrt{x-3}$, domain $[3, \infty)$.

31. $f(x) = |x - 1|$, domain $[-1, \infty)$, and $g(x) = |x + 1|$, domain $[1, \infty)$.

32. $f(x) = -|x + 5|$, domain $[-5, \infty)$, and $g(x) = |x - 5|$, domain $[5, \infty)$.

For each of the following functions that is one-to-one, write an equation for the inverse function in the form of $y = f^{-1}(x)$, and then graph f and f^{-1}.

33. $y = 3x - 4$

34. $y = 4x - 5$

35. $y = x^3 + 1$

36. $y = -x^3 - 2$

37. $x + 4y = 12$

38. $3x + y = 9$

39. $y = x^2$

40. $y = -x^2 + 2$

41. $y = \dfrac{1}{x}$

42. $xy = 4$

43. $y = \dfrac{8x + 3}{4x - 1}$

44. $y = \dfrac{-6x + 5}{3x - 1}$

45. $f(x) = 4 - x^2$, domain $(-\infty, 0]$

46. $f(x) = \sqrt{6 + x}$, domain $[-6, \infty)$

47. Let $f(x) = ax + b$ and $g(x) = cx + d$. Find all values of a, b, c, and d so that $f^{-1} = g$.

48. Let f be an odd one-to-one function. Show that f^{-1} exists and that f^{-1} is odd.

49. Let f be an even function. What can you say about f^{-1}?

3.7 Variation

In many applications of mathematics, it is necessary to formulate relationships between variables. If the quotient of two variables is constant, then one varies directly or is directly proportional to the other. The definition for this can be stated:

y varies directly as *x*, or *y* is *directly proportional* to *x*, means that a nonzero real number *k* (called the *constant of variation*) exists such that

$$y = kx.$$

Example 1 The cost of putting gasoline in a car varies directly as the number of gallons put into the tank. If it costs $6.72 to fill a tank with 6 gallons, find the cost to fill the tank with 11 gallons.

Since the cost varies directly as the number of gallons used,

$$C = kx,$$

where C is the cost, x is the number of gallons used, and k is a nonzero constant which we must find. When $x = 6$, then $C = 6.72$, so

$$6.72 = 6k,$$

or $k = 1.12$. Thus, the relationship between cost and the number of gallons is

$$C = 1.12x.$$

The cost to buy 11 gallons is

$$C = 1.12(11) = 12.32,$$

or $12.32. ▮

Sometimes y varies as a power of x:

Let n be a positive real number. Then y *varies directly as the nth power* of x, or y is *directly proportional to the nth power* of x, if there exists a real number k such that

$$y = kx^n.$$

For example, the area of a square is given by the formula $A = s^2$, so that the area varies directly as the square of the length of a side. Here $k = 1$.

Sometimes y increases as x decreases. This is the case with **inverse variation:**

Let n be a positive real number. Then y *varies inversely as the nth power* of x means that there exists a real number k such that

$$y = \frac{k}{x^n}.$$

If $n = 1$, then $y = k/x$, and y *varies inversely* as x.

Example 2   In a certain manufacturing process, the cost of producing a single item varies inversely as the square of the number of items produced. If 100 items are produced, each costs \$2. Find the cost per item if 400 items are produced.

We can let x represent the number of items produced and y the cost per item, so that

$$y = \frac{k}{x^2}$$

for some nonzero constant k. We know that $y = 2$ when $x = 100$.

Hence, $$2 = \frac{k}{100^2}$$

or $$k = 20{,}000.$$

Thus, the relationship between x and y is given by

$$y = \frac{20{,}000}{x^2}.$$

When 400 items are produced, the cost per item is given by

$$y = \frac{20{,}000}{400^2} = .125, \text{ or } 12.5\text{¢}. \quad \blacksquare$$

One variable may depend on more than one other variable. Such variation is called **combined variation.** If a variable depends on the product of two or more other variables, we refer to that as **joint variation:**

y *varies jointly* as the *n*th power of x and the *m*th power of z if there exists a real number k such that

$$y = kx^n z^m.$$

The next example shows combined variation.

Example 3 Suppose m varies directly as the square of p and inversely as q. Suppose also that $m = 8$ when $p = 2$ and $q = 6$. Find m if $p = 6$ and $q = 10$.

Here m depends on several variables. We can write

$$m = \frac{kp^2}{q}.$$

We know that $m = 8$ when $p = 2$ and $q = 6$. Thus,

$$8 = \frac{k \cdot 2^2}{6}$$

$$k = 12$$

and so

$$m = \frac{12p^2}{q}.$$

Let $p = 6$ and $q = 10$.

$$m = \frac{12 \cdot 6^2}{10}$$

$$m = \frac{216}{5} \quad \blacksquare$$

3.7 Exercises *Express each of the following as an equation.*

1. a varies directly as b.

2. m is proportional to n.

3. x is inversely proportional to y.

4. p varies inversely as y.

5. r varies jointly as s and t.

6. R is proportional to m and p.

7. w is proportional to x^2 and inversely proportional to y.

8. c varies directly as d and inversely as f^2 and g.

Solve each of the following.

9. If m varies directly as x and y, and $m = 10$ when $x = 4$ and $y = 7$; find m when $x = 11$ and $y = 8$.

10. Suppose m varies directly as z and p. If $m = 10$ when $z = 3$ and $p = 5$, find m when $z = 5$ and $p = 7$.

11. Suppose r varies directly as the square of m, and inversely as s. If $r = 12$ when $m = 6$ and $s = 4$, find r when $m = 4$ and $s = 10$.

12. Suppose p varies directly as the square of z, and inversely as r. If $p = \frac{32}{5}$ when $z = 4$ and $r = 10$, find p when $z = 2$ and $r = 16$.

13. Let a be proportional to m and n^2, and inversely proportional to y^3. If $a = 9$ when $m = 4$, $n = 9$, and $y = 3$, find a if $m = 6$, $n = 2$, and $y = 5$.

14. If y varies directly as x, and inversely as m^2 and r^2, and $y = \dfrac{5}{3}$ when $x = 1$, $m = 2$, and $r = 3$, find y if $x = 3$, $m = 1$, and $r = 8$.

15. Let r vary directly as p^2 and q^3, and inversely as z^2 and x. If $r = 334.6$ when $p = 1.9$, $q = 2.8$, $z = .4$, and $x = 3.7$, find r when $p = 2.1$, $q = 4.8$, $z = .9$, and $x = 1.4$.

16. Let p vary directly as x and z^2, and inversely as m, n, and q. If $p = 9.25$ when $x = 3.2$, $z = 10.1$, $m = 2$, $n = 1.7$, and $q = 8.3$, find p when $x = 8.1$, $z = 4.3$, $m = 4$, $n = 2.1$, and $q = 6.2$.

17. The distance a body falls from rest varies directly as the square of the time it falls (disregarding air resistance). If an object falls 1024 feet in 8 seconds, how far will it fall in 12 seconds?

18. Hooke's law for an elastic spring states that the distance a spring stretches varies directly as the force applied. If a force of 15 pounds stretches a certain spring 8 inches, how much will a force of 30 pounds stretch the spring?

19. In electric current flow, it is found that the resistance (measured in units called ohms) offered by a fixed length of wire of a given material varies inversely as the square of the diameter of the wire. If a wire .01 inches in diameter has a resistance of .4 ohm, what is the resistance of a wire of the same length and material but .03 inches in diameter?

20. The illumination produced by a light source varies inversely as the square of the distance from the source. The illumination of a light source at 5 meters is 70 candela. What is the illumination 12 meters from the source?

21. The pressure exerted by a certain liquid at a given point is proportional to the depth of the point below the surface of the liquid. If the pressure 20 meters below the surface is 70 kilograms per square centimeter, what pressure is exerted 40 meters below the surface?

22. The distance that a person can see to the horizon from a point above the surface of the earth varies directly as the square root of the height. A person on a hill 121 meters high can see for 15 kilometers to the horizon. How far is the horizon from a hill 900 meters high?

23. Simple interest varies jointly as principal and time. If $1000 left at interest for 2 years earned $110, find the amount of interest earned by $5000 for 5 years.

24. The volume of a right circular cylinder is jointly proportional to the square of the radius of the circular base and to the height. If the volume is 300 cubic centimeters when the height is 10.62 centimeters and the radius is 3 centimeters, find the volume for a cylinder with a radius of 4 centimeters and a height of 15.92 centimeters. Use 3.14 as an approximation for π.

25. The Downtown Construction Company is designing a building whose roof rests on round concrete pillars. The company's engineers know that the maximum load a cylindrical column of circular cross section can hold varies directly as the fourth power of the diameter and inversely as the square of the height. If a 9 meter column 1 meter in diameter will support a load of 8 metric tons, how many metric tons will be supported by a column 12 meters high and 2/3 meter in diameter?

26. The company's engineers also know that the maximum load of a horizontal beam which is supported at both ends varies directly as the width and square of the height and inversely as the length between supports. If a beam 8 meters long, 12 centimeters

wide, and 15 centimeters high can support a maximum of 400 kilograms, what will they find to be the maximum load of a beam of the same material 16 meters long, 24 centimeters wide, and 8 centimeters high?

27. The force needed to keep a car from skidding on a curve varies inversely as the radius of the curve and jointly as the weight of the car and the square of the speed. It takes 3000 pounds of force to keep a 2000 pound car from skidding on a curve of radius 500 feet at 30 mph. What force is needed to keep the same car from skidding on a curve of radius 800 feet at 60 mph?

28. The period of a pendulum varies directly as the square root of the length of the pendulum and inversely as the square root of the acceleration due to gravity. Find the period when the length is 121 centimeters and the acceleration due to gravity is 32 centimeters per second squared, if the period is 6π seconds when the length is 289 centimeters and the acceleration due to gravity is 32 centimeters per second squared.

29. The pressure on a point in a liquid is directly proportional to the distance from the surface to the point. In a certain liquid the pressure at a depth of 4 m is 60 kg per m^2. Find the pressure at a depth of 10 m.

30. The volume V of a gas varies directly as the temperature T and inversely as the pressure P. If V is 10 when T is 280 and P is 6, find V if T is 300 and P is 10.

31. A sociologist has decided to rank the cities in a nation by population, with population varying inversely as the ranking. If a city with a population of 1,000,000 ranks 8th, find the population of a city that ranks 2nd.

32. Under certain conditions, the length of time that it takes for fruit to ripen during the growing season varies inversely as the average maximum temperature during the season. If it takes 25 days for fruit to ripen with an average maximum temperature of 80°, find the number of days it would take at 75°.

33. The number of long distance phone calls between two cities in a certain time period varies directly as the populations p_1 and p_2 of the cities, and inversely as the distance between them. If 10,000 calls are made between two cities 500 miles apart, having populations of 50,000 and 125,000, find the number of calls between two cities 800 miles apart and having populations of 20,000 and 80,000.

34. The horsepower needed to run a boat through water varies as the cube of the speed. If 80 horsepower are needed to go 15 kilometers per hour in a certain boat, how many horsepower would be needed to go 30 kilometers per hour?

Chapter 3 Review Exercises

Graph the set of points satisfying the following conditions.

1. $x < 0$

2. $y \geq 0$

3. $xy > 0$

4. $x = 2$

Find the distance $d(P, Q)$ and the midpoint of segment PQ.

5. $P(3, -1)$ and $Q(-4, 5)$

6. $P(-8, 2)$ and $Q(3, -7)$

7. Find the other endpoint of a line segment having one end at $(-5, 7)$ and midpoint at $(1, -3)$.

8. Are the points $(5, 7)$, $(3, 9)$, $(6, 8)$ the vertices of a right triangle?

9. Find all possible values of k so that $(-1, 2)$ $(-10, 5)$, and $(-4, k)$ are the vertices of a right triangle.

10. Find all possible values of x so that the distance between $(x, -9)$ and $(3, -5)$ is 6.

11. Find all points (x, y) with $x = 6$ so that (x, y) is 4 units from $(1, 3)$.

12. Find all points (x, y) with $x + y = 0$ so that (x, y) is 6 units from $(-2, 3)$.

Prove each of the following.

13. The medians to the two equal sides of an isosceles triangle are equal in length.

14. The line segment connecting midpoints of two sides of a triangle is half as long as the third side.

Graph each of the following. Give the domain of those that are functions.

15. $x + y = 4$

16. $3x - 5y = 20$

17. $y = \dfrac{1}{2}x^2$

18. $y = 3 - x^2$

19. $y = \dfrac{-8}{x}$

20. $y = -2x^3$

21. $y = \sqrt{x - 7}$

22. $(x - 3)^2 + y^2 = 16$

Find equations of each of the following circles.

23. Center $(-2, 3)$, radius 5

24. Center $(\sqrt{5}, -\sqrt{7})$, radius $\sqrt{3}$

25. Center $(-8, 1)$, passing through $(0, 16)$

26. Center $(3, -6)$, tangent to the x-axis

Decide whether the following equations have graphs which are symmetric to the x-axis, the y-axis, the origin, or the line $y = x$.

27. $3y^2 - 5x^2 = 15$

28. $x + y^2 = 8$

29. $y^3 = x + 1$

30. $x^2 = y^3$

31. $|y| = -x$

32. $|x + 2| = |y - 3|$

33. $|x| = |y|$

34. $xy = 8$

35. Graph $y = |x|$.

Using your graph from Exercise 35, explain how each of the following graphs could be obtained. Sketch each graph.

36. $y = |x| - 3$

37. $y = -|x|$

38. $y = -|x| - 2$

39. $y = -|x + 1| + 3$

40. $y = 2|x - 3| - 4$

Give the domain of each of the following.

41. $y = -4 + |x|$

42. $y = 3x^2 - 1$

43. $y = (x - 4)^2$

44. $y^2 = 8 - x$

45. $y = \dfrac{8 + x}{8 - x}$

46. $y = -\sqrt{\dfrac{5}{x^2 + 9}}$

For each of the following, find $\dfrac{f(x + h) - f(x)}{h}$.

47. $f(x) = -2x^2 + 4x - 3$ **48.** $f(x) = -x^3 + 2x^2$

For the following functions, find (a) $(f + g)(x)$; (b) $(f \cdot g)(x)$; (c) $\left(\dfrac{f}{g}\right)(x)$; (d) $(f \cdot g)(4)$; (e) $\left(\dfrac{f}{g}\right)(-3)$.

49. $f(x) = 4x - 1$, $g(x) = 3x^2$ **50.** $f(x) = x^2 - 3x$, $g(x) = 5x^2$

Find $(f \circ g)(x)$ and $(g \circ f)(x)$ for each of the following.

51. $f(x) = 9x - 2$, $g(x) = 4 + 6x$

52. $f(x) = 8x^2$, $g(x) = 1 + x$

53. $f(x) = \dfrac{1}{x}$, $g(x) = \sqrt{3 + x}$

Decide whether the following functions are odd, even, or neither.

54. $g(x) = \dfrac{x}{|x|}$ $(x \neq 0)$

55. $h(x) = 9x^6 + 5|x|$

56. Let f be a function which gives the cost to rent a floor polisher for x hours. The cost is a flat \$3 for cleaning the polisher plus \$4 per day or fraction of a day for using the polisher. (a) Graph f. (b) Give the domain and range of f.

Which of the following functions are one-to-one?

57. $5y = 8x - 9$ **59.** $x = (y - 1)^2$

58. $y = -x^2 + 11$ **60.** $y = \sqrt{100 - x^2}$

Find all intervals where the following functions are increasing or decreasing.

61. $y = -(x + 1)^2$

62. $y = -3 + |x|$

63. $y = \dfrac{|x|}{x}$

64. $y = |x| + x^2$

For each of the following functions that is one-to-one, write an equation for the inverse function in the form $y = f^{-1}(x)$, and then graph f and f^{-1}.

65. $f(x) = 12x + 3$

66. $f(x) = \dfrac{2}{x - 9}$

67. $f(x) = x^3 - 3$

68. $f(x) = x^2 - 6$

69. $f(x) = \sqrt{25 - x^2}$, domain $[0, 5]$

70. $f(x) = -\sqrt{x - 3}$

Write each of the following as an equation.

71. m varies directly as the square of z.

72. y varies inversely as r.

73. Y varies directly as M and the square of N and inversely as the cube of X.

Solve each of the following problems.

74. Suppose r varies directly as x and inversely as the square of y. If r is 10 when x is 5 and y is 3, find r when x is 12 and y is 4.

75. Suppose m varies jointly as n and the square of p, and inversely as q. If m is 20 when n is 5, p is 6, and q is 18, find m when n is 7, p is 11, and q is 2.

76. The Energy Research and Development Administration is doing research on alternate forms of energy. Its scientists know that the power a windmill obtains from the wind varies directly as the cube of the wind velocity. If a 10 kph wind produces 10,000 units of power, how much power is produced by a wind of 15 kph?

77. Hooke's law for an elastic spring states that the distance a spring stretches varies directly as the force applied. If a force of 32 kilograms stretches a certain spring 48 centimeters, how much will a force of 24 kilograms stretch the spring?

78. The weight w of an object varies inversely as the square of the distance d between the object and the center of the earth. If a man weighs 90 kg on the surface of the earth, how much would he weigh 800 km above the surface? (The radius of the earth is about 6400 km.)

The following exercises are taken with permission from a standard calculus book.

79. Suppose function f is increasing.
    (a) Must $2f$ be increasing?
    (b) Must $-f$ be decreasing?
    (c) Must f^2 (or $f \cdot f$) be increasing?
    (d) If f is never zero, must $1/f$ be decreasing?

80. A function f has the following property: $f(x + 1) = f(x) + f(1) + 1$.
    (a) Find $f(0)$.
Suppose further that $f(1) = 1$. Find (b) $f(2)$, (c) $f(3)$.

81. A function g has the following property: $g(x + y) = g(x) + g(y)$.
    (a) Find $g(0)$
    (b) Prove that $g(-x) = -g(x)$.
    (c) Prove that $g(2x) = 2g(x)$.
Assume further that $g(1) = 1$. Find (d) $g(2)$, (e) $g(1/2)$.

82. Find a point that is equidistant from the three points $A(0, 1)$, $B(1, 0)$, $C(4, 3)$. What is the radius of the circle through A, B, and C?

83. If the distance from $P(x, y)$ to the point $(6, 0)$ is twice its distance from the point $(0, 3)$, show that P lies on a circle and find the center and radius.

84. According to Kepler's third law, the square of a planet's period of revolution around the sun is proportional to the cube of its distance from the sun. How many times as far are the following planets from the sun as the earth is, if the planets have periods (in years) as given: (a) Mercury, 0.24, (b) Venus, 0.615, (c) Mars, 1.9, (d) Jupiter, 11.9.

Exercises 79, 80, 81, and 84: Reproduced from *Calculus*, by Leonard Gillman and Robert H. McDowell, 2nd Edition, by permission of W. W. Norton & Company, Inc. Copyright © 1978, 1973 by W. W. Norton & Company, Inc. Exercises 82 and 83: George B. Thomas, Jr./Ross L. Finney, *Calculus and Analytic Geometry*, 5/E, © 1979, Addison-Wesley, Reading, Massachusetts. (Pp. 400 and 404.) Reprinted with permission.

Chapter 4

Some Important Functions

Polynomial functions are important in mathematics because of their simplicity. In this chapter we discuss first two special types of polynomial functions and then the general polynomial function. Rational functions, which are quotients of polynomials, are covered next. Another important group of functions are derived from the conic sections; these are discussed in Section 5. In the last section, we see how to use the graphs of these functions to graph several kinds of inequalities.

4.1 Linear Functions

A **polynomial function of degree** n (where n is a nonnegative integer) is a function of the form

$$f(x) = a_n x^n + a_{n-1} x^{n-1} + \ldots + a_1 x + a_0 x^0,$$

where $a_n, a_{n-1}, \ldots, a_0$ are real numbers and $a_n \neq 0$. A polynomial function of degree 1 is called a **linear function.** Thus, a linear function can be written as

$$f(x) = a_1 x + a_0,$$

where a_1 and a_0 are real numbers with $a_1 \neq 0$. We shall see that, as the name implies, every linear function has a graph which is a line.

We begin by determining the equation of a line. An important characteristic of a line is its slope, a numerical measure of the steepness of the line. To find this measure, let us consider the line through the two distinct points, (x_1, y_1) and (x_2, y_2), as shown in Figure 4.1(a) (we are assuming $x_1 \neq x_2$). The difference

$$x_2 - x_1$$

is called the **change in x,** and is denoted Δx (read "delta x"), where Δ is the Greek letter delta. In the same way, the **change in y** can be written

$$\Delta y = y_2 - y_1.$$

The **slope** of a line (usually denoted m) is defined to be the change in y divided by the change in x, or

$$m = \frac{\Delta y}{\Delta x} = \frac{y_2 - y_1}{x_2 - x_1} \qquad (\Delta x \neq 0).$$

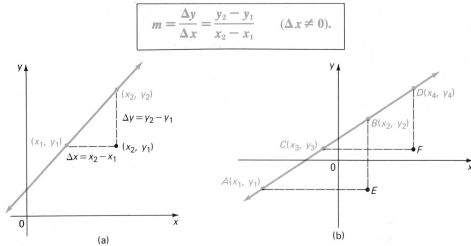

(a)   (b)

Figure 4.1

Figure 4.1(b) shows four points $A(x_1, y_1)$, $B(x_2, y_2)$, $C(x_3, y_3)$, and $D(x_4, y_4)$ all on the same straight line. Right triangles ABE and CDF have been completed. Since the lines through AE and CF are parallel, as are the lines through EB and FD, triangles ABE and CDF are similar. Similar triangles have corresponding sides proportional, so that

$$\frac{y_2 - y_1}{x_2 - x_1} = \frac{y_4 - y_3}{x_4 - x_3}.$$

The quotient on the left is the one we used in the definition of slope, and we have just proved that it equals the quotient on the right, for any choice of two distinct points on the line. Thus, the slope of a line is the same regardless of the choice of points made.

Example 1   Find the slope of the line through each of the following pairs of points.

(a) $(-4, 8)$, $(2, -3)$
We can choose $x_1 = -4$, $y_1 = 8$, $x_2 = 2$ and $y_2 = -3$. Then $\Delta y = -3 - 8 = -11$ and $\Delta x = 2 - (-4) = 6$. Thus the slope is $m = \frac{\Delta y}{\Delta x} = \frac{-11}{6}$.

(b) $(5, -3)$ and $(-2, -3)$
By the definition of slope, $m = \frac{-3 - (-3)}{-2 - 5} = 0$.

A line through the two points $(5, -3)$ and $(-2, -3)$ is horizontal. In general, *the slope of a horizontal line is 0.*

(c) $(2, 7)$ and $(2, -4)$
Use the definition of slope again: $m = \frac{-4 - 7}{2 - 2} = \frac{-11}{0}$.

Since division by 0 is meaningless, the line has no slope. The line through (2, 7) and (2, −4) is a vertical line. Thus, *a vertical line has no slope*. ▌

A line is determined if we know its slope and some point on the line. For example, if a line goes through (x_1, y_1), and has slope m, we can locate the line by first graphing the point (x_1, y_1), as in Figure 4.2. Then, to get a second point on the graph, start at (x_1, y_1) and go one unit to the right, parallel to the *x*-axis. Then turn and go $|m|$ units parallel to the *y*-axis; go up if $m > 0$, and down if $m < 0$. This locates a second point, which can be used with (x_1, y_1) to locate the line.

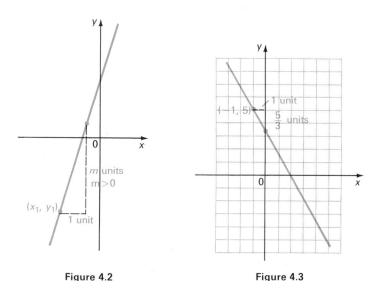

Figure 4.2   Figure 4.3

Example 2   Graph the line going through (−1, 5) with slope $-\dfrac{5}{3}$.

As shown in Figure 4.3, we first locate (−1, 5). Go one unit to the right, and $\dfrac{5}{3}$ units down. This gives a second point, which is used to draw the graph. Alternatively, we could have gone 3 units to the right and 5 down. ▌

Let us now find the equation of the line with slope m which goes through the point (x_1, y_1). Let (x, y) represent any other point on the line. Then, by the definition of slope,

$$\frac{y - y_1}{x - x_1} = m$$

or $$y - y_1 = m(x - x_1),$$

is an equation of the line called the **point-slope form.** We have proved the following theorem.

Theorem 4.1   *(Point-Slope Form)*   If a line has slope m and passes through the point (x_1, y_1), then the equation of the line is

$$y - y_1 = m(x - x_1).$$

Example 3   Write the equation of the line through $(-4, 1)$ with slope $m = -3$.

Here $x_1 = -4$, $y_1 = 1$, and $m = -3$. Using the point-slope form of the equation of a line,

$$y - 1 = -3(x - (-4))$$
$$y - 1 = -3(x + 4)$$
$$y - 1 = -3x - 12$$
$$3x + y = -11.$$

Example 4   Find the equation of the line through $(-3, 2)$ and $(2, -4)$.

In this case we find the slope first.

$$m = \frac{-4 - 2}{2 - (-3)} = \frac{-6}{5}.$$

We can use either $(-3, 2)$ or $(2, -4)$ for (x_1, y_1). If we let $x_1 = -3$ and $y_1 = 2$,

$$y - 2 = \frac{-6}{5}(x - (-3))$$
$$5(y - 2) = -6(x + 3)$$
$$5y - 10 = -6x - 18$$
$$6x + 5y = -8.$$

Verify that we get the same equation if we use $(2, -4)$ instead of $(-3, 2)$ in the point-slope form.

Two points which are useful for sketching the graph of a line are the *x*-intercept and the *y*-intercept. An **x-intercept** is the *x*-value at which the line crosses the *x*-axis. A **y-intercept** is the *y*-value at which the graph crosses the *y*-axis. To find the *x*-intercept of a line, let $y = 0$ in the equation for the line. (See Figure 4.4. Note that when the graph crosses the *x*-axis, $y = 0$.) Similarly, the *y*-intercept occurs when $x = 0$.

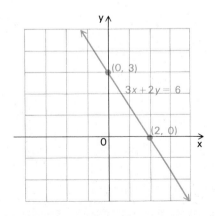

Figure 4.4

Example 5   Graph $3x + 2y = 6$.
The x-intercept occurs when $y = 0$.

$$3x + 2(0) = 6$$
$$3x = 6$$
$$x = 2.$$

Thus, the x-intercept is 2. In the same way, let $x = 0$ to find the y-intercept, 3. The graph is shown in Figure 4.4. (See previous page.)   ▌

Example 6   Graph $y = -3$.
To have an x-intercept there must be a value of x which makes $y = 0$. However, here $y = -3 \neq 0$. Hence the line has no x-intercept. This can happen only if the line is parallel to the x-axis, as shown in Figure 4.5.   ▌

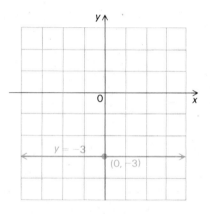

Figure 4.5

If we know the slope and y-intercept of a line, we can use the point-slope form to write the equation. Let m be the slope and b represent the y-intercept. Then the point $(0, b)$ is on the line, and the point-slope form of the equation is

$$y - b = m(x - 0)$$
$$y - b = mx.$$

If we solve this equation for y, we have

$$y = mx + b.$$

This is called the **slope-intercept** form of the equation of a line.

Theorem 4.2   (*Slope-Intercept Form*)   If a line has slope m and y-intercept b, then the equation of the line is

$$y = mx + b.$$

The slope-intercept form is especially useful when we want to find the slope of a line and we know the equation, as in the next example.

Example 7   Find the slope and y-intercept of $3x - y = 2$. Graph the line.

We first write $3x - y = 2$ in the form $y = mx + b$. Here solving for y gives $y = 3x - 2$. From this we see that the slope is $m = 3$ and the y-intercept is $b = -2$. To draw the graph first locate the y-intercept (See Figure 4.6). Here we know $m = 3 = 3/1$. Thus, if x changes 1 unit, y changes 3 units. We use this fact to find another point of the graph, as shown in Figure 4.6. ▌

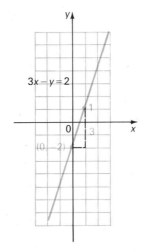

Figure 4.6

Example 8   Write the equation of the line with y-intercept -5 and slope $2/3$.

We use the slope-intercept form, $y = mx + b$. We have $m = 2/3$ and $b = -5$, so the equation in slope-intercept form is

$$y = \frac{2}{3}x - 5. \quad ▌$$

It can be shown that two lines are parallel if and only if they have the same slope or no slope (See Exercises 44 and 45). It can also be shown that two perpendicular lines (neither of which is vertical) have slopes with a product of -1. (See Exercises 56–59).

Example 9   Find the equation of the line through the point $(3, 5)$ and parallel to the line $2x + 5y = 4$.

We know that the point $(3, 5)$ is on the line, and we need the slope to use the point-slope form of the equation of a line. We can find the slope by writing the equation of the given line in slope-intercept form.

$$2x + 5y = 4$$

$$y = -\frac{2}{5}x + \frac{4}{5}$$

The slope is $-2/5$. Since the lines are parallel, $-2/5$ is also the slope of the line whose equation we are to find. Substituting $m = -2/5$, $x_1 = 3$, and $y_1 = 5$ into the point-slope form gives the desired equation.

$$y - y_1 = m(x - x_1)$$

$$y - 5 = \frac{-2}{5}(x - 3)$$

$$y - 5 = -\frac{2}{5}x + \frac{6}{5}$$

$$y = -\frac{2}{5}x + \frac{31}{5} \quad \blacksquare$$

Example 10   Find the slope of the line L perpendicular to the line with equation $5x - y = 4$. To find the slope, solve $5x - y = 4$ for y, which gives

$$y = 5x - 4.$$

Hence, the slope is 5. Since the lines are perpendicular, if line L has slope m, then

$$5m = -1$$

$$m = -\frac{1}{5}. \quad \blacksquare$$

We have seen that the graph of the equation $y = mx + b$ is a line. If we let $y = f(x)$, $m = a_1 \neq 0$ and $b = a_0$, we have the linear function

$$f(x) = a_1 x + a_0.$$

Thus, the graph of a linear function is a line.

Some applications require a function which consists of parts of two or more lines. The next example shows how to graph such a function.

Example 11   Graph the function

$$f(x) = \begin{cases} x + 1 \text{ if } x > 2 \\ -2x + 5 \text{ if } x \leq 2. \end{cases}$$

For $x > 2$, we graph $f(x) = x + 1$. For $x \leq 2$, we graph $f(x) = -2x + 5$, as shown in Figure 4.7. An open circle is used at $(2, 3)$ to show that this point is not part of the graph, while the filled-in circle at $(2, 1)$ shows that the point is part of the graph. $\quad \blacksquare$

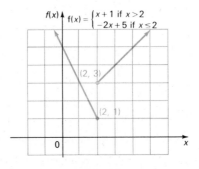

Figure 4.7

4.1 Exercises   *Find the slope of each of the following lines that has a slope.*

1. through $(4, 5)$ and $(-1, 2)$

2. through $(1, 5)$ and $(-2, 5)$

3. $y = 2x$

4. $y = 3x - 2$

5. $x = -6$

6. the x-axis

7. Find the slope of the line parallel to $2y - 4x = 7$.

8. Find the slope of the line perpendicular to $6x = y - 3$.

⊙ **9.** through $(-1.978, 4.806)$ and $(3.759, 8.125)$

10. through $(11.72, 9.811)$ and $(-12.67, -5.009)$

Use the slope to decide which of the following linear functions are increasing.

11. $2x + 3y = 8$ **13.** $x - y = 5$

12. $-4x + 6y = 9$ **14.** $3y = 4x + 7$

Write an equation of each of the following lines.

15. through $(1, 3)$, $m = -2$ **22.** through $(-3, 0)$ and $(0, -5)$

16. through $(2, 4)$, $m = -1$ **23.** x-intercept 3, y-intercept -2

17. through $(6, 1)$, $m = 0$ **24.** x-intercept -2, y-intercept 4

18. through $(-8, 1)$, no slope   **25.** vertical, through $(-6, 5)$

19. through $(4, 2)$ and $(1, 3)$ **26.** horizontal, through $(8, 7)$

20. through $(8, -1)$ and $(4, 3)$ ⊙ **27.** through $(-1.76, 4.25)$, with slope -5.081

21. through $(0, 3)$ and $(4, 0)$ **28.** through $(5.469, 11.08)$, with slope 4.723

Graph the following lines using the method of Example 2.

29. through $(-1, 3)$, $m = 3/2$ **31.** through $(3, -4)$, $m = -1/3$

30. through $(-2, 8)$, $m = -1$ **32.** through $(-2, -3)$, $m = -3/4$

Write an equation for each of the following lines.

33. through $(-1, 4)$, parallel to $x + 3y = 5$

34. through $(2, -5)$, parallel to $y - 4 = 2x$

35. through $(3, -4)$, perpendicular to $x + y = 4$

36. through $(-2, 6)$, perpendicular to $2x - 3y = 5$

37. x-intercept -2, parallel to $y = 2x$

38. y-intercept 3, parallel to $x + y = 4$

39. Do the points $(4, 3)$, $(2, 0)$, and $(-18, -12)$ lie on the same line? (Hint: find the equation of the line through two of the points.)

40. Do the points $(4, -5)$, $(3, -5/2)$, and $(-6, 18)$ lie on a line?

41. Find k so that the line through $(4, -1)$ and $(k, 2)$ is (a) parallel to $3y + 2x = 6$, (b) perpendicular to $2y - 5x = 1$.

42. Use slopes to show that the quadrilateral with vertices at $(1, 3)$, $(3/2, 2)$, $(7/2, -2)$, and $(2, 1)$ is a parallelogram.

43. Use slopes to show that the square with vertices at $(-2, 3)$, $(4, 3)$, $(4, -1)$, and $(-2, -1)$ has diagonals which are perpendicular.

44. Prove that two parallel lines have the same slope.

45. Prove that two lines with the same slope are parallel.

Graph the following functions.

46. $f(x) = \begin{cases} 2x - 1 & \text{if } x \leq 1 \\ -3x + 4 & \text{if } x > 1 \end{cases}$

47. $f(x) = \begin{cases} \dfrac{1}{2}x & \text{if } x \leq -2 \\ 2x + 3 & \text{if } x > -2 \end{cases}$

48. $f(x) = \begin{cases} x + 6 & \text{if } x \leq 0 \\ 2x + 6 & \text{if } x > 0 \end{cases}$

49. $f(x) = \begin{cases} -x - 1 & \text{if } x \leq -1 \\ 2x + 2 & \text{if } x > -1 \end{cases}$

50. $y = \begin{cases} x - 1 & \text{if } x \geq 1 \\ -(x - 1) & \text{if } x < 1 \end{cases}$

51. $y = \begin{cases} x + 3 & \text{if } x \geq -3 \\ -(x + 3) & \text{if } x < -3 \end{cases}$

52. $y = \begin{cases} -2x & \text{if } x < -3 \\ 3x + 1 & \text{if } -3 \leq x < 2 \\ -4x & \text{if } x \geq 2 \end{cases}$

53. $y = \begin{cases} 2 + x & \text{if } x < -4 \\ -x & \text{if } -4 \leq x \leq 5 \\ 3x & \text{if } x > 5 \end{cases}$

54. When a diabetic takes long-acting insulin, the insulin reaches its peak effect on the blood sugar level in about three hours. This effect remains fairly constant for five hours, then declines, and is very low until the next injection. In a typical patient, the level of insulin might be given by the following function.

$$i(t) = \begin{cases} 40t + 100 & \text{if } 0 \leq t \leq 3 \\ 220 & \text{if } 3 < t \leq 8 \\ -80t + 860 & \text{if } 8 < t \leq 10 \\ 60 & \text{if } 10 < t \leq 24 \end{cases}$$

Here $i(t)$ is the insulin level, in appropriate units, at time t measured in hours from the time of the injection. Chuck takes his insulin at 6 a.m. Find the insulin level at each of the following times: (a) 7 a.m., (b) 9 a.m., (c) 10 a.m., (d) noon, (e) 2 p.m., (f) 5 p.m., (g) midnight; (h) Graph $y = i(t)$. Is i a function?

55. To rent a midsized car from Avis costs $18 per day or fraction of a day. If you pick up the car in Boston and drop it off in Utica, there is a fixed $40 charge. Let $C(x)$ represent the cost of renting the car for x days, taking it from Boston to Utica. Find each of the following: (a) $C\left(\dfrac{3}{4}\right)$, (b) $C\left(\dfrac{9}{10}\right)$, (c) $C(1)$, (d) $C\left(1\dfrac{5}{8}\right)$, (e) $C\left(2\dfrac{1}{9}\right)$; (f) Graph $y = C(x)$. (g) Is $C(x)$ a function? (h) Is $C(x)$ a linear function?

To prove that two perpendicular lines, neither of which is vertical, have slopes with a product of -1, go through the following steps. Let line L_1 have equation $y = m_1x + b_1$, and let line L_2 have equation $y = m_2x + b_2$. Assume that L_1 and L_2 are perpendicular and complete right triangle MPN as shown in the figure.

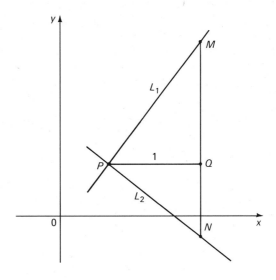

56. Show that MQ has a length m_1.

57. Show that QN has a length $-m_2$.

58. Show that triangles MPQ and PQN are similar.

59. Show that $m_1/1 = 1/-m_2$ and that $m_1m_2 = -1$.

4.2 Quadratic Functions

A **quadratic function** is a second-degree polynomial function of the form

$$f(x) = a_2x^2 + a_1x + a_0,$$

where a_2, a_1, and a_0 are real numbers ($a_2 \neq 0$). Quadratic functions are often written as

$$y = ax^2 + bx + c,$$

for real numbers $a \neq 0$, b, and c. The simplest quadratic function is $y = x^2$, where $a = 1$, $b = 0$, and $c = 0$. To find some ordered pairs belonging to the graphs of this function, we choose values for x and find the corresponding values for y, as shown on the chart with Figure 4.8 (on next page). These pairs are then graphed, and a smooth curve drawn through them. The reason that the curve is smooth depends on ideas from calculus. As we learned in Chapter 3, this curve is called a *parabola*. Since the coefficient of x^2 in the equation $y = x^2$ is positive, the parabola opens upward. On the other hand, the coefficient of x^2 in the equation $y = -x^2$ is negative, and the graph of this parabola opens downward.

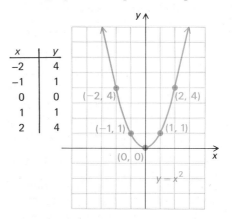

x	y
-2	4
-1	1
0	0
1	1
2	4

Figure 4.8

The parabola is an example of a graph which has symmetry about a line, in this case the y-axis. Every parabola is symmetric about a line, called the **axis** of the parabola. Recall that the lowest or highest point of a parabola is called its *vertex*.

Parabolas have many practical applications. For example, cross sections of spotlight reflectors, or radar dishes, form parabolas. Every quadratic function has a graph which is a parabola.

When b and c are not both 0, the equation of a parabola can be written in the form

$$y - k = a(x - h)^2$$

which essentially translates the parabola so that its vertex is now at (h, k). This translated equation is often written in the alternate form

$$y = a(x - h)^2 + k.$$

To translate the graph in this way, we *complete the square* on the $y = ax^2 + bx + c$ form, as shown in the next example. As we shall see, once we know where the vertex of the parabola is on the coordinate system, the curve is easier to draw.

Example 1   Graph $y = 2x^2 + 8x + 5$.

We want to write $y = 2x^2 + 8x + 5$ in the form $y = a(x - h)^2 + k$. To do so, first factor 2 out of $2x^2 + 8x$.

$$y = 2(x^2 + 4x \qquad) + 5$$

Now convert the expression in parentheses, $x^2 + 4x$, into a perfect square by adding an appropriate number. To find this number, take half the coefficient of $x \left(\frac{1}{2} \cdot 4 = 2 \right)$ and square the result ($2^2 = 4$). Add the square, 4, to the quantity inside the parentheses, and subtract 8 outside the parentheses to compensate for adding $2 \cdot 4 = 8$. The result is

$$y = 2(x^2 + 4x + 4) + 5 - 8.$$

Now write the expression as

$$y = 2(x + 2)^2 - 3.$$

Since $2(x + 2)^2 \geq 0$ for all real values of x, the lowest possible value of y is $y = -3$, and y has this value when $x = -2$. Thus, the vertex of this graph is $(-2, -3)$. The axis is the line $x = -2$.

Additional points on the graph can be found from the intercepts. To find the y-intercepts, let $x = 0$. (To find the intercepts, it is usually better to use the original form of the function.) If $x = 0$, then

$$y = 2 \cdot 0^2 + 8 \cdot 0 + 5 = 5,$$

giving the ordered pair $(0, 5)$. Letting $y = 0$ and using the quadratic theorem to find the x-intercepts leads approximately to the ordered pairs $(-.78, 0)$ and $(-3.22, 0)$. By using the intercepts and finding some other ordered pairs belonging to the function, we get the graph of Figure 4.9.

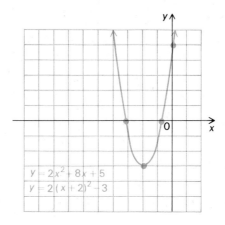

Figure 4.9

As this example suggests,

> When a parabola has its equation written in the form,
>
> $$y = a(x - h)^2 + k,$$
>
> the vertex is at (h, k). The axis is the line $x = h$.

Example 2 Graph $y = -3x^2 - 2x + 1$.

Before completing the square here, first rewrite the expression as

$$y = -3\left(x^2 + \frac{2}{3}x \qquad \right) + 1.$$

Then add $\left(\dfrac{1}{2}\cdot\dfrac{2}{3}\right)^2=\dfrac{1}{9}$ to the quantity inside the parentheses and, corresponding-

ly, subtract $\left(-3\right)\left(\dfrac{1}{9}\right)=-\dfrac{1}{3}$ outside the parentheses.

$$y=-3\left(x^2+\frac{2}{3}x+\frac{1}{9}\right)+1-\left(-\frac{1}{3}\right)$$

$$y=-3\left(x+\frac{1}{3}\right)^2+\frac{4}{3}$$

Since $-3\left(x+\dfrac{1}{3}\right)^2\le 0$ for all real values of x, the parabola will open downward,

and hence the vertex, $\left(-\dfrac{1}{3},\dfrac{4}{3}\right)$, will be the *highest* point on this graph. The axis

is the line $x=-\dfrac{1}{3}$. By finding the intercepts, selecting some ordered pairs of the

graph, and drawing a smooth curve through them, we get the result of Figure 4.10.

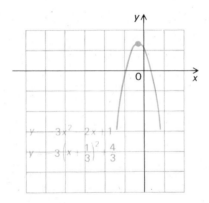

Figure 4.10

By completing the square on the general quadratic function,

$$y=ax^2+bx+c\qquad(a\ne 0),$$

we get the following formula for the vertex.

Theorem 4.3   The vertex of the graph of the quadratic function $y=ax^2+bx+c$ ($a\ne 0$) is given by

$$\left(-\frac{b}{2a},\frac{4ac-b^2}{4a}\right).$$

This vertex is the highest point on the graph if $a<0$, and the lowest point on the graph if $a>0$. The axis is the vertical line $x=\dfrac{-b}{2a}$.

Example 3 Find the vertex and axis of $y = -2x^2 + 3x - 5$.

Here $a = -2$, $b = 3$, and $c = -5$. Theorem 4.3 is a convenient way to find the vertex. Using the result of this theorem, the vertex is

$$\left(-\frac{b}{2a}, \frac{4ac - b^2}{4a}\right) = \left(\frac{-3}{2(-2)}, \frac{4(-2)(-5) - 3^2}{4(-2)}\right)$$

$$= \left(\frac{3}{4}, -\frac{31}{8}\right).$$

Since a is negative, the vertex is the highest point on the graph. The graph of this parabola could be obtained by plotting this vertex and some other ordered pairs that satisfy the equation, and drawing a smooth curve through them. The axis is the line $x = \frac{3}{4}$. ▌

Example 4 Find the axis of the parabola $y = 2x^2 - 5x + 3$.

By Theorem 4.3, with $a = 2$, $b = -5$, and $c = 3$, the vertex is the point $(5/4, -1/8)$. The equation of the axis is $x = 5/4$. ▌

The fact that the vertex point of a parabola is the highest or lowest point of the graph can be used in applications to find a maximum or minimum value. We shall not get into a precise definition of a maximum or minimum; but, intuitively, we can say a **maximum** value for an open interval is the maximum possible value of $f(x)$ for any value of x in the interval and a **minimum** is the lowest possible value of $f(x)$ for any x in the interval.

Example 5 Ms. Weintraub owns and operates Aunt Emma's Blueberry Pies. Always wanting to maximize her profits, she hires a consultant to analyze her business operations. The consultant tells her that her profit, $P(x)$, is given by the function

$$P(x) = 120x - x^2,$$

where x is the number of units of pies that she makes. How many units of pies should be made in order to maximize profit? What is the maximum profit?

The vertex of the parabola with equation $P(x) = 120x - x^2$ is (60, 3600). Figure 4.11 shows a graph of that portion of the profit function in Quadrant I.

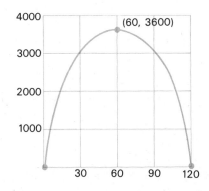

Figure 4.11

The maximum profit can be found from the vertex of the parabola. Thus the maximum profit of $3600 is obtained when 60 units of pies are made. In this case, profit increases as more and more pies are made, up to the point $x = 60$, and then decreases as more and more pies are made past this point. ▌

4.2 Exercises

1. Graph the following functions on the same coordinate system.
(a) $f(x) = 2x^2$
(b) $f(x) = 3x^2$
(c) $f(x) = \frac{1}{2}x^2$
(d) $f(x) = \frac{1}{3}x^2$
(e) How does the coefficient affect the shape of the graph?

2. Graph the following functions on the same coordinate system.
(a) $f(x) = x^2 + 2$
(b) $f(x) = x^2 - 1$
(c) $f(x) = x^2 + 1$
(d) $f(x) = x^2 - 2$
(e) How do these graphs differ from the graph of $y = x^2$?

3. Graph the following functions on the same coordinate system.
(a) $f(x) = (x - 2)^2$
(b) $f(x) = (x + 1)^2$
(c) $f(x) = (x + 3)^2$
(d) $f(x) = (x - 4)^2$
(e) How do these graphs differ from the graph of $f(x) = x^2$?

4. Use the quadratic formula to find the values of x when $f(x) = 0$. Use the two values you get to locate the x value of the vertex. Find the axis of each parabola.
(a) $f(x) = x^2 + 8x + 13$
(b) $f(x) = x^2 - 12x + 30$
(c) $f(x) = 3x^2 - 2x + 6$
(d) $f(x) = 5x^2 + 6x - 3$

Graph each of the following parabolas. Give the vertex and axis of each.

5. $y = (x - 2)^2$

6. $y = (x + 4)^2$

7. $y = (x + 3)^2 - 4$

8. $y = (x - 5)^2 - 4$

9. $y = -2(x + 3)^2 + 2$

10. $y = -3(x - 2)^2 + 1$

11. $y = -\frac{1}{2}(x + 1)^2 - 3$

12. $y = \frac{2}{3}(x - 2)^2 - 1$

13. $y = x^2 - 2x + 3$

14. $y = x^2 + 6x + 5$

15. $y = -x^2 - 4x + 2$

16. $y = -x^2 + 6x - 6$

17. $y = 2x^2 - 4x + 5$

18. $y = -3x^2 + 24x - 46$

⊙ *Find several points satisfying each of the following and then sketch the graph.*

19. $y = .14x^2 + .56x - .3$

20. $y = .82x^2 + 3.24x - .4$

21. $y = -.09x^2 - 1.8x + .5$

22. $y = -.35x^2 + 2.8x - .3$

Give the intervals where the following quadratic functions are increasing.

23. $y = (x - 2)^2$

24. $y = (x + 3)^2$

25. $y = -x^2 + 4$

26. $y = -x^2 - 6$

27. $y = -2x^2 - 5x + 3$

28. $y = -3x^2 - 9x + 2$

29. Glenview Community College wants to construct a rectangular parking lot on land bordered on one side by a highway. It has 320 feet of fencing which it will use to fence off the other three sides. What should be the dimensions of the lot if the enclosed area is to be a maximum? (Hint: let x represent the width of the lot and let $320 - 2x$ represent the length. Graph the area parabola, $A = x(320 - 2x)$, and investigate the vertex.)

30. What would be the maximum area that could be enclosed by the college's 320 feet of fencing if it decided to close the entrance by enclosing all four sides of the lot? (See Exercise 29.)

31. George runs a sandwich shop. By studying data concerning his past costs, he has found that the cost of operating his shop is given by

$$C(x) = 2x^2 - 1200x + 180,100,$$

where $C(x)$ is the daily cost to make x sandwiches. Find the number of sandwiches George must sell to minimize the cost. What is the minimum cost?

32. The revenue of a charter bus company depends on the number of unsold seats. If the revenue $R(x)$, is given by

$$R(x) = 5000 + 50x - x^2,$$

where x is the number of unsold seats, find the maximum revenue and the number of unsold seats which produce maximum revenue.

33. The number of mosquitoes, $M(x)$, in millions, in a certain area of Kentucky depends on the June rainfall, x, in inches, approximately as follows.

$$M(x) = 10x - x^2$$

Find the rainfall that will produce the maximum number of mosquitoes.

34. If an object is thrown upward with an initial velocity of 32 feet per second, then its height after t seconds is given by

$$h = 32t - 16t^2.$$

Find the maximum height attained by the object. Find the number of seconds it takes the object to hit the ground.

35. Find two numbers whose sum is 20 and whose product is a maximum. (Hint: Let x and $20 - x$ be the two numbers, and write an equation for the product.)

36. A charter flight charges a fare of $200 per person plus $4 per person for each unsold seat on the plane. If the plane holds 100 passengers, and if x represents the number of unsold seats, find the following.
    (a) An expression for the total revenue received for the flight. (Hint: Multiply the number of people flying, $100 - x$, by the price per ticket.)
    (b) The graph for the expression of part (a).
    (c) The number of unsold seats that will produce the maximum revenue.
    (d) The maximum revenue.

37. The demand for a certain type of cosmetic is given by

$$p = 500 - x,$$

where p is the price when x units are demanded.
    (a) Find the revenue, $R(x)$, that would be obtained at a price of x. (Hint: revenue = demand × price.)

(b) Graph the revenue function, $R(x)$.

(c) From the graph of the revenue function, estimate the price that will produce the maximum revenue.

(d) What is the maximum revenue?

38. Between the months of June and October, the percent of maximum possible chlorophyl production in a leaf is approximated by $C(x)$, where

$$C(x) = 10x + 50.$$

Here x is time in months, with $x = 1$ representing June. From October through December, $C(x)$ is approximated by

$$C(x) = -20(x - 5)^2 + 100,$$

where x is as above. Find the percent of maximum possible chlorophyl production in each of the following months: (a) June, (b) July, (c) September, (d) October, (e) November, (f) December.

39. Use your results in Exercise 38 to sketch a graph of $y = C(x)$, from June through December. In which month is chlorophyl production a maximum?

40. An arch is shaped like a parabola. It is 30 m wide at the base and 15 m high. How wide is it 10 m from the ground?

41. A culvert is shaped like a parabola, 18 cm across the top and 12 cm deep. How wide is the culvert 8 cm from the top?

4.3 Polynomial Functions

As mentioned earlier, any function of the form

$$f(x) = a_n x^n + a_{n-1} x^{n-1} + \ldots + a_1 x + a_0,$$

is called a polynomial function of degree n, for real numbers $a_n \neq 0$, $a_{n-1}, \ldots a_1, a_0$, and any nonnegative integer n. In Sections 4.1 and 4.2 we discussed first- and second-degree polynomial functions. In this section we consider polynomial functions of higher degree.

The simplest polynomial functions to graph are those where $f(x) = x^n$, so we shall discuss them first. To graph $f(x) = x^3$, find several ordered pairs which satisfy $y = x^3$, then plot them and connect the points with a smooth curve. A table of ordered pairs and the resulting graph shown as a solid curve are presented in Figure 4.12. Figure 4.12 also shows the graph of $f(x) = x^5$ as a broken line. We can sketch the graphs of $f(x) = x^4$ and $f(x) = x^6$ in a similar manner. Figure 4.13 shows $f(x) = x^4$ as a solid curve and $f(x) = x^6$ as a broken line.

As we saw in Exercise 1 of Section 4.2 with the graph of $f(x) = ax^2$, the value of a in $f(x) = ax^n$ affects the width of the graph. When $|a| > 1$, the graph is "thinner" than the graph of $f(x) = x^n$; when $0 < |a| < 1$, the graph is "fatter."

$y = x^3$

x	y
-2	-8
-1	-1
0	0
1	1
2	8

$y = x^5$

x	y
-1.5	-7.6
-1	-1
0	0
1	1
1.5	7.6

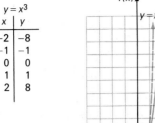

$y = x^4$

x	y
-2	16
-1	1
0	0
1	1
2	16

$y = x^6$

x	y
-1.5	11.4
-1	1
0	0
1	1
1.5	11.4

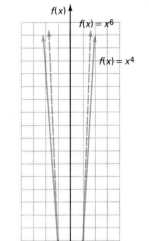

Figure 4.12

Figure 4.13

Example 1 Graph each of the following functions.

(a) $f(x) = \frac{1}{2}x^3$

First, find some ordered pairs.

x	-2	-1	0	1	2
y	-4	-1/2	0	1/2	4

Plotting these points leads to the graph in Figure 4.14. Note that the graph is "fatter" than that of $f(x) = x^3$.

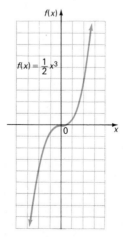

Figure 4.14

(b) $f(x) = \frac{3}{2}x^4$

The following table gives some ordered pairs.

x	-2	-1	0	1	2
y	24	$3/2$	0	$3/2$	24

The graph is shown in Figure 4.15. This graph is "thinner" than that of $f(x) = x^4$. ▌

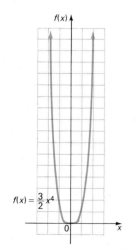

Figure 4.15

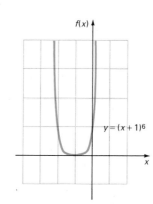

Figure 4.16

Figure 4.17

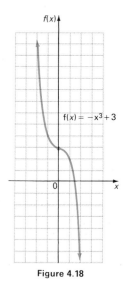

Figure 4.18

Example 2   Graph each of the following.
(a) $f(x) = x^5 - 2$
   The graph will be the same as that of $f(x) = x^5$ shifted down 2 units. See Figure 4.16.

(b) $f(x) = (x + 1)^6$
   This function has a graph like that of $f(x) = x^6$ shifted 1 unit to the left as shown in Figure 4.17.

(c) $f(x) = -x^3 + 3$
   The negative sign causes the graph to be reflected about the x-axis compared to the graph of $f(x) = x^3$. As shown in Figure 4.18, the graph is also shifted up 3 units. ▌

In general, the domain of a polynomial function is the set of all real numbers. The range of a polynomial function of odd degree is also the set of all real numbers. Some typical graphs of polynomial functions of odd degree are shown in Figure 4.19. These graphs illustrate that every polynomial function of odd degree has at least one real value of x that makes $f(x) = 0$. Those particular values of x are called the **real zeros** of the function; they are also the x-intercepts of the function.

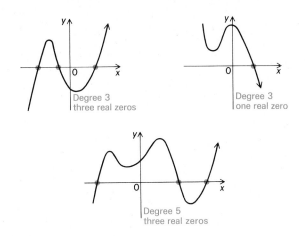

Figure 4.19

Polynomial functions of even degree have a range that takes the form $y \leq k$ or $y \geq k$ for some real number k. Figure 4.20 shows two typical graphs of polynomial functions of even degree.

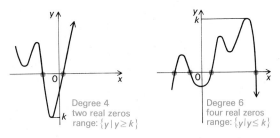

Figure 4.20

It is difficult to graph most polynomial functions without the use of calculus. A large number of points must be plotted to get a reasonably good graph. On the other hand, if a polynomial function can be factored, we can approximate its graph without plotting very many points, as shown in the next examples.

Example 3 Graph $f(x) = (2x + 3)(x - 1)(x + 2)$.

If $f(x)$ were multiplied out, it would be a third-degree polynomial, called a **cubic** polynomial. To sketch the graph, we first find the zeros of $f(x)$, by setting each factor equal to 0 and solving the resulting equations.

$$2x + 3 = 0 \quad \text{or} \quad x - 1 = 0 \quad \text{or} \quad x + 2 = 0$$

$$x = -\frac{3}{2} \qquad\qquad x = 1 \qquad\qquad x = -2$$

The three zeros, $-\dfrac{3}{2}$, 1, and -2, divide the x-axis into the four regions:

$$x < -2, \quad -2 < x < -\frac{3}{2}, \quad -\frac{3}{2} < x < 1, \quad 1 < x.$$

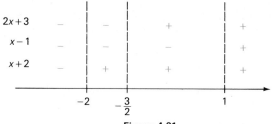

Figure 4.21

In any region, $f(x)$ is either always positive or always negative. We want to find the sign of $f(x)$ in each region. To do this, we find the sign of each factor in each region as shown in Figure 4.21.

From Figure 4.21, we see that all three factors are negative if $x < -2$. Thus, $f(x)$ is negative if $x < -2$. In the same way, we determine the sign of $f(x)$ in the other three regions. This information is summarized below.

Region	Sign of $f(x)$
$x < -2$	negative
$-2 < x < -3/2$	positive
$-3/2 < x < 1$	negative
$1 < x$	positive

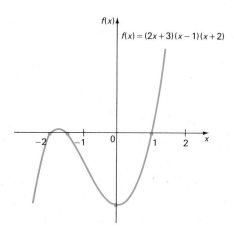

Figure 4.22

When $f(x)$ is negative, the graph is below the x-axis, and when $f(x)$ is positive, the graph is above the x-axis. Thus, we know the graph looks something like the sketch in Figure 4.22. We could improve the sketch by plotting one point in each region, especially if we chose a value much larger than 1 and a value much smaller than -2.

Example 4   Sketch the graph of $f(x) = 3x^4 + x^3 - 2x^2$.

The polynomial can be factored as follows.

$$3x^4 + x^3 - 2x^2 = x^2(3x^2 + x - 2)$$
$$= x^2(3x - 2)(x + 1)$$

The zeros are at $x = 0$, $x = 2/3$, and $x = -1$. They divide the x-axis into four regions:

$$x < -1, \qquad -1 < x < 0, \qquad 0 < x < 2/3, \qquad 2/3 < x$$

Find the sign of each factor in each region, as in Figure 4.23.

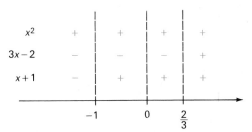

Figure 4.23

Then determine the sign of $f(x)$ in each region, by considering the signs of the three factors. We get the following information.

Region	Sign of $f(x)$	Location relative to axis
$x < -1$	positive	above
$-1 < x < 0$	negative	below
$0 < x < 2/3$	negative	below
$2/3 < x$	positive	above

By choosing a few values of x and finding the corresponding values of y, we can sketch the graph shown in Figure 4.24.   ▮

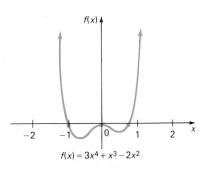

$f(x) = 3x^4 + x^3 - 2x^2$

Figure 4.24

4.3 Exercises   *Each of the following polynomial functions is symmetric about a line or a point. For each function, (a) graph and (b) name the line or point of symmetry.*

1. $f(x) = \dfrac{1}{4}x^6$

2. $f(x) = -\dfrac{2}{3}x^5$

3. $f(x) = \dfrac{-5}{4}x^5$

4. $f(x) = 2x^4$

5. $f(x) = \dfrac{1}{2}x^3 + 1$

6. $f(x) = -x^4 + 2$

7. $f(x) = -(x + 1)^3$

8. $f(x) = \dfrac{1}{3}(x + 3)^4$

9. $f(x) = (x - 1)^4 + 2$

10. $f(x) = (x + 2)^3 - 1$

Graph each of the following polynomial functions.

11. $f(x) = 2x(x - 3)(x + 2)$

12. $f(x) = x^2(x + 1)(x - 1)$

13. $f(x) = x^2(x - 2)(x + 3)^2$

14. $f(x) = x^2(x - 5)(x + 3)(x - 1)$

15. $f(x) = 3x^4 + 5x^3 - 2x^2$

16. $f(x) = 4x^3 + 2x^2 - 12x$

17. $f(x) = 2x^3(x^2 - 4)(x - 1)$

18. $f(x) = 5x^2(x^3 - 1)(x + 2)$

19. $f(x) = x^2(x - 3)^3(x + 1)$

20. $f(x) = x(x - 4)^2(x + 2)^2$

◉ **21.** The polynomial function

$$A(x) = -.015x^3 + 1.058x$$

gives the approximate alcohol concentration (in tenths of a percent) in an average person's bloodstream x hours after drinking about eight ounces of 100 proof whiskey. The function is approximately valid for $0 \le x \le 8$.
   (a) Graph $A(x)$.
   (b) Using the graph you drew for part (a), estimate the time of maximum alcohol concentration.
   (c) In one state, a person is legally drunk if the blood alcohol concentration exceeds .15%. Use the graph of part (a) to estimate the period in which this average person is legally drunk.

◉ *In calculus, techniques are developed for finding any maximum or minimum values of polynomial functions. We can find approximate maximums or minimums for given intervals, by first evaluating the function at the left endpoint of the given interval. Then add .1 to the value of x and reevaluate the polynomial. Keep doing this until the right endpoint of the interval is reached. Then identify the maximum and minimum values for the polynomial on the interval.*

22. $y = x^3 + 4x^2 - 8x - 8$, $[-3.8, -3]$, $[.3, 1]$

23. $y = 2x^3 - 5x^2 - x + 1$, $[-1, 0]$, $[1.4, 2]$

24. $y = x^4 - 7x^3 + 13x^2 + 6x - 28$, $[-2, -1]$, $[2, 3]$

4.4   Rational Functions

A function of the form

$$f(x) = \frac{P}{Q},$$

where P and Q are polynomials in x, is called a **rational function.** Since any values of x such that $Q = 0$ are excluded from the domain, a rational function usually has a graph which has one or more breaks in it.

The simplest rational function with a variable denominator is $f(x) = \dfrac{1}{x}$. The domain of this function is the set of all nonzero real numbers. To graph the function, it is helpful to see what happens to values of x close to 0. In the following table, we show what happens to $f(x)$ as x gets closer and closer to 0 from either side.

x	-1	$-.1$	$-.01$	$-.001$	$.001$	$.01$	$.1$	1
$f(x)$	-1	-10	-100	-1000	1000	100	10	1

From the table, we see that $|f(x)|$ gets larger as x gets closer to 0. Since x cannot equal 0, the graph will never intersect the vertical line $x = 0$. This line is called a **vertical asymptote.**

On the other hand, as $|x|$ gets larger and larger, $f(x)$ gets closer and closer to 0. (See the table.)

x	$-10,000$	-1000	-100	-10	10	100	1000	$10,000$
$f(x)$	$-.0001$	$-.001$	$-.01$	$-.1$	$.1$	$.01$	$.001$	$.0001$

Thus, as $|x|$ gets larger and larger, without bound (written $|x| \to \infty$), the graph of $y = \dfrac{1}{x}$ approaches closer and closer to the horizontal line $y = 0$. This straight line is called a **horizontal asymptote.**

From the equation, we see that $f(x) = \dfrac{1}{x}$ is symmetric to the origin. If we find and plot a point in the first quadrant, and let the graph approach the asymptotes, we get part of the graph as shown in Figure 4.25. The other part of the

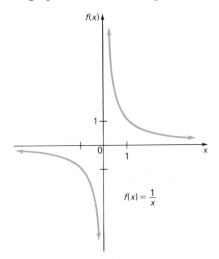

Figure 4.25

graph (in the third quadrant) can be found by plotting one or more points where $x < 0$. Note that the graph is indeed symmetric about the origin.

Example 1   Graph $f(x) = \dfrac{-2}{x}$.

The function can be written as

$$f(x) = -2 \cdot \frac{1}{x}.$$

Compared to $f(x) = 1/x$, the graph will be reflected about the x-axis (because of the negative sign), and each point will be twice as far from the x-axis. See Figure 4.26.   ▎

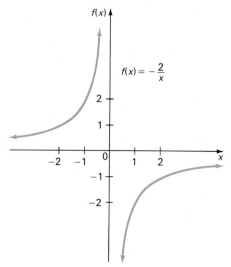

Figure 4.26

Example 2   Graph $f(x) = \dfrac{1}{x - 3}$.

Here, the domain is all real numbers except 3. As shown in Figure 4.27, the graph is the same as that of $f(x) = 1/x$, shifted 3 units to the right.   ▎

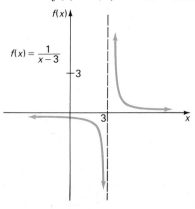

Figure 4.27

Example 3   Graph $y = \dfrac{1}{(x-1)(x+4)}$.

First, we note that this graph has no symmetry about either axis or the origin. There are vertical asymptotes at $x = 1$ and $x = -4$, as shown in the following charts.

as x approaches -4
↓

x	-4.1	-4.01	-4.001	-3.999	-3.99	-3.9
$f(x)$	1.96	19.96	199.96	-200.04	-20.04	-2.04

↑
values of $|f(x)|$ get larger and larger

as x approaches 1
↓

x	.9	.99	.999	1.001	1.01	1.1
$f(x)$	-2.04	-20.04	-200.04	199.96	19.96	1.96

↑
values of $|f(x)|$ get larger and larger

As $|x|$ gets larger and larger, $|(x-1)(x+4)|$ also gets larger and larger, thereby making y closer and closer to 0. This means that the x-axis is a horizontal asymptote. The vertical asymptotes divide the x-axis into three regions. It is often convenient to consider each region separately. If we find the intercepts and plot a few points, we get the result shown in Figure 4.28.

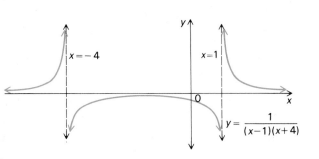

$y = \dfrac{1}{(x-1)(x+4)}$

Figure 4.28

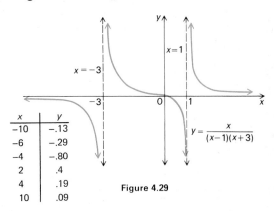

x	y
-10	$-.13$
-6	$-.29$
-4	$-.80$
2	.4
4	.19
10	.09

$y = \dfrac{x}{(x-1)(x+3)}$

Figure 4.29

Example 4   Graph $y = \dfrac{x}{(x-1)(x+3)}$.

There is no symmetry about either axis or the origin. There are two vertical asymptotes, $x = 1$ and $x = -3$. As $|x|$ gets larger and larger, both numerator and denominator get larger and larger. In this case, we cannot tell what happens to y. Therefore we must find selected ordered pairs of the function for values of x where $|x|$ is relatively large. (See the table next to the graph.) We plot the intercepts and selected ordered pairs and consider the vertical asymptotes. The graph is shown in Figure 4.29.

The rational functions we have discussed so far all had numerators of lower degree than their denominators. In general, when this is the case, the horizontal asymptote is $y = 0$, the x-axis.

Rational functions in which the degree of the numerator and denominator are the same, as in Example 5 below, also have a horizontal asymptote. If the rational function is of the form

$$f(x) = \frac{a_n x^n + \ldots + a_0}{b_n x^n + \ldots + b_0}, \qquad b_n \neq 0$$

the horizontal asymptote is

$$y = \frac{a_n}{b_n}.$$

Example 5   Graph $f(x) = \dfrac{2x + 1}{x - 3}$.

The vertical asymptote is $x = 3$. We can rewrite the function by dividing out the fraction.

$$
\begin{array}{r}
2 \\
x - 3 \overline{)\, 2x + 1} \\
\underline{2x - 6} \\
7
\end{array}
$$

Thus, $$f(x) = \frac{2x + 1}{x - 3} = 2 + \frac{7}{x - 3}.$$

As $|x|$ gets larger and larger, the fraction $7/(x - 3)$ approaches zero, and $f(x)$ approaches 2. Therefore, the horizontal asymptote is $y = 2$. By plotting the y-intercept and a few points, we get the graph as shown in Figure 4.30.

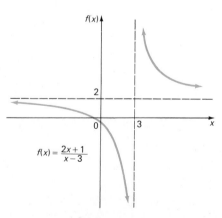

Figure 4.30

To summarize, when graphing a rational function, use the following procedure.

1. Find any vertical asymptotes by setting the denominator of the fraction equal
to zero and solving.

2. Determine any horizontal asymptotes. There are three possibilities:
    (a) If the numerator has lower degree than the denominator, the horizontal
asymptote is $y = 0$.
    (b) If the numerator and denominator have the same degree, and the func-
tion is of the form

$$f(x) = \frac{a_n x^n + \ldots + a_0}{b_n x^n + \ldots + b_0} \qquad b_n \neq 0,$$

then the horizontal asymptote is

$$y = \frac{a_n}{b_n}.$$

    (c) If the numerator is of degree higher than the denominator, methods
from calculus may be necessary to sketch the graph.

3. Find any intercepts.

4. Plot a few selected points; at least one in each region of the domain determined
by the vertical asymptotes.

5. Complete the sketch.

4.4 Exercises

1. Sketch the following graphs on the same axes and compare them with the graph of
$f(x) = \frac{1}{x}$.

    (a) $f(x) = \frac{1}{x^3}$ (b) $f(x) = \frac{1}{x^5}$

2. Sketch the following graphs on the same axes and compare them with each other.

    (a) $f(x) = \frac{1}{x^2}$ (b) $f(x) = \frac{1}{x^4}$ (c) $f(x) = \frac{1}{x^6}$

3. Sketch the following graphs and compare them with the graph of $f(x) = \frac{1}{x}$.

    (a) $f(x) = \frac{1}{x + 2}$ (c) $f(x) = \frac{3}{x + 2}$

    (b) $f(x) = \frac{3}{x}$ (d) $f(x) = \frac{1}{x} + 2$

4. Sketch the following graphs and compare them with the graph of $f(x) = \frac{1}{x^2}$.

    (a) $f(x) = \frac{1}{(x - 3)^2}$ (b) $f(x) = \frac{-2}{x^2}$ (c) $f(x) = \frac{-2}{(x - 3)^2}$

Graph each of the following.

5. $y = \frac{4}{5 + 3x}$ 6. $y = \frac{1}{(x - 2)(x + 4)}$ 7. $y = \frac{3}{(x + 4)^2}$

8. $y = \dfrac{3x}{(x+1)(x-2)}$

12. $y = \dfrac{3x}{x-1}$

15. $y = \dfrac{x-3}{x+5}$

9. $y = \dfrac{2x+1}{(x+2)(x+4)}$

13. $y = \dfrac{4x}{1-3x}$

16. $y = \dfrac{x}{x^2-9}$

10. $y = \dfrac{5x}{x^2-1}$

14. $y = \dfrac{x+1}{x-4}$

17. $y = \dfrac{3x}{x^2-16}$

11. $y = \dfrac{-x}{x^2-4}$

⦿ 18. In a recent year, the cost per ton, y, to build an oil tanker of x thousand deadweight tons is approximated by

$$y = \frac{110{,}000}{x+225}.$$

(a) Find y for $x = 25$, $x = 50$, $x = 100$, $x = 200$, $x = 300$, and $x = 400$.

(b) Graph the function.

19. Suppose the average cost per unit, $C(x)$, to produce x units of margarine is given by

$$C(x) = \frac{500}{x+30}.$$

(a) Find $C(10)$, $C(20)$, $C(50)$, $C(75)$, and $C(100)$.

(b) Would a more reasonable domain for C be $(0, \infty)$ or $[0, \infty)$? Why?

20. In situations involving environmental pollution, a cost-benefit model expresses cost as a function of the percentage of pollutant removed from the environment. Suppose a cost-benefit model is expressed as

$$y = \frac{6.7x}{100 - x},$$

where y is the cost in thousands of dollars of removing x percent of a certain pollutant.

(a) Graph the function.

(b) Is it possible, according to this function, to remove all the pollutant?

21. Antique-car fans often enter their cars in a concours d'elegance in which a maximum of 100 points can be awarded to a particular car. Points are awarded for the general attractiveness of the car. The function

$$C(x) = \frac{10x}{49(101 - x)}$$

expresses the cost, in thousands of dollars, of restoring a car so that it will win x points. Graph the function.

4.5 The Conic Sections

In Section 4.2, we discussed $y = ax^2 + bx + c$, where a, b, c are real numbers and $a \neq 0$. We found that the graph of this expression is a parabola. Exchanging x and y gives

$$x = ay^2 + by + c,$$

whose graph is also a parabola, but one that opens sideways.

The graph of $x = y^2$ is shown with a solid line in Figure 4.31. For comparison, we show the graph of $y = x^2$ with a dashed line. In general, the graph of $x = ay^2 + by + c$ is a sideways parabola, opening to the right if $a > 0$ and to the left if $a < 0$.

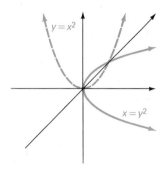

Figure 4.31

Example 1   Graph $x = 2y^2 + 4y + 3$.

Complete the square on y, just as we completed the square on x in a previous section.

$$x = 2(y^2 + 2y \qquad) + 3$$
$$ = 2(y^2 + 2y + 1) + 3 - 2$$
$$x = 2(y + 1)^2 + 1$$

From this we see that the vertex is $(1, -1)$. The parabola opens to the right, since $a = 2$, which is positive. By plotting a few additional points, we get the graph of Figure 4.32. The axis is the horizontal line $y = -1$.   ▌

Example 2   Graph $y = \sqrt{1 - x}$.

If we square both sides of this equation, we have $y^2 = 1 - x$ or $x = -y^2 + 1$. This equation has a graph which is a sideways parabola opening to the left with vertex at $(1, 0)$. Since the given expression has $y \geq 0$, we want only the upper half of the parabola, as shown in Figure 4.33.   ▌

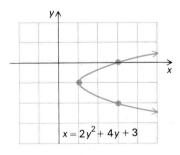

Figure 4.32

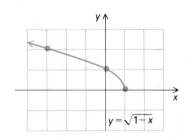

Figure 4.33

In general,

$$x = a(y - k)^2 + h \qquad a \neq 0$$

is a parabola with vertex at (h, k) and axis the horizontal line $y = k$. The parabola opens to the right if $a > 0$ and to the left is $a < 0$.

As we have seen in Chapter 3, a *circle* is the set of points in a plane which lie a fixed distance from a fixed point. The fixed distance is called the *radius* and the fixed point is the *center*.

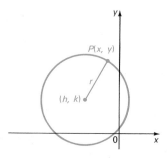

Figure 4.34

A circle is symmetric about its center and about any line through its center. To find the equation of the circle with center at (h, k) and radius r, use the distance formula. From Figure 4.34, the distance r from a point $P(x, y)$ on the circle to the center is

$$\sqrt{(x - h)^2 + (y - k)^2} = r.$$

If we square both sides, we get the formula originally given in Chapter 3.

Theorem 4.4   The equation of a circle with center at (h, k) and radius r is

$$(x - h)^2 + (y - k)^2 = r^2.$$

Example 3   Find the equation of the circle with center at $(-2, 4)$ and radius 4.
    By Theorem 4.4, the equation is $(x + 2)^2 + (y - 4)^2 = 16$. The graph is shown in Figure 4.35.   ▌

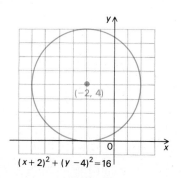

$(x + 2)^2 + (y - 4)^2 = 16$

Figure 4.35

If we start with $(x - h)^2 + (y - k)^2 = r^2$ and multiply, we end up with

$$x^2 - 2xh + h^2 + y^2 - 2yk + k^2 = r^2,$$

or $x^2 - 2xh + y^2 - 2yk + (h^2 + k^2 - r^2) = 0.$

where $h^2 + k^2 - r^2$ is a constant. Thus, if we begin with an expression of the form

$$Ax^2 + Bx + Cy^2 + Dy + E = 0 \qquad A \neq 0$$

and divide through by A, we get

$$x^2 + \frac{B}{A}x + \frac{C}{A}y^2 + \frac{D}{A}y + \frac{E}{A} = 0,$$

which might be the equation of a circle. To get the necessary y^2, instead of Cy^2/A, we must require that

$$C = A.$$

Thus, $Ax^2 + Bx + Cy^2 + Dy + E = 0$ might be a circle if $A = C$. (It might also be a single point, or no points at all.) To see if a given equation of this form represents a circle, complete the square as shown in the next two examples.

Example 4   Graph $x^2 - 6x + y^2 + 10y + 25 = 0$.

This equation might be a circle since both x^2 and y^2 have equal coefficients. To see if this equation really represents a circle, complete the square on both x and y.

$$(x^2 - 6x + 9) + (y^2 + 10y + 25) = -25 + 9 + 25$$
$$(x - 3)^2 + (y + 5)^2 = 9$$

The equation is that of a circle having center at $(3, -5)$ and radius 3, with the graph as shown in Figure 4.36 ▌

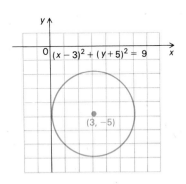

Figure 4.36

Example 5   Graph $x^2 + 10x + y^2 - 4y + 33 = 0$.

Completing the square gives

$$(x^2 + 10x + 25) + (y^2 - 4y + 4) = -33 + 25 + 4$$
$$(x + 5)^2 + (y - 2)^2 = -4.$$

There are no real ordered pairs (x, y) satisfying this condition. (Why?)

Example 6 Graph $y = \sqrt{16 - x^2}$.

If we square both sides, we have $y^2 = 16 - x^2$, or $x^2 + y^2 = 16$, which is a circle with center at the origin and radius 4. However, the original equation is $y = \sqrt{16 - x^2}$; therefore y can take on only nonnegative values. Hence, the graph is a semicircle, as shown in Figure 4.37. Because y is always the nonnegative square root of $16 - x^2$, each value of x leads to exactly one corresponding value of y. Thus, $y = \sqrt{16 - x^2}$ is a function. The domain of the function is $-4 \le x \le 4$, and the range is $0 \le y \le 4$.

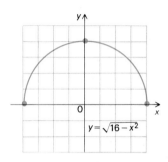

Figure 4.37

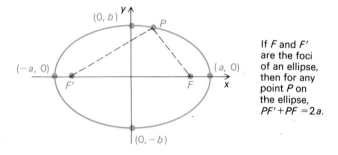

Figure 4.38

An **ellipse** is the set of points in a plane such that the sum of the distances from any point P on the ellipse to two given points in the plane is constant. The two fixed points are called the **foci** (singular, **focus**) of the ellipse. See Figure 4.38. If the foci are chosen to be on the x-axis (or y-axis) equidistant from the origin, and if the origin is the center of the ellipse, then we can use the distance formula and the definition of an ellipse to get the following theorem (see Exercise 45).

Theorem 4.5 The ellipse with x-intercepts $x = a$ and $x = -a$ and y-intercepts $y = b$ and $y = -b$ has the equation

$$\frac{x^2}{a^2}+\frac{y^2}{b^2}=1.$$

The coefficients of x^2 and y^2 are different, but both positive.

Example 7 Graph $4x^2 + 9y^2 = 36$.

To obtain the form of the equation of an ellipse shown in the theorem, divide by 36 to get

$$\frac{x^2}{9}+\frac{y^2}{4}=1.$$

The graph is an ellipse having x-intercepts $x = 3$ and $x = -3$, with y-intercepts $y = 2$ and $y = -2$. Additional ordered pairs which satisfy the equation of the ellipse may be found and plotted if a more accurate graph is desired. The graph of this ellipse is shown in Figure 4.39. ▎

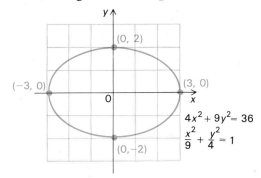

Figure 4.39

Like a circle, an ellipse is symmetric about its center. An ellipse centered at the origin is also symmetric about the lines through its x-intercepts and its y-intercepts. The line segment through the foci, and joining the intercepts, is called the **major axis** of the ellipse.

A **hyperbola** is the set of points in a plane such that the differences of the distances from any point P on the hyperbola to two given points (called foci) in the plane are constant. The following theorem depends upon the distance formula and the foci's being on the x-axis or y-axis, respectively.

Theorem 4.6 A hyperbola having x-intercepts $x = a$ and $x = -a$, centered about the origin and symmetric to the x-axis, has an equation of the form

$$\frac{x^2}{a^2}-\frac{y^2}{b^2}=1,$$

while a hyperbola having y-intercepts $y = a$ and $y = -a$, centered about the origin and symmetric to the y-axis, has an equation of the form

$$\frac{y^2}{a^2}-\frac{x^2}{b^2}=1.$$

Example 8   Graph the hyperbola $\dfrac{x^2}{16} - \dfrac{y^2}{9} = 1$.

By Theorem 4.6, the x-intercepts are $x = 4$ and $x = -4$. However, if $x = 0$, we have

$$-\frac{y^2}{9} = 1,$$

or

$$y^2 = -9,$$

which has no real solutions. Hence, the graph has no y-intercepts. To complete the graph find some other ordered pairs that belong to it. For example, if $x = 6$, we have

$$\frac{6^2}{16} - \frac{y^2}{9} = 1$$

$$-\frac{y^2}{9} = 1 - \frac{36}{16}$$

$$\frac{y^2}{9} = \frac{20}{16}$$

$$y^2 = \frac{180}{16} = \frac{45}{4}$$

$$y = \pm \frac{3\sqrt{5}}{2} \approx \pm 3.4.$$

Thus the graph includes the points $(6, 3.4)$ and $(6, -3.4)$. Also, if $x = -6$, we have $y \approx \pm 3.4$. Hence, the graph also includes $(-6, 3.4)$ and $(-6, -3.4)$, as shown in Figure 4.40.

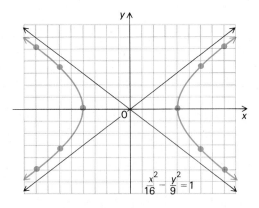

Figure 4.40

The straight lines approached by the graph of the hyperbola of Figure 4.40 are called the **asymptotes** of the hyperbola. A hyperbola of the form

$$\frac{x^2}{a^2} - \frac{y^2}{b^2} = 1$$

will have asymptotes whose equations are given by

$$\frac{x^2}{a^2} - \frac{y^2}{b^2} = 0.$$

This can be simplified by writing

$$\frac{x^2}{a^2} = \frac{y^2}{b^2},$$

from which

$$\frac{x}{a} = \frac{y}{b} \qquad \text{or} \qquad \frac{x}{a} = -\frac{y}{b},$$

so that

$$y = \frac{b}{a}x \qquad \text{or} \qquad y = -\frac{b}{a}x$$

are the equations of the asymptotes. In the same way,

$$\frac{y^2}{a^2} - \frac{x^2}{b^2} = 1$$

has asymptotes given by

$$y = \frac{a}{b}x \qquad \text{or} \qquad y = -\frac{a}{b}x$$

just as above. In general, then, we have the following result.

Theorem 4.7 The asymptotes of the hyperbola $\dfrac{x^2}{a^2} - \dfrac{y^2}{b^2} = 1$ are given by

$$y = \frac{b}{a}x \qquad \text{or} \qquad y = -\frac{b}{a}x,$$

while the asymptotes of the hyperbola $\dfrac{y^2}{a^2} - \dfrac{x^2}{b^2} = 1$ are given by

$$y = \frac{a}{b}x \qquad \text{or} \qquad y = -\frac{a}{b}x.$$

Example 9   Graph $4y^2 - x^2 = 16$.

Dividing both sides by 16 gives

$$\frac{y^2}{4} - \frac{x^2}{16} = 1.$$

The y-intercepts are 2 and -2. There are no x-intercepts. To find the asymptotes, use Theorem 4.7, or use the fact that the asymptotes are given by

$$\frac{y^2}{4} - \frac{x^2}{16} = 0.$$

Add $x^2/16$ to both sides to get

$$\frac{y^2}{4} = \frac{x^2}{16}$$

or

$$y^2 = \frac{x^2}{4},$$

so that

$$y = \frac{1}{2}x \quad \text{or} \quad y = -\frac{1}{2}x.$$

The asymptote $y = \frac{1}{2}x$ goes through $(4, 2)$ and $(-4, -2)$, while the asymptote $y = -\frac{1}{2}x$ goes through $(-4, 2)$ and $(4, -2)$. Using the intercepts and asymptotes gives the graph shown in Figure 4.41. ▌

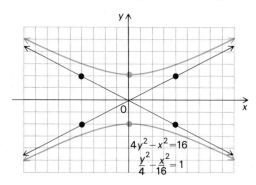

To graph the hyperbola:
(a) locate the asymptotes (shown in black)
(b) plot the intercepts (± 2 on the y-axis)
(c) sketch the two branches of the hyperbola

Figure 4.41

Example 10   Graph $x = -\sqrt{1 + 4y^2}$.

Squaring both sides to eliminate the radical gives $x^2 = 1 + 4y^2$ or $x^2 - 4y^2 = 1$. We can write this as

$$\frac{x^2}{1} - \frac{y^2}{1/4} = 1,$$

which is the equation of a hyperbola with intercepts $x = 1$ and $x = -1$. The asymptotes are $y = \frac{1}{2}x$ and $y = -\frac{1}{2}x$. Since the given equation restricts x to nonpositive values, the graph is the negative half of the hyperbola as shown in Figure 4.42.   ▌

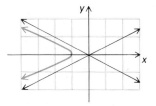

Figure 4.42

The graphs of the second-degree relations we have studied, *parabolas, hyperbolas, ellipses* and *circles,* are called **conic sections** since each can be obtained by cutting a cone with a plane, as shown in Figure 4.43.

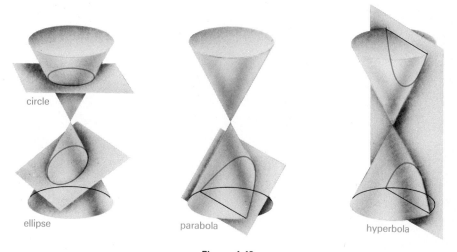

Figure 4.43

Note that all conic sections have second-degree equations of the form

$$Ax^2 + Bx + Cy^2 + Dy + E = 0$$

where either A or C must be nonzero. The special characteristics of each of the conic sections are summarized below.

Conic section	Characteristic
parabola	either A or C equals 0, but not both
circle	$A = C \neq 0$
ellipse	$A \neq C, AC > 0$
hyperbola	$AC < 0$

We can now summarize our work with the conic sections.

Equation	**Graph**	
$y = a(x-h)^2 + k$	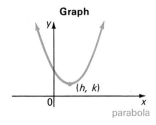 parabola	opens upwards if $a>0$, downward if $a<0$, vertex is at (h, k)
$x = a(y-k)^2 + h$	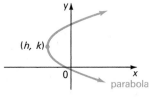 parabola	opens to right if $a>0$, to left if $a<0$, vertex is at (h, k)
$(x-h)^2 + (y-k)^2 = r^2$	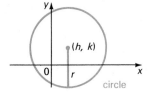 circle	center at (h, k), radius r
$\dfrac{x^2}{a^2} + \dfrac{y^2}{b^2} = 1$	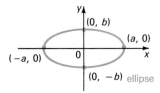 ellipse	x intercepts are a and $-a$ y intercepts are b and $-b$
$\dfrac{x^2}{a^2} - \dfrac{y^2}{b^2} = 1$	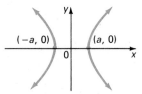 hyperbola	x intercepts are a and $-a$
$\dfrac{y^2}{a^2} - \dfrac{x^2}{b^2} = 1$	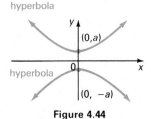 hyperbola	y intercepts are a and $-a$

Figure 4.44

4.5 Exercises   *Find the center and radius of each of the following that are circles.*

1. $x^2 + 6x + y^2 + 8y = -9$

2. $x^2 - 4x + y^2 + 12y = -4$

3. $x^2 - 12x + y^2 + 10y = -25$

4. $x^2 + 8x + y^2 - 6y + 16 = 0$

5. $2x^2 + 2y^2 = 4y + 96$

6. $3x^2 + 12x + 3y^2 - 63 = 0$

⊙   7. $x^2 - 2.84x + y^2 + 1.4y + 1.8664 = 0$

8. $x^2 + 7.4x + y^2 - 3.8y + 16.09 = 0$

Find the equations of the asymptotes of each of the following hyperbolas.

9. $\dfrac{x^2}{9} - \dfrac{y^2}{25} = 1$

10. $\dfrac{y^2}{9} - \dfrac{x^2}{16} = 1$

11. $\dfrac{x^2}{1/4} - \dfrac{y^2}{1/9} = 1$

12. $\dfrac{y^2}{9/16} - \dfrac{x^2}{25/36} = 1$

Sketch the graphs of each of the following.

13. $x = (y + 1)^2$

14. $x = (y - 3)^2$

15. $x = -2(y + 3)^2$

16. $x = -3(y - 1)^2 + 2$

17. $x = \dfrac{1}{2}(y + 1)^2 + 3$

18. $x = y^2 - 6y + 7$

19. $x = -2y^2 + 2y - 3$

20. $x = -4y^2 - 4y - 3$

21. $(x - 2)^2 + y^2 = 36$

22. $x^2 + (y + 3)^2 = 49$

23. $(x - 4)^2 + (y + 3)^2 = 4$

24. $(x + 3)^2 + (y - 2)^2 = 16$

25. $\dfrac{x^2}{16} + \dfrac{y^2}{36} = 1$

26. $\dfrac{x^2}{9} + y^2 = 1$

27. $\dfrac{y^2}{16} - \dfrac{x^2}{9} = 1$

28. $25x^2 + 9y^2 = 225$

29. $x^2 = 9 + y^2$

30. $y^2 = 16 + x^2$

31. $2x^2 + y^2 = 8$

32. $9x^2 - 25y^2 = 225$

33. $25x^2 - 4y^2 = -100$

34. $4y^2 - 16x^2 = 64$

35. $\dfrac{x^2}{1/9} + \dfrac{y^2}{1/16} = 1$

36. $\dfrac{x^2}{4/25} + \dfrac{y^2}{9/49} = 1$

37. $y = \sqrt{x + 4}$

38. $y = \sqrt{x - 3}$

39. $y = -\sqrt{2x + 6}$

40. $y = -\sqrt{3x - 9}$

41. $\dfrac{x}{4} = \sqrt{1 - \dfrac{y^2}{9}}$

42. $\dfrac{y}{2} = \sqrt{1 - \dfrac{x^2}{25}}$

43. $y = -\sqrt{1 + \dfrac{x^2}{25}}$

44. $x = -\sqrt{1 + \dfrac{y^2}{9}}$

45. Suppose $(c, 0)$ and $(-c, 0)$ are the foci of an ellipse. Suppose the sum of the distances from any point (x, y) of the ellipse to the two foci is $2a$. (See figure.)

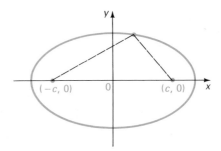

(a) Use the distance formula to show that the equation of the resulting ellipse is

$$\frac{x^2}{a^2} + \frac{y^2}{a^2 - c^2} = 1.$$

(b) Show that a and $-a$ are the x-intercepts.
(c) Let $b^2 = a^2 - c^2$, and show that b and $-b$ are the y-intercepts.

46. The **eccentricity** e of a conic is the ratio c/a where c is the distance from the center of the figure to a focus and a is the x-intercept. (See the figure for Exercise 45.)
(a) For an ellipse, $c = \sqrt{a^2 - b^2}$. Find e for the ellipses in Exercises 25–28.
(b) Compare c and a in the figure for Exercise 45. From this and your results in part (a), what are the restrictions on e for an ellipse?
(c) For a hyperbola, $c = \sqrt{a^2 + b^2}$. Find e for the hyperbolas in Exercises 29–34.
(d) Sketch a figure of a hyperbola with x-intercepts and determine c and a. From your sketch and your results in part (c), what are the restrictions on e for a hyperbola?

◉ *The orbit of Mars is an ellipse. The sun is at one focus. An approximate equation for this orbit is*

$$\frac{x^2}{5013} + \frac{y^2}{4970} = 1.$$

Here x and y are measured in millions of miles.

47. Find the widest possible distance across this ellipse.

48. Find the eccentricity of this ellipse.

4.6 Graphing Inequalities

Many mathematical descriptions of real-world situations are best expressed as inequalities rather than equalities. Perhaps the simplest way to see the solution of an inequality is to draw its graph. The graphs of inequalities are useful both in advanced work in mathematics and in applications of mathematics. Some applications of the graphs of inequalities are shown at the end of Chapter 9.

A line divides a plane into three sets of points—the points of the line itself and the points belonging to the two regions determined by the line. Each of these two regions is called a **half-plane.** In Figure 4.45, line r divides the plane into three different sets of points, line r, half-plane P, and half-plane Q. The points of r belong to neither P nor Q. Line r is the **boundary** of each half-plane.

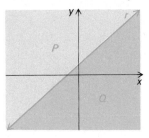

Figure 4.45

A **linear inequality** is one of the form $ax + by \leq c$, where a, b, and c are real numbers, with a and b not both equal to 0. (We could replace $\leq$ with $\geq$, $<$, or $>$.) The graph of a linear inequality turns out to be made up of a half-plane, perhaps together with its boundary. For example, to graph the linear inequality $3x - 2y \leq 6$, first graph the boundary, $3x - 2y = 6$, as shown in Figure 4.46.

Since the points of the line $3x - 2y = 6$ satisfy $3x - 2y \leq 6$, this line is part of the solution. To decide which half-plane—the one above the line $3x - 2y = 6$ or the one below the line—is part of the solution, solve the original inequality for y:

$$3x - 2y \leq 6$$
$$-2y \leq -3x + 6$$
$$y \geq \frac{3}{2}x - 3$$

If we choose a particular value of x, the inequality will be satisfied by all values of y which are *greater than* or equal to $\frac{3}{2}x - 3$. This means that the solution contains the half-plane *above* the line, as shown in Figure 4.47.

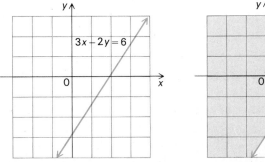

Figure 4.46   Figure 4.47

Example 1   Graph $x + 4y > 4$.

The boundary here is the straight line $x + 4y = 4$. Since the points on this line do not satisfy $x + 4y > 4$, it is customary to make the line dashed, as in Figure 4.48. To decide which half-plane gives the solution, solve for y.

$$x + 4y > 4$$
$$4y > -x + 4$$
$$y > -\frac{1}{4}x + 1$$

Since y is *greater than* $-\frac{1}{4}x + 1$, the solution is made up of the half-plane above the boundary, as shown in Figure 4.48.   █

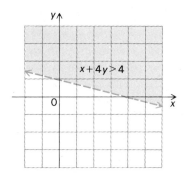

Figure 4.48

The methods we have used to graph linear inequalities can be used for other inequalities of the form $y \leq f(x)$ as summarized here:

> For a function f,
>
> the graph of $y < f(x)$ is made up of all the points which are *below* the graph of $y = f(x)$;
> the graph of $y > f(x)$ is made up of all the points which are *above* the graph of $y = f(x)$.

Example 2   Graph $y \leq 2x^2 - 3$.

First graph the boundary, the parabola $y = 2x^2 - 3$, as shown in Figure 4.49. Make the parabola a solid line. The inequality is already solved for y; here y is *less than* or equal to $2x^2 - 3$. The solution is thus made up of the region below the parabola as well as the points of the parabola itself. See Figure 4.49.   █

Example 3   Graph $y < |x - 2|$.

Begin by graphing the boundary, $y = |x - 2|$. This graph should be made dashed, since it is not part of the solution. Since y is *less than* $|x - 2|$, shade the region below the graph, as shown in Figure 4.50.   █

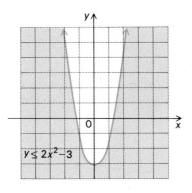

Figure 4.49

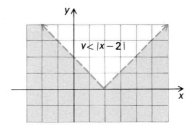

Figure 4.50

Example 4   Graph the intersection of $2x - y \leq 4$ and $x < 3$.

Figure 4.51 shows the graphs of both inequalities. The heavily shaded area represents the intersection of the two regions. The point of intersection of the boundary lines, $(3, 2)$, belongs to the first inequality but not the second. For this reason, $(3, 2)$ does not belong to the intersection. This is shown with an open dot on the graph at $(3, 2)$.

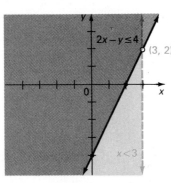

Figure 4.51

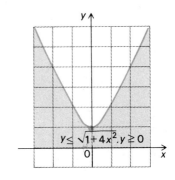

Figure 4.52

Example 5   Graph $y \leq \sqrt{1 + 4x^2}$, $y \geq 0$.

Squaring both sides of $y = \sqrt{1 + 4x^2}$ gives

$$y^2 = 1 + 4x^2$$

or

$$y^2 - 4x^2 = 1,$$

which is a hyperbola with y-intercepts 1 and -1. Since $\sqrt{1 + 4x^2}$ is always non-negative, we have only half a hyperbola, as shown in Figure 4.52.

Here we have $y \leq \sqrt{1 + 4x^2}$, so the solution is made up of points below the graph of $y = \sqrt{1 + 4x^2}$. However, we also have the restriction $y \geq 0$, so the solution is made up of only those points on or above the x-axis. The final graph is shown in Figure 4.52.

Example 6   Graph $16x^2 + y^2 \leq 16$.

This inequality has as its boundary the ellipse $16x^2 + y^2 = 16$, graphed in Figure 4.53. We cannot easily solve $16x^2 + y^2 = 16$ for y. To decide which region of the graph is part of the solution, we need an alternate method. For this alternate method, choose any point off the ellipse, such as $(0, 0)$. By substituting 0 for x and 0 for y in the inequality $16x^2 + y^2 \leq 16$, we get

$$16 \cdot 0^2 + 0^2 \leq 16$$
$$0 \leq 16,$$

a true statement. Thus, the solution includes the region containing $(0, 0)$, which is the region inside the ellipse. The final result is made up of this region and the boundary ellipse, as shown in Figure 4.53.   █

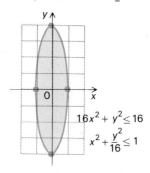

$16x^2 + y^2 \leq 16$

$x^2 + \dfrac{y^2}{16} \leq 1$

Figure 4.53

4.6 Exercises   *Graph each of the following.*

1. $y \leq -2$
2. $x + 2y \leq 6$
3. $x - y \geq 2$
4. $2x + 3y \geq 4$
5. $4y - 3x < 5$
6. $5x \leq 4y - 2$
7. $2x > 3 - 4y$
8. $y \leq |x|$
9. $y \geq |x + 2|$
10. $x > |y - 3|$
11. $x < |y + 1|$

12. $y < 3x^2 + 2$
13. $y \leq x^2 - 4$
14. $y > (x - 1)^2 + 2$
15. $y > 2(x + 3)^2 - 1$
16. $x^2 + (y + 3)^2 \leq 16$
17. $(x - 4)^2 + (y + 3)^2 \leq 9$
18. $4x^2 \leq 4 - y^2$
19. $x^2 + 9y^2 > 9$
20. $9x^2 - 16y^2 > 144$
21. $4x^2 \leq 36 + 9y^2$

Graph the intersection.

22. $2x + y > 5$ and $y \geq 0$
23. $3x + 2y \geq 6$ and $y \leq 2$
24. $4x + 3y \leq 6$ and $x \leq -2$
25. $x + 2y < 4$ and $3x - y > 5$

26. $4x + 1 < 2y$ and $-x > y - 3$
27. $3x - 4y > 6$ and $2x + 3y > 4$
28. $y \leq \sqrt{x + 3}$, $y \geq 0$
29. $x \leq \sqrt{1 - y}$, $x \geq 0$

30. $y \leq \sqrt{49 - x^2}, \ y \geq 0$

31. $x > \sqrt{16 - y^2}, \ x \geq 0$

32. $\dfrac{x}{6} < \sqrt{1 - \dfrac{y^2}{121}}, \ x \geq 0$

33. $\dfrac{y}{4} \leq \sqrt{1 + \dfrac{x^2}{25}}, \ y \geq 0$

34. $x^2 + y^2 \leq 49$ and $x^2 + y^2 \geq 36$

35. $x^2 + 4y^2 \geq 16$ and $4x^2 + y^2 \leq 36$

Chapter 4   Review Exercises

Find the slope for each of the following lines that has a slope.

1. through $(8, -2)$ and $(2, -2)$

2. through $(5, 6)$ and $(5, -2)$

3. a line parallel to $x - y = 2$

4. a line perpendicular to $3x - 5y = 7$

5. $9x - 4y = 2$

6. $11x + 2y = 3$

Write equations for each of the following lines.

7. through $(8, 7)$ and $\left(\dfrac{1}{2}, -2\right)$

8. through $(-3, 5)$ with slope 2

9. through $(1, -4)$ with no slope

10. through $(2, -1)$ and parallel to $3x - y = 1$

11. through $(0, 5)$ and perpendicular to $8x + 5y = 3$

12. through $(2, -10)$ and perpendicular to a line with no slope

Graph each of the following.

13. a line through $(2, 1)$ with slope $-\dfrac{3}{5}$

14. $y = \begin{cases} -4x + 2 & \text{if } x \leq 1 \\ 3x - 5 & \text{if } x > 1 \end{cases}$

Graph each of the following parabolas. Give the vertex and axis of each.

15. $y = x^2 - 4$

16. $y = 3(x + 1)^2 - 5$

17. $y = x^2 - 4x + 2$

18. $y = -3x^2 - 12x - 1$

Use parabolas to work each of the following problems.

19. Find two numbers whose sum is 11 and whose product is a maximum.

20. Find two numbers having a sum of 40 such that the sum of the square of one and twice the square of the other is maximum.

21. Find the rectangular region of maximum area that can be enclosed with 180 meters of fencing.

22. Find the rectangular region of maximum area that can be enclosed with 180 meters of fencing if no fencing is needed along one side of the region.

Graph each of the following.

23. $y = x^3 + 5$

24. $y = 1 - x^4$

25. $y = 2x^3 + 13x^2 + 15x$

26. $y = (4x - 3)(3x + 2)(x - 1)$

27. $y = x^2(2x + 1)(x - 2)$

28. $y = x(x - 1)(x + 2)(x - 3)$

29. $y = \dfrac{8}{x}$

30. $y = \dfrac{2}{3x - 1}$

31. $y = \dfrac{4x - 2}{3x + 1}$

32. $y = \dfrac{6x}{(x - 1)(x + 2)}$

33. $y = \dfrac{2x}{x^2 - 1}$

34. $y = \dfrac{8x + 3}{2x - 1}$

35. $x = y^2 - 2$

36. $x = y^2 - 4y$

37. $x = \sqrt{y - 2}$

38. $\dfrac{x^2}{4} + \dfrac{y^2}{36} = 1$

39. $25x^2 - 9y^2 = 225$

40. $\dfrac{y}{4} = -\sqrt{1 - \dfrac{x^2}{9}}$

41. $x = \sqrt{16 - y^2}$

42. $\dfrac{x^2}{25} - \dfrac{y^2}{9} = 1$

Find the center and radius of each of the following which are circles.

43. $x^2 - 4x + y^2 + 6y + 12 = 0$

44. $x^2 - 6x + y^2 - 10y + 30 = 0$

45. $x^2 + 7x + y^2 + 3y + 1 = 0$

46. $x^2 + 11x + y^2 - 5y + 46 = 0$

Graph each of the following inequalities.

47. $5x - 5y \le 20$

48. $25y^2 - 36x^2 > 900$

49. $|x - 4| \ge y$

50. $x^2 + y^2 \le 100$ and $25x^2 + 4y^2 \ge 100$

51. $x \le \sqrt{3y - y^2}$ and $x \ge 0$

52. $\dfrac{x^2}{9} + \dfrac{y^2}{4} \ge 1$ and $\dfrac{x^2}{16} + y^2 \le 1$

53. $y \le \sqrt{25 - x^2}$ and $x \ge 2$, $y \ge 0$

54. $|x - 1| \le 4$ and $y \le x^2$

55. The rental $R(x)$ on a roto-tiller is $5 plus $1 per hour or part of an hour. Find the cost to rent a roto-tiller for (a) 2 hours, (b) 5 hours, (c) $3\frac{1}{2}$ hours. (d) Graph R. (e) Is R a function?

56. Find the equation of the line through $(2, -5)$ which is perpendicular to $2y = 3x - 4$.

57. Find the equation of the line with slope 2/3 which goes through the center of the circle

$$(x - 4)^2 + (y + 2)^2 = 9.$$

58. Use slopes to show that the quadrilateral with vertices at $(-2, 2)$, $(4, 2)$, $(4, -1)$, and $(-2, 1)$ is a rectangle. (Hint: a rectangle is a quadrilateral with both pairs of opposite sides parallel and an adjacent pair of sides perpendicular.)

59. Find a value of k so that $5x - 3y = k$ goes through the point $(1, 4)$.

60. Find k so that the circle $x^2 - 4x + y^2 + 6y + k = 0$ goes through $(5, -3)$.

The following exercises are taken with permission from a standard calculus book.

61. An equilateral triangle is inscribed in the parabola $y = 4x^2$ with one vertex at the origin. Where are the other two?

62. An equilateral triangle is inscribed in the parabola $y = ax^2$ with one vertex at the origin. If its area is $3\sqrt{3}/4$, what is a?

63. A certain graph has an equation of the form

$$ay^2 + by = \frac{cx + d}{ex^2 + fx + g}$$

where a, b, c, d, e, f, and g are constants whose value in each case is either 0 or 1. From the following information about the graph, determine the constants and give a reason for your choice in each case.

Domain and range The curve does not exist for $x < -1$. All values of y are permissible.

Symmetry The curve is symmetric about the x-axis.

Intercepts No y-intercepts; x-intercept at $(-1, 0)$.

Asymptotes Both axes, no others.

Sketch the graph.

64. A point on the circle $x^2 + y^2 = 9$ has the property that its distance from the origin is equal to the slope of the line joining it to the origin. What is the point?

Find the equations of the circles with the given centers and tangent to the given circles.

65. $(6, 7)$, $(x + 2)^2 + (y - 1)^2 = 9$

66. $(-1, -3)$, $(x - 4)^2 + (y - 9)^2 = 16$

Exercises 61, 62, 64, 65, 66: Reproduced from *Calculus*, by Leonard Gillman and Robert H. McDowell, 2nd Edition, by permission of W. W. Norton & Company, Inc. Copyright © 1978, 1973 by W. W. Norton & Company, Inc. Exercise 63: George B. Thomas, Jr./Ross L. Finney, *Calculus and Analytic Geometry*, 5/E, © 1979, Addison-Wesley, Reading, Massachusetts. (P. 435.) Reprinted with permission.

Chapter 5

Exponential and
Logarithmic Functions

In this chapter, we study two kinds of functions which are quite different from those we have studied before. Exponential functions (studied in the first section) occur in many applications of mathematics, particularly those involving growth and decay of populations. Other applications, such as numerical calculations, depend on logarithmic functions, which we study later in the chapter. We shall see that these two types of functions are inverses of each other.

5.1 Exponential Functions

We know that if $a > 0$, we can define the symbol a^m for any rational value of m. In this section, we want to extend the definition of a^m to include all real, and not just rational, values of the exponent m. For example, what is meant by $2^{\sqrt{3}}$? The exponent, $\sqrt{3}$, can be approximated more and more closely by the numbers 1.7, 1.73, 1.732, and so on. Thus, it seems reasonable that $2^{\sqrt{3}}$ should be approximated more and more closely by the numbers $2^{1.7}$, $2^{1.73}$, $2^{1.732}$, and so on. In fact, this is exactly how $2^{\sqrt{3}}$ is defined (in a more advanced course).

We shall assume that the meaning given to real exponents is such that all our rules and theorems for exponents are valid for real number exponents as well as rational ones. In addition to the usual rules for exponents, we shall need the results of Theorem 5.1, which are stated without proof.

Theorem 5.1 For $a > 0$, $a \neq 1$, and any real number x,

(a) a^x is a unique real number.

(b) $a^b = a^c$ if and only if $b = c$.

(c) If $a > 1$ and $m < n$, then $a^m < a^n$.

(d) If $0 < a < 1$, and $m < n$, then $a^m > a^n$.

Part (a) of the theorem requires $a > 0$ so that a^x is always defined. For example, $(-6)^x$ is not a real number if $x = 1/2$. For part (b) to hold, a must not equal 1 since $1^4 = 1^5$, even though $4 \neq 5$. Parts (c) and (d) are illustrated by the graphs of Figure 5.1.

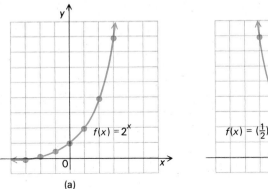

(a)   (b)

Figure 5.1

As we have said, the exponential a^x satisfies all the properties for exponents from Chapter 1. We can now define a function, $y = a^x$, whose domain is the set of all real numbers (and not just the rationals):

$$y = a^x, \qquad \text{where } a > 0 \text{ and } a \neq 1,$$

is an **exponential function with base** a.

Example 1   If $f(x) = 2^x$, find each of the following.

(a) $f(-1)$

Replace x with -1.

$$f(-1) = 2^{-1} = \frac{1}{2}$$

(b) $f(3) = 2^3 = 8$

(c) $f(5/2) = 2^{5/2} = (2^5)^{1/2} = 32^{1/2} = \sqrt{32} = 4\sqrt{2}.$ ▌

Figure 5.1(a) shows the graph of the exponential function $f(x) = 2^x$; the base of this exponential function is 2. This graph was found by obtaining a number of ordered pairs satisfying the function and then drawing a smooth curve through them. The domain of the function is the set of all real numbers, and the range is the set of all positive numbers. The function is increasing on its entire domain, and is thus a one-to-one function. The x-axis is a horizontal asymptote.

In Figure 5.1(b), the graph of $f(x) = (1/2)^x$ was obtained in a similar way. This graph is decreasing on its entire domain. Note that the graphs of $f(x) = 2^x$ and $f(x) = (1/2)^x$ are mirror images of each other with respect to the y-axis. This is because $\left(\dfrac{1}{2}\right)^x = (2^{-1})^x = 2^{-x}$. In general, $f(x) = a^x$ is increasing if $a > 1$, and decreasing if $0 < a < 1$.

Example 2   Graph $y = 2^{-x^2}$.

Since $y = 2^{-x^2} = 1/(2^{x^2})$, we have $0 < y \leq 1$ for all values of x. By plotting some typical points, such as $(-2, 1/16)$, $(-1, 1/2)$, $(0, 1)$, $(1, 1/2)$, and $(2, 1/16)$, and drawing a smooth curve through them, we get the graph of Figure 5.2. This graph is symmetric with respect to the y-axis. ▌

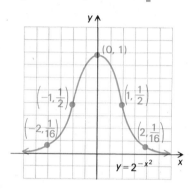

Figure 5.2

We can use the results of Theorem 5.1 to help solve equations, as shown by the next example.

Example 3   Solve $\left(\dfrac{1}{3}\right)^x = 81$.

First, write $1/3$ as 3^{-1}, so that $(1/3)^x = (3^{-1})^x = 3^{-x}$. Since $81 = 3^4$, we have

$$\left(\frac{1}{3}\right)^x = 81$$

$$3^{-x} = 3^4$$

$$-x = 4 \qquad \text{Theorem 5.1(b)}$$

$$x = -4 \quad ▌$$

(In Section 5.4 we discuss a method for solving equations of this type where this approach is not possible.)

Example 4   Find y if $y = 64^{-1/2}$.

Use the definitions of negative and rational exponents.

$$y = 64^{-1/2} = \frac{1}{64^{1/2}} = \frac{1}{\sqrt{64}} = \frac{1}{8} \quad ▌$$

Example 5   If $81 = b^{4/3}$, find b.

To solve for b, we need an exponent of 1 on b. Therefore, we take the 3/4 power on both sides of the equation.

$$81 = b^{4/3}$$

$$81^{3/4} = (b^{4/3})^{3/4}$$

$$(\sqrt[4]{81})^3 = b^1$$

$$3^3 = b$$

$$27 = b \quad ▌$$

Exponential functions have many practical applications. Frequently, these applications require the irrational number e as the base of the exponential function. It is shown in more advanced courses that, to seven places of accuracy,

$$e = 2.7182818.$$

In Figure 5.3, the functions $y = 2^x$, $y = e^x$, and $y = 3^x$ are graphed for comparison. The graph of $y = e^x$ can be found using a calculator or values from Table 3 in this book.

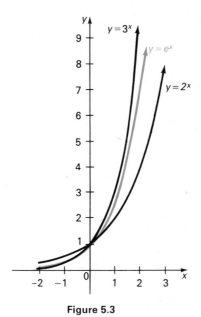

Figure 5.3

It can be shown that in many situations involving growth or decay of a population, the amount or number present at time t can be closely approximated by a function of the form

$$y = y_o e^{kt},$$

where y_o is the amount or number present at time $t = 0$ and k is a constant. (In other words, once the numbers y_o and k have been determined, population is a function of time.)

Example 6   Suppose the population of a midwestern city is

$$P(t) = 10{,}000e^{.04t},$$

where t represents time measured in years. The population at time $t = 0$ is

$$P(0) = 10{,}000e^{.04(0)}$$
$$= 10{,}000e^0$$
$$= 10{,}000(1)$$
$$= 10{,}000.$$

Thus, the population of the city is 10,000 at time $t = 0$, written $P_0 = 10,000$. The population of the city at year $t = 5$ is

$$P(5) = 10,000e^{.04(5)}$$
$$= 10,000e^{.2}$$

The number $e^{.2}$ can be found in Table 3 or by using a suitable calculator. By either of these methods, $e^{.2} \approx 1.22140$, so that

$$P(5) \approx 10,000(1.22140) = 12,214.$$

Thus, in 5 years the population of the city will be about 12,200 people. ▮

5.1 Exercises

1. Graph each of the following functions. Compare the graphs to that of $y = 2^x$.
   (a) $y = 2^x + 1$
   (b) $y = 2^x - 4$
   (c) $y = 2^{x+1}$
   (d) $y = 2^{x-4}$

2. Graph each of the following. Compare the graphs to that of $y = 3^{-x}$.
   (a) $y = 3^{-x} - 2$
   (b) $y = 3^{-x} + 4$
   (c) $y = 3^{-x-2}$
   (d) $y = 3^{-x+4}$

Graph each of the following functions.

3. $y = 10^{-x}$

4. $y = 10^x$

5. $y = e^{-x}$

6. $y = e^{2x}$

7. $y = 2^{|x|}$

8. $y = 2^{-|x|}$

9. $y = 2^x + 2^{-x}$

10. $y = \left(\frac{1}{2}\right)^x + \left(\frac{1}{2}\right)^{-x}$

⊙ *Graph each of the following.*

11. $y = \dfrac{e^x + e^{-x}}{2}$

12. $y = \dfrac{e^x - e^{-x}}{2}$

13. $y = x \cdot e^x$

14. $y = (1 - x)e^x$

Solve each of the following equations.

15. $3^x = 27$

16. $2^x = 1/8$

17. $4^x = 2$

18. $125^x = 5$

19. $(1/2)^x = 2$

20. $(2/3)^x = 9/4$

21. $2^{3-x} = 8$

22. $5^{2x+1} = 25$

23. $y = 2^3$

24. $y = 3^{-2}$

25. $y = 25^{1/2}$

26. $y = (1/27)^{1/3}$

27. $100 = b^2$

28. $125 = b^3$

29. $1/27 = b^{-3}$

30. $1/81 = b^{-4}$

31. $4 = b^{2/3}$

32. $32 = b^{5/2}$

33. Suppose the domain of $y = 2^x$ is restricted to only rational values of x (which are the only values discussed prior to this section). Describe in words the resulting graph.

34. For $a > 1$, how does the graph of a^x change as a increases? What if $0 < a < 1$?

Suppose the population of a city is

$$P(t) = 1,000,000e^{.02t},$$

where t represents time measured in years. Find each of the following values.

35. P_0 **36.** $P(2)$ **37.** $P(4)$ **38.** $P(10)$

39. Graph $P(t)$.

Suppose the quantity in grams of a radioactive substance present at time t is

$$Q(t) = 500e^{-.05t},$$

where t is measured in days. Find the quantity present at each of the following times.

40. $t = 0$. **41.** $t = 4$ **42.** $t = 8$ **43.** $t = 20$

44. Graph $Q(t)$.

It can be shown that P dollars compounded continuously (every instant) at i% annually, would amount to

$$A = Pe^{ni}$$

at the end of n years. How much would $20,000 amount to at 8% compounded continuously for the following number of years?

45. 1 year **46.** 5 years

⊙ *If P dollars is deposited into an account paying i% interest compounded m times a year, with the money left on deposit for n years, the account will end up with*

$$A = P\left(1 + \frac{i}{m}\right)^{nm}$$

dollars. Find the final amount on deposit for each of the following.

47. $4292 at 6% compounded annually for 10 years

48. $965.43 at 9% compounded annually for 15 years

49. $10,765 at 11% compounded semiannually for 7 years

50. $1593.24 at $10\frac{1}{2}$% compounded quarterly for 14 years

51. $68,922 at 10% compounded daily (365 days) for 4 years

52. $2964.58 at $11\frac{1}{4}$% compounded daily for 9 years

⊙ *Escherichia coli is a strain of bacteria that occurs naturally in many different situations. Under certain conditions, the number of these bacteria present in a colony is given by*

$$E(t) = E_0 \cdot 2^{t/30},$$

where E(t) is the number of bacteria present t minutes after the beginning of an experiment, and E_0 is the number present when $t = 0$. Let $E_0 = 2,400,000$, and find the number of bacteria at the following times.

53. $t = 5$ **54.** $t = 10$ **55.** $t = 60$ **56.** $t = 120$

◉ *The higher a student's grade-point average, the fewer applications that the student need send to medical schools (other things being equal). Using information given in a guide-book for prospective medical students, we constructed the function $y = 540e^{-1.3x}$ for the number of applications a student should send out. Here y is the number of applications for a student whose grade point average is x. The domain of x is $2.0 \le x \le 4.0$. Find the number of applications that should be sent out by students having a grade point average of*

57. 2.0   **58.** 3.0   **59.** 3.5   **60.** 3.9

Let $f(x) = a^x$ be an exponential function of base a.

61. Is f odd, even, or neither?

62. Prove that $f(m + n) = f(m) \cdot f(n)$ for any real numbers m and n.

◉ *In calculus, it is shown that*

$$e^x = 1 + x + \frac{x^2}{2 \cdot 1} + \frac{x^3}{3 \cdot 2 \cdot 1} + \frac{x^4}{4 \cdot 3 \cdot 2 \cdot 1} + \frac{x^5}{5 \cdot 4 \cdot 3 \cdot 2 \cdot 1} + \cdots.$$

63. Use the terms shown here and replace x with 1 to approximate $e^1 = e$ to three decimal places.

64. Use the terms shown here and replace x with $-.05$ to approximate $e^{-.05}$ to four decimal places.

5.2 Logarithmic Functions

In the previous section we discussed exponential functions of the form $y = a^x$, for all $a > 0$, $a \ne 1$. Since these functions are one-to-one (why?), they have inverse functions. We look at these inverse functions in this section.

The inverse of $y = a^x$ is written $y = \log_a x$; that is, for all real numbers y, all positive numbers a, $a \ne 1$,

$$y = \log_a x \quad \text{if and only if} \quad x = a^y.$$

Log is an abbreviation for "logarithm." Read $\log_a x$ as "the logarithm of x to the base a." A **logarithmic function** is a function of the form $y = \log_a x$, where $a > 0$, $a \ne 1$, $x > 0$.

Example 1   In the chart below we show several pairs of equivalent statements. The same statement is written in both exponential and logarithmic forms.

Exponential form	Logarithmic form
$2^3 = 8$	$\log_2 8 = 3$
$(1/2)^{-4} = 16$	$\log_{1/2} 16 = -4$
$10^5 = 100,000$	$\log_{10} 100,000 = 5$
$3^{-4} = 1/81$	$\log_3 (1/81) = -4$
$5^1 = 5$	$\log_5 5 = 1$
$(3/4)^0 = 1$	$\log_{3/4} 1 = 0$

In general, since $b^1 = b$ and $b^0 = 1$, for all positive b,

$$\log_b b = 1 \quad \text{and} \quad \log_b 1 = 0.$$

Exponential and logarithmic functions are inverses of each other. Since the domain of an exponential function is the set of all real numbers, the range of a logarithmic function will also be the set of all real numbers. In the same way, both the range of an exponential function and the domain of a logarithmic function are the set of all positive real numbers. Thus, we can find logarithms for positive numbers only.

In Figure 5.4(a), the graph of $y = 2^x$ is shown as a solid line. To get the graph of its inverse, reflect $y = 2^x$ about the 45° line $y = x$. The graph of the inverse, $y = \log_2 x$, is shown as a dashed line. As the graph shows, $y = \log_2 x$ is increasing for all its domain, is one-to-one, and has the y-axis as a vertical asymptote.

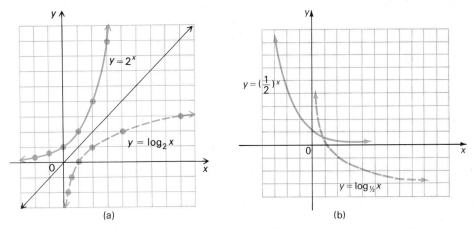

(a)   (b)

Figure 5.4

The graph of $y = (1/2)^x$ is shown as a solid line in Figure 5.4(b). Its inverse, $y = \log_{1/2} x$, shown dashed, is found by reflecting $y = (1/2)^x$ about the line $y = x$. The function $y = \log_{1/2} x$ is decreasing for all its domain, is one-to-one, and also has the y-axis for a vertical asymptote.

Example 2 Graph $y = \log_3 |x|$.

There are two ways to graph this function: we can choose values of x and find the corresponding values of y, as shown in the table below, or we can use the definition of logarithm to replace $y = \log_3 |x|$ with $|x| = 3^y$. In either case, we get the graph shown in Figure 5.5.

x	-3	-1	$-1/3$	$1/3$	1	3
y	1	0	-1	-1	0	1

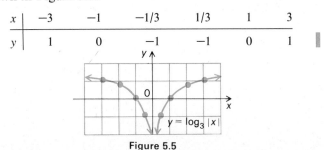

Figure 5.5

Example 3 Solve each of the following equations.

(a) $\log_x \dfrac{8}{27} = 3$

First, write the expression in exponential form.

$$x^3 = \dfrac{8}{27}$$

$$x^3 = \left(\dfrac{2}{3}\right)^3$$

$$x = \dfrac{2}{3} \qquad \text{Theorem 5.1(b)}$$

(b) $\log_4 x = \dfrac{5}{2}$

In exponential form, the statement becomes

$$4^{5/2} = x$$

$$(4^{1/2})^5 = x$$

$$2^5 = x$$

$$32 = x \qquad \blacksquare$$

Logarithms were originally important as an aid for numerical calculations, but the availability of inexpensive calculators has diminished the need for this application of logarithms. Yet the principles behind the use of logarithms for calculations are important and are based on the properties discussed in the next theorem.

Theorem 5.2 If x and y are any positive real numbers, r is any real number, and a is any positive real number, $a \neq 1$, then

(a) $\log_a xy = \log_a x + \log_a y$

(b) $\log_a \dfrac{x}{y} = \log_a x - \log_a y$

(c) $\log_a x^r = r \cdot \log_a x$

(d) $\log_a \sqrt[r]{x} = \dfrac{1}{r} \cdot \log_a x$

Example 4 Using the results of Theorem 5.2,

(a) $\log_6 7 \cdot 9 = \log_6 7 + \log_6 9$

(b) $\log_9 \dfrac{15}{7} = \log_9 15 - \log_9 7$

(c) $\log_5 \sqrt{8} = \log_5 8^{1/2} = \dfrac{1}{2} \log_5 8$

(d) $\log_a \dfrac{mnq}{p^2} = \log_a m + \log_a n + \log_a q - 2 \log_a p$

(e) $\log_a \sqrt[3]{m^2} = \dfrac{2}{3} \log_a m. \qquad \blacksquare$

Example 5   Write $2 \log_a m - 3 \log_a n$ as a single logarithm.

By Theorem 5.2,

$$2 \log_a m - 3 \log_a n = \log_a m^2 - \log_a n^3$$

$$= \log_a \frac{m^2}{n^3}. \quad \blacksquare$$

To prove part (a) of Theorem 5.2, let $m = \log_a x$ and $n = \log_a y$. Then, by the definition of logarithm,

$$a^m = x \quad \text{and} \quad a^n = y.$$

Hence,

$$a^m \cdot a^n = xy.$$

By a property of exponents,

$$a^{m+n} = xy.$$

Now use the definition of logarithm to write

$$\log_a xy = m + n.$$

Since $m = \log_a x$ and $n = \log_a y$,

$$\log_a xy = \log_a x + \log_a y.$$

To prove part (b) of the theorem, use m and n as defined above. Then

$$\frac{a^m}{a^n} = \frac{x}{y}.$$

Since

$$\frac{a^m}{a^n} = a^{m-n},$$

then

$$a^{m-n} = \frac{x}{y}.$$

By the definition of logarithms,

$$\log_a \frac{x}{y} = m - n,$$

or

$$\log_a \frac{x}{y} = \log_a x - \log_a y.$$

For part (c),

$$(a^m)^r = x^r \quad \text{or} \quad a^{mr} = x^r.$$

Again using the definition of logarithms,

$$\log_a x^r = mr,$$

or

$$\log_a x^r = r \cdot \log_a x.$$

Finally, part (d) is proved by using part (c) and replacing both r's with $1/r$.

Example 6 Assume $\log_{10} 2 = .3010$. Find the base 10 logarithms of 4 and 5.

Using the results of Theorem 5.2,

$$\log_{10} 4 = \log_{10} 2^2 = 2 \log_{10} 2 = 2(.3010) = .6020$$

$$\log_{10} 5 = \log_{10} \frac{10}{2} = \log_{10} 10 - \log_{10} 2 = 1 - .3010 = .6990. \quad \blacksquare$$

As mentioned above, historically, one of the main applications of logarithms has been as an aid to numerical calculation. Since our number system is base 10, logarithms to base 10 are most convenient for numerical calculations. Such logarithms are called **common logarithms.** Common logarithms are discussed in the next section.

Common logarithms have few applications other than numerical calculation. In most other practical applications of logarithms, the number $e \approx 2.7182818$ is used as base. Logarithms to base e are called **natural logarithms,** written in the form **ln x.**

A table of natural logarithms is given in Table 4. From this table we find, for example, that

$$\ln 55 = 4.0073$$
$$\ln 1.9 = 0.6419$$
$$\ln 0.4 = -.9163.$$

Example 7 Use Table 4 to find the following logarithms.

(a) $\ln 83$

Table 4 does not give $\ln 83$. However, we can use the properties of logarithms in Theorem 5.2 to write

$$\begin{aligned}
\ln 83 &= \ln(8.3 \times 10) \\
&= \ln 8.3 + \ln 10 \\
&\approx 2.1163 + 2.3026 \\
&= 4.4189
\end{aligned}$$

(b) $\ln 36$

Since 36 is not listed in Table 4, use the properties of logarithms.

$$\begin{aligned}
\ln 36 &= \ln 6^2 \\
&= 2 \cdot \ln 6 \\
&\approx 2(1.7918) \\
&= 3.5836. \quad \blacksquare
\end{aligned}$$

5.2 Exercises *Change each of the following to logarithmic form.*

1. $3^4 = 81$

2. $2^5 = 32$

3. $(1/2)^{-4} = 16$

4. $(2/3)^{-3} = 27/8$

5. $10^{-4} = .0001$

6. $(1/100)^{-2} = 10,000$

Change each of the following to exponential form.

7. $\log_6 36 = 2$

8. $\log_5 5 = 1$

9. $\log_{\sqrt 3} 81 = 8$

10. $\log_4 (1/64) = -3$

11. $\log_m k = n$

12. $\log_2 r = y$

Solve each of the following equations.

13. $\log_x 25 = -2$

14. $\log_x (1/16) = -2$

15. $\log_{36} x = 1/2$

16. $\log_9 x = 2$

17. $\log_9 27 = x$

18. $\log_8 4 = x$

19. $\log_x 8 = 3/4$

20. $\log_x 7 = 1/2$

Write each of the following as a sum, difference, or product of logarithms. Simplify the result if possible.

21. $\log_3 (2/5)$

22. $\log_4 (6/7)$

23. $\log_2 \dfrac{6x}{y}$

24. $\log_3 \dfrac{4p}{q}$

25. $\log_5 \dfrac{5\sqrt 7}{3}$

26. $\log_2 \dfrac{2\sqrt 3}{5}$

27. $\log_4 (2x + 4y)$

28. $\log_6 (7m - 3q)$

Write each of the following expressions as a single logarithm.

29. $\log_a x + \log_a y - \log_a m$

30. $(\log_b k - \log_b m) - \log_b a$

31. $2 \log_m a - 3 \log_m b^2$

32. $\dfrac{1}{2} \log_y p^3 q^4 - \dfrac{2}{3} \log_y p^4 q^3$

33. $-\dfrac{3}{4} \log_x a^6 b^8 + \dfrac{2}{3} \log_x a^9 b^3$

34. $\log_a (pq^2) + 2 \log_a (p/q)$

Find each of the following natural logarithms. Use Table 4 and the properties of logarithms as necessary.

35. $\ln 20$

36. $\ln 35$

37. $\ln 800$

38. $\ln 920$

39. $\ln 1440$

40. $\ln 490$

Suppose $\ln .01 = -4.6052$ *and* $\ln .001 = -6.9078$. *Use Table 4 and the properties of logarithms to find each of the following.*

41. $\ln .08$

42. $\ln .04$

43. $\ln .20$

44. $\ln .30$

45. $\ln .007$

46. $\ln .009$

47. Graph each of the following. Compare the graphs to that of $y = \log_2 x$.

    (a) $y = (\log_2 x) + 3$ (b) $y = \log_2 (x + 3)$ (c) $y = |\log_2 (x + 3)|$

48. Graph each of the following. Compare the graphs to that of $y = \log_{1/2} x$.

    (a) $y = (\log_{1/2} x) - 2$ (b) $y = \log_{1/2} (x - 2)$ (c) $y = |\log_{1/2} (x - 2)|$

Graph each of the following functions.

49. $y = \log_3 x$

50. $y = \log_{10} x$

51. $y = \log_{1/2} (-x + 1)$

52. $y = \log_{1/3} (-x + 3)$

53. $y = \log_2 x^2$

54. $y = \log_3 (x - 1)$

⊙ 55. $y = x \cdot \ln x$

56. $y = x^2 \cdot \ln x$

Given $\log_{10} 2 = .3010$ *and* $\log_{10} 3 = .4771$, *find each of the following without using calculators or tables.*

57. $\log_{10} 6$

58. $\log_{10} 12$

59. $\log_{10} 9$

60. $\log_{10} 20$

61. $\log_{10} 30$

62. $\log_{10} 36$

63. The population of an animal species that is introduced in a certain area may grow rapidly at first but then grows more slowly as time goes on. A logarithmic function can provide an excellent description of such growth. Suppose that the population of foxes, $F(t)$, in an area t months after the species is introduced into the area is

$$F(t) = 500 \ln (2t + 2).$$

Find the population of foxes at the following times:

(a) when they are first released into the area (that is, when $t = 0$); (b) after 3 months; (c) after 7 months; (d) after 15 months. (e) Graph F.

64. Use the definition of inverse function from Chapter 3 to show that $f(x) = a^x$ and $g(x) = \log_a x$ are inverses for $a > 0$, $a \neq 1$.

5.3 Common Logarithms

As we have said, base 10 logarithms are called common logarithms. For simplicity, $\log_{10} x$ is abbreviated as $\log x$. Some examples of common logarithms are:

$$\log 1000 = \log 10^3 = 3$$
$$\log 10 = \log 10^1 = 1$$
$$\log 1 = \log 10^0 = 0$$
$$\log .1 = \log 10^{-1} = -1$$
$$\log .001 = \log 10^{-3} = -3.$$

Though it can be shown that there is no rational number x such that $10^x = 6$ (and thus no rational number x such that $x = \log 6$), we can use a table of common logarithms or a calculator to find a decimal approximation for $\log 6$. From the excerpt of the logarithm table printed below, a decimal approximation of $\log 6$ is given by .7782, so that

$$\log 6 \approx .7782$$

(or, equivalently, $10^{.7782} \approx 6$). Since most logarithms are approximations, it is common to replace $\approx$ with $=$ and write

$$\log 6 = .7782.$$

Example 1 To find log 6.24, locate the first two significant digits, 62, in the left column of the table. Then find the third digit, 4, across the top. From the table,

$$\log 6.24 = .7952. \quad \blacksquare$$

Example 2 To find log 6240, use the properties of logarithms and scientific notation, as follows.

$$\log 6240 = \log (6.24 \times 10^3)$$
$$= \log 6.24 + \log 10^3$$

Find log 6.24 in the table, and use the definition of logarithm to see that $\log 10^3 = 3$. This gives

$$= .7952 + 3$$
$$= 3.7952. \quad \blacksquare$$

The decimal part of the logarithm, .7952 in Example 2, is called the **mantissa,** while the integer part, 3 here, is the **characteristic.** The mantissa must always be positive, and it can be found in the table; the characteristic may be any integer, positive, negative, or zero.

	0	1	2	3	4	5	6	7	8	9
5.7	.7559	.7566	.7574	.7582	.7589	.7597	.7604	.7612	.7619	.7627
5.8	.7634	.7642	.7649	.7657	.7664	.7672	.7679	.7686	.7694	.7701
5.9	.7709	.7716	.7723	.7731	.7738	.7745	.7752	.7760	.7767	.7774
6.0	.7782	.7789	.7796	.7803	.7810	.7818	.7825	.7832	.7839	.7846
6.1	.7853	.7860	.7868	.7875	.7882	.7889	.7896	.7903	.7910	.7917
6.2	.7924	.7931	.7938	.7945	.7952	.7959	.7966	.7973	.7980	.7987
6.3	.7993	.8000	.8007	.8014	.8021	.8028	.8035	.8041	.8048	.8055
6.4	.8062	.8069	.8075	.8082	.8089	.8096	.8102	.8109	.8116	.8122
6.5	.8129	.8136	.8142	.8149	.8156	.8162	.8169	.8176	.8182	.8189
6.6	.8195	.8202	.8209	.8215	.8222	.8228	.8235	.8241	.8248	.8254

Example 3 Find log .00587.

Use scientific notation:

$$\log .00587 = \log 5.87 \times 10^{-3}$$
$$= \log 5.87 + \log 10^{-3}$$
$$= .7686 + (-3)$$

There are now at least two ways to proceed. If we add .7686 and -3 we get

$$\log .00587 = -2.2314$$

This is the answer a calculator would give if we entered .00587 and pushed the correct keys for common logarithms. For pencil and paper calculations, this form is not the best since it is not clear what is the mantissa and what is the characteristic. For this reason, the characteristic of -3 is written as $-3 = 7 - 10$; thus,

$$\log .00587 = .7686 + (-3)$$
$$= .7686 + (7 - 10)$$
$$= 7.7686 - 10$$

Either -2.2314 or $.7686 - 3$ or $7.7686 - 10$ is equally correct — the best choice depends on your anticipated use of the logarithm. ▌

Example 4   Find each of the following.
   (a) $\log (2.73)^4$
Use a property of logarithms:

$$\log (2.73)^4 = 4 \cdot \log 2.73$$
$$= 4(.4362)$$
$$= 1.7448$$

   (b) $\log \sqrt[3]{.00762}$

We find that

$$\log \sqrt[3]{.00762} = \frac{1}{3} \log .00762$$

$$= \frac{1}{3}(7.8820 - 10)$$

This calculation can be simplified if we write the characteristic, -3, as $27 - 30$. Then we have

$$\log \sqrt[3]{.00762} = \frac{1}{3}(27.8820 - 30) = 9.2940 - 10.$$

Alternatively,

$$\log \sqrt[3]{.00762} = \frac{1}{3} \log .00762$$

$$= \frac{1}{3}(.8820 - 3)$$

$$= \frac{1}{3}(-2.1180)$$

$$= -.7060 \quad ▌$$

Sometimes we know the logarithm of a number and wish to find the number. We call the number the **antilogarithm**, abbreviated "antilog." For example, .756 is the antilogarithm of $9.8785 - 10$, since

$$\log .756 = 9.8785 - 10.$$

To find this result, look for .8785 in the body of the logarithm table. You should find 7.5 at the left and 6 at the top. Since the characteristic of 9.8785 − 10 is 9 − 10 = −1, the antilogarithm is

$$7.56 \times 10^{-1} = .756.$$

Example 5 Find each of the following antilogarithms.

(a) log x = 2.5340

Find .5340 in the body of the table; 3.4 is at the left and 2 is at the top. Thus,

$$\begin{aligned} \log x &= 2 + .5340 \\ &= \log 10^2 + \log 3.42 \qquad \text{(from Table 2)} \\ &= \log (3.42 \times 10^2) \\ &= \log 342 \end{aligned}$$

Since log x = log 342,

$$x = 342,$$

and 342 is the antilogarithm of 2.5340.

(b) log x = 7.7536 − 10

Table 3 shows that the antilogarithm of 7.7536 − 10 is

$$5.67 \times 10^{-3} = .00567$$

(c) log x = −4.0670

$$\begin{aligned} &= -4 + (-.0670) \\ &= -4 + (-1) + [1 + (-.0670)] \\ &= -5 + .9330 \\ \log x &= \log .0000857 \\ x &= .0000857 \quad \blacksquare \end{aligned}$$

We can now use Table 2 and the properties of logarithms to help with a numerical calculation.

Example 6 Calculate $(\sqrt[3]{42})(76.9)(.00283)$.

Use the properties of logarithms and Table 2.

$$\log (\sqrt[3]{42})(76.9)(.00283) = \frac{1}{3} \log 42 + \log 76.9 + \log .00283$$

$$= \frac{1}{3}(1.6232) + 1.8859 + (7.4518 - 10)$$

$$= .5411 + 1.8859 + (7.4518 - 10)$$

$$= 9.8788 - 10.$$

From the logarithm table, .756 is the antilogarithm of 9.8788 − 10, and so

$$(\sqrt[3]{42})(76.9)(.00283) \approx .756. \quad \blacksquare$$

Example 7   The cost in dollars, $C(x)$, of manufacturing x picture frames, where x is measured in thousands, is

$$C(x) = 5000 + 2000 \log (x + 1).$$

Find the cost of manufacturing 19,000 frames.

To find the cost of producing 19,000 frames, let $x = 19$. This gives

$$
\begin{aligned}
C(19) &= 5000 + 2000 \log (19 + 1) \\
&= 5000 + 2000 \log 20 \\
&= 5000 + 2000 \,(1.3010) \\
&= 7602.
\end{aligned}
$$

Thus, 19,000 frames cost a total of about $7600 to produce.   ▌

5.3 Exercises   *Find the characteristic of the logarithms of each of the following.*

1. 2,400,000
2. 875000
3. .00023

4. .098
5. .000042
6. .000000257

Find the logarithms of the following numbers.

7. 875
8. 3750
9. 12800
10. 653000
11. .000893
12. .00376
13. 68,200

14. 103,000
15. .000382
◉ 16. 1157
17. 42,967
18. 1.51172
19. .00809432
20. .0000439761

Find the antilogarithms of each of the following.

21. 1.5366
22. 2.9253
23. 8.8733 − 10

24. 9.2504 − 10
25. −3.4283
26. −4.2933

Use logarithms to find approximations to three significant digits for each of the following.

27. $\dfrac{(79.6)(4.83)(9.3)}{43.8}$

28. $\dfrac{(123)(7.892)(.436)}{2.81}$

29. $\dfrac{(21.3)^2}{(.86)^3}$

30. $\dfrac{(.893)^2}{(.624)^3}$

31. $(8.16)^{1/3}$

32. $\sqrt{276}$

33. $\dfrac{(7.06)^3}{(31.7)(\sqrt{1.09})}$

34. $\dfrac{(2.51)^2}{(\sqrt{1.52})(3.94)}$

35. $(115)^{1/2} + (35.2)^{2/3}$

36. $(778)^{1/3} + (159)^{3/4}$

37. $(10.2)^{1/2} + (3.58)^2$

38. $(8.63)^{1/3} + (42.5)^{1/4}$

Use logarithms to solve each of the following applications.

39. Philadelphia Chemicals, Inc., has to store a new gas it plans to produce. The pressure p (pounds per cubic foot) and volume v (cubic feet) of the gas are related by the formula

$$pv^{1.6} = 800.$$

What is p if $v = 7.6$ cubic feet?

40. The approximate period T (in seconds) of a simple pendulum of length L (in feet) is

$$T \approx 2\pi\sqrt{\frac{L}{32}}$$

Find the period of a pendulum of length $L = 26$ feet.

41. The number of years, n, since two independently evolving languages split off from a common ancestral language is approximated by

$$n \approx \frac{500 \log r}{\log .86},$$

where r is the proportion of words from the ancestral language common to both languages. Find n if (a) $r = .9$; (b) $r = .3$; (c) How many years have elapsed since the split if half of the words of the ancestral language are common to both languages?

42. Midwest Creations finds that its total sales, $T(x)$, from the distribution of x catalogs, measured in thousands, is approximated by $T(x) = 5000 \log (x + 1)$. Find the total sales resulting from the distribution of (a) 0 catalogs; (b) 5000 catalogs; (c) 24,000 catalogs; (d) 49,000 catalogs.

*In chemistry, the **pH** of a solution is defined as*

$$pH = -log\ [H_3O^+]$$

where $[H_3O^+]$ is the hydronium ion concentration in moles per liter. Find the pH of each of the following, whose hydronium ion concentration is given.

43. Grapefruit, 6.3×10^{-4}

44. Crackers, 3.9×10^{-9}

45. Limes, 1.6×10^{-2}

46. Sodium hydroxide (lye), 3.2×10^{-14}

Find $[H_3O^+]$ for each of the following, whose pH is given.

47. Soda pop, 2.7

48. Wine, 3.4

49. Beer, 4.8

50. Drinking water, 6.5

5.4   **Exponential and Logarithmic Equations**

In Section 5.1 we solved exponential equations such as $(1/3)^x = 81$ by writing both sides of the equation as a power of 3. However, we can't use that method to solve an equation such as $3^x = 5$ since we can't easily write 5 as a power of 3. Thus, we need another method; the method we use depends on the following theorem.

Theorem 5.3   If $x > 0$, $y > 0$, $b > 0$, and $b \neq 1$, then

$$x = y \qquad \text{if and only if} \qquad \log_b x = \log_b y.$$

Example 1   Solve the equation $7^x = 12$.

If we use Theorem 5.3 and take base 10 logarithms of both sides, we get

$$\log 7^x = \log 12$$
$$x \cdot \log 7 = \log 12$$
$$x = \frac{\log 12}{\log 7}$$

If desired, we can get a decimal approximation for x. First use Table 2 or a calculator to get

$$x = \frac{\log 12}{\log 7} = \frac{1.0792}{.8451}.$$

To do the actual division of 1.0792 and .8451, use a calculator:

$$x = 1.277. \quad \blacksquare$$

Example 2   Solve $3^{2x-1} = 4^{x+2}$

Take base 10 logarithms on both sides.

$$\log 3^{2x-1} = \log 4^{x+2}$$

or

$$(2x - 1) \log 3 = (x + 2) \log 4,$$

leads to

$$2x \log 3 - \log 3 = x \log 4 + 2 \log 4$$

or

$$2x \log 3 - x \log 4 = 2 \log 4 + \log 3.$$

Factor out x on the left to get

$$x(2 \log 3 - \log 4) = 2 \log 4 + \log 3$$

or

$$x = \frac{2 \log 4 + \log 3}{2 \log 3 - \log 4}.$$

Using the properties of logarithms, this can be expressed as

$$x = \frac{\log 16 + \log 3}{\log 9 - \log 4}$$

or finally,
$$x = \frac{\log 48}{\log \dfrac{9}{4}}.$$

This quotient could be approximated by a decimal if desired:
$$x = \frac{\log 48}{\log 2.25} = \frac{1.6812}{.3522} = 4.773. \quad \blacksquare$$

Example 3 Solve $\log (x + 4) - \log (x + 2) = \log x$.
Use a property of logarithms and Theorem 5.3.

$$\log \frac{x + 4}{x + 2} = \log x$$

$$\frac{x + 4}{x + 2} = x$$

$$x + 4 = x(x + 2)$$

$$x + 4 = x^2 + 2x$$

$$x^2 + x - 4 = 0$$

By the quadratic formula,
$$x = \frac{-1 \pm \sqrt{1 + 16}}{2}$$

$$x = \frac{-1 + \sqrt{17}}{2} \quad \text{or} \quad x = \frac{-1 - \sqrt{17}}{2}.$$

We cannot evaluate $\log x$ for
$$x = \frac{-1 - \sqrt{17}}{2},$$

since this number is negative and hence not in the domain of $\log x$. Thus the only valid solution is the positive number
$$x = \frac{-1 + \sqrt{17}}{2}. \quad \blacksquare$$

Example 4 Solve $\log (3x + 2) + \log (x - 1) = 1$.
Since $1 = \log 10$,

$$\log (3x + 2)(x - 1) = \log 10$$

$$(3x + 2)(x - 1) = 10$$

$$3x^2 - x - 2 = 10$$

$$3x^2 - x - 12 = 0.$$

Now use the quadratic formula.

$$x = \frac{1 \pm \sqrt{1 + 144}}{6}$$

$$x = \frac{1 + \sqrt{145}}{6} \quad \text{or} \quad x = \frac{1 - \sqrt{145}}{6}.$$

If $x = (1 - \sqrt{145})/6$, then $x - 1 < 0$, and so log $(x - 1)$ does not exist. Hence, this proposed solution must be discarded and the only solution is

$$x = \frac{1 + \sqrt{145}}{6}.$$ ▌

Example 5 Suppose the function

$$P(t) = 10,000e^{.4t},$$

gives the population of a city at time t (in years). In how many years will the population double?

We want to find the value of t for which $P(t) = 20,000$. Thus,

$$20,000 = 10,000e^{.4t}$$
$$2 = e^{.4t}$$

To solve for t, take logarithms on both sides. Since the base is e, it is convenient to use base e or natural logarithms.

$$\ln 2 = \ln e^{.4t}$$
$$\ln 2 = .4t \ln e$$

We used Theorem 5.2(c) in the last step. Since $\ln e = 1$,

$$\ln 2 = .4t$$
$$t = \frac{\ln 2}{.4}.$$

Using Table 4 to find ln 2 and logarithms or a calculator to find the quotient to three-digit accuracy, we get $t \approx 1.73$. Thus, the population will double in about 1.73 years. ▌

Example 6 Solve the equation $y = \dfrac{1 - e^x}{1 - e^{-x}}$ for x.

Begin by multiplying both sides by $1 - e^{-x}$:

$$y(1 - e^{-x}) = 1 - e^x$$

or

$$y - ye^{-x} = 1 - e^x.$$

Get the equation equal to 0.

$$e^x + y - 1 - ye^{-x} = 0.$$

Multiply both sides by e^x.

$$e^{2x} + (y - 1)e^x - y = 0.$$

Rewrite this equation as

$$(e^x)^2 + (y - 1)e^x - y = 0,$$

an equation quadratic in e^x. We can solve this equation by using the quadratic formula with $a = 1$, $b = y - 1$, and $c = -y$.

$$e^x = \frac{-(y-1) \pm \sqrt{(y-1)^2 - 4(1)(-y)}}{2(1)}$$

$$= \frac{-(y-1) \pm \sqrt{y^2 - 2y + 1 + 4y}}{2}$$

$$= \frac{-(y-1) \pm \sqrt{y^2 + 2y + 1}}{2}$$

$$= \frac{-(y-1) \pm \sqrt{(y+1)^2}}{2}$$

$$e^x = \frac{-y + 1 \pm (y+1)}{2}$$

Use the + sign:

$$e^x = \frac{-y + 1 + y + 1}{2} = \frac{2}{2} = 1.$$

We cannot have $e^x = 1$ in the original equation since $e^x = 1$ forces $e^{-x} = 1$ also, giving a zero denominator.

Try the − sign:

$$e^x = \frac{-y + 1 - y - 1}{2} = \frac{-2y}{2} = -y.$$

If $e^x = -y$, then we may take natural logarithms to get

$$\ln e^x = \ln(-y)$$
$$x \cdot \ln e = \ln(-y)$$
$$x \cdot 1 = \ln(-y)$$
$$x = \ln(-y).$$

This result will be satisfied by all values of y less than 0.   ▮

5.4 Exercises   *Solve each of the following equations.*

1. $3^x = 6$

2. $4^x = 12$

3. $7^x = 8$

4. $13^x = 55$

5. $3^{x-1} = 4$

6. $5^{2-x} = 12$

7. $6^{2x-1} = 8$

8. $2^{3x-7} = 5$

9. $\left(1 + \dfrac{r}{2}\right)^5 = 9$

10. $\left(1 + \dfrac{n}{4}\right)^3 = 12$

11. $\log(x - 1) = 1$

12. $\log x^2 = 1$

13. $\log(x - 3) = 1 - \log x$

14. $\log(x - 6) = 2 - \log(x + 15)$

15. $\log (x + 2) = \log (x - 7) + 1$

16. $\log x - \log (x + 1) = \log 5$

17. $\log (x - 3) = 1 + \log (x + 1)$

18. $\log x + \log (3x - 13) = 1$

19. $\log \sqrt{2x^2 - 1} = 1/2$

20. $\log (\log x) = 1$

21. $\log x = \sqrt{\log x}$

22. $\log x^2 = (\log x)^2$

◉ *Find the solution of each of the following to three significant digits.*

23. $\log_x 7 = 2$

24. $\log_x 10 = 3$

25. $1.8^{x+4} = 9.31$

26. $3.7^{5x-1} = 5.88$

Solve the following equations for x. Use natural logarithms.

27. $y = \dfrac{1 + e^{-x}}{1 + e^x}$

28. $y = \dfrac{e^x}{1 - e^x}$

29. $y = \dfrac{e^x + e^{-x}}{2}$

30. $y = \dfrac{e^x - e^{-x}}{2}$

Solve each of the following equations for the indicated variables. Use logarithms to the appropriate bases.

31. $P = P_0 e^{kt/1000}$,   for t

32. $I = \dfrac{E}{R}(1 - e^{-Rt/2})$,   for t

33. $T = T_0 + (T_1 - T_0) \, 10^{-kt}$,   for t

34. $A = \dfrac{Pi}{1 - (1 + i)^{-n}}$,   for n

35. The amount of a radioactive specimen present at time t (measured in seconds) is $A(t) = 5000(10)^{-.02t}$, where $A(t)$ is measured in grams. Find the half-life of the specimen, that is, the time it will take for half the specimen to remain.

A large cloud of radioactive debris from a nuclear explosion has floated over the Pacific Northwest, contaminating much of the hay supply. Consequently, farmers in the area are concerned that the cows who eat this hay will give contaminated milk. (The tolerance level for radioactive iodine in milk is 0.) The percent of the initial amount of radioactive iodine still present in the hay after t days is approximated by $P(t) = 100 \, e^{-.1t}$, where t is time measured in days.

36. Some scientists feel that the hay is safe after the percent of radioactive iodine has declined to 10% of the original amount. Find the number of days before the hay can be used.

37. Other scientists believe that the hay is not safe until the level of radioactive iodine has declined to only 1% of the level. Find the number of days this would take.

38. Use the formula $A = Pe^{ni}$ for continuous compounding of interest to find the number of years it will take for $1000, compounded continuously at 5%, to double.

5.5 Change of Base

As mentioned earlier in this chapter, today natural logarithms have more practical applications than common logarithms. Table 4 gives the natural logarithms of many numbers, but we often need natural logarithms that cannot be found with this table. The following theorem can be used to convert common logarithms to natural logarithms, or, in fact, a logarithm from any acceptable base to any other acceptable base.

Theorem 5.4   If x is any positive number and if a and b are positive real numbers, $a \neq 1$, $b \neq 1$, then

$$\log_a x = \frac{\log_b x}{\log_b a}.$$

To prove this result, we can use the definition of logarithm to write $y = \log_a x$, as $x = a^y$ or $x = a^{\log_a x}$ (for positive x and positive a, $a \neq 1$). If we now take logarithms to base b of both sides of the last equation, we have

$$\log_b x = \log_b a^{\log_a x}$$

or $$\log_b x = (\log_a x)(\log_b a),$$

from which we obtain

$$\log_a x = \frac{\log_b x}{\log_b a}.$$

We can use this result to find the natural logarithm of a number. For example, to find $\ln 47.2$, let $x = 47.2$, $a = e$, and $b = 10$. Using these values, we have

$$\ln 47.2 = \log_e 47.2 = \frac{\log_{10} 47.2}{\log_{10} e}$$

$$\ln 47.2 = \frac{\log 47.2}{\log e}.$$

Since $e \approx 2.71828$, $\log e$ can be estimated to equal approximately .4343. Thus,

$$\ln 47.2 = \frac{\log 47.2}{.4343}.$$

Since $1/(.4343) \approx 2.3026$, this last statement becomes

$$\ln 47.2 = (2.3026)(\log 47.2)$$
$$= (2.3026)(1.6739)$$
$$= 3.8543.$$

Using this same principle, we can prove the next result.

Theorem 5.5   For all positive real numbers x,

$$\ln x = (2.3026) \log x.$$

Example 1 $\ln .427 = (2.3026)(\log .427)$
$$= (2.3026)(-1 + .6304)$$
$$= (2.3026)(-.3696)$$
$$\ln .427 = -.8510 \quad \blacksquare$$

Example 2   Find $\log_5 27$.

Theorem 5.4 can be used to find logarithms to any base. Here $a = 5$, $x = 27$. Use 10 for b:

$$\log_5 27 = \frac{\log_{10} 27}{\log_{10} 5} = \frac{1.4314}{.6990} = 2.05.$$

In the last step, the division can be done with a calculator.   ▮

Example 3   One measure of the diversity of the species in an ecological community is given by

$$H = -[P_1 \, \log_2 P_1 + P_2 \, \log_2 P_2 + \ldots + P_n \, \log_2 P_n],$$

where $P_1, P_2, \ldots, P_n$ are the proportion of a sample belonging to each of n species found in the sample. For example, in a community with two species, where there are 99 of one kind and 1 of the other, $P_1 = 99/100 = .99$ and $P_2 = 1/100 = .01$. Thus,

$$H = -[.99 \, \log_2 .99 + .01 \, \log_2 .01].$$

To find $\log_2 .99$ and $\log_2 .01$, use Theorem 5.4:

$$\log_2 .99 = \frac{\log .99}{\log 2} = \frac{-.0044}{.3010} = -.0146$$

$$\log_2 .01 = \frac{\log .01}{\log 2} = \frac{-2.0000}{.3010} = -6.6445.$$

Therefore,

$$H = -[.99(-.0146) + .01(-6.6445)] = .081.   ▮$$

Example 4   Suppose the amount, y, of a certain radioactive substance present at a time t is given by

$$y = y_0 e^{-.1t},$$

where y_0 is the amount present initially and t is measured in days. Find the half-life of the substance. (The **half-life** of a radioactive substance is the time it takes for exactly half the sample to decay.)

We want to know the time t that must elapse for y to be reduced to a value equal to $\frac{1}{2}y_0$. This is, we want to solve the equation

$$\frac{1}{2}y_0 = y_0 e^{-.1t}.$$

Here we have $\frac{1}{2} = e^{-.1t}$, and if we now take natural logs of both sides, we get

$$\ln \frac{1}{2} = \ln e^{-.1t}$$

$$\ln \frac{1}{2} = -.1t(\ln e).$$

Since ln $e = 1$, we have

$$\ln \frac{1}{2} = -.1t$$

$$t = \frac{-\ln \frac{1}{2}}{.1}$$

From the table we have $\ln \frac{1}{2} = \ln .5 = 9.3069 - 10 = -.6931$. Then

$$t \approx 6.9 \text{ days.} \quad \blacksquare$$

5.5 Exercises   *Find each of the following to the nearest hundredth.*

1. ln 125
2. ln 63.1
3. ln .98
4. ln 1.53

5. $\log_5 10$
6. $\log_9 12$
7. $\log_{15} 5$
8. $\log_6 8$

9. $\log_{1/2} 3$
10. $\log_{12} 62$
11. $\log_{100} 83$
12. $\log_{200} 375$

13. Suppose a sample of a small community shows two species with 50 individuals each. Find the index of diversity H.

14. A virgin forest in northwestern Pennsylvania has 4 species of large trees with the following proportions of each: hemlock, .521; beech, .324; birch, .081; maple, .074. Find the index of diversity H.

The number of species in a sample is given by

$$S(n) = a \ln\left(1 + \frac{n}{a}\right),$$

where n is the number of individuals in the sample and a is a constant which indicates the diversity of species in the community. If $a = .36$, find $S(n)$ for the following values of n.

15. 100
16. 200
17. 150
18. 10

19. Find n if $S(n) = 9$ and $a = .36$.

Suppose the number of rabbits in a colony increases according to the relationship

$$y = y_0 e^{.4t},$$

where t represents time in months and y_0 is the initial population of rabbits.

20. Find the number of rabbits present at time $t = 4$ if $y_0 = 100$.

21. How long will it take for the number of rabbits to triple?

A city in Ohio finds its residents moving into the suburbs. Its population is declining according to the relationship

$$P = P_0 e^{-.04t},$$

where t is time measured in years and P_0 is the population at time $t = 0$.

22. If $P_0 = 1,000,000$, find the population at time $t = 1$.

23. If $P_0 = 1,000,000$, estimate the time it will take for the population to be reduced to 750,000.

24. How long will it take for the population to be cut in half?

Carbon 14 is a radioactive isotope of carbon which has a half-life of about 5600 years. The atmosphere contains much carbon, mostly in the form of carbon dioxide, with small traces of carbon 14. Most of this atmospheric carbon is in the form of the nonradioactive isotope carbon 12. The ratio of carbon 14 to carbon 12 is virtually constant in the atmosphere. However, as a plant absorbs carbon dioxide from the air in the process of photosynthesis, the carbon 12 stays in the plant while the carbon 14 decays by conversion to nitrogen. Thus, the ratio of carbon 14 to carbon 12 is smaller in the plant than it is in the atmosphere. Even when the plant is eaten by an animal, this ratio will continue to decrease. Based on these facts, a method of dating objects called carbon 14 dating *has been developed. It is explained in the following problems.*

25. Suppose an Egyptian mummy is discovered in which the ratio of carbon 14 to carbon 12 is only about half the ratio found in the atmosphere. About how long ago did the Egyptian die?

26. Let R be the (nearly constant) ratio of carbon 14 to carbon 12 found in the atmosphere, and let r be the ratio found in a fossil. It can be shown that the relationship between R and r is given by

$$\frac{R}{r} = e^{(t \ln 2)/5600},$$

where t is the age of the fossil in years. Verify the formula for $t = 0$.

27. Verify the formula in Exercise 26 for $t = 5600$ and then for $t = 11,200$.

28. Solve the formula of Exercise 26 for t.

29. Suppose a specimen is found in which $r = \frac{2}{3}R$. Estimate the age of specimen.

30. If an object is fired vertically upward and is subject only to the force of gravity, g, and to air resistance, then the maximum height, H, attained by the object is

$$H = \frac{1}{K}\left(V_0 - \frac{g}{K} \ln \frac{g + V_0 K}{g}\right),$$

where V_0 is the initial velocity of the object and K is a constant. Find H if $K = 2.5$, $V_0 = 1000$ feet per second, and $g = 32$ feet per second per second.

⦿ 31. The following formula* can be used to estimate the population of the United States, where t is time in years measured from 1914 (times before 1914 are negative):

$$N = \frac{197,273,000}{1 + e^{-.03134t}}.$$

---

*The formula is given in Alfred J. Lotka, *Elements of Mathematical Biology*, reprinted by Dover Press, 1957, p. 67.

Complete the following chart.

Year	Observed population	Predicted population
1790	3,929,000	3,929,000
1810	7,240,000	
1860	31,443,000	30,412,000
1900	75,995,000	
1970	204,000,000	

⊙ **32.** Turnage† has shown that the pull, P, of a tracked vehicle on dry sand under certain conditions is approximated by

$$P = W\left[.2 + .16 \ln \frac{G(bl)^{3/2}}{W}\right]$$

where G is an index of sand strength, W is the load on the vehicle, b is the width of the track, and l is the length of the track. Find P if $W = 10$, $G = 5$, $b = 30.5$ cm, and $l = 61.0$ cm.

Appendix   Interpolation

The table of logarithms included in this book contains decimal approximations of common logarithms to four significant digits. More accurate tables are available; however, more accuracy may be obtained from the table included in this book by the process of **linear interpolation.** As an example, let us use linear interpolation to approximate log 75.37.

First, we can establish that log 75.3 < log 75.37 < log 75.4.

Figure 5.6 shows the portion of the curve $y = \log x$ between $x = 75.3$ and $x = 75.4$. We shall use the line segment PR to approximate the logarithm curve (this

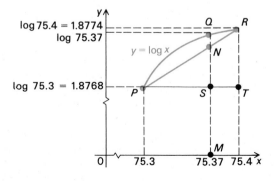

Figure 5.6

†Gerald W. Turnage, *Prediction of Track Pull Performance in a Desert Sand*, unpublished MS thesis, The Florida State University, 1971.

approximation is usually adequate for values of x that are close together.) From the figure, log 75.37 is given by the length of segment MQ, which we cannot find. We can, however, find MN, which we shall use as our approximation to log 75.37. By properties of similar triangles,

$$\frac{PS}{PT} = \frac{SN}{TR}.$$

In this case, $PS = 75.37 - 75.3 = .07$, $PT = 75.4 - 75.3 = .1$, and $RT = \log 75.4 - \log 75.3 = 1.8774 - 1.8768 = .0006$. Hence,

$$\frac{.07}{.1} = \frac{SN}{.0006}$$

or
$$SN = .7(.0006) \approx .0004.$$

(This is 7/10 of the difference of the two logarithms.) Since log $75.37 = MN = MS + SN$, and since $MS = \log 75.3 = 1.8768$,

$$\log 75.37 = 1.8768 + .0004 = 1.8772.$$

Example 1   Find log 8726.

All the work of the example above can be condensed as follows.

$$10\left\{6\left\{\begin{array}{l}\log 8720 = 3.9405 \\ \log 8726 = \\ \log 8730 = 3.9410\end{array}\right\}x\right\}.0005$$

From this display,

$$\frac{6}{10} = \frac{x}{.0005}$$

$$x = \frac{6(.0005)}{10}$$

$$x = .0003.$$

Thus, log $8726 = 3.9405 + .0003 = 3.9408$.

Example 2   Find log .0005958.

Work as above.

$$10\left\{8\left\{\begin{array}{l}\log .0005950 = -4 + .7745 \\ \log .0005958 = \\ \log .0005960 = -4 + .7752\end{array}\right\}x\right\}.0007$$

We get
$$\frac{8}{10} = \frac{x}{.0007},$$

or
$$x = .0006,$$

and
$$\log .0005958 = (-4 + .7745) + .0006$$
$$= -4 + .7751$$
$$= 6.7751 - 10.$$

We can also interpolate when finding an antilogarithm, as shown in the next example.

Example 3   Find x such that $\log x = .3275$.
From the logarithm table,

$$\log 2.12 = .3263 < .3275 < .3284 = \log 2.13$$

Set up the work as follows.

$$.01 \left\{ {}^{y} \left| \begin{array}{l} \log 2.12 = .3263 \\ \log x \ \ \ = .3275 \\ \log 2.13 = .3284 \end{array} \right. \right\} .0012 \Big\} .0021$$

$$\frac{y}{.01} = \frac{.0012}{.0021}$$

$$y = \frac{(.01)(.0012)}{.0021}$$

$$y = .006$$

Thus, $x = 2.12 + .006 = 2.126$, and

$$\log 2.126 = .3275. \quad \blacksquare$$

Appendix Exercises   *Interpolate to find logarithms of the following numbers.*

1. 2345   3. 48.26   5. .06273   7. 27.05

2. 1.732   4. 351.9   6. .003471   8. 342.6

Use interpolation to find the antilogarithms of the following logarithms.

9. 1.7942   11. 7.6565 − 10   13. 5.6930   15. −3.7778

10. 3.9225   12. 8.7296 − 10   14. 12.6268   16. −4.1323

Use logarithms (and interpolation) to find approximations to four-digit accuracy for each of the following.

17. $\dfrac{(26.13)(5.427)}{101.6}$ 19. $\sqrt{\dfrac{6.532}{2.718}}$ 21. $(.2374)^{.05}$

18. $\dfrac{(32.68)(142.8)}{973.4}$ 20. $\left(\dfrac{27.46}{58.29}\right)^3$ 22. $(1.792)^{.23}$

23. $(49.83)^{1/2} + (2.917)^2$

24. $(38.42)^{1/3} + (86.13)^{1/4}$

25. The maximum load L that a cylindrical column can hold is given by

$$L = \frac{d^4}{h^2},$$

where d is the diameter of the cylindrical cross section and h is the height of the column. Find L if $d = 2.143$ feet and $h = 12.25$ feet.

26. Two electrons repel each other with a force $F = d^{-2}$, where d is the distance between the electrons. Find F if $d = .0005241$ cm.

Chapter 5   Review Exercises

Graph each of the following.

1. $y = 2^x$ **2.** $y = 2^{-x}$ **3.** $y = (1/2)^{x+1}$ **4.** $y = 4^x + 4^{-x}$

Solve each of the following equations.

5. $8^p = 32$ **6.** $9^{2y-1} = 27^y$ **7.** $\dfrac{8}{27} = b^{-3}$ **8.** $\dfrac{1}{2} = \left(\dfrac{b}{4}\right)^{1/4}$

The amount of a certain radioactive material, in grams, present after t days, is given by

$$A(t) = 800e^{-.04t}.$$

Find $A(t)$ if

9. $t = 0$.   **10.** $t = 5$

Suppose P dollars is compounded continuously at i% annually; the final amount on deposit would be $A = Pe^{ni}$ dollars after n years. How much would $1200 amount to at 10% compounded continuously for the following number of years:

11. 4 years   **12.** 10 years

13. Historically, the consumption of electricity has increased at a continuous rate of 6% per year. If it continued to increase at this rate, find the number of years before exactly twice as much electricity would be needed.

14. Suppose a conservation campaign together with higher rates caused demand for electricity to increase at only 2% per year. (See Exercise 13.) Find the number of years before twice as much electricity would be needed.

Write each of the following in logarithmic form.

15. $2^5 = 32$ **16.** $100^{1/2} = 10$

Write each of the following in exponential form.

17. $\log_{10} .001 = -3$ **18.** $\log_2 \sqrt{32} = 5/2$

Use properties of logarithms to write each of the following as a sum, difference, or product of logarithms.

19. $\log_3 \dfrac{mn}{p}$ **20.** $\log_2 \dfrac{\sqrt{5}}{3}$ **21.** $\log_5 x^2 y^4 \sqrt[5]{m^3 p}$

Find the common logarithm of each of the following numbers.

22. 8.47   **23.** .00421

Find the antilogarithm of each of the following numbers.

24. 3.4983   **25.** 9.7243   **26.** 8.6493 − 10

Use common logarithms to approximate each of the following.

27. $\dfrac{6^{2.1}}{\sqrt{52}}$ **29.** $\sqrt[5]{\dfrac{27.1}{4.33}}$

28. $2.43^{3.2}$

Solve each of the following equations.

30. $6^k = 12$

32. $\log_{64} y = 1/3$

34. $\log 6x - \log (x + 1) = \log 4$

31. $5^{2r-3} = 17$

33. $\log_2 (y + 3) = 5$

35. $\log_{16} \sqrt{x + 1} = 4^{-1}$

Solve for x.

36. $y = \dfrac{5^x - 5^{-x}}{2}$

37. $y = \dfrac{1}{2(5^x - 5^{-x})}$

Find each of the following.

38. $\ln 896$

40. $\log_5 8$

42. $\log_{1/2} 9.45$

39. $\ln .0000509$

41. $\log_{3.4} 15.8$

43. $\log_3 769$

The height, in meters, of the members of a certain tribe is approximated by

$$h = .5 + \log t,$$

where t is the tribe member's age in years, and $1 \le t \le 20$. Find the height of a tribe member of age

44. 2 years

46. 10 years

45. 5 years

47. 20 years

The formula

$$A = P\left(1 + \frac{i}{m}\right)^{mn}$$

of Section 5.1 gives the amount of money in an account after n years if P dollars is deposited at i% compounded m times per year. If A is known, then P is called the present value of A. (Think of present value as the value today of a sum of money to be received at some time in the future.) Find the present value of the following sums.

48. $4500 at 6% compounded annually for 9 years

49. $11,500 at 4% compounded annually for 12 years

50. $2000 at 4% compounded semiannually for 11 years

51. $2000 at 6% compounded quarterly for 8 years

52. If money can be invested at 4% compounded quarterly, which is larger, $1000 now or $1210 in 5 years? (Hint: find the present value of the $1210.)

53. If money can be invested at 8% compounded annually, which is larger, $10,000 now or $17,000 in 10 years?

If R dollars is deposited at the end of each year in an account paying a rate of interest i compounded annually, then after n years the account will contain a total of

$$R\left[\frac{(1 + i)^n - 1}{i}\right]$$

dollars. Find the final amount on deposit for each of the following. Use logarithms or a calculator.

54. $R = 800$, $i = .06$, 10 years

56. $R = 375$, $i = .10$, 12 years

55. $R = 1500$, $i = .08$, 25 years

57. $R = 2200$, $i = .11$, 20 years

58. Pam Parker deposits $1000 at the end of each year for 8 years in an account paying 5% compounded annually. She then leaves the money alone, with no further deposit, for an additional 6 years. Find the final amount on deposit after the entire 14-year period.

59. Chuck deposits $10,000 at the end of each year for 12 years in an account paying 6% compounded annually. He then puts this total amount on deposit in another account paying 6% compounded semiannually for another 9 years. Find the final amount on deposit after the entire 21-year period.

Use interpolation to find each of the following.

60. log 18.99

61. log 4.763

62. log .009814

Find the antilogarithm of each of the following.

63. 1.9255

64. 8.7468 − 10

65. −3.7067

Use interpolation and logarithms to find each of the following to four significant digits of accuracy.

66. $\dfrac{8.937}{.4288}$

67. $(12.11)^2 + (95.09)^2$

68. $\sqrt[4]{4.213}$

The following exercises are taken with permission from a standard calculus book.

69. Suppose you had a table of natural logarithms giving $\ln x$ for each $x > 0$. How could you use this to find $\log_{10} N$, where

$$\log_{10} N = b \qquad \text{means} \qquad N = 10^b?$$

In particular, find $\log_{10} 2$, given $\ln 2 = 0.69315$, $\ln 10 = 2.30259$.

70. For what positive values of x does $x^{(x^x)} = (x^x)^x$?

71. Stirling's formula says that if n is large, then

$$n! \approx \sqrt{2\pi} \cdot n^{n+.5} \cdot e^{-n}$$

[where $n! = n(n - 1)(n - 2) \ldots (3)(2)(1)$, for any integer $n \geq 1$]. For what value of the constant m can we replace e^{-n} by 10^{-mn} in the formula?

72. Prove: for $a > 0$, $a \neq 1$, $b > 0$, $b \neq 1$, $(\log_b a)(\log_a b) = 1$.

Exercises 69, 71, 72: George B. Thomas, Jr./Ross L. Finney, *Calculus and Analytic Geometry*, 5/E, © 1979, Addison-Wesley, Reading, Massachusetts. (Pp. 311, 321, 323.) Reprinted with permission. Exercise 72: Reproduced from *Calculus*, by Leonard Gillman and Robert H. McDowell, 2nd Edition, by permission of W. W. Norton & Company, Inc. Copyright © 1978, 1973 by W. W. Norton & Company, Inc.

Chapter 6

Trigonometric Functions

We have discussed many different types of functions throughout this book, including linear, quadratic, polynomial, exponential, and logarithmic. In this chapter we introduce the trigonometric functions, which differ in a fundamental way from those previously studied: the trigonometric functions describe a *periodic* or *repetitive* relationship.

An example of a periodic relationship is shown by this electrocardiogram, a graph of the human heartbeat. The EKG shows electrical impulses from the heart. Each small square represents .04 second, and each large square represents .2 seconds. How often does this (abnormal) heart beat?

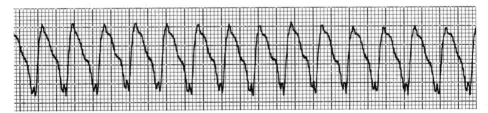

There are many practical applications of these trigonometric functions, particularly in surveying and navigation. These functions also describe many natural phenomena and, hence, are important in the study of optics, heat, electronics, X rays, acoustics, seismology, and many other areas. Trigonometric functions occur again and again in calculus.

6.1 The Unit Circle

A circle with center at the origin and radius of one unit is called a **unit circle.** Start at the point (1, 0) on the unit circle, and let (x, y) be any other point on the unit circle. By measuring along the arc of the circle in a counterclockwise direction from (1, 0) to (x, y), we can find a unique positive real number s that gives the length of this arc. There is also a unique negative number which gives the length of the arc from $(1, 0)$ to (x, y), measured in a clockwise direction. An arc with $s > 0$ is shown in Figure 6.1.

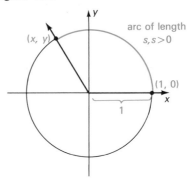

Figure 6.1

The circumference of a circle of radius r is given by the formula $C = 2\pi r$. Thus, the circumference of the unit circle is 2π, so that s may take values from 0 to 2π or from -2π to 0. We can extend the domain of s to include all real numbers by allowing arcs which wrap around the circle more than once. For example, $s = 3\pi$ would correspond to the same point on the circle as $s = \pi$ or $s = -\pi$. Figure 6.2 shows how s can take any real number as a value by wrapping a real number line around the unit circle.

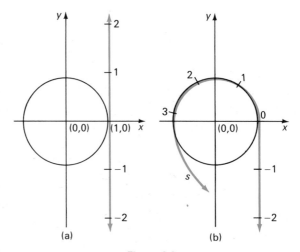

Figure 6.2

Example 1   Find the coordinates of the points on the unit circle corresponding to the following arc lengths.

(a) π
   Since π is one-half the circumference of the unit circle, an arc of length π which starts at $(1, 0)$ would end at the point $(-1, 0)$, as shown in Figure 6.3.

(b) $\pi/2$
   An arc of length $\pi/2$ corresponds to the point $(0, 1)$. See Figure 6.4.

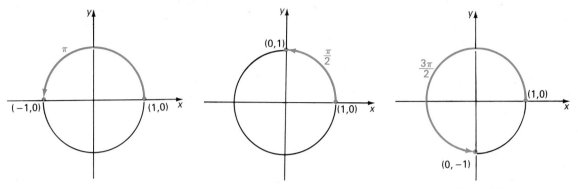

Figure 6.3   Figure 6.4   Figure 6.5

(c) $\dfrac{3\pi}{2}$

As Figure 6.5 shows, the arc of length $\dfrac{3\pi}{2}$ corresponds to $(0, -1)$.   ▌

Example 2   Find the coordinates of the point P on the unit circle which corresponds to $s = \pi/4$.

The point P on the unit circle which corresponds to $s = \pi/4$ is halfway between $(1, 0)$ and $(0, 1)$, as shown in Figure 6.6. This point also lies on the line $y = x$. Since the equation of the unit circle is $x^2 + y^2 = 1$, we have, for point P,

$$x^2 + x^2 = 1$$
$$2x^2 = 1$$
$$x^2 = \frac{1}{2}$$
$$x = \frac{1}{\sqrt{2}}$$
$$x = \frac{\sqrt{2}}{2}.$$

Also, since $y = x$, we have $\qquad y = \dfrac{\sqrt{2}}{2}.$

Thus, the point on the unit circle which corresponds to $s = \pi/4$ is $(\sqrt{2}/2, \sqrt{2}/2)$.   ▌

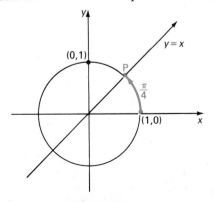

Figure 6.6

Example 3 Find the coordinates of the point Q on the unit circle which corresponds to each of the following.

  (a) $s = 3\pi/4$

   Figure 6.7 shows point Q and point P from the discussion above. Note that $3\pi/4 = \pi - \pi/4$. By symmetry, Q has the same y-coordinate as P, but an x-coordinate with opposite sign. Thus, the coordinates of Q are $(-\sqrt{2}/2, \sqrt{2}/2)$.

  (b) $s = -\pi/4$

   As Figure 6.8 shows, this time the coordinates of Q are $\left(\dfrac{\sqrt{2}}{2}, \dfrac{-\sqrt{2}}{2}\right)$.

  (c) $s = 5\pi/4$

   Since $5\pi/4 = \pi + \pi/4$, by symmetry again, the coordinates are $(-\sqrt{2}/2, -\sqrt{2}/2)$. See Figure 6.9. ∎

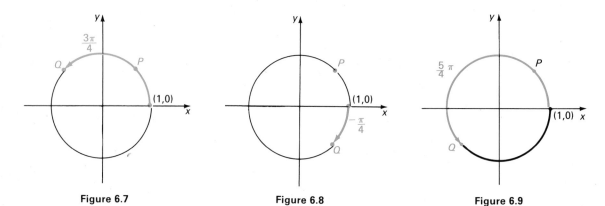

Figure 6.7   Figure 6.8   Figure 6.9

Using the correspondence between an arc of length s and a point (x, y) on the unit circle, we can define two functions. For each value of s, we have a unique value of x and a unique value of y. The function which associates each arc length s with the y-value of the corresponding point is called the **sine function**, abbreviated

$$\sin s = y.$$

The function which associates each arc length s with the x-value of the corresponding point is called the **cosine function**, abbreviated

$$\cos s = x.$$

By these definitions, the coordinates of the point associated with an arc of length s can be written as $(\cos s, \sin s)$.

  Both the sine and cosine functions have the set of real numbers as domain.

The values of cos s (or x) range from 1 at $s = 0$ to -1 at $s = \pi$. Cos s is 0 when s is $\pi/2$ or $3\pi/2$. Similarly, sin s ranges from -1 when s is $3\pi/2$ to 1 for $s = \pi/2$, with sin $s = 0$ when s is 0 or π.

If 2π is added to any value of s, the corresponding values of sin s and cos s are unchanged. That is,

$$\sin s = \sin(s + 2\pi) \tag{1}$$

and

$$\cos s = \cos(s + 2\pi). \tag{2}$$

A function of this type, which describes a cyclic relationship, is called a **periodic function.** Here, the number 2π is called the **period** of the function, because it is the smallest positive number which satisfies statements (1) and (2) above. It is also true, for example, that sin $s = \sin(s + 4\pi)$ and sin $s = \sin(s + 6\pi)$, but 2π is the period since it is the *smallest* positive number that can be used.

Example 4   Find each of the following function values.

(a) sin 0

If $s = 0$, the corresponding point is $(1, 0)$. Since sin $s = y$, we have sin $0 = 0$.

(b) cos $\pi/2$

The point corresponding to $s = \pi/2$ is $(0, 1)$. We know cos $s = x$, so cos $\pi/2 = 0$.

(c) cos $\pi/4$

In Example 2, we saw that $(\sqrt{2}/2, \sqrt{2}/2)$ corresponds to $\pi/4$. Thus, cos $\pi/4 = \sqrt{2}/2$.   ▮

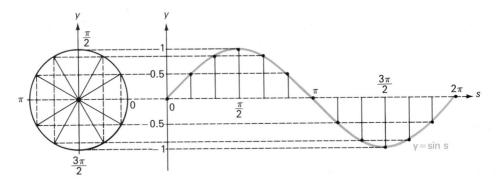

Figure 6.10

While we shall not graph sine and cosine functions in detail until later in this chapter, it is beneficial to sketch the basic graphs now. To do this, we use the definitions of sine and cosine in terms of the unit circle. A unit circle with various arc lengths s is shown in Figure 6.10. The vertical dotted lines give the corresponding values of y, which is sin s. By projecting horizontally, we get points on the graph of $y = \sin s$. Figure 6.10 shows only *one period* of the graph; the complete graph would extend indefinitely to the right and to the left. A similar process can be used to get the graph of $y = \cos s$, shown in Figure 6.11. Again, the portion shown here is only one period of the graph.

The following chart summarizes the intervals where sine and cosine are increasing and decreasing. The results in the chart can be found by inspecting the graphs of Figure 6.10 and Figure 6.11.

interval	$[0, \pi/2]$	$[\pi/2, \pi]$	$[\pi, 3\pi/2]$	$[3\pi/2, 2\pi]$
quadrant	I	II	III	IV
sin s	increases from 0 to 1	decreases from 1 to 0	decreases from 0 to −1	increases from −1 to 0
cos s	decreases from 1 to 0	decreases from 0 to −1	increases from −1 to 0	increases from 0 to 1

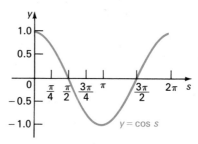

Figure 6.11

6.1 Exercises   *For each of the following arc lengths, find the coordinates of the corresponding point on the unit circle.*

1. $5\pi/4$

2. $7\pi/4$

3. π

4. -3π

5. 4π

6. 17π

7. -2π

8. $-\dfrac{\pi}{2}$

9. $\dfrac{5\pi}{2}$

10. $\dfrac{11\pi}{2}$

11. $\dfrac{-11\pi}{4}$

12. $\dfrac{-7\pi}{4}$

13. 2.25π

14. 1.5π

15. $.75\pi$

16. -2.25π

In each of the following exercises, the point which corresponds to arc length s is given. Use symmetry to find the coordinates of the point that corresponds to (a) −s; (b) s + 2π; (c) s + π; (d) π − s.

17. $\left(\dfrac{2}{3}, \dfrac{\sqrt{5}}{3}\right)$

18. $\left(\dfrac{5}{13}, \dfrac{12}{13}\right)$

19. $\left(\dfrac{4}{5}, \dfrac{3}{5}\right)$

20. $\left(\dfrac{3}{4}, \dfrac{\sqrt{7}}{4}\right)$

21. $\left(-\dfrac{1}{2}, \dfrac{\sqrt{3}}{2}\right)$

22. $\left(\dfrac{\sqrt{3}}{2}, -\dfrac{1}{2}\right)$

23. $\left(-\dfrac{2}{5}, \dfrac{-\sqrt{21}}{5}\right)$

24. $\left(\dfrac{-3}{5}, \dfrac{-4}{5}\right)$

For each of the following arc lengths, find sin s and cos s.

25. 0

26. $\dfrac{\pi}{2}$

27. $\dfrac{\pi}{4}$

28. $\dfrac{3\pi}{4}$

29. $\dfrac{3\pi}{2}$

30. 987π

31. -1423π

32. -2π

33. $-\dfrac{\pi}{4}$

34. $\dfrac{-\pi}{2}$

35. $\dfrac{-3\pi}{4}$

36. $\dfrac{-7\pi}{4}$

⦿ *Identify the quadrant in which arcs having the following lengths would terminate.*

37. $s = 10$

38. $s = 18$

39. $s = 36$

40. s $= 92$

41. $s = -896.1$

42. $s = -1046.001$

⦿ *Show that the following points lie (approximately) on the unit circle.*

43. $(.39852144, .91715902)$

44. $(-.81745602, -.57599102)$

Follow the method used in Examples 2 and 3 to work the following problems.

45. (a) Use a $30°-60°-90°$ triangle to show that the arc length $\pi/3$ corresponds to a point on the unit circle which is also on the line $y = \sqrt{3}\,x$.
  (b) Find the coordinates of the point on the unit circle which corresponds to $\pi/3$.
  (c) Use symmetry to find the coordinates of the points on the unit circle which correspond to $-\pi/3$, $2\pi/3$, and $4\pi/3$.

46. (a) Use a $30°-60°-90°$ triangle to show that the arc length $\pi/6$ corresponds to a point on the unit circle which is also on the line $\sqrt{3}\,y = x$.
  (b) Find the coordinates of the point on the unit circle which corresponds to $\pi/6$.
  (c) Use symmetry to find the coordinates of the points on the unit circle which correspond to $-\pi/6$, $5\pi/6$, and $7\pi/6$.

Use the results of Exercises 45 and 46 to find each of the following.

47. $\sin \pi/3$

48. $\cos \pi/3$

49. $\cos 2\pi/3$

50. $\sin 2\pi/3$

51. $\sin 4\pi/3$

52. $\cos -\pi/3$

53. $\sin 5\pi/6$

54. $\cos 5\pi/6$

6.2 The Trigonometric Functions

In the previous section, we defined the sine and cosine functions as $\sin s = y$ and $\cos s = x$, where (x, y) is the point on the unit circle which corresponds to an arc of length s. We now define four additional functions derived from these two basic functions: the **tangent, cotangent, cosecant,** and **secant** functions, abbreviated as tan, cot, csc, and sec, respectively.

$$\tan s = \frac{y}{x} \quad (x \neq 0) \qquad \csc s = \frac{1}{y} \quad (y \neq 0)$$

$$\cot s = \frac{x}{y} \quad (y \neq 0) \qquad \sec s = \frac{1}{x} \quad (x \neq 0)$$

These six functions are called the **trigonometric functions** or the *circular functions.*

Example 1   Find tan $\pi/4$, cot $\pi/4$, csc $\pi/4$, and sec $\pi/4$.

In the last section (Example 2), we saw that $(\sqrt{2}/2, \sqrt{2}/2)$ corresponds to $s = \pi/4$. Thus $x = \sqrt{2}/2$ and $y = \sqrt{2}/2$. By their definitions,

$$\tan\frac{\pi}{4} = \frac{y}{x} = \frac{\sqrt{2}/2}{\sqrt{2}/2} = 1$$

$$\cot\frac{\pi}{4} = \frac{x}{y} = \frac{\sqrt{2}/2}{\sqrt{2}/2} = 1$$

$$\csc\frac{\pi}{4} = \frac{1}{y} = \frac{1}{\sqrt{2}/2} = \frac{2}{\sqrt{2}} = \sqrt{2}$$

$$\sec\frac{\pi}{4} = \frac{1}{x} = \frac{1}{\sqrt{2}/2} = \frac{2}{\sqrt{2}} = \sqrt{2}.$$

Like the sine and cosine functions, the four new trigonometric functions are periodic. The cosecant and secant functions have the same period as sine and cosine, 2π. The tangent and cotangent functions, however, have a period of π. We shall prove this fact in the next chapter.

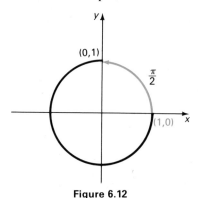

Figure 6.12

Example 2   Find the values of the trigonometric functions for an arc of length $\pi/2$.

As shown in Figure 6.12, the point which corresponds to an arc of length $\pi/2$ is $(0, 1)$, so that $x = 0$ and $y = 1$. Use the definitions of the various functions.

$$\sin\frac{\pi}{2} = y = 1 \qquad\qquad \cot\frac{\pi}{2} = \frac{x}{y} = \frac{0}{1} = 0$$

$$\cos\frac{\pi}{2} = x = 0 \qquad\qquad \csc\frac{\pi}{2} = \frac{1}{y} = \frac{1}{1} = 1$$

$$\tan\frac{\pi}{2} = \frac{y}{x} = \frac{1}{0} \quad\text{(undefined)} \qquad \sec\frac{\pi}{2} = \frac{1}{x} = \frac{1}{0} \quad\text{(undefined)}$$

Several important properties of the trigonometric functions can be obtained from the definitions of the functions. First, recall that the *reciprocal* of a number a is $1/a$. (There is no reciprocal for 0.) The numbers $1/x$ and $x/1$ are reciprocals.

From the definitions of the trigonometric functions, we see that $1/x$ is sec s and $x/1$ (or x) is cos s. Thus, cos s and sec s are reciprocals, so that

$$\cos s = \frac{1}{\sec s} \quad \text{and} \quad \sec s = \frac{1}{\cos s},$$

whenever the denominators are not zero. In the same way,

$$\sin s = \frac{1}{\csc s} \quad \text{and} \quad \csc s = \frac{1}{\sin s}$$

$$\tan s = \frac{1}{\cot s} \quad \text{and} \quad \cot s = \frac{1}{\tan s},$$

whenever the denominators are not zero. These results are called the **reciprocal identities.**

Example 3   Suppose tan $s = 3/4$. Find cot s.
   Since cot $s = 1/\tan s$, we have

$$\cot s = \frac{1}{3/4} = \frac{4}{3}. \quad \blacksquare$$

   We can use the definitions to determine the signs of the trigonometric functions in each of the four quadrants. For example, if s terminates in quadrant I, then both x and y are positive, and all the trigonometric functions have positive values. In quadrant II, x is negative, and y is positive. Thus, cos $s = x$ is negative, sin $s = y$ is positive, tan $s = y/x$ is negative, and so on.

Example 4   Suppose s terminates in quadrant II and sin $s = 2/3$. Find the values of the other trigonometric functions.
   Since sin $s = y$, $y = 2/3$. To find x, use the fact that on the unit circle $x^2 + y^2 = 1$.

$$x^2 + \left(\frac{2}{3}\right)^2 = 1$$

$$x^2 + \frac{4}{9} = 1$$

$$x^2 = \frac{5}{9}$$

$$x = \frac{\pm\sqrt{5}}{3}$$

We know s terminates in quadrant II. Therefore, x must be negative, so $x = -\sqrt{5}/3$.

The remaining functions can now be found from their definitions.

$$\cos s = -\frac{\sqrt{5}}{3}$$

$$\tan s = \frac{2/3}{-\sqrt{5}/3} = \frac{2}{-\sqrt{5}} = \frac{-2\sqrt{5}}{5}$$

$$\cot s = \frac{-\sqrt{5}/3}{2/3} = \frac{-\sqrt{5}}{2}$$

$$\sec s = \frac{1}{-\sqrt{5}/3} = \frac{-3}{\sqrt{5}} = \frac{-3\sqrt{5}}{5}$$

$$\csc s = \frac{1}{2/3} = \frac{3}{2}$$ ▌

We can also derive other relationships among the trigonometric functions by starting with the definitions of these functions. The equation of the unit circle is $x^2 + y^2 = 1$; since $\cos s = x$ and $\sin s = y$, we have

$$(\cos s)^2 + (\sin s)^2 = 1.$$

It is customary to write $(\sin s)^2$ as $\sin^2 s$, giving

$$\boxed{\sin^2 s + \cos^2 s = 1.}$$

Starting with $x^2 + y^2 = 1$, we can divide through by x^2, and then by y^2, to get two additional identities:

$$\boxed{1 + \tan^2 s = \sec^2 s \quad \text{and} \quad \cot^2 s + 1 = \csc^2 s.}$$

Finally, we have two more identities derived from the equalities $\cos s = x$ and $\sin s = y$.

$$\boxed{\begin{array}{ll} \tan s = \dfrac{\sin s}{\cos s} \quad \text{and} \quad \cot s = \dfrac{\cos s}{\sin s} \\ (\cos s \neq 0) \qquad\qquad\quad (\sin s \neq 0) \end{array}}$$

For proofs of these results, see Exercises 43 – 46 below.

Using these relationships, we can find all values of the trigonometric functions for a particular value of s, given the value of one function and the quadrant in which the arc of length s terminates.

Example 5   Suppose that $\tan t = 1/4$, and t terminates in quadrant III. Find the other five trigonometric function values for t.

Since $\cot t = 1/\tan t$,

$$\cot t = \frac{1}{1/4} = 4.$$

We know that $1 + \tan^2 t = \sec^2 t$. Since $\tan t = 1/4$,

$$1 + \left(\frac{1}{4}\right)^2 = \sec^2 t$$

$$1 + \frac{1}{16} = \sec^2 t$$

$$\frac{17}{16} = \sec^2 t$$

Before we take the square root of both sides to find sec t, we need to know whether the result is positive or negative. We are told that the arc terminates in quadrant III, where secant is negative. Thus,

$$-\frac{\sqrt{17}}{4} = \sec t.$$

Since $\cos t = 1/\sec t$, we have $\cos t = -4\sqrt{17}/17$. Finally, we know that

$$\tan t = \frac{\sin t}{\cos t}$$

or $\sin t = (\tan t)(\cos t)$. Using our values,

$$\sin t = \left(\frac{1}{4}\right)\left(-\frac{4\sqrt{17}}{17}\right) = -\frac{\sqrt{17}}{17}.$$

Finally, $\csc t = 1/\sin t = -\sqrt{17}$. ∎

6.2 Exercises

For each of the following, find tan s, cot s, sec s, and csc s.

1. $\sin s = 1/2$, $\cos s = \sqrt{3}/2$
2. $\sin s = 3/4$, $\cos s = \sqrt{7}/4$
3. $\sin s = 4/5$, $\cos s = -3/5$
4. $\sin s = -1/2$, $\cos s = -\sqrt{3}/2$
5. $\sin s = -\sqrt{3}/2$, $\cos s = 1/2$
6. $\sin s = 12/13$, $\cos s = 5/13$

For each of the following, find the values of the six trigonometric functions. For Exercises 13–18, use the results of Exercises 49 and 50 of Section 6.1.

7. π
8. $3\pi/2$
9. $3\pi/4$
10. $5\pi/4$
11. $-\pi/4$
12. $-\pi/2$
13. $\pi/6$
14. $\pi/3$
15. $2\pi/3$
16. $5\pi/6$
17. $7\pi/6$
18. $4\pi/3$

Complete the following table of signs of the trigonometric functions.

	Quadrant	sin	cos	tan	cot	sec	csc
19.	I	+	+	—	—	+	+
20.	II	+	—	—	—	—	—
21.	III	—	—	—	—	—	—
22.	IV	—	—	—	—	—	—

Decide what quadrant(s) s must terminate in to satisfy the following conditions for $0 \leq s < 2\pi$.

23. $\sin s > 0$, $\cos s < 0$

24. $\cos s > 0$, $\tan s > 0$

25. $\sec s < 0$, $\csc s < 0$

26. $\tan s > 0$, $\cot s > 0$

27. $\cos s < 0$

28. $\tan s > 0$

29. $\csc s < 0$

For each of the following find the values of the other trigonometric functions.

30. $\sin s = \dfrac{3}{4}$, s terminates in quadrant I

31. $\cos s = \dfrac{-4}{9}$, s terminates in quadrant II

32. $\csc s = 2$, s terminates in quadrant II

33. $\tan s = \dfrac{3}{2}$, $\csc s = \dfrac{\sqrt{13}}{3}$

34. $\sec s = -2$, $\cot s = \dfrac{\sqrt{3}}{3}$

35. $\sin t = \dfrac{\sqrt{5}}{5}$, $\cos t < 0$

36. $\tan t = -\dfrac{3}{5}$, $\sec t > 0$

37. $\sin s = a$, s is in quadrant I

38. $\tan t = m$, t is in quadrant III

● *Find the values of the other trigonometric functions.*

39. $\cos s = -.428193$, s terminates in quadrant II

40. $\sec t = 28.4096$, t terminates in quadrant IV

41. $\csc t = -10.4349$, $\sec t > 0$

42. $\cot t = -.139725$, $\cos t > 0$

Use the definitions of the trigonometric functions to prove the following statements.

43. $\tan^2 s + 1 = \sec^2 s$

44. $1 + \cot^2 s = \csc^2 s$

45. $\tan s = \dfrac{\sin s}{\cos s}$, $\cos s \neq 0$

46. $\cot s = \dfrac{\cos s}{\sin s}$ ($\sin s \neq 0$)

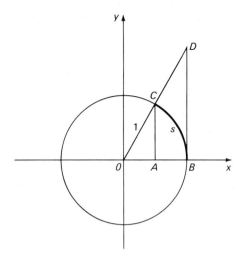

In the figure above, line segments CA and DB are perpendicular to OB. We defined sin s and cos s in terms of the line segments AC and OA. Use geometric relationships to show the following.

47. The length of line segment BD equals tan s. (Hint: since tan $s = y/x$, you must show that $AC/OA = BD$.)

48. The length of line segment OD equals sec s.

6.3 Angles and the Unit Circle

A basic idea of trigonometry is the angle, which we define in this section. Figure 6.13 shows a line through points A and B. This line is named *line AB*. The portion of the line between A and B, including points A and B, is called *line segment AB*. The portion of line AB that starts at A and continues through B, and on past B, is called *ray AB*. Point A is the endpoint of the ray.

An **angle** is formed by rotating a ray around its endpoint. The initial position of the ray is called the *initial side* of the angle and the endpoint of the ray is called the *vertex* of the angle. The location of the ray at the end of its rotation is called the *terminal side* of the angle. Figure 6.14 shows the initial and terminal sides of an angle with vertex A.

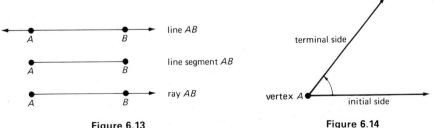

Figure 6.13   **Figure 6.14**

If the rotation of an angle is counterclockwise, we call the angle *positive.* If the rotation is clockwise, the angle is *negative.* Figure 6.15 shows both types.

An angle can be named by using the name of its vertex. For example, the angle on the right in Figure 6.15 can be called angle C. Also, an angle can be named by using three letters. For example, the angle on the right could also be named angle *ACB*. (Put the vertex in the middle.)

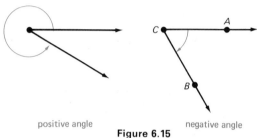

positive angle   negative angle

Figure 6.15

An angle is in **standard position** if its vertex is at the origin of a coordinate system and its initial side is along the positive *x*-axis. The two angles of Figure 6.16 are in standard position. An angle in standard position is said to lie in the quadrant where its terminal side lies.

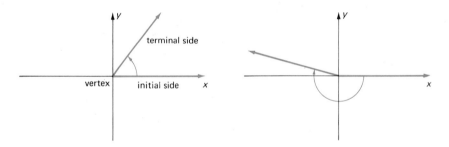

Figure 6.16

Example 1 Find the quadrants for the angles in Figure 6.16.

The angle on the left in Figure 6.16 is a quadrant I angle. The angle on the right is a quadrant II angle. ▌

An angle in standard position whose terminal side coincides with the *x*-axis or *y*-axis is called a **quadrantal angle.** Two angles with the same initial side and the same terminal side, but different amounts of rotation, are called **coterminal angles.** Figure 6.17 shows a pair of coterminal angles.

There are two systems commonly used to measure angles. In most work in applied trigonometry, angles are measured in degrees. Degree measure has remained unchanged since the Babylonians developed it over 4000 years ago. To use degree measure, assign 360 degrees to the rotation of a ray through a com-

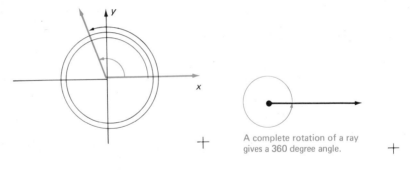

Figure 6.17   Figure 6.18

plete circle. As Figure 6.18 shows, the terminal side corresponds with its initial side when it makes a complete rotation. **One degree,** 1°, represents 1/360 of a rotation. One sixtieth of a degree is called a *minute,* and one sixtieth of a minute is a *second.* The measure 12° 42′ 38″ represents 12 degrees, 42 minutes, 38 seconds.

An angle having a measure between 0° and 90° is called an *acute angle.* An angle whose measure is exactly 90° is a *right angle.* An angle measuring more than 90° but less than 180° is an *obtuse angle,* and an angle of exactly 180° is a *straight angle.*

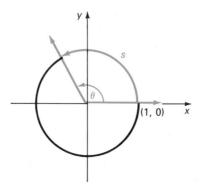

Figure 6.19

In advanced work in trigonometry, and in calculus, angles are measured in **radians.** Radian measure simplifies many formulas. Figure 6.19 shows an angle θ (θ is the Greek letter theta) in standard position. As shown in the figure, angle θ determines an arc of positive length s on the unit circle. Thus, it is reasonable to use the real number s as a measure of θ. We say that

$$\theta = s \text{ radians}$$

or simply $\theta = s$.

Several angles and their radian measures are shown in Figure 6.20. Since the radian measure of an angle is just a real number, no dimensions are associated with radian measure.

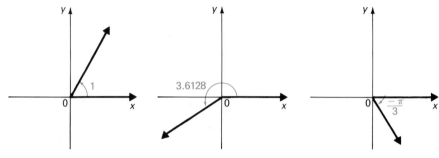

Figure 6.20

An angle of measure 360° would correspond to an arc that went entirely around the unit circle. Thus, the radian measure of a 360° angle is 2π, or

$$360° = 2\pi.$$

This result gives us a basis for comparing degree measure and radian measure. Dividing both sides by 2 gives

$$180° = \pi.$$

Since π radians = 180°, we divide both sides by π to find that

$$\boxed{1 \text{ radian} = \frac{180°}{\pi},}$$

or, approximately, 1 radian = 57° 17′ 45″.

On the other hand,

$$180° = \pi \text{ radians}$$

$$\boxed{1° = \frac{\pi}{180} \text{ radians,}}$$

or, approximately, 1° = .0174533 radians.

Example 2   Convert each of the following degree measures to radians.

(a) 45°

Since $1° = \pi/180$ radians,

$$45° = 45\left(\frac{\pi}{180}\right) \text{ radians} = \frac{45\pi}{180} \text{ radians} = \frac{\pi}{4} \text{ radians.}$$

The word *radian* is often omitted, so that we could simply write $45° = \pi/4$.

(b) 240°

$$240° = 240\left(\frac{\pi}{180}\right) = \frac{4\pi}{3}. \quad \blacksquare$$

Example 3   Convert each of the following radian measures to degrees.

(a) $\dfrac{9\pi}{4}$

We know that 1 radian $= 180°/\pi$. Thus,

$$\dfrac{9\pi}{4} \text{ radians} = \dfrac{9\pi}{4}\left(\dfrac{180°}{\pi}\right)$$

$$\dfrac{9\pi}{4} \text{ radians} = 405°.$$

(b) $\dfrac{11\pi}{3} \text{ radians} = \dfrac{11\pi}{3}\left(\dfrac{180°}{\pi}\right) = 660°.$ ∎

Many calculators will convert back and forth from radian measure to degree measure. A difficulty that often comes up is that the calculator works with decimal degrees, rather than degrees, minutes, and seconds. The next example shows how to handle this.

Example 4   Convert as indicated.

(a) 146° 18′ 34″ to radians
Since $1' = 1/60°$, and $1'' = 1/60' = 1/3600°$, we have

$$146°\ 18'\ 34'' = 146° + 18\left(\dfrac{1}{60}\right)° + 34\left(\dfrac{1}{3600}\right)°$$

$$= 146° + \dfrac{18°}{60} + \dfrac{34°}{3600}.$$

Using calculator memory as necessary, we have

$$= 146° + .3° + .00944°$$
$$= 146.30944°.$$

Now activate the appropriate keys on your calculator to get:

$$146.30944° \approx 2.55358 \text{ radians}$$

(b) .97682 radians to degrees

Enter .97682 into your calculator and activate the keys that convert to degrees. You should get .97682 $= 55.967663°$.

Subtract 55, to get .967663. Multiply by 60, to get

$$55.967663° = 55° + .967663°$$
$$= 55° + (60)(.967663)'$$
$$= 55° + 58.05978'$$
$$= 55° + 58' + .05978'$$
$$= 55° + 58' + 60(.05978)''$$
$$= 55° + 58' + 4''$$
$$= 55°\ 58'\ 4''.$$ ∎

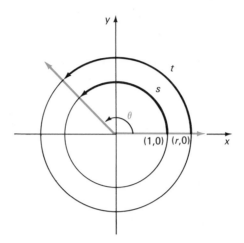

Figure 6.21

We can find the radian measure of an angle using a circle other than the unit circle. Figure 6.21 shows an angle θ, a unit circle, and a circle of radius r. Angle θ is a *central angle* (an angle whose vertex is at the center of the circle) for both circles. From geometry, we know that the ratio of the arcs is the same as the ratio of the lengths of the radii. Therefore,

$$\frac{t}{s} = \frac{r}{1}, \quad \text{or} \quad \frac{t}{s} = r.$$

By definition, $\theta = s$, so that

$$\frac{t}{\theta} = r$$

$$t = r\theta$$

$$\boxed{\theta = \frac{t}{r}.}$$

Any units of measure for t and r would be the same and would be eliminated in this division; this is an additional reason for omitting the word "radian" when using radian measure.

Example 5   Find the radian measure of a central angle which cuts off an arc of length 8 inches on a circle with a radius of 5 inches.

We know that $\theta = t/r$. Here, t is 8 inches and r is 5 inches. Thus,

$$\theta = \frac{8 \text{ inches}}{5 \text{ inches}} = 1.6. \quad \blacksquare$$

The relationship $\theta = t/r$ also gives us a way to find an arc length on a circle when the central angle and radius are known. This is useful in applications, as the next example shows.

Example 6   Reno, Nevada, is approximately due north of Los Angeles. The latitude of Reno is 40° N, while that of Los Angeles is 34° N. (The N means that the location is north of the equator.) If the radius of the earth is 4.0×10^3 miles, find the north-south distance between the two cities.

Latitude gives the measure of a central angle whose initial side goes through the earth's equator and whose terminal side goes through the location in question. As shown in Figure 6.22, the central angle between Reno and Los Angeles is 6°. The distance between the two cities can thus be found by the formula $t = r\theta$, after 6° is first converted to radians.

$$6° = 6\left(\frac{\pi}{180}\right) = \frac{\pi}{30} \text{ radians}$$

The distance between the two cities is thus

$$t = r\theta$$

$$= (4.0 \times 10^3)\left(\frac{\pi}{30}\right) \text{ miles}$$

$$= \frac{400\pi}{3} \text{ miles}$$

$$t = 420 \text{ miles} \qquad \text{(to two significant digits).} \qquad \blacksquare$$

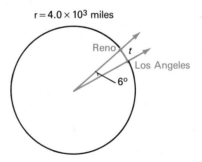

$r = 4.0 \times 10^3$ miles

Reno t

Los Angeles

6°

Figure 6.22

6.3 Exercises   *Find the angles of smallest positive measure coterminal with the following angles.*

1. −40°	**3.** −125°	**5.** 450°	**7.** 539°
2. −98°	**4.** −203°	**6.** 489°	**8.** 699°

Convert each of the following degree measures to radians. Leave answers as multiples of π.

9. 60°	**12.** 120°	**15.** 300°	**18.** 20°
10. 30°	**13.** 135°	**16.** 390°	**19.** 140°
11. 90°	**14.** 270°	**17.** 405°	**20.** 320°

Convert each of the following radian measures to degrees.

21. $\pi/3$	**25.** $11\pi/6$	**29.** 5π
22. $8\pi/3$	**26.** $15\pi/4$	**30.** 7π
23. $7\pi/4$	**27.** $-\pi/6$	**31.** $7\pi/20$
24. $2\pi/3$	**28.** $-\pi/4$	**32.** $17\pi/20$

● *Convert as indicated. Write radian measure with four significant digits and degree measure to the nearest second.*

33. 56° 25′ to radians   **35.** .735114 to degrees

34. 289° 14′ 45″ to radians   **36.** 12.69734 to degrees

Find the radian measure (as a multiple of π) of the smallest angle between the hands of a clock at the following times. Assume that the hour hand stays exactly on the given hour.

37. 12:15   **38.** 12:30   **39.** 2:40   **40.** 3:35

41. A tire is rotating 600 times per minute. How many degrees does a point on the edge of the tire revolve through in 1/2 second?

42. An airplane propeller rotates 1000 times per minute. Find the number of degrees that a point on the edge of the propeller would rotate through in 1 second.

Find the measure of the central angle in radians for each of the following.

43. $r = 8$ inches, $t = 12$ inches

44. $r = 18$ mm, $t = 6$ mm

45. $r = 16.4$ m, $t = 20.1$ m

46. $r = 5.80$ cm, $t = 12.3$ cm

● **47.** $r = 1.93470$ cm, $t = 5.98421$ cm

48. $r = 294.893$ m, $t = 122.097$ m

Find the distance in miles between the following pairs of cities whose latitudes are given. Assume the cities are on a north-south line and that the radius of the earth is 4.0×10^3 miles. Give answers to two significant digits.

49. Grand Portage, Minnesota, 44° N, and New Orleans, Louisiana, 30° N

50. Charleston, South Carolina, 33° N, and Toronto, Ontario, 43° N

51. Panama City, Panama, 9° N, and Pittsburgh, Pennsylvania, 40° N

52. Farmersville, California, 36° N and Penticton, British Columbia, 49° N

53. New York City, 41° N, and Lima, Peru, 12° S

Medicine Wheel is a large Indian structure in northern Wyoming. The circular structure is perhaps 200 years old. There are 32 spokes in the wheel, all equally spaced.

54. Find the measure, in degrees and radians, of each central angle that consecutive pairs of spokes make.

55. If the radius of the wheel is 76 feet, find the circumference.

56. Find the length of each arc cut off by consecutive pairs of spokes.

Angular velocity *is a measure of how fast the terminal side of an angle is rotating. The symbol ω (the Greek letter omega) is used for angular velocity. The distance traveled in t seconds by a point on the edge of a circle of radius r that is rotating through ω radians per second is given by rωt.*

57. Find ω for the hour hand of a clock.

58. Find ω for the second hand of a clock.

59. Find ω for a line from the center to the edge of a phonograph record revolving 33 1/3 times per minute.

60. Find the distance traveled in 9 seconds by a point on the edge of a circle of radius 6 cm, which is rotating through $\pi/3$ radians per second.

61. A point on the edge of a circle travels $8\pi/9$ m in 12 seconds. The radius of the circle is 4/3 m. Find ω.

62. Find the number of seconds it would take for a point on the edge of a circle to move $12\pi/5$ m, if the radius of the circle is 1.5 m and the circle is rotating through $2\pi/5$ radians per second.

● **63.** Eratosthenes (*ca.* 230 B.C.)* made a famous measurement of the earth. He observed at Syene [the modern Aswan], at noon and at the summer solstice, that a vertical stick had no shadow, while at Alexandria (on the same meridian as Syene) the sun's rays were inclined 1/50 of a complete circle to the vertical. [See the figure.] He then calculated the circumference of the earth from the known distance of 5000 stades between Alexandria and Syene. Obtain Eratosthenes' result of 250,000 stades for the circumference of the earth. There is reason to suppose that a stade is about equal to 516.7 feet. Assuming this, calculate from the above result the polar diameter of the earth in miles. (The actual polar diameter of the earth, to the nearest mile, is 7900 miles.)

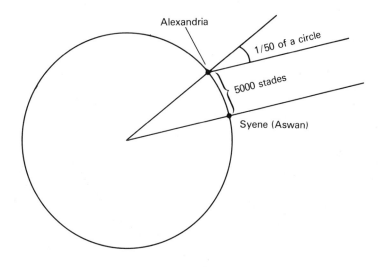

*From *A Survey of Geometry,* Vol. I by Howard Eves. Copyright © 1963 by Allyn & Bacon, Inc. Reprinted by permission of Allyn & Bacon, Inc.

6.4 Trigonometric Functions of Angles

The trigonometric functions we have defined so far have had sets of real numbers for domains. We can extend this domain to include angles by using the radian measure of the angle. For example, from Figure 6.23, we have θ in degrees equal to s in radians, and thus $\sin \theta = \sin s$, $\cos \theta = \cos s$, and so on.

Thus, the trigonometric functions lead to the same function values whether the domain represents arc lengths or angle measures.

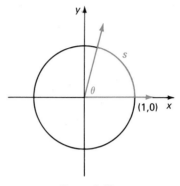

Figure 6.23

Example 1 Find the trigonometric functions of the following angles.

(a) $\sin 90°$

We know that $90° = \pi/2$ radians. Then

$$\sin 90° = \sin \frac{\pi}{2} = 1.$$

(b) $\tan 45°$

Since $45° = \pi/4$ radians, and using results from Section 6.2,

$$\tan 45° = \tan \frac{\pi}{4} = 1. \quad \blacksquare$$

We defined the trigonometric functions in terms of the coordinates of point P on the unit circle. We now extend the definitions so that P need not be on the unit circle. Figure 6.24 shows an angle θ in standard position, a point P' on the unit circle, and a point P which lies r units from the origin. The distance r from 0 to P is called the *radius vector*. Triangles OPQ and $OP'Q'$ are both right triangles and OP has length r. From the figure,

$$\frac{y'}{1} = \frac{y}{r} \text{ and } \frac{x'}{1} = \frac{x}{r}.$$

Since $\sin \theta = y'$ and $\cos \theta = x'$, we have

$$\sin \theta = \frac{y}{r} \qquad \text{and} \qquad \cos \theta = \frac{x}{r}.$$

The other trigonometric functions can be defined as follows.

$$\tan \theta = \frac{y}{x} \qquad \cot \theta = \frac{x}{y}$$

$$\csc \theta = \frac{r}{y} \qquad \sec \theta = \frac{r}{x}.$$

As we can see by looking at Figure 6.24, the new definitions of the trigonometric functions allow us to think of the trigonometric functions as ratios of the sides of a right triangle.

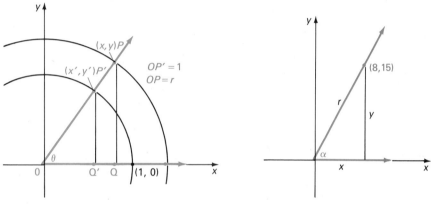

Figure 6.24   Figure 6.25

Example 2   The terminal side of an angle α goes through the point (8, 15). Find the values of the trigonometric functions of α.

Figure 6.25 shows angle α and the triangle formed by dropping a perpendicular from the point (8, 15). We have $x = 8$ and $y = 15$. To find the radius vector r, use the Pythagorean theorem:

$$r^2 = x^2 + y^2 \qquad \text{or} \qquad r = \sqrt{x^2 + y^2}.$$

(Recall that $\sqrt{a}$ represents the *positive* square root of *a*.)

$$r = \sqrt{8^2 + 15^2}$$
$$= \sqrt{64 + 225}$$
$$r = \sqrt{289}.$$

By using a calculator, or from Table 1 in the Appendix, we have $r = 17$. The values of the trigonometric functions of angle α are now found by the definitions given above.

$$\sin \alpha = \frac{y}{r} = \frac{15}{17} \qquad \cos \alpha = \frac{x}{r} = \frac{8}{17} \qquad \tan \alpha = \frac{y}{x} = \frac{15}{8}$$

$$\csc \alpha = \frac{r}{y} = \frac{17}{15} \qquad \sec \alpha = \frac{r}{x} = \frac{17}{8} \qquad \cot \alpha = \frac{x}{y} = \frac{8}{15} \qquad ▌$$

Now that we have defined the trigonometric functions for angles, we can use some results from geometry to find the trigonometric functions for 30°, 45°, and 60°. (We could also use the methods of Exercises 45 and 46 of Section 6.1.) The trigonometric functions of 30° and 60° are found by considering a 30°–60° right triangle. Such a triangle can be obtained from an *equilateral triangle*, a triangle with all sides equal in length. Each angle of such a triangle has a measure of 60°.

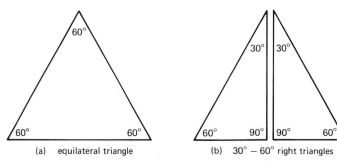

(a)   equilateral triangle   (b)   30° − 60° right triangles

Figure 6.26

If we bisect one angle of an equilateral triangle, we obtain two right triangles, each of which has angles of 30°, 60°, and 90°, as shown in Figure 6.26(b). If the hypotenuse of one of these right triangles has a length of 2, then the shortest side will have a length of 1. (Why?) We use x to represent the length of the medium side, then use the Pythagorean theorem.

$$2^2 = 1^2 + x^2$$
$$4 = 1 + x^2$$
$$3 = x^2$$
$$\sqrt{3} = x.$$

The length of the medium side is thus $\sqrt{3}$. In summary, in a 30°–60° right triangle, the hypotenuse is always twice as long as the shortest side, and the medium side has a length which is $\sqrt{3}$ times as long as that of the shortest side. Also, the shortest side is opposite the 30° angle, and the medium side is opposite the 60° angle.

Now we can find the trigonometric functions for an angle of 30°. To do so, place a 30° angle in standard position, as shown in Figure 6.27. Choose a point P on the terminal side of the angle so that $r = 2$. By the work above, P will have coordinates $(\sqrt{3}, 1)$. Thus, $x = \sqrt{3}$, $y = 1$, and $r = 2$. By the definitions of the trigonometric functions,

$$\sin 30° = \frac{1}{2} \qquad \tan 30° = \frac{\sqrt{3}}{3} \qquad \sec 30° = \frac{2\sqrt{3}}{3}$$

$$\cos 30° = \frac{\sqrt{3}}{2} \qquad \cot 30° = \sqrt{3} \qquad \csc 30° = 2.$$

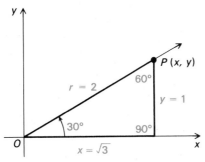

Figure 6.27

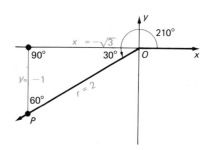

Figure 6.28

Example 3   Find the values of the trigonometric functions for 210°.

Draw an angle of 210° in standard position, as shown in Figure 6.28. Choose point P on the terminal side of the angle so that $r=2$. By our knowledge of 30°–60° right triangles, the coordinates of point P are $(-\sqrt{3}, -1)$. Thus, $x = -\sqrt{3}$, $y = -1$, and $r = 2$, with

$$\sin 210° = -\frac{1}{2} \qquad \tan 210° = \frac{\sqrt{3}}{3} \qquad \sec 210° = -\frac{2\sqrt{3}}{3}$$

$$\cos 210° = -\frac{\sqrt{3}}{2} \qquad \cot 210° = \sqrt{3} \qquad \csc 210° = -2. \quad \blacksquare$$

To find the values of the trigonometric functions for 45°, let us start with a 45°–45° right triangle, as shown in Figure 6.29. Such a triangle is *isosceles* and thus has two sides of equal length.

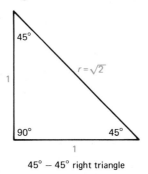

45° − 45° right triangle

Figure 6.29

If we let the sides of shorter length each have length 1 and if r represents the length of the hypotenuse, then

$$1^2 + 1^2 = r^2$$
$$2 = r^2$$
$$\sqrt{2} = r.$$

In general, in a 45°–45° right triangle, the hypotenuse has a length which is $\sqrt{2}$ times as long as the length of either of the shorter sides.

To find the values of the trigonometric functions for 45°, place a 45° angle in standard position, as in Figure 6.30. Choose point P on the terminal side of the angle so that $r = \sqrt{2}$. Then the coordinates of P become (1, 1). Hence, $x = 1$, $y = 1$, and $r = \sqrt{2}$, so that

$$\sin 45° = \frac{\sqrt{2}}{2} \qquad \tan 45° = 1 \qquad \sec 45° = \sqrt{2}$$

$$\cos 45° = \frac{\sqrt{2}}{2} \qquad \cot 45° = 1 \qquad \csc 45° = \sqrt{2}.$$

To find the values of sin 45° and cos 45°, we rationalized the denominators.

Figure 6.31 shows an acute angle θ in standard position. A right triangle (triangle with a 90° angle) has been drawn. By the work above, we know that $\sin \theta = y/r$. It is convenient to call y the length of the *side opposite* angle θ, with r the length of the *hypotenuse*. Also, x is the length of the *side adjacent* to θ. Using these terms, we have

$$\sin \theta = \frac{\text{side opposite}}{\text{hypotenuse}} \qquad \cos \theta = \frac{\text{side adjacent}}{\text{hypotenuse}} \qquad \tan \theta = \frac{\text{side opposite}}{\text{side adjacent}}$$

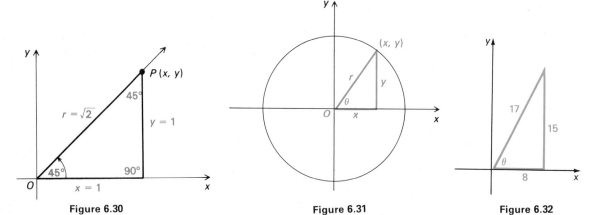

Figure 6.30   Figure 6.31   Figure 6.32

Example 4 Find the values of sin θ, cos θ, and tan θ for angle θ of Figure 6.32.

As shown in the figure, the length of the hypotenuse is 17, the length of the side opposite θ is 15, and the length of the side adjacent to θ is 8. Thus,

$$\sin \theta = \frac{15}{17}, \qquad \cos \theta = \frac{8}{17}, \qquad \text{and} \qquad \tan \theta = \frac{15}{8}. \qquad \blacksquare$$

6.4 Exercises   *Find the values of the six trigonometric functions for the following angles.*

1. 120°   3. 150°   5. 240°   7. 330°

2. 135°   4. 225°   6. 300°   8. 390°

| **9.** 420° | **11.** 510° | **13.** 180° | **15.** −90° |
| **10.** 495° | **12.** 570° | **14.** 270° | **16.** −180° |

Complete the following table.

	θ	$\sin\theta$	$\cos\theta$	$\tan\theta$	$\cot\theta$	$\sec\theta$	$\csc\theta$
17.	30°	1/2	$\sqrt{3}/2$	_____	_____	$2\sqrt{3}/3$	2
18.	45°	_____	_____	1	1	_____	_____
19.	60°	_____	1/2	$\sqrt{3}$	_____	2	_____
20.	120°	$\sqrt{3}/2$	_____	$-\sqrt{3}$	_____	_____	$2\sqrt{3}/3$
21.	135°	$\sqrt{2}/2$	$-\sqrt{2}/2$	_____	_____	$-\sqrt{2}$	$\sqrt{2}$
22.	150°	_____	$-\sqrt{3}/2$	$-\sqrt{3}/3$	_____	_____	2
23.	210°	−1/2	_____	$\sqrt{3}/3$	$\sqrt{3}$	_____	−2
24.	240°	$-\sqrt{3}/2$	−1/2	_____	_____	−2	$-2\sqrt{3}/3$

Find the six trigonometric function values of θ where the point given below is on the terminal side of angle θ in standard position.

| **25.** (−3, 4) | **27.** (24, 7) | **29.** (−12, −5) | **31.** (−9, −12) |
| **26.** (−4, −3) | **28.** (−7, 24) | **30.** (6, 8) | **32.** (5, −12) |

Find the six trigonometric function values of θ.

33.
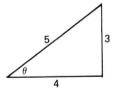

35.
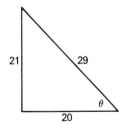

37.
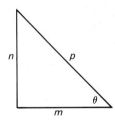

34.
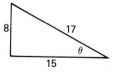

36.
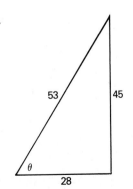

38.
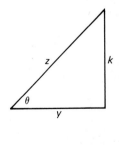

◉ *Find sin A, cos A, and tan A for the following right triangles.*

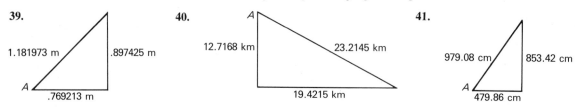

39.
1.181973 m   .897425 m
A
.769213 m

40.
A
12.7168 km   23.2145 km
19.4215 km

41.
979.08 cm   853.42 cm
A
479.86 cm

Answer true *or* false *for each of the following.*

42. $\sin 30° + \sin 60° = \sin (30° + 60°)$

43. $\sin (30° + 60°) = \sin 30° \cdot \cos 60° + \sin 60° \cdot \cos 30°$

44. $\cos 60° = 2 \cos^2 30° - 1$

45. $\cos 60° = 2 \cos 30°$

46. $\sin 120° = \sin 150° - \sin 30°$

47. $\sin 210° = \sin 180° + \sin 30°$

48. $\sin 120° = \sin 180° \cdot \cos 60° - \sin 60° \cdot \cos 180°$

49. $\cos 300° = \cos 240° \cdot \cos 60° - \sin 240° \cdot \sin 60°$

50. $\cos 150° = \cos 120° \cdot \cos 30° - \sin 120° \cdot \sin 30°$

◉ *Find each of the following values on a calculator. Then explain why these answers are not really "correct" if the exact value has been requested.*

51. $\sin 45°$ **52.** $\tan 60°$

6.5   Values of Trigonometric Functions

Up to now, we have discussed values of the trigonometric functions only for certain special values of θ. The methods we used were primarily based on geometry. Certainly, there are many values of θ for which geometric methods are inadequate and for which more advanced methods, beyond the level of this course, are required.

Approximate values of the trigonometric functions can be found with a calculator or by using special tables, such as Table 5 in the Appendix. This table gives the values of the trigonometric functions for values of θ where $0° \leq \theta \leq 90°$ or $0 \leq \theta \leq \pi/2$. Most of the values in Table 5 are four decimal place approximations. However, for convenience, we use the equality symbol with the understanding that the values are actually approximations. The table is designed to give the value of θ in the first two columns (in degrees, then radians) for $0° \leq \theta \leq 45°$ (or $0 \leq \theta \leq \pi/4$) and in the last two columns for $45° \leq \theta \leq 90°$ (or $\pi/4 \leq \theta \leq \pi/2$). When locating values for $45° \leq \theta \leq 90°$ (or $\pi/4 \leq \theta \leq \pi/2$), read *up* the table and refer to the names of the trigonometric functions at the *bottom* of the page. Function values of real numbers can be found by using the "radian" column of Table 5.

Example 1   Use Table 5 to find each of the following.
    (a) sin 10° 20'
        Find 10° 20' at the side. Since this angle is at the left, use the function names at the top of the page.

$$\sin 10° \, 20' = 0.1794$$

    (b) cos 48° 10'
        This angle is at the right of the page, so we use function names on the bottom of the page.

$$\cos 48° \, 10' = 0.6670$$

    (c) tan 82° 00' = 7.115
    (d) sin .2676 = 0.2644   (Use the "radian" column of the table.)
    (e) cot 1.2043 = 0.3839   ▌

When the required value is not in the table, linear interpolation may be used, as shown in the next example.

Example 2   Find each of the following.
    (a) tan 40° 52'
        The value for tan 40° 52' lies 2/10 or .2 of the way between the values for tan 40° 50' and tan 41°00'.

$$10 \left\{ 2 \left\{ \begin{array}{l} \tan 40° \, 50' = .8642 \\ \tan 40° \, 52' = ? \\ \tan 41° \, 00' = .8693 \end{array} \right\} .0051 \right.$$

$$\tan 40° \, 52' = .2(.8693 - .8642) + .8642$$
$$= .2(.0051) + .8642$$
$$= .8652$$

    (b) cos 63° 34'
        Work as follows.

$$10 \left\{ 4 \left\{ \begin{array}{l} \cos 63° \, 30' = .4462 \\ \cos 63° \, 34' = ? \\ \cos 63° \, 40' = .4436 \end{array} \right\} .0026 \right.$$

$$\cos 63° \, 34' = .4462 - (.4)(.4462 - .4436)$$
$$= .4462 - .4(.0026)$$
$$= .4452 \quad ▌$$

Here we had to *subtract* from .4462 rather than add because the cosine function *decreases* as θ increases for $0 < \theta < \pi/2$.

Example 3   Find a value of θ satisfying each of the following.
(a) $\sin \theta = .5807$; θ in degrees
Use Table 5 and read columns having sine at either the top or the bottom. Here we find .5807 in a column having sine at the top. Thus, we use angles at the left to read the value of θ.

$$\theta = 35° \ 30'$$

(b) $\tan \theta = 2.699$; θ in degrees
Here 2.699 is in a column having tangent at the bottom. Thus, we use angles at the right to read the value of θ.

$$\theta = 69° \ 40' \quad \blacksquare$$

Table 5 gives values only for angles between 0° and 90°, inclusive, or for real numbers between 0 and $\pi/2$, inclusive. For values outside this range, we need to use some of our earlier work with trigonometric functions. As we have seen, we can find the trigonometric function values for $90° < \theta < 360°$ by referring to the appropriate value of θ in the interval $0° < \theta < 90°$ and affixing the correct sign. For any value θ in the interval $90° < \theta < 360°$, the positive acute angle made by the terminal side of angle θ and the x-axis is called the **related** or **reference angle** for θ; this new angle is written θ'. See Figure 6.33. For example, if $\theta = 135°$, the related angle θ' is 45°. If $\theta = 200°$, then $\theta' = 20°$. If $\theta = -\pi/6$, then $\theta' = \pi/6$.

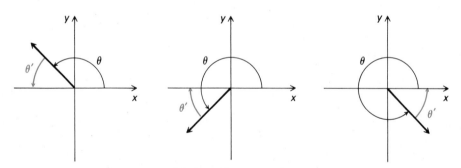

related or reference angles

Figure 6.33

Example 4   Find the related angle for each of the following.
(a) 218°
As shown in Figure 6.34, the positive acute angle made by the terminal side of this angle and the x-axis is $218° - 180° = 38°$.
(b) 321° 10′
The positive acute angle made by the terminal side of this angle and the x-axis is $360° - 321° \ 10'$. Write 360° as 359° 60′ so that the related angle is

$$359° \ 60' - 321° \ 10' = 38° \ 50'.$$

By the way, an angle of $-38°$ 50′, which has the same terminal ray as 321° 10′, also has a related angle of 38° 50′.

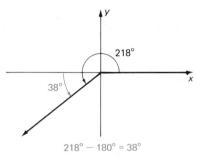

218° − 180° = 38°

Figure 6.34

(c) 2.5685
The related angle is found by subtracting from π. (See Figure 6.35.) Using the four-decimal-place approximation 3.1416 for π gives

$$3.1416 - 2.5685 = 0.5731.$$

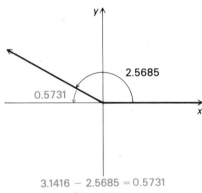

3.1416 − 2.5685 = 0.5731

Figure 6.35

Example 5   Find each of the following.
(a) sin 409°
If $\theta = 409°$, draw a sketch to see that $\theta' = 49°$. Since θ terminates in quadrant I, sin θ is positive, and

$$\sin 409° = \sin 49° = 0.7547.$$

(b) cot (−185°)
The reference angle here is $\theta' = 5°$. Since −185° terminates in quadrant II, where cotangent is negative, we have

$$\cot (-185°) = -\cot 5° = -11.43.$$

(c) sec 3.0369
Use 3.1416 as an approximation for π. With this, if $\theta = 3.0369$, then $\theta' = 0.1047$, and

$$\sec 3.0369 = -\sec 0.1047 = -1.006.$$

(Why was a minus sign used?)

As we saw in the last section, the trigonometric functions can be obtained from the lengths of the sides of a right triangle. The next example shows another application of this fact.

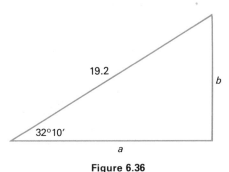

Figure 6.36

Example 6   A surveyor gathered the data shown on the triangle of Figure 6.36. Find the lengths of sides a and b of the triangle.

Let us first find b. The sine of angle B (the angle opposite b) is given by

$$\sin B = \frac{\text{side opposite}}{\text{hypotenuse}}.$$

Substitute in the known values.

$$\sin 32° \ 10' = \frac{b}{19.2}.$$

Use Table 5 or a calculator.

$$.5324 = \frac{b}{19.2}$$
$$19.2(.5324) = b$$
$$10.2 = b$$

Use the cosine of angle B to find that $a = 16.3$.   ▌

We shall study right triangle applications in more detail in Chapter 8.

6.5 Exercises   *Find the related angle for each of the following. Use 3.1416 as an approximation for π.*

1. 215°   **4.** −12°   **7.** 3.21   **10.** −1.7861

2. 550°   **5.** −110° 10′   **8.** 2.4   **11.** −4.0230

3. −143°   **6.** −429° 30′   **9.** 5.9690   **12.** −2.4580

Use Table 5 or a calculator to get a value for each of the following. Use 3.1416 as an approximation for π.

13. sin 39° 20′   **15.** sin (−38° 40′)   **17.** cos (−124° 50′)

14. cos 58° 40′   **16.** csc (−168° 30′)   **18.** sec 274° 30′

19. sec 1.9024

20. cot 3.1998

21. sin 7.5835

22. tan 6.4752

23. cos (−4.0230)

24. cot (−3.8426)

Use interpolation to find each of the following values.

25. tan 29° 42′

26. sin 56° 38′

27. tan 49° 17′

28. sin 78° 32′

29. sin .1635

30. cos (−1.3870)

31. tan (−.3034)

32. csc .2518

Use Table 5 or a calculator to find a value of θ in degrees for each of the following.

33. sin $\theta = 0.8480$

34. cot $\theta = 1.257$

35. sec $\theta = 2.759$

Use Table 5 or a calculator to find a value of s in radians for each of the following.

36. cos $s = 0.7826$

37. sin $s = 0.9936$

38. tan $s = 2.605$

For small real number values of x, sin x ≈ x. (A graph that makes this plausible is given in the next section.) Use this fact to find approximate values of the following without using tables or a calculator.

39. sin .001

40. sin .009

41. sin .01

42. sin .05

As we know, tan x = sin x/cos x. For small values of x, cos x ≈ 1 and sin x ≈ x. Thus, tan x ≈ x. Use this fact to find approximate values of the following without using tables or a calculator.

43. tan .01

44. tan .005

45. tan .10

46. tan .05

Approximate the value of the following without using tables or a calculator.

47. $\dfrac{\sin .01}{.01}$

48. $\dfrac{\sin .009}{.009}$

49. $\dfrac{\sin .05}{\tan .05}$

50. $\dfrac{\tan .10 + \sin .10}{\sin .10}$

⦿ *In calculus courses sin x and cos x are expressed as infinite sums, where x is measured in radians. For all real numbers x and all natural numbers n, the following hold.*

$$\cos x = 1 - \frac{x^2}{2!} + \frac{x^4}{4!} - \ldots + (-1)^{n-1}\frac{x^{2n-2}}{(2n-2)!} + \ldots$$

and

$$\sin x = x - \frac{x^3}{3!} + \frac{x^5}{5!} - \ldots + (-1)^{n-1}\frac{x^{2n-1}}{(2n-1)!} + \ldots$$

where $2! = 2 \cdot 1; \quad 3! = 3 \cdot 2 \cdot 1; \quad 4! = 4 \cdot 3 \cdot 2 \cdot 1;$

and $n! = n(n-1)(n-2) \ldots (2)(1).$

Using these formulas, sin x and cos x can be evaluated to any desired degree of accuracy. For example, let us find cos 0.5 using the first three terms of the definition and compare this with the result using the first four terms. Using the first three terms, we have

$$\cos 0.5 = 1 - \frac{(0.5)^2}{2!} + \frac{(0.5)^4}{4!}$$

$$= 1 - \frac{.25}{2} + \frac{.0625}{24}$$

$$= 1 - 0.125 + 0.00260$$

$$= .87760$$

If we use four terms, the result is

$$\cos 0.5 = 1 - \frac{(0.5)^2}{2!} + \frac{(0.5)^4}{4!} - \frac{(0.5)^6}{6!}$$

$$= 1 - 0.125 + 0.00260 - 0.00002$$

$$= 0.87758$$

The two results differ by only 0.00002, so that the first three terms give results which are accurate to the fourth decimal place. From the tables, using interpolation, cos 0.5 = .87754.

Use the first three terms of the definitions given above for sin x and cos x to find the following. Compare your results with the values in Table 5 in the Appendix.

51. sin 1

52. sin 0.1

53. sin 0.01

54. cos 0.1

55. cos 0.01

Find the lengths of the missing sides in each of the following right triangles.

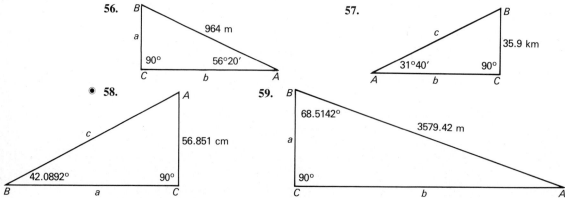

56.   **57.**

58.   **59.**

60. A woman stands 59.7 m from the base of a tree. The angle her line of sight makes to the top of the tree is 39° 20′. If the woman's eyes are 1.74 m above the ground, find the height of the tree.

61. A ladder leans against a building, making an angle of 24° 10′ with the building. If the ladder is 4.88 m in length, find the distance between the bottom of the ladder and the building.

6.6 Graphs of the Sine and Cosine Functions

In Section 6.1 we mentioned that sin x and cos x were periodic functions with a period of 2π. The repeating nature of these functions is evident in their graphs, shown there and later in this section. In general, a **periodic function** has the property

$$f(x) = f(x + p)$$

for any real number x and some positive real number p. The smallest value of p that will work is called the **period.**

The sine function, $y = \sin x$, has all real numbers for its domain, and its range is $-1 \le y \le 1$. Since the sine function has period 2π, we can sketch the graph of the sine function by concentrating on values of x between 0 and 2π. We can then repeat this portion of the graph for other values of x.

As we have seen, for x-values from 0 to $\pi/2$, sin x increases from 0 to 1, and for x-values from $\pi/2$ to π, sin x decreases from 1 back to 0.

We know that sin x is negative for $\pi < x < 2\pi$. Therefore, for x-values from π to $3\pi/2$, sin x decreases from 0 to -1, and for x-values from $3\pi/2$ to 2π, sin x increases from -1 back to 0. These facts are summarized in the table of values shown below. (Decimals have been rounded to the nearest tenth.)

x	0	$\pi/4$	$\pi/2$	$3\pi/4$	π	$5\pi/4$	$3\pi/2$	$7\pi/4$	2π
sin x	0	.7	1	.7	0	$-.7$	-1	$-.7$	0

Plotting the points from the table of values and connecting them with a smooth curve, we get the solid portion of the graph of Figure 6.37. Since $y = \sin x$ is periodic and has all real numbers as its domain, the graph continues in both directions indefinitely, as shown by the dashed lines of the figure.

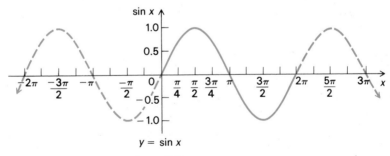

$y = \sin x$

Figure 6.37

From Figure 6.37, we see that the graph of $y = \sin x$ is symmetric about the origin. Based on our discussion of symmetry in Chapter 3, this means that we can replace x with $-x$ and y with $-y$ without changing the function. Thus,

$$y = \sin x \quad \text{becomes} \quad -y = \sin(-x),$$

and upon replacing $-y$ with $-\sin x$,

$$\sin(-x) = -\sin x.$$

(See also Exercise 41, where this same result is derived using the unit circle.)

The graph of $y = \cos x$ in Figure 6.38 can be found by plotting points just as we did for $y = \sin x$. Figure 6.38 shows that the graph of $y = \cos x$ is symmetric about the y-axis. Thus, we should be able to substitute $-x$ for x in $y = \cos x$ without changing its value. Doing this gives $y = \cos(-x)$. Since $\cos x = y$, we have

$$\cos(-x) = \cos x$$

(See also Exercise 42.)

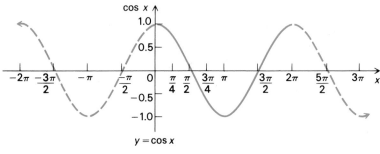

$$y = \cos x$$

Figure 6.38

Example 1 Graph $y = 2 \sin x$.

For each value of x, the value of y is twice as large as it would be for $y = \sin x$, as shown in the table of values. Thus, the only change in the graph is in the range, which becomes $-2 \leq y \leq 2$. (See Figure 6.39.)

x	0	$\pi/2$	π	$3\pi/2$	2π
$\sin x$	0	1	0	-1	0
$2 \sin x$	0	2	0	-2	0

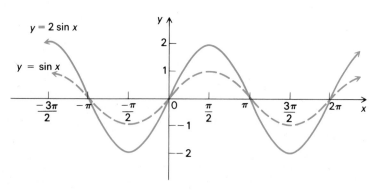

Figure 6.39

In general, the graph of $y = a \sin x$ will have the same form as $y = \sin x$ with range $-|a| \leq y \leq |a|$. The number $|a|$ is called the **amplitude**.

Also, the graph of $y = a \cos x$ has the same shape as $y = \cos x$, but has a range of $-|a| \leq y \leq |a|$. Again, $|a|$ is called the *amplitude*. No matter the value of a, the period of $y = a \sin x$ and $y = a \cos x$ is still 2π.

Example 2 Graph $y = \sin 2x$.

Note the comparison between the functional values for $\sin x$ and $\sin 2x$.

x	0	$\pi/4$	$\pi/2$	$3\pi/4$	π	$5\pi/4$	$3\pi/2$	$7\pi/4$
$2x$	0	$\pi/2$	π	$3\pi/2$	2π	$5\pi/2$	3π	$7\pi/2$
$\sin 2x$	0	1	0	-1	0	1	0	-1

As the table shows, multiplying x by 2 results in shortening the period by half. The range is not changed. Figure 6.40 shows the graph of $y = \sin 2x$. ▌

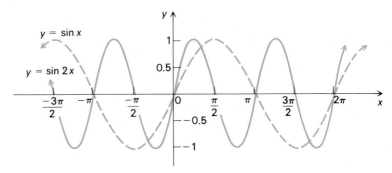

Figure 6.40

In general, the graph of $y = \sin bx$ will look like that of $\sin x$, but with period $|2\pi/b|$. (See Exercises 43 and 44.) The graph of $y = \cos bx$ has a similar period change.

Example 3 Graph $y = \cos \dfrac{1}{2}x$.

The period here is $|2\pi/(1/2)| = 4\pi$. The amplitude is 1. The graph is shown in Figure 6.41. ▌

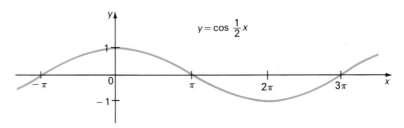

$y = \cos \dfrac{1}{2}x$

Figure 6.41

Example 4 Graph $y = \sin\left(x - \dfrac{\pi}{3}\right)$

Based on our work with translations in Chapter 3, this graph is the same as the graph of $y = \sin x$, except that it is shifted $\pi/3$ units to the right. The graph of $y = \sin (x - \pi/3)$ is the solid line of Figure 6.42.

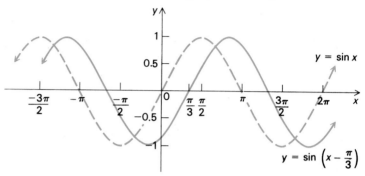

Figure 6.42

In general, $y = \sin (x - c)$ will have the shape of the basic graph $y = \sin x$, but will be translated $|c|$ units—to the left if $c < 0$, and to the right if $c > 0$. The number c is the **phase shift** of the graph.

Also, $y = \cos (x - c)$ has the shape of $y = \cos x$, but is translated $|c|$ units—to the left if $c < 0$ and to the right if $c > 0$. Again, c is the *phase shift*.

Example 5 Graph $y = -2 \cos (3x + \pi)$.

The amplitude of this graph is $|-2| = 2$. The period is $|2\pi/3| = 2\pi/3$. To find the phase shift, let

$$3x + \pi = 0$$
$$3x = -\pi$$
$$x = -\frac{\pi}{3}.$$

The graph is shifted $\pi/3$ units to the left, as shown in the graph of Figure 6.43.

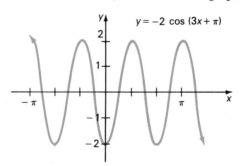

Figure 6.43

Example 6 Radio stations send out a carrier signal in the form of a sine wave having equation

$$y = A_0 \sin (2\pi \omega_0 t),$$

where A_0 is the amplitude of the carrier signal, ω_0 is the number of periods the signal oscillates through in one second (its *frequency*), and t is time. A carrier signal received by a radio would be a pure tone. To transmit music and voices, the station might change or *modulate* A_0 according to the function

$$A_0(t) = A_0 + mA_0 \sin(2\pi\omega t),$$

where ω is the frequency of a pure tone and m is a constant called the *degree of modulation*. The transmitted signal has equation

$$y = A_0 \sin(2\pi\omega_0 t) + A_0 m \sin(2\pi\omega t) \sin(2\pi\omega_0 t)$$
$$= A_0[1 + m \sin(2\pi\omega t)] \sin(2\pi\omega_0 t).$$

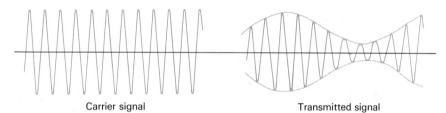

Carrier signal   Transmitted signal

Figure 6.44

A typical carrier signal and a typical graph of y are shown in Figure 6.44. This process of sending out a radio signal is called *amplitude modulation,* or AM, radio.

Frequency modulation, or FM, radio involves altering the frequency of the carrier signal rather than its amplitude. A typical graph is shown in Figure 6.45.

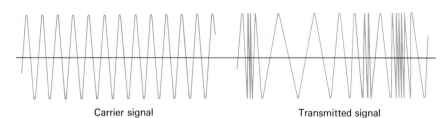

Carrier signal   Transmitted signal

Figure 6.45

6.6 Exercises   *Graph each of the following functions over a two-period interval. Give the period and amplitude of each.*

1. $y = 2 \cos x$

2. $y = \dfrac{1}{2} \sin x$

3. $y = -3 \cos x$

4. $y = \sin \dfrac{1}{2}x$

5. $y = \cos \dfrac{1}{8}x$

6. $y = \cos 2x$

7. $y = \sin 3x$

8. $y = -\sin 4x$

9. $y = -\cos 6x$

10. $y = -2 \cos 3x$

11. $y = 2 \sin \dfrac{1}{4}x$

12. $y = 3 \sin 2x$

Graph each of the following over a one-period interval.

13. $y = \cos \left(x - \dfrac{\pi}{2}\right)$

14. $y = \sin \left(x + \dfrac{\pi}{4}\right)$

15. $y = \sin \left(x - \dfrac{\pi}{4}\right)$

16. $y = \cos \left(x + \dfrac{\pi}{3}\right)$

17. $y = 2 \cos \left(x - \dfrac{\pi}{3}\right)$

18. $y = 3 \sin \left(x + \dfrac{3\pi}{2}\right)$

19. $y = \dfrac{3}{2} \sin 2\left(x - \dfrac{\pi}{4}\right)$

20. $y = -\dfrac{1}{2} \cos 4\left(x + \dfrac{\pi}{2}\right)$

21. $y = -4 \sin (2x - \pi)$

22. $y = 3 \cos (4x + \pi)$

23. $y = \dfrac{1}{2} \cos \left(\dfrac{1}{2}x - \dfrac{\pi}{4}\right)$

24. $y = -\dfrac{1}{4} \sin \left(\dfrac{3}{4}x + \dfrac{\pi}{8}\right)$

25. Is the function $y = \sin x$ even, odd, or neither?

26. Is the function $y = \cos x$ even, odd, or neither?

27. Graph $y = \sin \left(\theta - \dfrac{\pi}{2}\right)$. What trigonometric function has the same graph?

28. Graph $y = \cos \left(\theta - \dfrac{\pi}{2}\right)$. What trigonometric function has the same graph?

Pure sounds produce single sine waves on an oscilloscope. Find the amplitude and period of each sine wave in the following photographs. On the vertical scale, each square represents .5, and on the horizontal scale each square represents $\pi/6$.

29.

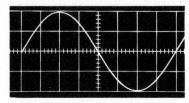

30.

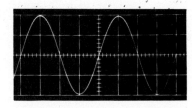

Scientists believe that the average annual temperature in a given location is periodic. The overall temperature at a given place during a given season fluctuates as time goes on, from colder to warmer, and back to colder. The graph below shows an idealized description of the temperature for the last few thousand years of a location at the latitude of Anchorage.

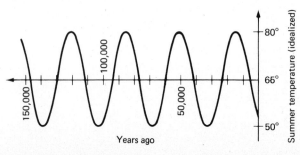

31. An alternate definition of amplitude is half the difference of the highest and lowest points on the graph. Use this definition to find the amplitude of the graph shown in the figure.

32. Find the period of this graph.

33. What is the trend of the temperature now?

Many of the activities of living organisms are periodic. For example, the graph below shows the time that flying squirrels begin their evening activity.

34. Find the amplitude and period of this graph.

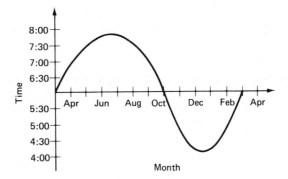

The graph shown here gives the variation in blood pressure for a typical person. Systolic and diastolic pressures are the upper and lower limits of the periodic changes in pressure which produce the pulse. The length of time between peaks is called the period of the pulse.

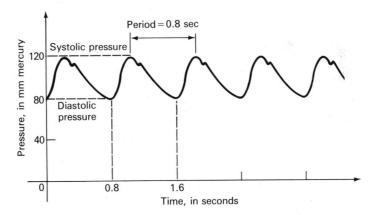

35. Find the amplitude of this graph.

36. Find the pulse rate for this person — the number of pulse beats in one minute.

Graph each of the following functions. Give the period of each. Use the definition of Exercise 31 to find the amplitude of each.

37. $y = 2 + \cos x$ **39.** $y = 3 - 2 \sin x$

38. $y = \sin x - 1$ **40.** $y = -5 + 3 \cos x$

Figure for Exercises 35 and 36: From *Calculus for the Life Sciences* by Rodolfo De Sapio. W. H. Freeman and Company. Copyright © 1978.

Use a sketch of a unit circle to show that

41. $\sin(-x) = -\sin x$

42. $\cos(-x) = \cos x$

43. To find the period of $y = \sin bx$, where $b > 0$, first observe that as bx varies from 0 to 2π, we get one period of the graph of $y = \sin bx$. Show that x must therefore vary from 0 to $2\pi/b$, so that the period of $y = \sin bx$ is $2\pi/b$.

44. In Exercise 43, show that the period of $y = \sin bx$ is $|2\pi/b|$, no matter whether b is positive or negative.

● **45.** Sketch the graph of $y = \sin x$ for real number values of x from 0 to .2 in increments of .02. On the same axes, draw $y = x$. Use this sketch to argue that for small values of x, $\sin x \approx x$.

● **46.** The quotient $(\sin x)/x$ is very important in calculus. Find the value of this quotient, starting with $x = .1$. Then let x decrease by steps of .01 until $x = .01$ is reached. (Why can't we let x decrease all the way to 0?) What number does the quotient seem to be approaching as x gets closer and closer to 0?

Graph one period of each of the following.

47. $y = \sin^2 x$

48. $y = \cos^2 x$

49. $y = \sin^2 2x$

50. $y = 4\cos^2 x$

6.7   Graphs of the Other Trigonometric Functions

In this section, we continue our discussion of the graphs of the trigonometric functions, beginning with $y = \tan x$. As we shall see in the next chapter, the period of $y = \tan x$ is π, so that we need to investigate the tangent function only within an interval of π units. A convenient interval for this purpose is $-\pi/2 < x < \pi/2$. Although the endpoints $-\pi/2$ and $\pi/2$ are not in the domain of tangent (why?), $\tan x$ exists for all other values in the interval.

There is no point on the graph of $y = \tan x$ at $x = -\pi/2$ or $x = \pi/2$. However, in the interval $0 < x < \pi/2$, $\tan x$ is positive. As x goes from 0 to $\pi/2$, we see from Table 5 that $\tan x$ gets larger and larger. The graph approaches the vertical line $x = \pi/2$ but never touches it. The line $x = \pi/2$ is called a *vertical asymptote*. The lines $x = \pi/2 + k\pi$, where k is an integer, are all vertical asymptotes. We indicate these asymptotes on the graph with a dashed black line. (See Figure 6.46.) In the interval $-\pi/2 < x < 0$, $\tan x$ is negative, and as x goes from 0 to $-\pi/2$, $\tan x$ gets smaller and smaller. A table of values for $\tan x$, where $-\pi/2 < x < \pi/2$, is given below. This interval is shown by the solid colored line in Figure 6.46.

x	$-\pi/3$	$-\pi/4$	$-\pi/6$	0	$\pi/6$	$\pi/4$	$\pi/3$
$\tan x$	-1.7	-1	$-.6$	0	.6	1	1.7

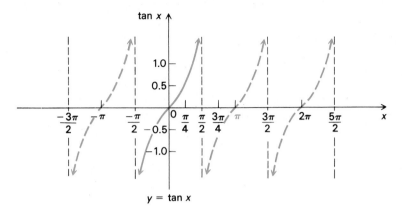

Figure 6.46

As shown in Figure 6.46, the graph of $y = \tan x$, like that of $y = \sin x$, is symmetric about the origin. Replacing y with $-y$ and x with $-x$ gives $-y = \tan(-x)$. Then, substituting from $y = \tan x$ gives $-\tan x = \tan(-x)$ or

$$\tan(-x) = -\tan x.$$

Example 1   Graph $y = \tan 2x$.

As we saw in the last section, multiplying x by a positive number b results in the period being changed to π/b. Here we have $b = 2$, so the period becomes $\pi/2$. Note that $x = \dfrac{\pi}{2}$ leads to $y = \tan \pi$, $x = \pi/4$ leads to $y = \tan \pi/2$, and so on. Thus, the graph of $y = \tan 2x$ is the same as the graph of $y = \tan x$ except for the change in the period. See Figure 6.47.   ▌

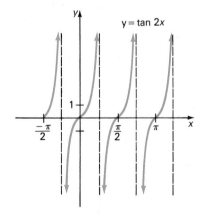

Figure 6.47

The remaining three functions can be graphed by using the fact that they are reciprocals of the three functions we have already discussed. The cotangent function, like tangent, has a period of π. Since $\cot x = 1/\tan x$, we can find some information about the cotangent graph by considering the values of $1/\tan x$. The tangent function is 0 when $x = 0$. Thus, cot 0 is undefined. In fact, cot $(0 + k\pi)$ is undefined for all integer values of k. The lines $x = 0$, $x = \pi$, $x = 2\pi$, and so on, are vertical asymptotes. When tan x is undefined, cot $x = 0$. This occurs at $\pi/2 + k\pi$. Since cot $x = 1/\tan x$, the function will be positive when tangent x is positive (in quadrants I and III) and negative when tangent x is negative (in quadrants II and IV). By taking reciprocals of the values of tan x for $0 < x < \pi$, plotting some points, and considering the information mentioned above, we get the graph shown in Figure 6.48.

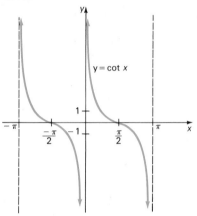

Figure 6.48

The graph of $y = \csc x$ is restricted to values of $x \neq k\pi$, where k is any integer. (Why?) Hence, the lines $x = k\pi$ are asymptotes. Since $\csc x = 1/\sin x$, the period is 2π, the same as for sin x. When sin $x = 1$, we have csc $x = 1$, and when $0 < \sin x < 1$, then csc $x > 1$. Thus, the graph takes the shape of the solid line shown in Figure 6.49. To show how the two curves are related, the graph of $y = \sin x$ is also shown, as a dashed curve. The graph of sec x, which is related to the graph of cos x in a similar way, is left for the exercises.

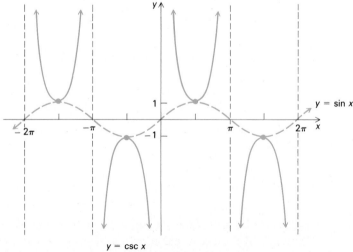

$y = \csc x$

Figure 6.49

Example 2   Graph $y = \dfrac{3}{2} \csc\left(x - \dfrac{\pi}{2}\right)$.

Compared with $y = \csc x$, this graph is translated $\pi/2$ units to the right. Also, it has no values of y between $3/2$ and $-3/2$; note how this relates to the increased amplitude of $y = 3/2 \sin x$ as compared with $y = \sin x$. See Figure 6.50. |

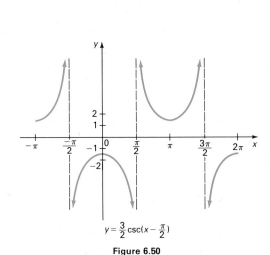

$y = \dfrac{3}{2} \csc(x - \dfrac{\pi}{2})$

Figure 6.50

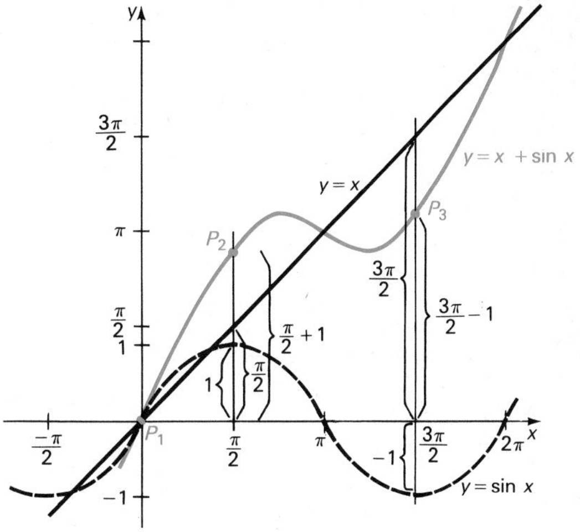

Figure 6.51

To graph trigonometric functions which are the sum of two or more terms, we can use a method called **addition of ordinates.** An **ordinate** is the y-value of an ordered pair. For example, in the ordered pair $(\pi, -1)$, the number -1 is the ordinate. This graphing method is best described by examples.

Example 3   Graph $y = x + \sin x$.

Begin by graphing the functions $y = x$ and $y = \sin x$ separately on the same coordinate axes. Figure 6.51 shows the two graphs. (We use a dashed line for $y = \sin x$ to make it easier to keep the two graphs separate.) Then select some x-values, and for these values add the two corresponding ordinates to get the ordinate of the sum, $x + \sin x$. For example, when $x = 0$, both ordinates are 0, so that $P_1 = (0, 0)$ is a point on the graph of $y = x + \sin x$. When $x = \pi/2$, the ordinates are $\pi/2$ and 1; their sum is $\pi/2 + 1$, and $P_2 = (\pi/2, \pi/2 + 1)$ is on the graph. At $x = 3\pi/2$, the sum is $3\pi/2 + (-1)$ or $3\pi/2 - 1$. The point with ordinate $3\pi/2 - 1$ is indicated by P_3 on the graph. As many points as necessary can be located in this way. The graph is then completed by drawing a smooth curve through the points. The graph of $y = x + \sin x$ is shown in color in Figure 6.51. |

As shown on the graph of Figure 6.51, we actually treat the ordinates as line segments. For example, the ordinate of P_2 is found by adding the two line segments which represent the ordinates of $\sin x$ and x at $\pi/2$. The same is true for the ordinate of P_3 as well as each of the other ordinates.

Example 4   Graph $y = \cos x - \sin x$.

When graphing a difference of functions, like $y = \cos x - \sin x$, it is easier to change the problem to a sum by rewriting it as $\cos x + (-\sin x)$. Then graph

$y = \cos x$ and $y = -\sin x$ on the same axes, as in Figure 6.52. At $x = 0$, the ordinates are 1 and 0, so the ordinate of $y = \cos x + (-\sin x)$ is $1 + 0 = 1$, and the point $(0, 1)$ is on the graph. Other points where one ordinate is 0 such as P_1 and P_4, are easy to plot. At any point where the graphs of $\cos x$ and $-\sin x$ cross, the ordinates are the same. Therefore, the ordinate of $y = \cos x + (-\sin x)$ is twice as large as the common ordinate. See P_2 and P_5 on the graph in Figure 6.52 for example. When $x = \pi/4$, the two ordinates are $\sqrt{2}/2$ and $-\sqrt{2}/2$, with a sum of 0. A zero sum occurs again at $x = 5\pi/4$. The finished graph is shown in color in Figure 6.52. ▌

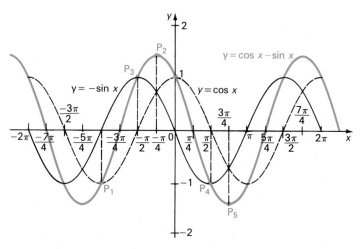

Figure 6.52

6.7 Exercises   *Graph each of the following over a two-period interval.*

1. $y = \cot \dfrac{1}{2} x$

2. $y = 5 \tan x$

3. $y = \sec x$

4. $y = \cot 2x$

5. $y = -\tan x$

6. $y = 3 \csc x$

7. $y = \sec 2x$

8. $y = \cot \dfrac{1}{4} x$

9. $y = \csc x + 4$

10. $y = \sec \dfrac{1}{2} x - 1$

11. $y = \tan x + 1$

12. $y = 3 \sec x + 2$

Graph each of the following over a one-period interval.

13. $y = \tan\left(x - \dfrac{\pi}{4}\right)$

14. $y = \cot\left(x + \dfrac{3\pi}{4}\right)$

15. $y = \sec\left(x + \dfrac{\pi}{3}\right)$

16. $y = 3 \csc\left(x + \dfrac{3\pi}{2}\right)$

17. $y = 2 + \tan\left(\dfrac{1}{2}x + \dfrac{\pi}{3}\right)$

18. $y = \csc\left(\dfrac{1}{2}x - \dfrac{\pi}{4}\right) - 1$

Use the method of addition of ordinates to graph each of the following.

19. $y = x + \cos x$

20. $y = \sin x - 2x$

21. $y = 3x - \cos 2x$

22. $y = x + 2 - \sin x$

23. $y = \sin x + \sin 2x$

24. $y = \cos x - \cos \frac{1}{2}x$

25. $y = \sin x + \tan x$

26. $y = \sin x + \csc x$

27. $y = 2 \cos x - \sec x$

28. $y = 2 \sec x + \sin x$

29. $y = \cos x + \cot x$

30. $y = \sin x - 2 \cos x$

31. $y = -x + \sec x$

32. $y = x + \csc x$

6.8 Inverse Trigonometric Functions

In Chapter 3 we defined the inverse of a one-to-one function. In this section we consider inverses of the trigonometric functions.

We begin with $y = \sin x$. Recall that a function must be one-to-one before it can have an inverse. From the graph of sine in Figure 6.37, it is clear that $y = \sin x$ is not a one-to-one function since different values of x can lead to the *same* value of y. However, by suitably restricting the domain of the sine function, we can define a one-to-one function. It is customary to restrict the domain of $y = \sin x$ to $-\pi/2 \le x \le \pi/2$, which is the solid portion of the graph in Figure 6.53. Reflecting that portion of the sine graph about the 45° line $y = x$ gives the graph of the inverse function, shown in Figure 6.54.

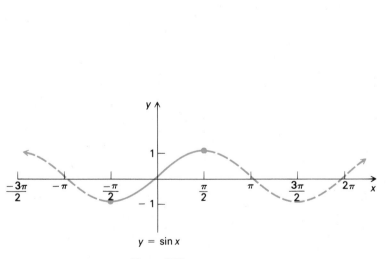

$y = \sin x$

Figure 6.53

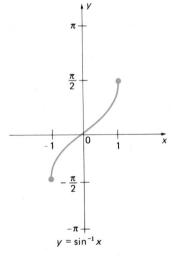

$y = \sin^{-1} x$

Figure 6.54

The inverse of the sine function, restricted to $-\pi/2 \le x \le \pi/2$, is written $y = \sin^{-1} x$; that is,

$$y = \sin^{-1}x \qquad \text{if and only if} \qquad x = \sin y.$$

The domain of $y = \sin^{-1} x$ is $-1 \le x \le 1$, while the range is $-\pi/2 \le y \le \pi/2$.

For each of the other trigonometric functions, we can define an inverse function by a suitable restriction on the range of the inverse function. The three most commonly used **inverse trigonometric functions** and their ranges are

$$y = \sin^{-1} x, \qquad -\pi/2 \le y \le \pi/2$$
$$y = \cos^{-1} x, \qquad 0 \le y \le \pi$$
$$y = \tan^{-1} x, \qquad -\pi/2 < y < \pi/2.$$

The graphs of $y = \cos^{-1} x$ and $y = \tan^{-1} x$ are shown in Figures 6.55 and 6.56, respectively.

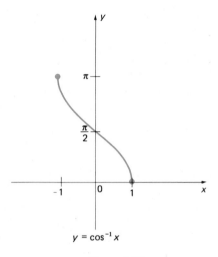

$y = \cos^{-1} x$

Figure 6.55

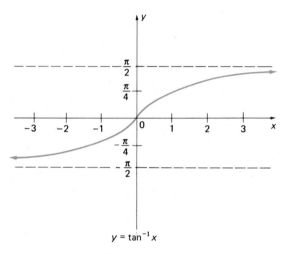

$y = \tan^{-1} x$

Figure 6.56

Example 1   Find $\sin^{-1} 1/2$.

Let $y = \sin^{-1} 1/2$. Then by the definition of the inverse sine function, $\sin y = 1/2$. Since $\sin \pi/6 = 1/2$ and $\pi/6$ is in the range of $y = \sin^{-1} x$, we have

$$\sin^{-1} 1/2 = \pi/6. \quad \blacksquare$$

Example 2   Find $\cos^{-1} -\sqrt{2}/2$.

Since we have the restriction $0 \le \cos^{-1} x \le \pi$, the angle represented by $\cos^{-1} x$ can terminate only in quadrants I and II. Since $-\sqrt{2}/2$ is negative, we are restricted to quadrant II. Let $y = \cos^{-1} -\sqrt{2}/2$. Then $\cos y = -\sqrt{2}/2$. In quadrant II, $\cos 3\pi/4 = -\sqrt{2}/2$, so

$$\cos^{-1} -\frac{\sqrt{2}}{2} = \frac{3\pi}{4}. \quad \blacksquare$$

Example 3   Find $\sin (\tan^{-1}(-3/2))$ without using tables or a calculator.

Let $y = \tan^{-1} (-3/2)$, so that $\tan y = -3/2$. Since $\tan^{-1} x$ is defined only in quadrants I and IV $(-\pi/2 < \tan^{-1} x < \pi/2)$, and since we have $x = -3/2$, we must work in quadrant IV. Sketch y in quadrant IV and label a triangle as shown in

Figure 6.57. The hypotenuse has a length of $\sqrt{13}$, so that $\sin y = -3/\sqrt{13}$, or

$$\sin\left(\tan^{-1} -\frac{3}{2}\right) = \frac{-3}{\sqrt{13}} = \frac{-3\sqrt{13}}{13}. \quad \blacksquare$$

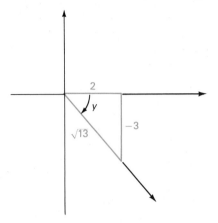

u can be in either quadrant I or IV

Figure 6.57   **Figure 6.58**

Example 4   Solve the equation $y = 2 \sin^{-1}(x + 4)$ for x.
First multiply by 1/2 to get

$$\frac{y}{2} = \sin^{-1}(x + 4).$$

Use the definition of the inverse sine function to get

$$\sin\frac{y}{2} = x + 4$$

or

$$x = \left(\sin\frac{y}{2}\right) - 4. \quad \blacksquare$$

Example 5   Write $\sec(\tan^{-1} x)$ as an algebraic expression.
Let $\tan^{-1} x = u$. Then $\tan u = x$. Since $-\pi/2 < \tan^{-1} x < \pi/2$, u is in quadrant I or quadrant IV. As shown in Figure 6.58, in either case

$$\sec(\tan^{-1} x) = \sec u = \sqrt{x^2 + 1}. \quad \blacksquare$$

There is an alternate notation for inverse trigonometric functions used in some books: $y = \sin^{-1} x$ is written $y = \text{Arcsin } x$, $y = \cos^{-1} x$ is written $y = \text{Arccos } x$, and $y = \tan^{-1} x$ is written $y = \text{Arctan } x$. In the exercise set below, we shall use these notations interchangeably.

6.8 Exercises   *For the following, give the value of y in radians without using tables or a calculator.*

1. $y = \sin^{-1}\dfrac{-\sqrt{3}}{2}$

2. $y = \cos^{-1}\dfrac{\sqrt{3}}{2}$

3. $y = \tan^{-1} 1$

4. $y = \tan^{-1} -1$

5. $y = \sin^{-1} -1$

6. $y = \cos^{-1} -1$

7. $y = \cos^{-1} 1/2$

8. $y = \sin^{-1}\dfrac{-\sqrt{2}}{2}$

9. $y = \text{Arccos} \dfrac{-\sqrt{2}}{2}$

10. $y = \text{Arctan} \dfrac{\sqrt{3}}{3}$

11. $y = \text{Arctan} -\sqrt{3}$

12. $y = \text{Arccos} -1/2$

For the following, give the value in degrees.

13. $y = \sin^{-1}(-0.1334)$

14. $y = \cos^{-1}(-0.1334)$

15. $y = \cos^{-1}(-0.3987)$

16. $y = \sin^{-1} 0.7990$

17. $y = \cos^{-1} 0.9272$

18. $y = \tan^{-1} 1.767$

19. $y = \tan^{-1} 1.111$

20. $y = \sin^{-1} 0.8192$

21. $y = \text{Arctan}(-0.9217)$

22. $y = \text{Arctan}(-0.2867)$

Give the value of the following in radians to four significant digits.

23. $\sin^{-1} 0.7214$

24. $\cos^{-1} 0.3004$

25. $\tan^{-1} -4.114$

26. $\sin^{-1} -0.9946$

27. Enter 1.003 in your calculator and push the keys for inverse sine. The machine will tell you that something is wrong. What is wrong?

28. Enter 1.003 in your calculator and push the keys for inverse tangent. This time, unlike in Exercise 27, you get an answer easily. What is the difference?

Find each of the following to the nearest second.

29. $\sin^{-1}(-0.443981)$

30. $\tan^{-1}(-0.394511)$

31. $\cos^{-1} 0.91441$

32. $\tan^{-1} 14.76892$

Give the value of each of the following without using tables.

33. $\tan(\cos^{-1} 2/3)$

34. $\sin(\cos^{-1} 1/4)$

35. $\cos(\tan^{-1} -2)$

36. $\sec(\sin^{-1} -1/3)$

37. $\cot(\sin^{-1} -2/5)$

38. $\cos(\tan^{-1} 8/5)$

39. $\sin(\text{Arctan} -3)$

40. $\tan(\text{Arccos} -4/5)$

Solve each of the following equations for x.

41. $y = 4 \sin^{-1} x$

42. $3y = \cos^{-1} x$

43. $2y = \tan^{-1} 2x$

44. $y = 3 \sin^{-1}(x/2)$

45. $y = \sin^{-1}(x + 2)$

46. $y = \tan^{-1}(2x - 1)$

Write each of the following as an algebraic expression.

47. $\sin(\cos^{-1} x)$

48. $\tan(\cos^{-1} x)$

49. $\sec(\cos^{-1} x)$

50. $\csc(\sin^{-1} x)$

51. $\cot(\sin^{-1} x)$

52. $\cos(\sin^{-1} x)$

Graph each of the following and give the domain and range.

53. $y = 2 \cos^{-1} x$

54. $y = \tan^{-1} 2x$

55. $y = \sin^{-1} x + 2$

56. $y = \tan^{-1}(x + 1)$

⊙ **57.** We know that $\sin^{-1}(\sin x) = x$. Enter 1.74283 in your calculator (set for radians), and push the sine key. Then push the keys for $\sin^{-1}$. You get 1.398763 instead of 1.74283. What happened?

⊙ *The following were used by the mathematicians that computed the value of π to 100,000 decimal places. Use a calculator to verify that each is (approximately) correct.*

58. $\pi = 16 \tan^{-1}\dfrac{1}{5} - 4 \tan^{-1}\dfrac{1}{239}$

59. $\pi = 24 \tan^{-1}\dfrac{1}{8} + 8 \tan^{-1}\dfrac{1}{57} + 4 \tan^{-1}\dfrac{1}{239}$

60. $\pi = 48 \tan^{-1}\dfrac{1}{18} + 32 \tan^{-1}\dfrac{1}{57} - 20 \tan^{-1}\dfrac{1}{239}$

Answer true *or* false *for each of the following.*

61. $2 \cos^{-1} x = \cos^{-1} 2x$

62. $\cot x = 1/\tan^{-1} x$

63. $\tan^{-1} x = \sin^{-1} x/\cos^{-1} x$

64. $\sin^{-1}(-x) = -\sin^{-1} x$

65. $y = \sin^{-1} x$ is an even function

66. $y = \cos^{-1} x$ is an even function

67. $y = x \cdot \sin^{-1} x$ is an odd function

68. $y = x^2 \cdot \cos^{-1} x$ is an even function

Chapter 6   Review Exercises

For each of the following arc lengths, find the coordinates of the corresponding point on the unit circle.

1. $-\pi/4$ **2.** $2\pi/3$ **3.** 3π

For each of the following values of s, find sin s, cos s, and tan s.

4. $5\pi/4$ **5.** $5\pi/3$ **6.** $-\pi/3$

The point $(-2/3, \sqrt{5}/3)$ is the endpoint of arc s on the unit circle. Find the coordinates of the endpoints of the following arcs.

7. $-s$ **8.** $\pi + s$ **9.** $\pi - s$

Give the quadrant in which θ terminates.

10. $\sin \theta > 0$, $\cos \theta < 0$ **12.** $\tan \theta > 0$, $\sin \theta < 0$

11. $\cos \theta > 0$, $\cot \theta < 0$ **13.** $\sec \theta > 0$, $\tan \theta < 0$

For each of the following, find the values of the other trigonometric functions.

14. $\sin s = 2/3$, s terminates in quadrant I

15. $\cos s = 4/5$, s terminates in quadrant IV

16. $\sec s = \sqrt{5}$, $\cot s = -1/2$ **17.** $\tan s = -4/3$, $\sec s = -5/3$

Convert radian measures to degrees, and degree measures to radians.

18. $3\pi/4$ **20.** $31\pi/5$ **22.** $480°$

19. $4\pi/5$ **21.** $270°$

Find the exact value of each of the following.

23. $\sin \pi/3$ **25.** $\tan 240°$ **27.** $\sec 900°$

24. $\cos 120°$ **26.** $\cot 390°$ **28.** $\cot (-1020°)$

Find the values for the six trigonometric functions for angles in standard position having the following points on their terminal sides.

29. $(-3, -4)$ **30.** $(\sqrt{3}, 1)$

Find the values of each of the following. Use Table 5. Interpolate as necessary.

31. $\tan 235°$ **33.** $\sin 247° \ 10'$ **35.** $\cos 58° \ 4'$

32. $\sec (-87°)$ **34.** $\sec 28° \ 17'$ **36.** $\cos (-3.1998)$

Use Table 5 to find θ in degrees for each of the following.

37. $\tan \theta = 5.226$ **38.** $\cos \theta = 0.4384$ **39.** $\sin \theta = 0.8871$

Use Table 5 to find a value of s in radians for each of the following.

40. $\tan s = 0.7581$ **41.** $\sin s = 0.9596$

42. Find the lengths of the missing sides in this right triangle.

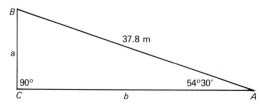

Give the amplitude, period, and phase shift for each of the following.

43. $y = -2 \sin (x - \pi)$ **45.** $y = -\cos 4x$

44. $y = \dfrac{3}{4} \cos \left(x + \dfrac{\pi}{4}\right)$ **46.** $y = 6 \sin (11x - 2\pi)$

Graph each of the following over a two-period interval.

47. $y = -\cos x$

48. $y = \sin 3x$ **52.** $y = \sec \dfrac{1}{2}x$

49. $y = -\dfrac{1}{2} \sin \left(x - \dfrac{\pi}{2}\right)$ **53.** $y = \tan \left(x - \dfrac{\pi}{6}\right)$

50. $y = -2 \cos (2x - \pi)$ **54.** $y = \sec (2x - \pi)$

51. $y = \tan 2x$

Graph by the method of addition of ordinates.

55. $y = x - \sin x$ **56.** $y = \cos x + \cos 2x$

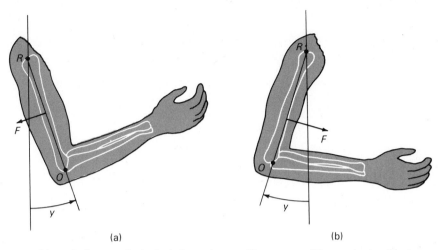

(a)   (b)

Schematic diagrams of a rhythmically moving arm. The upper arm *RO* rotates back and forth about the point *R;* the position of the arm is measured by the angle *y* between the actual position and the downward vertical position.

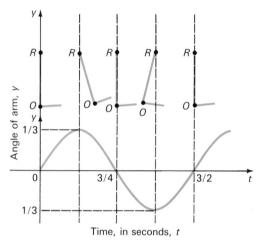

This graph shows the relationship between angle *y* and time *t* in seconds.

57. Find an equation of the form $y = a \sin kt$ for the graph immediately above.

58. How long does it take for a complete movement of the arm?

Find each of the following. Give answers in radians.

59. $y = \sin^{-1} \sqrt{2}/2$

60. $y = \cos^{-1} -1/2$

61. $y = \tan^{-1} -\sqrt{3}$

62. $y = \text{Arctan } 1.780$

63. $y = \text{Arcsin } -0.6604$

64. $y = \cos^{-1} 0.8039$

65. Graph $y = 2 \cos^{-1} x$.

66. Graph $y = \sin^{-1} 3x$.

67. Graph $y = -1 + \tan^{-1} x$.

Figures for Exercises 57 and 58: From *Calculus for the Life Sciences* by Rodolfo De Sapio. W. H. Freeman and Company. Copyright © 1978.

68. Solve for x: $2y = 1 + \tan^{-1}(x + 1)$.

Find each of the following without using tables.

69. $\tan (\sin^{-1} 1/3)$ **70.** $\cos^{-1}(\tan -\pi/4)$

The following exercises are taken with permission from a standard calculus book.

71. Show that the area of a sector of a circle having central angle θ and radius r is $\frac{1}{2}r^2\theta$, if θ is measured in radians.

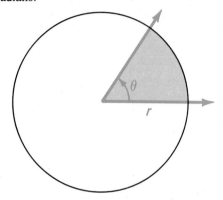

72. Let $A(r, 0)$ be the point where the positive x-axis cuts a circle of radius r, center at the origin O. Let $P(r \cos \theta, r \sin \theta)$ be a point on the circle in the first quadrant, with angle $AOP = \theta$ radians. Let AT be tangent to the circle at A and suppose it intersects the line OP at T. By considering the areas of triangle AOP, sector AOP, and triangle AOT, prove the following inequality.

$$\sin \theta < \theta < \tan \theta \qquad \text{if } 0 < \theta < \pi/2.$$

Chapter 7

Trigonometric Identities and Equations

An *equation*, such as $2x + 1 = 9$ or $m^2 - 2m - 3 = 0$, is true for *certain* values in its domain. For example, $2x + 1 = 9$ is true only for $x = 4$, and $m^2 - 2m - 3 = 0$ is true only for $m = 3$ and $m = -1$. On the other hand, an *identity* is a statement that is true for *every* value in its domain. Examples of identities include $5(x + 3) = 5x + 15$, $(m + 3)^2 = m^2 + 6m + 9$, and $p^0 = 1$.

In this chapter we discuss identities that involve trigonometric functions. The variables in the trigonometric functions represent either angles or real numbers. The domain is all values for which a given function is defined. We shall also look at equations involving trigonometric functions.

7.1 Fundamental Identities

Let us begin by restating the fundamental identities introduced in Chapter 6.

$$\sin s = \frac{1}{\csc s} \qquad \cos s = \frac{1}{\sec s} \qquad \tan s = \frac{1}{\cot s}$$

$$\cot s = \frac{1}{\tan s} \qquad \csc s = \frac{1}{\sin s} \qquad \sec s = \frac{1}{\cos s}$$

$$\tan s = \frac{\sin s}{\cos s} \qquad \cot s = \frac{\cos s}{\sin s}$$

$$\sin^2 s + \cos^2 s = 1 \qquad \tan^2 s + 1 = \sec^2 s$$

$$1 + \cot^2 s = \csc^2 s$$

The unit circle in Figure 7.1 on page 266 shows an arc of length s starting at $(1, 0)$, with endpoint (x, y). The same figure also shows an arc of length $-s$, again starting at $(1, 0)$. This arc has endpoint $(x, -y)$. Since $\sin s = y$, we have

$$\sin (-s) = -y = -\sin s,$$

also,

$$\cos (-s) = x = \cos s$$

and

$$\tan (-s) = \frac{-y}{x} = -\tan s.$$

In summary,

$$\sin (-s) = -\sin s \qquad \cos (-s) = \cos s$$
$$\tan (-s) = -\tan s.$$

(These identities were derived in Chapter 6 through an analysis of the symmetry of the graphs of the three functions. Note that the sine and tangent functions are odd, while the cosine function is even.)

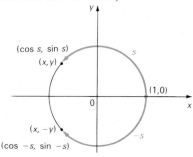

Figure 7.1

Trigonometric identities are useful in several ways. One use of trigonometric identities is in finding values of the other trigonometric functions from the value of a given trigonometric function. For example, if we are given a value of tan s, we can find the value of cot s by using the identity cot $s = 1/\tan s$. In fact, given tan s and the quadrant in which s lies, we can find the value of all the other trigonometric functions by using identities, as shown below.

Example 1 If tan $s = -5/3$ and s is in quadrant II, find the values of the other trigonometric functions.

We know cot $s = 1/\tan s$, so that cot $s = -3/5$. Also, $\tan^2 s + 1 = \sec^2 s$.

$$\left(-\frac{5}{3}\right)^2 + 1 = \sec^2 s$$

$$\frac{25}{9} + 1 = \sec^2 s$$

$$\frac{34}{9} = \sec^2 s$$

$$-\sqrt{\frac{34}{9}} = \sec s$$

$$-\frac{\sqrt{34}}{3} = \sec s.$$

We choose the negative square root since sec s is negative in quadrant II. Since cos s is the reciprocal of sec s,

$$\cos s = \frac{-3}{\sqrt{34}} = \frac{-3\sqrt{34}}{34},$$

after rationalizing the denominator. Now find sin s by using the identity $\sin^2 s + \cos^2 s = 1$.

$$\sin^2 s + \left(\frac{-3\sqrt{34}}{34}\right)^2 = 1$$

$$\sin^2 s = 1 - \frac{9}{34}$$

$$\sin^2 s = \frac{25}{34}$$

$$\sin s = \frac{5}{\sqrt{34}} \quad \text{or} \quad \sin s = \frac{5\sqrt{34}}{34}.$$

Here we choose the positive square root because $\sin s$ is positive in quadrant II. Finally, since $\csc s$ is the reciprocal of $\sin s$, $\csc s = \sqrt{34}/5$. ▌

Example 2   Express $\cos x$ in terms of $\tan x$.
Start with $\tan^2 x + 1 = \sec^2 x$. Then

$$\frac{1}{\tan^2 x + 1} = \frac{1}{\sec^2 x}$$

or

$$\frac{1}{\tan^2 x + 1} = \cos^2 x.$$

Take the square root of both sides:

$$\pm\sqrt{\frac{1}{\tan^2 x + 1}} = \cos x$$

or

$$\cos x = \frac{\pm 1}{\sqrt{\tan^2 x + 1}}.$$

Here, the $+$ or the $-$ sign is chosen, depending on the quadrant of x. ▌

Another use of identities is to simplify trigonometric expressions by substituting one half of an identity for the other half. For example, the expression $\sin^2 \theta + \cos^2 \theta$ can be simplified to just 1, as in the following example.

Example 3   Use the fundamental identities to write $\tan \theta + \cot \theta$ in terms of $\sin \theta$ and $\cos \theta$. Then simplify.
From the fundamental identities,

$$\tan \theta + \cot \theta = \frac{\sin \theta}{\cos \theta} + \frac{\cos \theta}{\sin \theta}.$$

A common denominator on the right is $\cos \theta \cdot \sin \theta$.

$$= \frac{\sin^2 \theta}{\cos \theta \sin \theta} + \frac{\cos^2 \theta}{\cos \theta \sin \theta}$$

$$= \frac{\sin^2 \theta + \cos^2 \theta}{\cos \theta \sin \theta}$$

Now substitute 1 for $\sin^2 \theta + \cos^2 \theta$, to get

$$\tan \theta + \cot \theta = \frac{1}{\cos \theta \sin \theta}. \qquad \blacksquare$$

Later on, we shall see that it is often a good idea to write complicated expressions in terms of sine and cosine, as was done in this example.

7.1 Exercises   *Find sin s for each of the following.*

1. $\cos s = 3/4$, s is in quadrant I

2. $\cot s = -\frac{1}{3}$, s is in quadrant IV

3. $\cos s = \sqrt{5}/5$, $\tan s < 0$

4. $\tan s = -\sqrt{7}/2$, $\sec s > 0$

5. Find $\tan \theta$ if $\cos \theta = -2/5$ and $\sin \theta < 0$.

6. Find $\csc \alpha$ if $\tan \alpha = 6$ and $\cos \alpha > 0$.

Use the fundamental identities to find the remaining five trigonometric functions for the given angle.

7. $\sin \theta = \frac{2}{3}$, θ in quadrant II

8. $\tan \theta = \frac{2}{3}$, θ in quadrant III

9. $\sec \theta = -3$, θ in quadrant II

10. $\csc \theta = -\frac{5}{2}$, θ in quadrant III

11. $\cot s = \frac{4}{3}$, $\sin s > 0$

12. $\sin s = -\frac{4}{5}$, $\cos s < 0$

13. $\sec s = \frac{4}{3}$, $\sin s < 0$

14. $\tan s = -5$, $\cos s < 0$

For each trigonometric expression in List I, choose the expression from List II which completes a fundamental identity.

List I	List II
15. $\dfrac{\cos x}{\sin x}$	(a) $\sin^2 x + \cos^2 x$
16. $\tan x$	(b) $\cot x$
17. $\cos (-x)$	(c) $\sec^2 x$
18. $\tan^2 x + 1$	(d) $\dfrac{\sin x}{\cos x}$
19. 1	(e) $\cos x$

For each expression in List I, choose the expression from List II which completes an identity. You will have to rewrite one or both expressions, using a fundamental identity, to recognize the matches.

List I   List II

20. $-\tan x \cos x$ (a) $\dfrac{\sin^2 x}{\cos^2 x}$

21. $\sec^2 x - 1$ (b) $\dfrac{1}{\sec^2 x}$

22. $\dfrac{\sec x}{\csc x}$ (c) $\sin(-x)$

23. $1 - \sin^2 x$ (d) $\csc^2 x - \cot^2 x - \sin^2 x$

24. $\cos^2 x$ (e) $\tan x$

In each of the following, use the fundamental identities to get an equivalent expression involving only sines and cosines and then simplify it.

25. $\csc^2 \beta - \cot^2 \beta$

26. $\dfrac{\tan(-\theta)}{\sec \theta}$

27. $\tan(-\alpha) \cos(-\alpha)$

28. $\cot^2 x \,(1 + \tan^2 x)$

29. $\tan^2 \theta - \dfrac{\sec^2 \theta}{\csc^2 \theta}$

30. $\dfrac{\tan x \csc x}{\sec x}$

31. $\sec \theta + \tan \theta$

32. $\dfrac{\sec \alpha}{\tan \alpha + \cot \alpha}$

33. $1 + \cot^2 \alpha$

34. $\dfrac{1 + \tan^2 \theta}{\cot^2 \theta}$

35. $\dfrac{1 - \sin^2 t}{\csc^2 t}$

36. $\cot^2 \beta \sin^2 \beta + \tan^2 \beta \cos^2 \beta$

37. $\sec^2 x + \cos^2 x$

38. $\dfrac{\cot^2 \alpha + \csc^2 \alpha}{\cos^2 \alpha}$

39. $1 - \tan^4 \theta$

40. $\tan^4 \gamma - \cot^4 \gamma$

Write all the trigonometric functions in terms of

41. $\sin x$

42. $\cos x$

43. Write $\tan x$ in terms of $\csc x$.

44. Write $\sec \alpha$ in terms of $\tan \alpha$.

45. Express $\cot s$ in terms of $\sec s$.

46. Express $\csc t$ in terms of $\tan t$.

47. Prove that $|\tan x| \geq |\sin x|$ for all real numbers x in the domain of both functions.

48. Prove that $|\sec x| > |\tan x|$ for all real numbers x in the domain of both functions.

49. Let $\cos x = 1/5$. Find all possible values for

$$\frac{(\sec x - \tan x)}{\sin x}.$$

50. Let $\csc x = -3$. Find all possible values for

$$\frac{(\sin x + \cos x)}{\sec x}.$$

Prove that each of the following is not *an identity.*

51. $(\sin s + \cos s)^2 = 1$

52. $(\tan s + 1)^2 = \sec^2 s$

53. $2 \sin s = \sin 2s$

54. $\sin x = \sqrt{1 - \cos^2 x}$

7.2 Verifying Trigonometric Identities

One of the skills required for more advanced work in mathematics (and especially in calculus) is the ability to use the trigonometric identities to write trigonometric expressions in alternate forms. To develop this skill, we use the fundamental identities to verify that a trigonometric equation is an identity (for those values of the variable for which it is defined). This process is a skill that must be learned with practice. Here are some hints that may help you get started.

1. Memorize the fundamental identities given in the last section. Whenever you see one half of a fundamental identity, the other half should come to mind.

2. Try to rewrite the more complicated side of the equation so that it is identical to the simpler side.

3. It is often helpful to express all other trigonometric functions in the equation in terms of sine and cosine and then simplify the result.

4. You should usually perform any indicated algebraic operations. For example, the expression $\sin^2 x + 2 \sin x + 1$ can be factored as $(\sin x + 1)^2$. The sum or difference of two trigonometric expressions, such as

$$\frac{1}{\sin \theta} + \frac{1}{\cos \theta}$$

can be added or subtracted in the same way as any other rational expression. For example,

$$\frac{1}{\sin \theta} + \frac{1}{\cos \theta} = \frac{\cos \theta}{\sin \theta \cos \theta} + \frac{\sin \theta}{\sin \theta \cos \theta}$$

$$= \frac{\cos \theta + \sin \theta}{\sin \theta \cos \theta}$$

5. Keep in mind the side you are not changing as you select substitutions. It represents your goal. For example, if you are to verify the identity

$$\tan^2 x + 1 = \frac{1}{\cos^2 x},$$

try to think of an identity that relates $\tan x$ to $\cos x$. Here, since $\sec x = 1/\cos x$ and $\sec^2 x = \tan^2 x + 1$, the secant function is the best link between the two sides of the equation.

We use these hints in the following examples.

Example 1   Verify that the equation

$$\cot s + 1 = \csc s(\cos s + \sin s)$$

is an identity.

We use the fundamental identities to rewrite one side of the equation so that it is identical to the other. Since the right side is more complicated, we work with it. Here we use the method of changing all the trigonometric functions to sine or cosine.

$$\csc s(\cos s + \sin s) = \frac{1}{\sin s}(\cos s + \sin s)$$

$$= \frac{\cos s}{\sin s} + \frac{\sin s}{\sin s}$$

$$\csc s(\cos s + \sin s) = \cot s + 1.$$

The equation is an identity because the right side equals the left side, for any value of s. █

As an alternative to the method of solving identities given above, each side of the statement may be reduced to the same expression. As long as all steps on both sides are reversible, this then proves that the original statement is an identity. This procedure is shown in the next example.

Example 2   Verify that the equation

$$\tan^2 \alpha (1 + \cot^2 \alpha) = \frac{1}{1 - \sin^2 \alpha}$$

is an identity.

Working first with the left side gives

$$\tan^2 \alpha (1 + \cot^2 \alpha) = \tan^2 \alpha + \tan^2 \alpha \cot^2 \alpha$$

$$= \tan^2 \alpha + 1$$

$$= \sec^2 \alpha.$$

On the right side,

$$\frac{1}{1 - \sin^2 \alpha} = \frac{1}{\cos^2 \alpha}$$

$$= \sec^2 \alpha.$$

Since both the left side and the right side equal $\sec^2 \alpha$, the given statement must be an identity. █

Example 3   Show that

$$\frac{\tan t - \cot t}{\sin t \cos t} = \sec^2 t - \csc^2 t.$$

Work with the left side.

$$\frac{\tan t - \cot t}{\sin t \cos t} = \frac{\tan t}{\sin t \cos t} - \frac{\cot t}{\sin t \cos t}$$

$$= \tan t \cdot \frac{1}{\sin t \cos t} - \cot t \cdot \frac{1}{\sin t \cos t}$$

$$= \frac{\sin t}{\cos t} \cdot \frac{1}{\sin t \cdot \cos t} - \frac{\cos t}{\sin t} \cdot \frac{1}{\sin t \cos t}$$

$$= \frac{1}{\cos^2 t} - \frac{1}{\sin^2 t}$$

$$= \sec^2 t - \csc^2 t. \quad █$$

7.2 Exercises   *For each of the following, perform the indicated operations and simplify the result.*

1. $\tan \theta + \dfrac{1}{\tan \theta}$

2. $\dfrac{\cos x}{\sin x} + \dfrac{\sin x}{\cos x}$

3. $\cot s(\tan s + \sin s)$

4. $\dfrac{1}{\csc^2 \theta} + \dfrac{1}{\sec^2 \theta}$

5. $\dfrac{1}{\sin \alpha - 1} - \dfrac{1}{\sin \alpha + 1}$

6. $\dfrac{\cos \gamma}{\sin \gamma} + \dfrac{\sin \gamma}{1 + \cos \gamma}$

7. $(1 + \sin t)^2 + \cos^2 t$

8. $(1 + \tan s)^2 - 2 \tan s$

Factor each of the following trigonometric expressions.

9. $\sin^2 \gamma - 1$

10. $\sec^2 \theta - 1$

11. $(\sin x + 1)^2 - (\sin x - 1)^2$

12. $(\tan x + \cot x)^2 - (\tan x - \cot x)^2$

13. $2 \sin^2 x + 3 \sin x + 1$

14. $4 \tan^2 \beta + \tan \beta - 3$

15. $\cos^4 x + 2 \cos^2 x + 1$

16. $\cot^4 s + 3 \cot^2 s + 2$

Use the fundamental identities to simplify each of the given expressions.

17. $\tan \theta \cos \theta$

18. $\cot t \tan t$

19. $\dfrac{\sin \beta \tan \beta}{\cos \beta}$

20. $\dfrac{\csc \theta \sec \theta}{\cot \theta}$

21. $\sec^2 x - 1$

22. $\csc^2 t - 1$

23. $\dfrac{\sin^2 x}{\cos^2 x} + \sin x \csc x$

24. $\dfrac{1}{\tan^2 \alpha} + \cot \alpha \tan \alpha$

Verify each of the following trigonometric identities.

25. $1 - \sec \alpha \cos \alpha = \tan \alpha \cot \alpha - 1$

26. $\csc^4 \theta = \cot^4 \theta + 2 \cot^2 \theta + 1$

27. $\dfrac{\sin^2 \theta}{\cos^2 \theta} = \sec^2 \theta - 1$

28. $\cot \beta \sin \beta = \cos \beta$

29. $\sec^2 x - \tan^2 x = \cos^2 x + \sin^2 x$

30. $\sin^2 s - 1 = -\cos^2 s$

31. $\dfrac{\sin^2 \gamma}{\cos \gamma} = \sec \gamma - \cos \gamma$

32. $(1 + \tan^2 x) \cos^2 x = 1$

33. $\cot s + \tan s = \sec s \csc s$

34. $\dfrac{\cos \alpha}{\sec \alpha} + \dfrac{\sin \alpha}{\csc \alpha} = \sec^2 \alpha - \tan^2 \alpha$

35. $\dfrac{\cos \alpha}{\sin \alpha \cot \alpha} = 1$

36. $\sin^4 \theta - \cos^4 \theta = 2 \sin^2 \theta - 1$

37. $\dfrac{1 + \sin x}{\cos x} = \dfrac{\cos x}{1 - \sin x}$

38. $(1 - \cos^2 \alpha)(1 + \cos^2 \alpha) = 2 \sin^2 \alpha - \sin^4 \alpha$

39. $\dfrac{1}{1 - \sin \theta} + \dfrac{1}{1 + \sin \theta} = 2 \sec^2 \theta$

40. $\dfrac{1 - \cos x}{1 + \cos x} = (\cot x - \csc x)^2$

41. $\dfrac{\sec^4 s - \tan^4 s}{\sec^2 s + \tan^2 s} = \sec^2 s - \tan^2 s$

42. $\dfrac{\cot^2 t - 1}{1 + \cot^2 t} = 1 - 2 \sin^2 t$

43. $\dfrac{\tan^2 t - 1}{\sec^2 t} = \dfrac{\tan t - \cot t}{\tan t + \cot t}$

44. $(1 + \sin x + \cos x)^2 = 2(1 + \sin x)(1 + \cos x)$

45. $(\sin s + \cos s)^2 \cdot \csc s = 2 \cos s + \dfrac{1}{\sin s}$

46. $\dfrac{\sin^3 t - \cos^3 t}{\sin t - \cos t} = 1 + \sin t \cos t$

47. $\dfrac{\tan t + 1}{\tan t - 1} = \dfrac{\sec t + \csc t}{\sec t - \csc t}$

48. $(2 \sin x + 3 \cos x)^2 + (2 \cos x - 3 \sin x)^2 = 13$

49. $\dfrac{\tan s}{1 + \cos s} + \dfrac{\sin s}{1 - \cos s} = \cot s + \sec s \csc s$

50. $\dfrac{1}{\tan \alpha - \sec \alpha} + \dfrac{1}{\tan \alpha + \sec \alpha} = -2 \tan \alpha$

51. $\dfrac{\cot \alpha + 1}{\cot \alpha - 1} = \dfrac{1 + \tan \alpha}{1 - \tan \alpha}$

52. $\sin^2 \alpha \sec^2 \alpha + \sin^2 \alpha \csc^2 \alpha = \sec^2 \alpha$

53. $\sec^4 x - \sec^2 x = \tan^4 x + \tan^2 x$

54. $\dfrac{1 - \sin \theta}{1 + \sin \theta} = \sec^2 \theta - 2 \sec \theta \tan \theta + \tan^2 \theta$

55. $\sin \theta + \cos \theta = \dfrac{\sin \theta}{1 - \dfrac{\cos \theta}{\sin \theta}} + \dfrac{\cos \theta}{1 - \dfrac{\sin \theta}{\cos \theta}}$

56. $\dfrac{\sin \theta}{1 - \cos \theta} - \dfrac{\sin \theta \cos \theta}{1 + \cos \theta} = \csc \theta + \csc \theta \cos^2 \theta$

57. $(\sec \alpha + \csc \alpha)(\cos \alpha - \sin \alpha) = \cot \alpha - \tan \alpha$

58. $\dfrac{\sin^4 \alpha - \cos^4 \alpha}{\sin^2 \alpha - \cos^2 \alpha} = 1$

59. $\dfrac{\cot^2 x + \sec^2 x + 1}{\cot^2 x} = \sec^4 x$

60. $\dfrac{\cos x - (\sin x - 1)}{\cos x + (\sin x - 1)} = \dfrac{\sin x}{1 - \cos x}$

61. $\ln e^{|\sin x|} = |\sin x|$

62. $\ln |\sin s| = -\ln |\csc s|$

63. $\ln |\sec x - \tan x| = -\ln |\sec x + \tan x|$

64. $-\ln |\csc t - \cot t| = \ln |\csc t + \cot t|$

● *Given a complicated equation involving trigonometric functions, it is a good idea to decide whether or not it really is an identity before trying to* prove *that it is. Substitute s = 1 and s = 2 into each of the following. If you get the same results on both sides of the equation, it* may *be an identity. Then prove that it is.*

65. $\dfrac{2 + 5 \cos s}{\sin s} = 2 \csc s + 5 \cot s$

68. $\dfrac{1}{1 + \sin s} + \dfrac{1}{1 - \sin s} = \sec^2 s$

66. $1 + \cot^2 s = \dfrac{\sec^2 s}{\sec^2 s - 1}$

69. $\dfrac{1 - \tan^2 s}{1 + \tan^2 s} = \cos^2 s - \sin s$

67. $\dfrac{\tan s - \cot s}{\tan s + \cot s} = 2 \sin^2 s$

70. $\dfrac{\sin^3 s - \cos^3 s}{\sin s - \cos s} = \sin^2 s + 2 \sin s \cos s + \cos^2 s$

71. $\sin^2 s + \cos^2 s = \dfrac{1}{2}(1 - \cos 4s)$

72. $\cos 3s = 3 \cos s + 4 \cos^3 s$

Show that the following are not *identities for real numbers s and t.*

73. $\sin (\csc s) = 1$

75. $\sqrt{\cos^2 s} = \cos s$

74. $\sin^{-1} (\csc s) = 1$

76. $\csc t = \sqrt{1 + \cot^2 t}$

7.3 Sum and Difference Identities for Cosine

Sometimes we need to express a trigonometric function value for the sum or difference of two real numbers (or angles) in terms of the trigonometric function values for each real number (or angle). For example, let us express $\cos(s - t)$ in terms of trigonometric function values of s and t themselves.

To do this, let $A(1, 0)$, $B(x_1, y_1)$, $C(x_2, y_2)$, and $D(x_3, y_3)$ be points on the unit circle such that the length of arc AD, written $\overset{\frown}{AD}$, is s, $\overset{\frown}{AB} = t$, and $\overset{\frown}{AC} = s - t$. (See Figure 7.2.) Here we assume that $0 < t < s < 2\pi$ although the results we get are valid for any values of s and t. Arc BD also has a length $s - t$, so that $\overset{\frown}{AC} = \overset{\frown}{BD}$. Since these arcs are equal in length, line segments AC and BD must also be equal in length. By the distance formula,

$$\sqrt{(x_2 - 1)^2 + (y_2 - 0)^2} = \sqrt{(x_3 - x_1)^2 + (y_3 - y_1)^2}.$$

Squaring both sides and simplifying gives

$$x_2^2 - 2x_2 + 1 + y_2^2 = x_3^2 - 2x_3x_1 + x_1^2 + y_3^2 - 2y_3y_1 + y_1^2. \qquad (1)$$

Since points B, C, and D are on the unit circle,

$$x_1^2 + y_1^2 = 1, \qquad x_2^2 + y_2^2 = 1, \qquad \text{and } x_3^2 + y_3^2 = 1.$$

Substituting these results into equation (1) gives

$$2 - 2x_2 = 2 - 2x_3x_1 - 2y_3y_1$$

or

$$x_2 = x_3x_1 + y_3y_1.$$

Since $x_2 = \cos(s - t)$, $x_3 = \cos s$, $x_1 = \cos t$, $y_3 = \sin s$, and $y_1 = \sin t$, we end up with

$$\cos(s - t) = \cos s \cos t + \sin s \sin t.$$

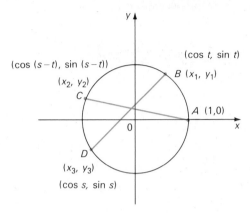

Figure 7.2

Example 1 Find the value of cos 15°.

To find cos 15°, write 15° as the difference of two angles whose function values we know. Since $15° = 45° - 30°$,

$$\cos 15° = \cos(45° - 30°) = \cos 45° \cos 30° + \sin 45° \sin 30°$$

$$= \frac{\sqrt{2}}{2} \cdot \frac{\sqrt{3}}{2} + \frac{\sqrt{2}}{2} \cdot \frac{1}{2}$$

$$= \frac{\sqrt{6} + \sqrt{2}}{4}. \quad \blacksquare$$

We have found a formula for $\cos(s - t)$. It is not necessary to work as hard to find $\cos(s + t)$. To do so, use the result for $\cos(s - t)$, and write $s + t$ as $s - (-t)$.

$$\cos(s + t) = \cos[s - (-t)]$$

$$= \cos s \cos(-t) + \sin s \sin(-t)$$

$$= \cos s \cos t + \sin s \,(-\sin t)$$

$$= \cos s \cos t - \sin s \sin t$$

In summary,

$$\cos(s + t) = \cos s \cos t - \sin s \sin t.$$

Example 2 Find $\cos \frac{5}{12}\pi$.

$$\cos \frac{5}{12}\pi = \cos \left(\frac{\pi}{6} + \frac{\pi}{4}\right)$$

$$= \cos \frac{\pi}{6} \cos \frac{\pi}{4} - \sin \frac{\pi}{6} \sin \frac{\pi}{4}$$

$$= \frac{\sqrt{3}}{2} \cdot \frac{\sqrt{2}}{2} - \frac{1}{2} \cdot \frac{\sqrt{2}}{2}$$

$$\cos \frac{5}{12}\pi = \frac{\sqrt{6} - \sqrt{2}}{4} \quad \blacksquare$$

Example 3   Suppose $\sin x = 1/2$, $\cos y = -12/13$, and both x and y are in quadrant II. Find $\cos(x + y)$.

We know that $\cos(x + y) = \cos x \cos y - \sin x \sin y$. We are given the values of $\sin x$ and $\cos y$. To use the formula for $\cos(x + y)$, we need to find $\cos x$ and $\sin y$.

To find $\cos x$, we use the fact that $\sin^2 x + \cos^2 x = 1$, and then substitute $1/2$ for $\sin x$.

$$\sin^2 x + \cos^2 x = 1$$

$$\left(\frac{1}{2}\right)^2 + \cos^2 x = 1$$

$$\frac{1}{4} + \cos^2 x = 1$$

$$\cos^2 x = \frac{3}{4}$$

$$\cos x = \pm \frac{\sqrt{3}}{2}$$

Since x is in quadrant II, $\cos x$ is negative, so $\cos x = -\sqrt{3}/2$.

We find $\sin y$ as follows.

$$\sin^2 y + \cos^2 y = 1$$

$$\sin^2 y + \left(-\frac{12}{13}\right)^2 = 1$$

$$\sin^2 y + \frac{144}{169} = 1$$

$$\sin^2 y = \frac{25}{169}$$

$$\sin y = \pm \frac{5}{13}$$

Since y is in quadrant II, $\sin y = 5/13$.

Now we find $\cos(x + y)$.

$$\cos(x + y) = \cos x \cos y - \sin x \sin y$$

$$= -\frac{\sqrt{3}}{2} \cdot \left(-\frac{12}{13}\right) - \frac{1}{2} \cdot \frac{5}{13}$$

$$= \frac{12\sqrt{3}}{26} - \frac{5}{26}$$

$$\cos(x + y) = \frac{12\sqrt{3} - 5}{26} \qquad \blacksquare$$

The identities for the cosine of the sum and difference of two angles can be used to derive other identities. For example, if we substitute $\pi/2$ for s in the identity for $\cos(s - t)$, we have

$$\cos(\pi/2 - t) = \cos \pi/2 \cdot \cos t + \sin \pi/2 \cdot \sin t$$

$$= 0 \cdot \cos t + 1 \cdot \sin t$$

$$\cos(\pi/2 - t) = \sin t.$$

This result is true for any value of t since the identity for $\cos(s - t)$ is true for any values of s and t. The identity $\cos(\pi/2 - t) = \sin t$ is an example of a **cofunction identity.** The common cofunction identities are

$$\cos(\pi/2 - t) = \sin t$$
$$\sin(\pi/2 - t) = \cos t$$
$$\tan(\pi/2 - t) = \cot t$$
$$\cot(\pi/2 - t) = \tan t.$$

The derivation of the cofunction identities is included in Exercises 51–54 below.

Example 4 Find a number s which satisfies each of the following.

(a) $\cot s = \tan \pi/12$
   Since tangent and cotangent are cofunctions, we have

$$\cot s = \tan(\pi/2 - s) = \tan 5\pi/12$$

   Thus, $\pi/2 - s = \pi/12$, and $s = 5\pi/12$.

(b) $\sin \theta = \cos(-30°)$
   In a similar way,

$$\sin \theta = \cos(90° - \theta) = \cos(-30°)$$
$$90° - \theta = -30°$$

Thus,

$$\theta = 120°. \qquad \blacksquare$$

Example 5 Write $\cos(\pi - t)$ as a function of t.
   Use the identity for $\cos(s - t)$. Replace s with π.

$$\cos(\pi - t) = \cos \pi \cdot \cos t + \sin \pi \cdot \sin t$$
$$= (-1) \cdot \cos t + (0) \cdot \sin t$$
$$= -\cos t \qquad \blacksquare$$

7.3 Exercises   *Write each of the following in terms of cofunctions.*

1. tan 87°

2. sin 15°

3. cos $\pi/12$

4. sin $2\pi/5$

5. csc $(-14°\ 24')$

6. sin 142° 14'

7. sin $5\pi/8$

8. cot $9\pi/10$

9. sec 146° 42'

10. tan 174° 3'

Identify each of the following as true or false.

11. cos 42° = cos (30° + 12°)

12. cos (−24°) = cos 16° − cos 40°

13. cos 74° = cos 60° cos 14° + sin 60° sin 14°

14. cos 140° = cos 60° cos 80° − sin 60° sin 80°

15. cos (−10°) = cos 90° cos 80° + sin 90° sin 80°

16. cos (10°) = cos 90° cos 80° + sin 90° sin 80°

Use the cofunction identities to find the angle θ which makes each of the following true.

17. tan θ = cot (45° + 2θ)

18. sin θ = cos (2θ − 10°)

19. sec θ = csc ($\theta/2$ + 20°)

20. cos θ = sin (3θ + 10°)

21. sin (3θ − 15°) = cos (θ + 25°)

22. cot (θ − 10°) = tan (2θ + 20°)

Use the sum and difference identities for cosine to find each of the following without using tables or calculator.

23. cos 285°

24. cos (−15°)

25. cos $\left(-\dfrac{5\pi}{12}\right)$

26. cos $\dfrac{7\pi}{12}$

27. cos 14° cos 31° − sin 14° sin 31°

28. cos 40° cos 50° − sin 40° sin 50°

29. cos 80° cos 35° + sin 80° sin 35°

30. cos (−10°) cos 35° + sin (−10°) sin 35°

Write as a function of x or θ.

31. cos (30° + θ)

32. cos (45° − θ)

33. cos (60° + θ)

34. cos (θ − 30°)

35. cos $\left(\dfrac{3\pi}{2} - x\right)$

36. cos $\left(x + \dfrac{\pi}{4}\right)$

For each of the following, find cos (s + t) and cos (s − t).

37. sin $t = 5/13$ and cos $s = 3/5$, s and t in quadrant I

38. sin $t = 3/5$ and cos $s = -1/5$, s and t in quadrant II

39. sin $t = -1/3$ and sin $s = 2/3$, s in quadrant II and t in IV

40. sin $t = -12/13$ and sin $s = 3/5$, s in quadrant I and t in III

41. cos $s = -8/17$ and cos $t = -3/5$, s and t in quadrant III

42. cos $s = -15/17$ and sin $t = 4/5$, s in quadrant II and t in I

Verify each of the following identities.

43. $\cos (\pi/2 + x) = -\sin x$

44. $\sec (\pi - x) = -\sec x$

45. $\cos 2x = \cos^2 x - \sin^2 x$ (Hint: cos $2x = \cos (x + x)$)

46. $\cos (x + y) + \cos (x - y) = 2 \cos x \cos y$

47. $\dfrac{\cos (\alpha - \theta) - \cos (\alpha + \theta)}{\cos (\alpha - \theta) + \cos (\alpha + \theta)} = \tan \theta \tan \alpha$

48. $1 + \cos 2x - \cos^2 x = \cos^2 x$ (Hint: use the result in Exercise 45)

49. $\cos (\pi + s - t) = -\sin s \sin t - \cos s \cos t$

50. $\cos (\pi/2 + s - t) = \sin (t - s)$

51. Use the identities for the cosine of the sum and difference of two angles to complete each of the following.

$\cos (0 - t) =$ $\cos (0 + t) =$
$\cos (\pi/2 - t) =$ $\cos (\pi/2 + t) =$
$\cos (\pi - t) =$ $\cos (\pi + t) =$
$\cos (3\pi/2 - t) =$ $\cos (3\pi/2 + t) =$

52. Use the identity cos $(\pi/2 - t) = \sin t$; replace t with $\pi/2 - t$, and derive the identity cos $t = \sin (\pi/2 - t)$.

53. Derive the identity tan $t = \cot (\pi/2 - t)$.

54. Prove that csc $t = \sec (\pi/2 - t)$.

⊙ *Let sin s = −0.09463 and cos t = 0.83499, where s terminates in quadrant III and t in quadrant IV. Find each of the following.*

55. cos $(s - t)$

56. cos $(s + t)$

57. cos $2s$

58. cos $2t$

59. Let $f(x) = \cos x$. Prove that $\dfrac{f(x + h) - f(x)}{h} = \cos x\left(\dfrac{\cos h - 1}{h}\right) - \sin x\left(\dfrac{\sin h}{h}\right)$.

Use the identities of this section to find each of the following.

60. cos $(\tan^{-1} 5/12 - \cos^{-1} 4/5)$

61. cos $(\sin^{-1} 8/17 + \tan^{-1} 3/4)$

62. cos $(\sin^{-1} 1/3 - \cos^{-1} 2/5)$

7.4 Sum and Difference Identities for Sine and Tangent

Formulas for sin $(s + t)$ and sin $(s - t)$ can be developed from the results of the previous section. From a cofunction identity,

$$\sin (s + t) = \cos \left[\frac{\pi}{2} - (s + t) \right]$$

$$= \cos \left[\left(\frac{\pi}{2} - s \right) - t \right].$$

Using the identity for cos $(s - t)$ from the previous section gives

$$= \cos \left(\frac{\pi}{2} - s \right) \cdot \cos t + \sin \left(\frac{\pi}{2} - s \right) \sin t$$

$$\boxed{\sin (s + t) = \sin s \cos t + \cos s \sin t}$$

In the last step we substituted from the cofunction relationships.

If we now write sin $(s - t)$ as sin $[s + (-t)]$ and use the identity for sin $(s + t)$ we have

$$\boxed{\sin (s - t) = \sin s \cos t - \cos s \sin t.}$$

Using the identities for sin $(s + t)$, cos $(s + t)$, sin $(s - t)$, and cos $(s - t)$, and the identity tan $x = \sin x / \cos x$, we can get the following identities.

$$\boxed{\begin{aligned} \tan (s + t) &= \frac{\tan s + \tan t}{1 - \tan s \tan t} \\[1em] \tan (s - t) &= \frac{\tan s - \tan t}{1 + \tan s \tan t} \end{aligned}}$$

We show the proof for the first of these two identities. The proof of the other is very similar.

$$\tan (s + t) = \frac{\sin (s + t)}{\cos (s + t)}$$

$$= \frac{\sin s \cos t + \cos s \sin t}{\cos s \cos t - \sin s \sin t}$$

To express this result in terms of the tangent function, multiply both numerator and denominator by 1/cos s cos t.

$$= \frac{\dfrac{\sin s \cos t + \cos s \sin t}{1}}{\dfrac{\cos s \cos t - \sin s \sin t}{1}} \cdot \frac{\dfrac{1}{\cos s \cos t}}{\dfrac{1}{\cos s \cos t}}$$

$$\tan (s + t) = \dfrac{\dfrac{\sin s \cos t}{\cos s \cos t} + \dfrac{\cos s \sin t}{\cos s \cos t}}{\dfrac{\cos s \cos t}{\cos s \cos t} - \dfrac{\sin s \sin t}{\cos s \cos t}}$$

Using the identity $\tan x = \sin x/\cos x$, gives

$$\tan (s + t) = \frac{\tan s + \tan t}{1 - \tan s \tan t}.$$

Similar formulas can be found for the remaining trigonometric functions. However, they are seldom used, so we do not give them here.

Example 1 Use identities to find the exact value of each of the following.

(a) $\sin 75°$

$$\sin 75° = \sin (45° + 30°)$$
$$= \sin 45° \cos 30° + \cos 45° \sin 30°$$
$$= \frac{\sqrt{2}}{2} \cdot \frac{\sqrt{3}}{2} + \frac{\sqrt{2}}{2} \cdot \frac{1}{2}$$
$$\sin 75° = \frac{\sqrt{6} + \sqrt{2}}{4}$$

(b) $\tan \dfrac{7}{12}\pi = \tan \left(\dfrac{\pi}{3} + \dfrac{\pi}{4} \right)$

$$= \frac{\tan \dfrac{\pi}{3} + \tan \dfrac{\pi}{4}}{1 - \tan \dfrac{\pi}{3} \tan \dfrac{\pi}{4}}$$

$$= \frac{\sqrt{3} + 1}{1 - \sqrt{3} \cdot 1}$$

To simplify this result, rationalize the denominator by multiplying numerator and denominator by $1 + \sqrt{3}$.

$$= \frac{\sqrt{3} + 1}{1 - \sqrt{3}} \cdot \frac{1 + \sqrt{3}}{1 + \sqrt{3}}$$

$$= \frac{3 + 2\sqrt{3} + 1}{1 - 3}$$

$$\tan \frac{7}{12}\pi = -\sqrt{3} - 2. \quad ∎$$

Example 2 If $\sin s = 4/5$ and $\cos t = -5/13$, where s is in quadrant II and t is in quadrant III, find each of the following.

(a) $\sin (s + t)$

Use the identity for the sine of the sum of two angles,

$$\sin (s + t) = \sin s \cos t + \cos s \sin t.$$

To use this identity we need to find cos s and sin t. To do so, use the identity $\sin^2 x + \cos^2 x = 1$. Let us first find cos s.

$$\sin^2 s + \cos^2 s = 1$$

$$\frac{16}{25} + \cos^2 s = 1$$

$$\cos^2 s = \frac{9}{25}$$

$$\cos s = -\frac{3}{5} \qquad (s \text{ is in quadrant II})$$

In the same way, check that sin $t = -12/13$. Now we have

$$\sin (s + t) = \frac{4}{5}\left(-\frac{5}{13}\right) + \left(-\frac{3}{5}\right)\left(-\frac{12}{13}\right)$$

$$= -\frac{20}{65} + \frac{36}{65}$$

$$\sin (s + t) = \frac{16}{65}.$$

(b) tan $(s + t)$
We know that

$$\tan (s + t) = \frac{\tan s + \tan t}{1 - \tan s \tan t}.$$

Here we have tan $s = -4/3$ and tan $t = 12/5$ (where did we get these values?) so that

$$\tan (s + t) = \frac{-\frac{4}{3} + \frac{12}{5}}{1 - \left(-\frac{4}{3}\right)\left(\frac{12}{5}\right)} = \frac{16}{63}. \qquad ▌$$

Example 3 Write each of the following as a function of θ.
(a) sin $(30° + \theta)$
Using the identity for sin $(s + t)$, we have

$$\sin (30° + \theta) = \sin 30° \cos \theta + \cos 30° \sin \theta$$

$$\sin (30° + \theta) = \frac{1}{2}\cos \theta + \frac{\sqrt{3}}{2} \sin \theta$$

(b) $\tan (45° - \theta) = \dfrac{\tan 45° - \tan \theta}{1 + \tan 45° \tan \theta}$

$$\tan (45° - \theta) = \frac{1 - \tan \theta}{1 + \tan \theta}. \qquad ▌$$

Expressions of the form $a \sin x + b \cos x$ occur so often in mathematics that it is useful to know how to rewrite these expressions in simpler form. In particular, these expressions must often be graphed, which can be done more easily with the procedure developed here. Figure 7.3 shows a circle of radius r with the point (a, b) on the circle. The circle has equation $x^2 + y^2 = r^2$, so that

$$a^2 + b^2 = r^2, \quad \text{or} \quad r = \sqrt{a^2 + b^2}.$$

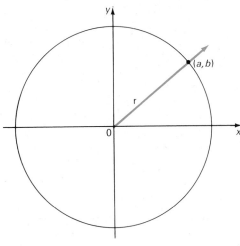

Figure 7.3   Figure 7.4

Let α be the angle shown in Figure 7.4. Then

$$\sin \alpha = \frac{b}{r} = \frac{b}{\sqrt{a^2 + b^2}} \quad \text{and} \quad \cos \alpha = \frac{a}{r} = \frac{a}{\sqrt{a^2 + b^2}}.$$

Now rewrite $a \sin x + b \cos x$:

$$a \sin x + b \cos x = \frac{a}{1} \cdot \frac{\sqrt{a^2 + b^2}}{\sqrt{a^2 + b^2}} \sin x + \frac{b}{1} \cdot \frac{\sqrt{a^2 + b^2}}{\sqrt{a^2 + b^2}} \cos x$$

$$= \sqrt{a^2 + b^2} \left(\frac{a}{\sqrt{a^2 + b^2}} \sin x + \frac{b}{\sqrt{a^2 + b^2}} \cos x \right)$$

$$= \sqrt{a^2 + b^2} \left(\sin x \, \frac{a}{\sqrt{a^2 + b^2}} + \cos x \, \frac{b}{\sqrt{a^2 + b^2}} \right).$$

Substitute $\sin \alpha$ and $\cos \alpha$ from above.

$$= \sqrt{a^2 + b^2} \, (\sin x \cos \alpha + \cos x \sin \alpha)$$

Using the identity for $\sin (s + t)$, we end up with

$$a \sin x + b \cos x = \sqrt{a^2 + b^2} \, \sin (x + \alpha).$$

In summary, we have the **reduction identity:**

$$a \sin x + b \cos x = \sqrt{a^2 + b^2} \, \sin(x + \alpha),$$

where $\quad \sin \alpha = \dfrac{b}{\sqrt{a^2 + b^2}} \quad$ and $\quad \cos \alpha = \dfrac{a}{\sqrt{a^2 + b^2}}$

Example 4   Simplify $\dfrac{1}{2} \sin x + \dfrac{\sqrt{3}}{2} \cos x$, using the reduction identity.

Here $a = 1/2$ and $b = \sqrt{3}/2$, so that

$$\sqrt{a^2 + b^2} = \sqrt{\left(\frac{1}{2}\right)^2 + \left(\frac{\sqrt{3}}{2}\right)^2} = 1.$$

To find α, first find $\sin \alpha$ and $\cos \alpha$.

$$\sin \alpha = \frac{b}{\sqrt{a^2 + b^2}} = \frac{\dfrac{\sqrt{3}}{2}}{1} = \frac{\sqrt{3}}{2}$$

$$\cos \alpha = \frac{a}{\sqrt{a^2 + b^2}} = \frac{\dfrac{1}{2}}{1} = \frac{1}{2}$$

A value of α satisfying these conditions is $\alpha = \pi/3$. Thus,

$$\frac{1}{2} \sin x + \frac{\sqrt{3}}{2} \cos x = 1 \cdot \sin\left(x + \frac{\pi}{3}\right)$$

$$= \sin\left(x + \frac{\pi}{3}\right) \quad \blacksquare$$

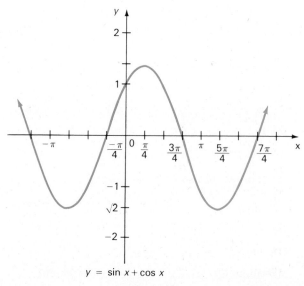

$y = \sin x + \cos x$

Figure 7.5

Example 5   Graph $y = \sin x + \cos x$.

Reduce $\sin x + \cos x$ as follows. Since $a = b = 1$, we have $\sqrt{a^2 + b^2} = \sqrt{1^2 + 1^2} = \sqrt{2}$. To find α, let

$$\sin \alpha = \frac{b}{\sqrt{a^2 + b^2}} = \frac{1}{\sqrt{2}} \qquad \text{and} \qquad \cos \alpha = \frac{a}{\sqrt{a^2 + b^2}} = \frac{1}{\sqrt{2}},$$

Thus, $\alpha = \pi/4$, and

$$y = \sin x + \cos x = \sqrt{2} \sin \left(x + \frac{\pi}{4} \right).$$

The graph of this function has an amplitude of $\sqrt{2}$, a period of 2π, and a phase shift of $\pi/4$ to the left, as shown in Figure 7.5. ▌

7.4 Exercises   *Use the identities of this section to find each of the following without using tables.*

1. $\sin 15°$

2. $\sin 105°$

3. $\sin (-105°)$

4. $\tan \dfrac{5\pi}{12}$

5. $\sin \dfrac{5\pi}{12}$

6. $\sin 285°$

7. $\sin 76° \cos 31° - \cos 76° \sin 31°$

8. $\sin 40° \cos 50° + \cos 40° \sin 50°$

9. $\dfrac{\tan 80° + \tan 55°}{1 - \tan 80° \tan 55°}$

10. $\dfrac{\tan 80° - \tan (-55°)}{1 + \tan 80° \tan (-55°)}$

11. $\sin 80° \cos (-55°) - \cos 80° \sin (-55°)$

12. $\sin 100° \cos 10° - \cos 100° \sin 10°$

Write each of the following as a function of t.

13. $\sin (\pi/4 + t)$

14. $\sin (t - \pi/6)$

15. $\tan (\pi/3 - t)$

16. $\sin (\pi - t)$

17. $\tan (\pi + t)$

18. $\tan (0 - t)$

19. $\sin (\pi + t)$

20. $\tan (\pi - t)$

For each of the following, find sin (s + t), sin (s − t), tan (s + t), and tan (s − t).

21. $\sin t = 5/13$ and $\cos s = 3/5$, s and t in quadrant I

22. $\sin t = 3/5$ and $\cos s = -1/5$, s and t in quadrant II

23. $\sin t = -1/3$ and $\sin s = 2/3$, s in quadrant II and t in quadrant IV

24. $\sin t = -12/13$ and $\sin s = 3/5$, s in quadrant I and t in quadrant III

25. $\cos s = -8/17$ and $\cos t = -3/5$, s and t in quadrant III

26. $\cos s = -15/17$ and $\sin t = 4/5$, s in quadrant II and t in quadrant I

Verify that each of the following are identities.

27. $\sin\left(\dfrac{\pi}{2} + x\right) = \cos x$

28. $\sin\left(\dfrac{3\pi}{2} + x\right) = -\cos x$

29. $\tan\left(\dfrac{\pi}{2} + x\right) = -\cot x$

30. $\tan\left(\dfrac{\pi}{4} + x\right) = \dfrac{1 + \tan x}{1 - \tan x}$

31. $\sin 2x = 2 \sin x \cos x$

32. $\sin (x + y) + \sin (x - y) = 2 \sin x \cos y$

33. $\sin (x + y) - \sin (x - y) = 2 \cos x \sin y$

34. $\tan (x - y) - \tan (y - x) = \dfrac{2(\tan x - \tan y)}{1 + \tan x \tan y}$

35. $\sin (30° + \alpha) + \cos (60° + \alpha) = \cos \alpha$

36. $\sin (210° + x) - \cos (120° + x) = 0$

37. $\dfrac{\cos (\alpha - \beta)}{\cos \alpha \sin \beta} = \tan \alpha + \cot \beta$

38. $\dfrac{\sin (s + t)}{\cos s \cos t} = \tan s + \tan t$

A painting 1 meter high and 3 meters from the floor will cut off an angle θ to an observer, where $\theta = \tan^{-1} [x/(x^2 + 2)]$. Assume the observer is x meters from the wall displaying the painting and that the eyes of the observer are 2 meters above the ground. (See the figure.) Find the value of θ for each of the following values of x. Round to the nearest degree.

39. 1   **40.** 2   **41.** 3

42. Derive the formula for θ. Use the identity for $\tan (\theta + \alpha)$.

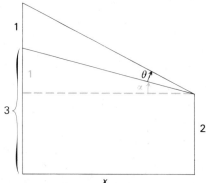

Use the reduction identity to simplify each of the following for angles between $0°$ and $360°$. Find angles to the nearest degree.

43. $-\sin x + \cos x$

44. $\sqrt{3} \sin x - \cos x$

45. $5 \sin \theta - 12 \cos \theta$

46. $12 \sin A + 5 \cos A$

47. $15 \sin B - 8 \cos B$

48. $-7 \sin s - 24 \cos s$

49. $24 \cos s - 7 \sin s$

50. $3 \sin x + 4 \cos x$

Graph each of the following by first changing to a function of the form $y = a \sin (x + \alpha)$.

51. $y = \sqrt{3} \sin x + \cos x$

52. $y = \sin x - \sqrt{3} \cos x$

53. $y = -\sin x + \cos x$

54. $y = -\sin x - \cos x$

55. Let $f(x) = \sin x$. Show that $\dfrac{f(x + h) - f(x)}{h} = \sin x \left(\dfrac{\cos h - 1}{h}\right) + \cos x \left(\dfrac{\sin h}{h}\right)$.

⊙ *Let $\sin s = 0.599832$, where s terminates in quadrant II. Let $\sin t = -0.845992$, where t terminates in quadrant III. Find each of the following.*

56. $\sin (s + t)$ **57.** $\sin (s - t)$ **58.** $\tan (s + t)$ **59.** $\sin 2s$

Use the identities of this section to find each of the following.

60. $\sin (\cos^{-1} 5/13 + \tan^{-1} 3/4)$

61. $\sin (\sin^{-1} 2/3 + \tan^{-1} 1/4)$

62. $\sin (\cos^{-1} 1/2 - \tan^{-1} -3)$

63. $\tan (\tan^{-1} 4/5 - \sin^{-1} 5/13)$

64. Use the results of Exercise 17 above to help show that the period of tangent is π.

7.5 Multiple-Angle Identities

Some special cases of the identities for the sum of two angles are used often enough to be expressed as separate identities. These are the identities that result from the addition identities when $s = t$, so that $s + t = 2s$. These identities are called **double-angle identities.** In the identity for $\cos(s + t)$, we let $t = s$ to derive an expression for $\cos 2s$.

$$\cos 2s = \cos(s + s)$$
$$= \cos s \cos s - \sin s \sin s$$

$$\boxed{\cos 2s = \cos^2 s - \sin^2 s}$$

By substitution from either $\cos^2 s = 1 - \sin^2 s$ or $\sin^2 s = 1 - \cos^2 s$, we get

$$\boxed{\begin{aligned}\cos 2s &= 1 - 2 \sin^2 s\\ \cos 2s &= 2 \cos^2 s - 1.\end{aligned}}$$

or

We can do the same thing with $\sin(s + t)$.

$$\sin 2s = \sin(s + s)$$
$$= \sin s \cos s + \cos s \sin s$$

$$\boxed{\sin 2s = 2 \sin s \cos s}$$

We can also find $\tan 2s$ from the identity for $\tan(s + t)$.

$$\tan 2s = \tan(s + s)$$
$$= \frac{\tan s + \tan s}{1 - \tan s \tan s}$$

$$\boxed{\tan 2s = \frac{2 \tan s}{1 - \tan^2 s}}$$

These identities, together with the addition identities, allow us to rewrite trigonometric functions of multiple values of s in terms of s.

Example 1   Write $\sin 3s$ in terms of $\sin s$.

$$\begin{aligned} \sin 3s &= \sin(2s + s) \\ &= \sin 2s \cos s + \cos 2s \sin s \\ &= (2 \sin s \cos s) \cos s + (\cos^2 s - \sin^2 s) \sin s \\ &= 2 \sin\!s \cos^2 s + \cos^2 s \sin s - \sin^3 s \\ &= 2 \sin s(1 - \sin^2 s) + (1 - \sin^2 s) \sin s - \sin^3 s \\ &= 2 \sin s - 2 \sin^3 s + \sin s - \sin^3 s - \sin^3 s \\ \sin 3s &= 3 \sin s - 4 \sin^3 s \quad \blacksquare \end{aligned}$$

The double-angle identities for $2s$ can be used to find values of the trigonometric functions of s as shown in the following example.

Example 2   Find the values of the six trigonometric functions of θ if $\cos 2\theta = 4/5$ and θ terminates in quadrant II.
Use one of the double-angle identities for cosine.

$$\cos 2\theta = 1 - 2 \sin^2 \theta$$

$$\frac{4}{5} = 1 - 2 \sin^2 \theta$$

$$-\frac{1}{5} = -2 \sin^2 \theta$$

$$\frac{1}{10} = \sin^2 \theta$$

$$\sin \theta = \frac{\sqrt{10}}{10}.$$

We use the positive square root since θ terminates in quadrant II. Values of $\cos \theta$ and $\tan \theta$ can now be found using the fundamental identities.

$$\sin^2 \theta + \cos^2 \theta = 1$$

$$\frac{1}{10} + \cos^2 \theta = 1$$

$$\cos^2 \theta = \frac{9}{10}$$

$$\cos \theta = \frac{-3}{\sqrt{10}}$$

$$\cos \theta = \frac{-3\sqrt{10}}{10}$$

Verify that $\tan \theta = \sin \theta / \cos \theta = -1/3$. Find the other three functions using reciprocals.

$$\csc \theta = \frac{1}{\sin \theta} = \sqrt{10} \qquad \sec \theta = \frac{1}{\cos \theta} = \frac{-\sqrt{10}}{3} \qquad \cot \theta = \frac{1}{\tan \theta} = -3 \quad \blacksquare$$

Example 3   Given $\cos \theta = 3/5$, where $3\pi/2 < \theta < 2\pi$, find $\cos 2\theta$, $\sin 2\theta$, and $\tan 2\theta$.

Since $\cos \theta = 3/5$, we can show that $\sin \theta = \pm 4/5$ by using the identity $\sin^2 \theta + \cos^2 \theta = 1$. Since θ terminates in quadrant IV, we choose $\sin \theta = -4/5$. Then, using the double-angle identities, we have

$$\sin 2\theta = 2 \sin \theta \cos \theta = 2\left(-\frac{4}{5}\right)\left(\frac{3}{5}\right) = -\frac{24}{25}$$

$$\cos 2\theta = \cos^2 \theta - \sin^2 \theta = \frac{9}{25} - \frac{16}{25} = -\frac{7}{25}$$

$$\tan 2\theta = \frac{\sin 2\theta}{\cos 2\theta} = \frac{-24/25}{-7/25} = \frac{24}{7}.$$

We can also find $\tan 2\theta$ by noting that $\tan \theta = -4/3$, so that

$$\tan 2\theta = \frac{2 \tan \theta}{1 - \tan^2 \theta} = \frac{2\left(-\frac{4}{3}\right)}{1 - \frac{16}{9}} = \frac{-\frac{8}{3}}{-\frac{7}{9}} = \frac{24}{7}. \quad \blacksquare$$

From the alternate forms of the double-angle identity for cosine, we can derive three additional identities. These **half-angle identities,** listed below, are quite useful in the study of calculus.

$$\cos \frac{s}{2} = \pm \sqrt{\frac{1 + \cos s}{2}} \qquad \sin \frac{s}{2} = \pm \sqrt{\frac{1 - \cos s}{2}} \qquad \tan \frac{s}{2} = \pm \sqrt{\frac{1 - \cos s}{1 + \cos s}}$$

$$\tan \frac{s}{2} = \frac{\sin s}{1 + \cos s} \qquad \text{and} \qquad \tan \frac{s}{2} = \frac{1 - \cos s}{\sin s}$$

In these identities, the plus or minus sign is selected according to the quadrant in which $s/2$ terminates. For example, if s represents an angle of 324°, then $s/2 = 162°$, which lies in quadrant II. Thus, $\cos s/2$ and $\tan s/2$ would be negative, while $\sin s/2$ would be positive.

To derive the identity for $\sin s/2$, start with the following identity.

$$\cos 2x = 1 - 2 \sin^2 x$$

$$2 \sin^2 x = 1 - \cos 2x$$

$$\sin x = \pm \sqrt{\frac{1 - \cos 2x}{2}}$$

Now let $2x = s$, so that $x = s/2$, and substitute into this last expression.

$$\sin \frac{s}{2} = \pm \sqrt{\frac{1 - \cos s}{2}}$$

The identity for $\cos s/2$ is derived in exactly the same way, by starting with the double-angle identity $\cos 2x = 2 \cos^2 x - 1$. The first identity for $\tan s/2$ comes from the half-angle identities for sine and cosine.

$$\tan \frac{s}{2} = \frac{\pm \sqrt{\dfrac{1 - \cos s}{2}}}{\pm \sqrt{\dfrac{1 + \cos s}{2}}} = \pm \sqrt{\frac{1 - \cos s}{1 + \cos s}}$$

The other two identities for $\tan \dfrac{s}{2}$ that are given above are proven in Exercises 46 and 47 below.

Example 4   Find $\cos 112.5°$.

Since $112.5° = 225°/2$, we use the identity for $\cos s/2$. Also, $112.5°$ is in quadrant II, where cosine is negative, so that the $-$ sign must be used on the radical.

$$\cos 112.5° = \cos \frac{225°}{2} = -\sqrt{\frac{1 + \cos 225°}{2}}$$

$$= -\sqrt{\frac{1 - \dfrac{\sqrt{2}}{2}}{2}}$$

$$= -\sqrt{\frac{2 - \sqrt{2}}{4}}$$

$$= -\frac{\sqrt{2 - \sqrt{2}}}{2} \qquad \blacksquare$$

Example 5   Find $\tan 22.5°$.

Use the identity $\tan \dfrac{s}{2} = \dfrac{\sin s}{1 + \cos s}$, with $s = 45°$.

$$\tan 22.5° = \tan \frac{45°}{2} = \frac{\sin 45°}{1 + \cos 45°}$$

$$= \frac{\dfrac{\sqrt{2}}{2}}{1 + \dfrac{\sqrt{2}}{2}}$$

$$= \frac{\sqrt{2}}{2 + \sqrt{2}}$$

$$= \sqrt{2} - 1 \quad \blacksquare$$

(Here we rationalized the denominator.) See also Exercise 54 below.

Example 6 Given $\cos s = 2/3$, with $3\pi/2 < s < 2\pi$, find $\cos s/2$, $\sin s/2$ and $\tan s/2$.

Since $3\pi/2 < s < 2\pi$, we have $3\pi/4 < s/2 < \pi$. Thus, $s/2$ terminates in quadrant II and $\cos s/2$ and $\tan s/2$ are negative, while $\sin s/2$ is positive. Using the half-angle identities gives

$$\sin \frac{s}{2} = \sqrt{\frac{1 - \dfrac{2}{3}}{2}} = \sqrt{\frac{1}{6}} = \frac{\sqrt{6}}{6}$$

$$\cos \frac{s}{2} = -\sqrt{\frac{1 + \dfrac{2}{3}}{2}} = -\sqrt{\frac{5}{6}} = -\frac{\sqrt{30}}{6}$$

$$\tan \frac{s}{2} = \frac{\dfrac{\sqrt{6}}{6}}{-\dfrac{\sqrt{30}}{6}} = \frac{-\sqrt{5}}{5}. \quad \blacksquare$$

7.5 Exercises *Use the identities of this section to complete the following.*

1. $2 \sin \dfrac{\pi}{5} \cos \dfrac{\pi}{5} = \sin$ _____

2. $\cos^2 10° - \sin^2 10° = \cos$ _____

3. $4 \cos^2 x - 2 = 2(\underline{\hspace{1cm}})$

4. $\dfrac{2 \tan \dfrac{\pi}{3}}{1 - \tan^2 \dfrac{\pi}{3}} = \tan$ _____

5. $\sin 320° = 2 \sin \underline{\hspace{0.8cm}} \cos \underline{\hspace{0.8cm}}$

6. $\tan 8k = \dfrac{2 \tan \underline{\hspace{0.6cm}}}{1 - \underline{\hspace{1cm}}}$

7. $\cos 6x = \underline{\hspace{0.8cm}} 3x - \underline{\hspace{0.8cm}} 3x$

8. $\tan 10x = \dfrac{\underline{\hspace{0.8cm}} 5x}{1 - \underline{\hspace{1cm}}}$

9. $\sin \underline{\hspace{0.8cm}} = \sqrt{\dfrac{1 - \cos 18°}{2}}$

10. $\cos \underline{\hspace{0.8cm}} = \sqrt{\dfrac{\underline{\hspace{0.6cm}} \cos 44°}{2}}$

11. $\underline{\hspace{1cm}} = -\sqrt{\dfrac{1 - \cos 340°}{1 + \cos 340°}}$

12. $\underline{\hspace{1cm}} = \sqrt{\dfrac{1 + \cos 40°}{2}}$

Determine whether the positive or negative square root should be selected.

13. $\sin 195° = \pm\sqrt{\dfrac{1 - \cos 390°}{2}}$

15. $\tan 225° = \pm\sqrt{\dfrac{1 - \cos 450°}{1 + \cos 450°}}$

14. $\cos 58° = \pm\sqrt{\dfrac{1 + \cos 116°}{2}}$

16. $\sin (-10°) = \pm\sqrt{\dfrac{1 - \cos (-20°)}{2}}$

Find each of the following.

17. $\cos x$, given $\cos 2x = -5/12$ and $\pi/2 < x < \pi$

18. $\sin x$, given $\cos 2x = 2/3$ and $\pi < x < 3\pi/2$

19. $\cos \alpha/2$, given $\cos \alpha = 1/4$ and $\pi < \alpha < 3\pi/2$

20. $\sin \beta/2$, given $\cos \beta = 3/4$ and $3\pi/2 < \beta < 2\pi$

Use the identities of this section to find the sine, cosine, and tangent for each of the following.

21. $\theta = 22.5°$

22. $\theta = 15°$

23. $\theta = 195°$

24. $x = -\pi/8$

25. $x = 5\pi/2$

26. $x = 3\pi/2$

Use the identities of this section to find values of the six trigonometric functions for each of the following.

27. x, given $\cos 2x = -5/12$ and $\pi/2 < x < \pi$

28. t, given $\cos 2t = 2/3$ and $\pi/2 < t < \pi$

29. 2θ, given $\sin \theta = 2/5$ and $\cos \theta < 0$

30. 2β, given $\cos \beta = -12/13$ and $\sin \beta > 0$

31. $2x$, given $\tan x = 2$ and $\cos x > 0$

32. $2x$, given $\tan x = 5/3$ and $\sin x < 0$

33. $\alpha/2$, given $\cos \alpha = 1/3$ and $\sin \alpha < 0$

34. $\theta/2$, given $\cos \theta = -2/3$ and $\sin \theta > 0$

Verify that each of the following equations is an identity.

35. $(\sin \gamma + \cos \gamma)^2 = \sin 2\gamma + 1$

36. $\cos 2s = \cos^4 s - \sin^4 s$

37. $\sec 2x = \dfrac{\sec^2 x + \sec^4 x}{2 + \sec^2 x - \sec^4 x}$

38. $\cot s + \tan s = 2 \csc 2s$

39. $\sin 4\alpha = 4 \sin \alpha \cos \alpha \cos 2\alpha$

40. $\dfrac{1 + \cos 2x}{\sin 2x} = \cot x$

41. $\sec^2 \dfrac{x}{2} = \dfrac{2}{1 + \cos x}$

42. $\cot^2 \dfrac{x}{2} = \dfrac{(1 + \cos x)^2}{\sin^2 x}$

43. $\sin^2 \dfrac{x}{2} = \dfrac{\tan x - \sin x}{2 \tan x}$

44. $\dfrac{\sin 2x}{2 \sin x} = \cos^2 \dfrac{x}{2} - \sin^2 \dfrac{x}{2}$

45. $\dfrac{2}{1 + \cos x} - \tan^2 \dfrac{x}{2} = 1$

46. $\tan \dfrac{s}{2} = \dfrac{\sin s}{1 + \cos s}$

47. $\tan \dfrac{s}{2} = \dfrac{1 - \cos s}{\sin s}$

48. $\tan \dfrac{\gamma}{2} = \csc \gamma - \cot \gamma$

Express each of the following as trigonometric functions of x.

49. $\tan^2 2x$ **50.** $\cos^2 2x$ **51.** $\sin 3x$ **52.** $\sin 4x$ **53.** $\cos 4x$

54. In Example 5, we used the identity tan $s/2 = \sin s/(1 + \cos s)$ to find that tan 22.5° = $\sqrt{2} - 1$. Find tan 22.5° using the identity tan $s/2 = \pm\sqrt{(1 - \cos s)/(1 + \cos s)}$, and show that the two answers are equal.

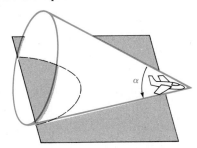

An airplane flying faster than sound sends out sound waves that form a cone, as shown in the figure. The cone intersects the ground to form a hyperbola. As this hyperbola passes over a particular point on the ground, a sonic boom is heard at that point. If α is the angle at the vertex of the cone, then

$$\sin \frac{\alpha}{2} = \frac{1}{m}$$

where m is the mach number of the plane. (We assume $m > 1$.) The mach number is the ratio of the speed of the plane and the speed of sound. Thus, a speed of mach 1.4 means that the plane is flying 1.4 times the speed of sound. Find α or m, as necessary, for each of the following.

55. $m = 3/2$ **57.** $m = 2$ **59.** $\alpha = 30°$

56. $m = 5/4$ **58.** $m = 5/2$ **60.** $\alpha = 45°$

● *Let* $\sin s = -0.481143$, *with* $7\pi/4 < s < 2\pi$. *Find each of the following.*

61. $\sin 2s$ **63.** $\cos 2s$ **65.** $\tan 2s$

62. $\sin \frac{1}{2}s$ **64.** $\cos \frac{1}{2}s$ **66.** $\tan \frac{1}{2}s$

Simplify each of the following.

67. $\sin^2 2x + \cos^2 2x$ **69.** $1 + \tan^2 4x$

68. $\sin^2 \frac{x}{2} + \cos^2 \frac{x}{2}$ **70.** $\cot^2 \frac{x}{3} + 1$

7.6 Sum and Product Identities

One group of identities in this section can be used to rewrite a product of two functions as a sum or difference. The other group can be used to rewrite a sum or difference of two functions as a product. Some of these identities can also be used to rewrite an expression involving both sine and cosine functions as one with only one of these functions. In the next section on conditional equations, the need for this kind of change will become clear. These identities are also useful in graphing and in calculus.

The identities that we discuss in this section all result from the sum and difference identities for sine and cosine. Adding the two addition identities for $\sin (s + t)$ and $\sin (s - t)$ gives

$$\sin (s + t) = \sin s \cos t + \cos s \sin t$$
$$\underline{\sin (s - t) = \sin s \cos t - \cos s \sin t}$$
$$\sin (s + t) + \sin (s - t) = 2 \sin s \cos t,$$

or

$$\sin s \cos t = \frac{1}{2} [\sin (s + t) + \sin (s - t)].$$

If we subtract $\sin (s - t)$ from $\sin (s + t)$, the result is

$$\cos s \sin t = \frac{1}{2} [\sin (s + t) - \sin (s - t)].$$

If we use the identities for $\cos (s + t)$ and $\cos (s - t)$ in a similar manner we get

$$\cos s \cos t = \frac{1}{2} [\cos (s + t) + \cos (s - t)]$$

$$\sin s \sin t = \frac{1}{2} [\cos (s - t) - \cos (s + t)].$$

Example 1   Rewrite $\cos 2\theta \sin \theta$ as the sum or difference of two functions.
Using the identity for $\cos s \sin t$ gives

$$\cos 2\theta \sin \theta = \frac{1}{2}(\sin 3\theta - \sin \theta)$$

$$\cos 2\theta \sin \theta = \frac{1}{2} \sin 3\theta - \frac{1}{2} \sin \theta. \quad \blacksquare$$

Example 2   Evaluate $\cos 15° \cos 45°$.
Use the identity for $\cos s \cos t$.

$$\cos 15° \cos 45° = \frac{1}{2} [\cos (15° + 45°) + \cos (15° - 45°)]$$

$$= \frac{1}{2} [\cos 60° + \cos (-30°)]$$

$$= \frac{1}{2} (\cos 60° + \cos 30°)$$

$$= \frac{1}{2} \left(\frac{1}{2} + \frac{\sqrt{3}}{2} \right)$$

$$\cos 15° \cos 45° = \frac{1 + \sqrt{3}}{4} \quad \blacksquare$$

Now we can use the identities from above to obtain further identities that are used in calculus. To begin, let $s + t = x$, and let $s - t = y$. Then we have

$$s = \frac{x+y}{2} \quad \text{and} \quad t = \frac{x-y}{2}.$$

(To get these results, add the two equations, and then subtract them.) With these results, the identity

$$\sin s \cos t = \frac{1}{2}[\sin(s+t) + \sin(s-t)]$$

becomes

$$\sin\left(\frac{x+y}{2}\right) \cos\left(\frac{x-y}{2}\right) = \frac{1}{2}(\sin x + \sin y),$$

or

$$\boxed{\sin x + \sin y = 2 \sin\left(\frac{x+y}{2}\right) \cos\left(\frac{x-y}{2}\right).}$$

Three other identities can be obtained in a very similar way.

$$\boxed{\begin{array}{l} \sin x - \sin y = 2 \cos\left(\frac{x+y}{2}\right) \sin\left(\frac{x-y}{2}\right) \\[2mm] \cos x + \cos y = 2 \cos\left(\frac{x+y}{2}\right) \cos\left(\frac{x-y}{2}\right) \\[2mm] \cos x - \cos y = -2 \sin\left(\frac{x+y}{2}\right) \sin\left(\frac{x-y}{2}\right) \end{array}}$$

Example 3 Write $\sin 2\gamma - \sin 4\gamma$ as a product of two functions.
Use the identity for $\sin x - \sin y$.

$$\sin 2\gamma - \sin 4\gamma = 2 \cos\left(\frac{2\gamma + 4\gamma}{2}\right) \sin\left(\frac{2\gamma - 4\gamma}{2}\right)$$

$$= 2 \cos \frac{6\gamma}{2} \sin \frac{-2\gamma}{2}$$

$$= 2 \cos 3\gamma \sin(-\gamma)$$

$$\sin 2\gamma - \sin 4\gamma = -2 \cos 3\gamma \sin \gamma. \quad \blacksquare$$

Example 4 Verify that $\dfrac{\sin 3s + \sin s}{\cos s + \cos 3s} = \tan 2s$ is an identity.

Work as follows.

$$\frac{\sin 3s + \sin s}{\cos s + \cos 3s} = \frac{2 \sin\left(\frac{3s+s}{2}\right) \cos\left(\frac{3s-s}{2}\right)}{2 \cos\left(\frac{s+3s}{2}\right) \cos\left(\frac{s-3s}{2}\right)}$$

$$= \frac{\sin 2s \cos s}{\cos 2s \cos(-s)} = \frac{\sin 2s}{\cos 2s} = \tan 2s. \quad \blacksquare$$

7.6 Exercises   *Rewrite each of the following as a sum or difference of trigonometric functions.*

1. $\cos 35° \sin 25°$

2. $2 \sin 2x \sin 4x$

3. $3 \cos 5x \cos 3x$

4. $2 \sin 74° \cos 114°$

5. $\sin (-\theta) \sin (-3\theta)$

6. $4 \cos (-32°) \sin 15°$

7. $-8 \cos 4y \cos 5y$

8. $2 \sin 3k \sin 14k$

Rewrite each of the following as a product of trigonometric functions.

9. $\sin 60° - \sin 30°$

10. $\sin 28° + \sin (-18°)$

11. $\cos 42° + \cos 148°$

12. $\cos 2x - \cos 8x$

13. $\sin 12\beta - \sin 3\beta$

14. $\cos 5x + \cos 10x$

15. $-3 \sin 2x + 3 \sin 5x$

16. $-\cos 8s + \cos 14s$

Verify that each of the following is an identity.

17. $\tan x = \dfrac{\sin 3x - \sin x}{\cos 3x + \cos x}$

18. $\dfrac{\sin 5t + \sin 3t}{\cos 3t - \cos 5t} = \cot t$

19. $\dfrac{\cot 2\theta}{\tan 3\theta} = \dfrac{\cos 5\theta + \cos \theta}{\cos \theta - \cos 5\theta}$

20. $\dfrac{\cos \alpha + \cos \beta}{\cos \alpha - \cos \beta} = -\cot \left(\dfrac{\alpha + \beta}{2}\right) \cot \left(\dfrac{\alpha - \beta}{2}\right)$

21. $\dfrac{1}{\tan 2s} = \dfrac{\sin 3s - \sin s}{\cos s - \cos 3s}$

22. $\dfrac{\sin^2 5\alpha - 2 \sin 5\alpha \sin 3\alpha + \sin^2 3\alpha}{\sin^2 5\alpha - \sin^2 3\alpha} = \dfrac{\tan \alpha}{\tan 4\alpha}$

23. $\sin 6\theta \cos 4\theta - \sin 3\theta \cos 7\theta = \sin 3\theta \cos \theta$

24. $\sin 8\beta \sin 4\beta + \cos 10\beta \cos 2\beta = \cos 6\beta \cos 2\beta$

25. $\sin^2 u - \sin^2 v = \sin (u + v) \sin (u - v)$

26. $\cos^2 u - \cos^2 v = -\sin (u + v) \sin (u - v)$

27. Show that the double-angle identity for sine can be considered a special case of the identity $\sin s \cos t = (1/2) [\sin (s + t) + \sin (s - t)]$.

28. Show that the double-angle identity $\cos 2s = 2 \cos^2 s - 1$ is a special case of the identity $\cos s \cos t = \dfrac{1}{2} [\cos (s + t) + \cos (s - t)]$.

7.7 Trigonometric Equations

So far in this chapter we have discussed trigonometric identities, statements which are true for every value in the domain of the variable. Here we discuss conditional equations which involve trigonometric functions. A **conditional equation** is an equation in which some replacements for the variable make the statement true, while others make it false. For example, $2x + 3 = 5$, $x^2 - 5x = 10$, and $2^x = 8$ are conditional equations. Conditional equations with trigonometric functions can usually be solved by using algebraic methods and trigonometric identities to simplify the equations.

Example 1 Solve $3 \sin x = \sqrt{3} + \sin x$.

Treat $\sin x$ as the variable. Collect all terms with $\sin x$ on one side of the equation. Then solve for $\sin x$.

$$3 \sin x = \sqrt{3} + \sin x$$
$$2 \sin x = \sqrt{3}$$
$$\sin x = \frac{\sqrt{3}}{2}$$

From earlier work, we know that $\sin 60° = \sqrt{3}/2$. However, $\sin 120° = \sqrt{3}/2$ also, as does $\sin 420°$, and so on. There are an infinite number of values of x which satisfy the equation $\sin x = \sqrt{3}/2$. We can express the infinite number of solutions as

$$x = 60° + 360° \cdot n \quad \text{or} \quad x = 120° + 360° \cdot n,$$

where n is any integer. ▌

Usually, we need the solutions of a trigonometric equation only for some specified interval, as shown in the next examples.

Example 2 Find all solutions of $\tan^2 x + \tan x - 2 = 0$ in the interval $[0, 2\pi)$.

If we let $y = \tan x$, the equation becomes $y^2 + y - 2 = 0$, which is factorable as $(y - 1)(y + 2) = 0$. Substituting $\tan x$ back for y, we have

$$(\tan x - 1)(\tan x + 2) = 0$$
$$\tan x - 1 = 0 \qquad \tan x + 2 = 0$$
$$\tan x = 1 \qquad \tan x = -2.$$

If $\tan x = 1$, then for the interval $[0, 2\pi)$ we get $x = \pi/4$ or $x = 5\pi/4$. If $\tan x = -2$, then using Table 5, we find that (approximately) $x = 2.0333$ or 5.1749. The solutions are $\pi/4$, $5\pi/4$, 2.0333, and 5.1749. ▌

When an equation involves more than one trigonometric function, it is often helpful to use a suitable identity to rewrite the equation in terms of just one trigonometric function as in the following example.

Example 3   Find all solutions for $\sin x + \cos x = 0$ in the interval $[0, 360°)$.

Since $\sin x/\cos x = \tan x$ and $\cos x/\cos x = 1$, we can divide both sides of the equation by $\cos x$ (assuming $\cos x \neq 0$) to get

$$\sin x + \cos x = 0$$

$$\frac{\sin x}{\cos x} + \frac{\cos x}{\cos x} = \frac{0}{\cos x}$$

$$\tan x + 1 = 0$$

$$\tan x = -1.$$

The solutions in the given interval for the last equation are

$$x = 135° \quad \text{and} \quad x = 315.°$$

We assumed here that $\cos x \neq 0$. If $\cos x = 0$, our equation becomes $\sin x + 0 = 0$, or $\sin x = 0$. If $\cos x = 0$, it is not possible for $\sin x = 0$, so that no solutions were missed by assuming $\cos x \neq 0$.   ∎

Example 4   Find all solutions for $\sin x \tan x = 3 \sin x$ in the interval $[0°, 360°)$.

Subtract $3 \sin x$ on both sides and then factor.

$$\sin x \tan x = 3 \sin x$$

$$\sin x \tan x - 3 \sin x = 0$$

$$\sin x (\tan x - 3) = 0$$

Set each factor equal to 0.

$$\sin x = 0 \quad \text{or} \quad \tan x - 3 = 0$$

$$x = 0° \text{ or } x = 180° \qquad \tan x = 3$$

$$x = 71°30' \text{ or } x = 251°30'   ∎$$

Example 5   Find all solutions for $2 \sin x/2 = 1$ in the interval $[0°, 360°)$.

We begin as before by solving for the trigonometric function.

$$2 \sin \frac{x}{2} = 1$$

$$\sin \frac{x}{2} = \frac{1}{2}$$

If we let $x/2 = \theta$, then we have

$$\sin \theta = \frac{1}{2}$$

$$\theta = 30° \quad \text{or} \quad \theta = 150°.$$

Since $x = 2\theta$, then $x = 60°$ or $x = 300°$.   ∎

Example 6 Find all solutions for $2 \sin x/2 = -1$ in the interval $[0°, 360°)$.

Divide by 2 to get

$$\sin \frac{x}{2} = -\frac{1}{2}$$

Let $x/2 = \theta$, giving

$$\sin \theta = -\frac{1}{2},$$

from which we get $\theta = 210°$ or $\theta = 330°$. Since $x = 2\theta$, we end up with $x = 420°$ or $x = 660°$, which are not in the interval $[0°, 360°)$. Thus, *in this interval*, the equation has no solution. ▌

Sometimes equations with multiple angles can be solved by using an appropriate identity as in the next example.

Example 7 Find all solutions for $\cos 2x = \cos x$ in the interval $[0, 2\pi)$.

$$\cos 2x = \cos x$$
$$2 \cos^2 x - 1 = \cos x$$
$$2 \cos^2 x - \cos x - 1 = 0$$
$$(2 \cos x + 1)(\cos x - 1) = 0$$

$2 \cos x + 1 = 0 \qquad \cos x - 1 = 0$

$\cos x = -\dfrac{1}{2} \qquad \cos x = 1$

$x = \dfrac{2\pi}{3}$ or $\dfrac{4\pi}{3} \qquad x = 0$

The solutions are 0, $2\pi/3$, and $4\pi/3$. ▌

Example 8 Find all solutions for $4 \sin x \cos x = \sqrt{3}$ in the interval $[0°, 360°)$.

The identity $2 \sin x \cos x = \sin 2x$ is useful here.

$$4 \sin x \cos x = \sqrt{3}$$
$$2(2 \sin x \cos x) = \sqrt{3}$$
$$2 \sin 2x = \sqrt{3}$$
$$\sin 2x = \frac{\sqrt{3}}{2}$$

$$2x = 60°, \ 120°, \ 420°, \ \text{or} \ 480°$$
$$x = 30°, \ 60°, \ 210°, \ \text{or} \ 240°$$

In this case the domain $0° \le x < 360°$ implies $0° \le 2x < 720°$, which allows four solutions for x. ▌

Example 9 Find all solutions of $\cos 6x - \cos 2x = -\sin 4x$ in the interval $[0, 2\pi)$.

Use the identity

$$\cos x - \cos y = -2 \sin \left(\frac{x + y}{2}\right) \sin \left(\frac{x - y}{2}\right)$$

to rewrite the given equation as

$$-2 \sin \left(\frac{6x + 2x}{2}\right) \sin \left(\frac{6x - 2x}{2}\right) = -\sin 4x$$

$$-2 \sin 4x \sin 2x = -\sin 4x$$

or

$$2 \sin 4x \sin 2x - \sin 4x = 0.$$

Factor:

$$\sin 4x \,(2 \sin 2x - 1) = 0$$

$$\sin 4x = 0 \qquad \text{or} \qquad 2 \sin 2x - 1 = 0$$

$$\sin 2x = \frac{1}{2}$$

The solutions of $\sin 4x = 0$ are given by $4x = 0 + n \cdot \pi$. Thus,

$$x = 0 + n \cdot \frac{\pi}{4}.$$

For $n = 0, 1, 2, 3, 4, 5, 6, 7$ we get the solutions

$$0, \ \pi/4, \ \pi/2, \ 3\pi/4, \ \pi, \ 5\pi/4, \ 3\pi/2, \ \text{and} \ 7\pi/4.$$

From $\sin 2x = 1/2$, we get $2x = \pi/6 + n \cdot 2\pi$, and $2x = 5\pi/6 + n \cdot 2\pi$. The first of these produces the solutions $\pi/12$ and $13\pi/12$, while the second produces $5\pi/12$ and $17\pi/12$. In summary, the solutions of the original equation are

$$0, \ \pi/4, \ \pi/2, \ 3\pi/4, \ \pi, \ 5\pi/4, \ 3\pi/2, \ 7\pi/4, \ \pi/12, \ 13\pi/12, \ 5\pi/12, \ \text{and} \ 17\pi/12. \qquad \blacksquare$$

The next example shows how to solve equations involving inverse trigonometric functions.

Example 10 Solve $\sin^{-1} x - \cos^{-1} x = \pi/6$.

Begin by adding $\cos^{-1} x$ to both sides of the equation to get

$$\sin^{-1} x = \cos^{-1} x + \frac{\pi}{6}.$$

By the definition of the inverse sine, this becomes

$$\sin \left(\cos^{-1} x + \frac{\pi}{6}\right) = x.$$

Let $u = \cos^{-1} x$. Then

$$\sin \left(u + \frac{\pi}{6}\right) = x.$$

Use the identity for $\sin(s + t)$, which gives

$$\sin u \cos \frac{\pi}{6} + \cos u \sin \frac{\pi}{6} = x. \qquad (1)$$

Since $u = \cos^{-1} x$, we have $\cos u = x$. We know that $\sin^2 u + \cos^2 u = 1$, so

$$\sin^2 u = 1 - \cos^2 u = 1 - x^2$$

and $\sin u = \pm\sqrt{1 - x^2}$.

Replace $\sin u$ with $\pm\sqrt{1 - x^2}$, $\sin \pi/6$ with $1/2$, $\cos \pi/6$ with $\sqrt{3}/2$, and $\cos u$ with x, so that equation (1) becomes

$$\pm\sqrt{1 - x^2} \cdot \frac{\sqrt{3}}{2} + x \cdot \frac{1}{2} = x$$

$$\pm\sqrt{1 - x^2} \cdot \sqrt{3} + x = 2x$$

$$\pm\sqrt{3} \cdot \sqrt{1 - x^2} = x$$

Squaring both sides gives

$$3(1 - x^2) = x^2$$

$$3 - 3x^2 = x^2$$

$$3 = 4x^2$$

$$x = \pm\sqrt{\frac{3}{4}}$$

$$x = \pm\frac{\sqrt{3}}{2}$$

Check that $\sqrt{3}/2$ is a solution of the original equation, while $-\sqrt{3}/2$ is not. ▍

7.7 Exercises   *Find all solutions for the following equations in the interval $[0, 2\pi)$. Use 3.1416 as an approximation for π when you need values from Table 5.*

1. $3 \tan x + 5 = 2$

2. $\tan x + 1 = 2$

3. $2 \sec x + 1 = \sec x + 3$

4. $\tan^2 x - 1 = 0$

5. $(\cot x - \sqrt{3})(2 \sin x + \sqrt{3}) = 0$

6. $(\tan x - 1)(\cos x - 1) = 0$

7. $(\sec x - 2)(\sqrt{3} \sec x - 2) = 0$

8. $(2 \sin x + 1)(\sqrt{2} \cos x + 1) = 0$

9. $\cos^2 x + 2 \cos x + 1 = 0$

10. $2 \cos^2 x - \sqrt{3} \cos x = 0$

11. $-2 \sin^2 x = 3 \sin x + 1$

12. $3 \sin^2 x - \sin x = 2$

13. $\cos^2 x - \sin^2 x = 0$

14. $\dfrac{2 \tan x}{3 - \tan^2 x} = 1$

15. $\sin 2x = 0$

16. $\cos 2x = 1$

17. $3 \tan 2x = \sqrt{3}$

18. $\cot 2x = \sqrt{3}$

19. $\sqrt{2} \cos 2x = -1$

20. $2\sqrt{3} \sin 2x = -3$

21. $\sin \dfrac{x}{2} = \sqrt{2} - \sin \dfrac{x}{2}$

22. $\cos 2x - \cos x = 0$

Find all solutions for the following equations in the interval $[0°, 360°)$. Find θ to the nearest ten minutes.

23. $\tan \theta + 6 \cot \theta = 5$

24. $\csc \theta = 2 \sin \theta + 1$

25. $\sec^2 \theta = 2 \tan \theta + 4$

26. $2 \tan^2 \theta \sin \theta - \tan^2 \theta = 0$

27. $5 \sec^2 \theta = 6 \sec \theta$

28. $\cos^2 \theta = \sin^2 \theta + 1$

29. $\csc^2 \theta - 2 \cot \theta = 0$

30. $3 \cot^3 \theta = \cot \theta$

31. $\sin^2 \theta \cos^2 \theta = 0$

32. $\sec^2 \theta \tan \theta = 2 \tan \theta$

33. $2 \sin 2\theta = \sqrt{3}$

34. $2 \cos 2\theta = \sqrt{2}$

35. $\cos \dfrac{\theta}{2} = 1$

36. $\sin \dfrac{\theta}{2} = 1$

37. $2\sqrt{3} \sin \dfrac{\theta}{2} = 3$

38. $2\sqrt{3} \cos \dfrac{\theta}{2} = -3$

39. $2 \sin \theta = 2 \cos 2\theta$

40. $\cos \theta - 1 = \cos 2\theta$

41. $\sin 2\theta = 2 \cos^2 \theta$

42. $\csc^2 \dfrac{\theta}{2} = 2 \sec \theta$

43. $\cos \theta = \sin^2 \dfrac{\theta}{2}$

44. $4 \cos 2\theta = 8 \sin \theta \cos \theta$

45. $2 \cos^2 2\theta = 1 - \cos 2\theta$

46. $\sin \theta = \cos \dfrac{\theta}{2}$

Give all solutions (to the nearest ten minutes) for each of the following. Write the solutions in the form used in Example 1.

47. $\sin x - \cos x = 1$

48. $\cos 2x = 1$

49. $\cos x \left(\sin x - \dfrac{1}{2} \right) = 0$

50. $(2 \sin x - \sqrt{3})(\cos x + 1) = 0$

51. $\tan^2 x + 2 \tan x = 3$

52. $\cot^2 x - 4 \cot x - 5 = 0$

53. $\sin 2x = \cos 2x$

54. $\tan \dfrac{1}{2}x = \cot \dfrac{1}{2}x$

⦿ *To solve the following equations, you will need the quadratic formula. Find all solutions in the interval [0°, 360°). Give solutions to the nearest ten minutes.*

55. $9 \sin^2 x - 6 \sin x = 1$

56. $4 \cos^2 x + 4 \cos x = 1$

57. $\tan^2 x + 4 \tan x + 2 = 0$

58. $3 \cot^2 x - 3 \cot x - 1 = 0$

59. $\sin^2 x - 2 \sin x + 3 = 0$

60. $2 \cos^2 x + 2 \cos x - 1 = 0$

For the following equations, use the sum and product identities of Section 7.6. Give all solutions in the interval [0, 2π).

61. $\sin x + \sin 3x = \cos x$

62. $\cos 4x - \cos 2x = \sin x$

63. $\sin 3x - \sin x = 0$

64. $\cos 2x + \cos x = 0$

65. $\sin 4x + \sin 2x = 2 \cos x$

66. $\cos 5x + \cos 3x = 2 \cos 4x$

In an electric circuit, let V represent the electromotive force in volts at t seconds. Assume V = 5 cos 2t. Find the value of t for each of the following values of V.

67. $V = 0$

68. $V = .5$

Solve each of the following equations.

69. $\sin^{-1} x = \tan^{-1} 3/4$

70. $\tan^{-1} x = \cos^{-1} 5/13$

71. $\text{Arccos } x = \text{Arcsin } 3/5$

72. $\text{Arctan } x = \text{Arcsin } -4/5$

73. $\sin^{-1} x - \tan^{-1} 1 = -\pi/4$

74. $\cos^{-1} x + \cos^{-1} 1 = \pi/2$

75. $\cos^{-1} x + 2 \sin^{-1} \sqrt{3}/2 = \pi$

76. $\sin^{-1} x + \tan^{-1} \sqrt{3} = 2\pi/3$

77. $\sin^{-1} 2x + \cos^{-1} x = \pi/6$

78. $\sin^{-1} 2x + \sin^{-1} x = \pi/2$

79. $\cos^{-1} x + \tan^{-1} x = \pi/2$

80. $\tan^{-1} x + \cos^{-1} x = \pi/4$

Chapter 7   Review Exercises

1. Use the trigonometric identities to find the remaining five trigonometric functions of x, given that $\cos x = 3/5$ and x is in quadrant IV.

2. Given $\tan x = -5/4$, where x is in the interval $(\pi/2, \pi)$, use trigonometric identities to find the other trigonometric functions of x.

3. Given $\sin x = -1/4$, $\cos y = -4/5$, and both x and y are in quadrant III, find $\sin (x + y)$ and $\cos (x - y)$.

4. Given $\sin 2\theta = \sqrt{3}/2$ and 2θ terminates in quadrant II, use trigonometric identities to find $\tan \theta$.

5. Given $x = \pi/8$, use trigonometric identities to find $\sin x$, $\cos x$, and $\tan x$.

For each item in List I, give the letter of the item in List II which completes an identity.

List I	List II
6. $\sin 35°$	(a) $\sin (-35°)$
7. $\tan (-35°)$	(b) $\cos 55°$
8. $\cos 35°$	(c) $\sqrt{\dfrac{1 + \cos 150°}{2}}$
9. $\cos 75°$	
10. $\sin 75°$	(d) $2 \sin 150° \cos 150°$
11. $\sin 300°$	(e) $\cos 150° \cos 60° - \sin 150° \cos 60°$
12. $\cos 300°$	(f) $\cot (-35°)$
	(g) $\cos^2 150° - \sin^2 150°$
	(h) $\sin 15° \cos 60° + \cos 15° \sin 60°$
	(i) $\cos (-35°)$
	(j) $\cot 125°$

For each item in List I give the letter of the item in List II which completes an identity.

List I		List II	
13. $\csc x$ **16.** $\sin^2 x$		(a) $\dfrac{1}{\sin x}$ (e) $\dfrac{1}{\cos^2 x}$	
14. $\tan x$ **17.** $\tan^2 x + 1$		(b) $\dfrac{1}{\cos x}$ (f) $\dfrac{\cos x}{\sin x}$	
15. $\cot x$ **18.** $\tan^2 x$		(c) $\dfrac{\sin x}{\cos x}$ (g) $\dfrac{1}{\sin^2 x}$	
		(d) $\dfrac{1}{\cot^2 x}$ (h) $1 - \cos^2 x$	

Use identities to express each of the following in terms of $\sin \theta$ and $\cos \theta$ and simplify.

19. $\sec^2 \theta - \tan^2 \theta$

20. $\dfrac{\cot \theta}{\sec \theta}$

21. $\tan^2 \theta(1 + \cot^2 \theta)$

22. $\csc \theta + \cot \theta$

23. $\csc^2 \theta + \sec^2 \theta$

24. $\tan \theta - \sec \theta \csc \theta$

Show that each of the following is an identity.

25. $\dfrac{\sin 2x}{\sin x} = \dfrac{2}{\sec x}$

26. $2 \cos A - \sec A = \cos A - \dfrac{\tan A}{\csc A}$

27. $\dfrac{2 \tan B}{\sin 2B} = \sec^2 B$

28. $\tan \beta = \dfrac{1 - \cos 2\beta}{\sin 2\beta}$

32. $2 \cos (A + B) \sin (A + B) = \sin 2A \cos 2B + \sin 2B \cos 2A$

33. $\dfrac{2 \cot x}{\tan 2x} = \csc^2 x - 2$

34. $\sin t = \dfrac{\cos t \sin 2t}{1 + \cos 2t}$

35. $\tan \theta \sin 2\theta = 2 - 2 \cos^2 \theta$

36. $\csc A \sin 2A - \sec A = \cos 2A \sec A$

37. $2 \tan x \csc 2x - \tan^2 x = 1$

38. $2 \cos^2 \theta - 1 = \dfrac{1 - \tan^2 \theta}{1 + \tan^2 \theta}$

39. $\dfrac{\tan \dfrac{x}{2} + \cot \dfrac{x}{2}}{\cot \dfrac{x}{2} - \tan \dfrac{x}{2}} = \sec x$

40. $1 - \tan^2 \dfrac{\theta}{2} = \dfrac{2 \cos \theta}{1 + \cos \theta}$

41. $\dfrac{\sin 2\alpha - 2 \sin \alpha}{2 \sin \alpha + \sin 2\alpha} = -\tan^2 \dfrac{\alpha}{2}$

42. $8 \sin^2 \dfrac{\gamma}{2} \cos^2 \dfrac{\gamma}{2} = 1 - \cos 2\gamma$

43. $\cos^2 \dfrac{x}{2} = \dfrac{1 + \sec x}{2 \sec x}$

29. $1 + \tan^2 \alpha = 2 \tan \alpha \csc 2\alpha$

30. $-\dfrac{\sin (A - B)}{\sin (A + B)} = \dfrac{\cot A - \cot B}{\cot A + \cot B}$

31. $\dfrac{\sin t}{1 - \cos t} = \cot \dfrac{t}{2}$

44. $\tan \theta \cos^2 \theta = \dfrac{2 \tan \theta \cos^2 \theta - \tan \theta}{1 - \tan^2 \theta}$

45. $\tan 8k - \tan 8k \cdot \tan^2 4k = 2 \tan 4k$

46. $\sin 2\gamma = \dfrac{2 \tan \gamma}{1 + \tan^2 \gamma}$

47. $-\tan 2\theta = \dfrac{2 \tan \theta}{\sec^2 \theta - 2}$

48. $\dfrac{2 \cos 2\alpha}{\sin 2\alpha} = \cot \alpha - \tan \alpha$

49. $\tan 2\beta - \sec 2\beta = \dfrac{\tan \beta - 1}{\tan \beta + 1}$

50. $\dfrac{\sin^3 t - \cos^3 t}{\sin t - \cos t} = \dfrac{2 + \sin 2t}{2}$

51. $-\cot \dfrac{x}{2} = \dfrac{\sin 2x + \sin x}{\cos 2x - \cos x}$

52. $2 \cos^3 x - \cos x = \dfrac{\cos^2 x - \sin^2 x}{\sec x}$

Find all solutions for the following equations in the interval $[0, 2\pi)$.

53. $\sin^2 x = 1$

54. $2 \tan x - 1 = 0$

55. $2 \sin^2 x - 5 \sin x + 2 = 0$

56. $\tan x = \cot x$

57. $\sec^4 2x = 4$

58. $\tan^2 2x - 1 = 0$

59. $\sin \dfrac{x}{2} = \cos \dfrac{x}{2}$

60. $\sec \dfrac{x}{2} = \cos \dfrac{x}{2}$

61. $\cos 2x + \cos x = 0$

62. $\sin x \cos x = \dfrac{1}{4}$

Find all solutions for the following equations in the interval $[0°, 360°)$.

63. $2 \cos \theta = 1$

64. $(\tan \theta + 1)\left(\sec \theta - \dfrac{1}{2}\right) = 0$

65. $\sin^2 \theta + 3 \sin \theta + 2 = 0$

66. $\sin 2\theta = \cos 2\theta + 1$

67. $\dfrac{\sin \theta}{\cos \theta} = \tan^2 \theta$

68. $4 \sin \theta \cos \theta = 1$

Exact values of the trigonometric functions of 15° can be found by the following method, an alternative to the use of the half-angle formulas. Start with a right triangle ABC having a 60° angle at A and a 30° angle at B. Let the hypotenuse of this triangle have length 2. Extend side BC and draw a semicircle with diameter along BC extended, center at B, and radius AB. Draw segment AE. (See the figure.) Since any angle inscribed in a semicircle is a right angle, triangle AED is a right triangle.

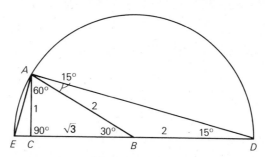

69. Show that triangle *ABD* is isosceles.

70. Show that angle *ABD* is 150°.

71. Show that angle *DAB* is 15°, as is angle *ADB*.

72. Show that *DC* has length $2 + \sqrt{3}$.

73. Since *AC* has length 1, the length of *AD* is given by

$$(AD)^2 = 1^2 + (2 + \sqrt{3})^2.$$

Reduce this to $\sqrt{8 + 4\sqrt{3}}$, and show that this result equals $\sqrt{6} + \sqrt{2}$.

74. Use angle *ADB* of triangle *ADE* and find cos 15°.

75. Show that *AE* has length $\sqrt{6} - \sqrt{2}$.

76. Find sin 15°.

77. Use triangle *ACE* and find tan 15°.

78. Find cot 15°.

The following exercises are taken with permission from a standard calculus book.

79. Let α and β be two given numbers.
  (a) Prove that if sin $(\alpha + \beta)$ = sin $(\alpha - \beta)$, then either α is an odd multiple of $\pi/2$ or β is a multiple of π, or both.
  (b) Prove that if cos $(\alpha + \beta)$ = cos $(\alpha - \beta)$, then either α is a multiple of π or β is a multiple of π, or both.
  (c) Prove that if tan $(\alpha + \beta)$ = tan $(\alpha - \beta)$, then β is a multiple of π.

80. Note that for $\alpha = 18°$, we have cos 3α = sin 2α. Use the formula

$$\cos 3\alpha = 3 \sin \alpha - 4 \sin^3 \alpha$$

and show that sin 18° = $(\sqrt{5} - 1)/4$.

Chapter 8

Triangles and Vectors

Trigonometry is over 3000 years old. The ancient Egyptians, Babylonians, and Greeks developed trigonometry to find the lengths of the sides of triangles and the measures of their angles. Every triangle has three sides and three angles. In this chapter we see that if we know any three of the six measures of a triangle (if at least one measure is a side), then we can find the other three measures. This process is called **solving a triangle.**

8.1 Right-Triangle Applications

We briefly mentioned right-triangle applications of trigonometry in Chapter 6. We shall discuss more such applications in this section. First, recall that if θ is an acute angle of a right triangle, then $\sin \theta$, $\cos \theta$, and $\tan \theta$ can be found from the lengths of the sides of the triangle:

$$\sin \theta = \frac{\text{side opposite}}{\text{hypotenuse}} \qquad \cos \theta = \frac{\text{side adjacent}}{\text{hypotenuse}} \qquad \tan \theta = \frac{\text{side opposite}}{\text{side adjacent}}.$$

The other three functions, $\cot \theta$, $\sec \theta$, and $\csc \theta$, can be defined in a similar way. (See Figure 8.1.)

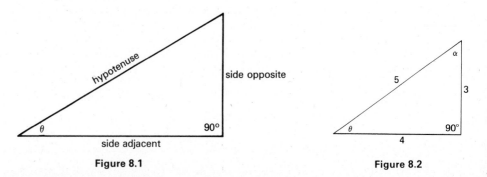

Figure 8.1   **Figure 8.2**

Example 1   The right triangle of Figure 8.2 has sides of lengths 3, 4, and 5. Find each of the following.

(a) $\sin \theta$, $\cos \theta$, and $\tan \theta$

Use the ratios given above.

$$\sin \theta = \frac{\text{side opposite}}{\text{hypotenuse}} = \frac{3}{5} \qquad \cos \theta = \frac{\text{side adjacent}}{\text{hypotenuse}} = \frac{4}{5}$$

$$\tan \theta = \frac{\text{side opposite}}{\text{side adjacent}} = \frac{3}{4}$$

(b) the degree measure of angle θ.

Since $\sin \theta = 3/5 = .6000$, we can use a calculator or Table 5 to find that $\theta = \sin^{-1} .6000 = 36° \ 50'$, to the nearest ten minutes.

(c) $\sin \alpha$, $\cos \alpha$, and $\tan \alpha$.

$$\sin \alpha = \frac{4}{5}, \qquad \cos \alpha = \frac{3}{5}, \qquad \text{and} \qquad \tan \alpha = \frac{4}{3}$$

(d) the degree measure of angle α.

We know that $\theta = 36° \ 50'$, and that $\alpha + \theta = 90°$. Thus,

$$\alpha = 90° - \theta$$
$$= 90° - 36° \ 50'$$
$$= 89° \ 60' - 36° \ 50'$$
$$\alpha = 53° \ 10'. \quad \blacksquare$$

In solving triangles, we shall use a to represent the length of the side opposite angle A, b for the length of the side opposite angle B, and so on. In a right triangle the letter c represents the hypotenuse and C represents the right angle.

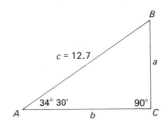

Figure 8.3

Example 2   Solve right triangle ABC, with $A = 34° \ 30'$ and $c = 12.7$. See Figure 8.3.

We solve the triangle by finding the measures of the remaining sides and angles. We know $C = 90°$, so we want to find a, b, and B.

By the definitions given above, $\sin A = a/c$. Since $A = 34° \ 30'$ and $c = 12.7$,

$$\sin A = \frac{a}{c}$$

$$\sin 34° \ 30' = \frac{a}{12.7}$$

or, upon multiplying both sides by 12.7,

$$a = 12.7 \sin 34° \ 30'$$
$$a \approx 12.7 \ (.5664)$$
$$a \approx 7.19.$$

We could use the Pythagorean theorem to find b. However, to do so, we would have to use the value of a just calculated. It is best to use the information given in the problem rather than a calculated result. If a mistake had been made in finding a, then b would also be incorrect. It is better to use cosine to find b.

$$\cos A = \frac{\text{side adjacent}}{\text{hypotenuse}} = \frac{b}{c}$$

$$\cos 34° \, 30' = \frac{b}{12.7}$$

$$b = 12.7 \cos 34° \, 30'$$

$$b \approx 12.7 \, (.8241)$$

$$b \approx 10.5$$

The Pythagorean theorem can be used as a check once b is found. All that remains to find is angle B. Since $A + B = 90°$, and $A = 34° \, 30'$, we have

$$A + B = 90°$$

$$B = 90° - A$$

$$B = 90° - 34° \, 30'$$

$$= 89° \, 60' - 34° \, 30'$$

$$B = 55° \, 30'.$$

Triangle ABC is now solved—we know the lengths of all sides and the measures of all angles.

In Example 2 above, we were told that $c = 12.7$. Since this measure for c is given to three significant digits, we must give both a and b to no more than three significant digits as the number of significant digits in an answer cannot exceed the least number of significant digits in any number used to find the answer. Also, an angle given to the nearest degree is assumed to have *two* significant digits; to the nearest ten minutes implies *three* significant digits; to the nearest minute implies *four* significant digits.

Figure 8.4 shows an angle of elevation and an angle of depression. For the **angle of elevation,** assume you are standing at point X and looking up at point Y. For the **angle of depression,** assume you are standing at point X and looking down at point Y.

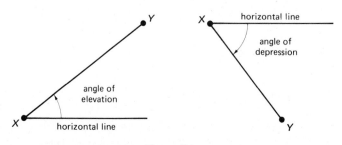

Figure 8.4

Example 3   Private Spence knows that when she stands 123 feet from the base of a flagpole, the angle of elevation to the top is 26°40′. If her eyes are 5.30 feet above the ground, find the height of the flagpole.

We know the length of the side adjacent to Private Spence (see Figure 8.5) and we want to find the length of the side opposite her. The ratio that involves these two values is the tangent. Thus,

$$\tan A = \frac{\text{side opposite}}{\text{side adjacent}}$$

$$\tan 26° \ 40' = \frac{a}{123}$$

$$a = 123 \tan 26°40'$$

$$a \approx 123(.5022)$$

$$a \approx 61.8 \text{ feet}$$

Since Spence's eyes are 5.30 feet above the ground, the height of the flagpole is

$$61.8 + 5.30 = 67.1 \text{ feet.}$$

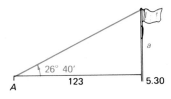

Figure 8.5

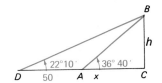

Figure 8.6

Example 4   Francisco needs to find the height of a tower on the opposite side of a river. From a given point on the ground on this side of the river, he finds that the angle of elevation to the top of the tower is 36°40′. He then moves back 50 feet. From the second point, the angle of elevation to the top of the tower is 22°10′. (See Figure 8.6.) Find the height of the tower.

Here we have two unknowns, x, the distance from the base of the tower to the point where the first observation was made, and h, the height of the tower. Since we know nothing about the length of the hypotenuse of either triangle ABC or triangle BCD, we use a ratio which doesn't involve hypotenuses, that is, the tangent. We have

in triangle ABC $\tan 36° \ 40' = \dfrac{h}{x}$ or $h = x \tan 36° \ 40'$

in triangle BCD $\tan 22° \ 10' = \dfrac{h}{50 + x}$ or $h = (50 + x) \tan 22° \ 10'$.

Since we have two expressions equaling h, these expressions must be equal.

$$x \tan 36° \ 40' = (50 + x) \tan 22° \ 10'$$

Now we use algebra to solve for x.

$$x \tan 36° \, 40' = 50 \tan 22° \, 10' + x \tan 22° \, 10'$$
$$x \tan 36° \, 40' - x \tan 22° \, 10' = 50 \tan 22° \, 10'$$
$$x(\tan 36° \, 40' - \tan 22° \, 10') = 50 \tan 22° \, 10'$$

$$x = \frac{50 \tan 22° \, 10'}{\tan 36° \, 40' - \tan 22° \, 10'}$$

$$= \frac{50 \,(.4074)}{.7445 - .4074}$$

$$= \frac{50 \,(.4074)}{.3371}$$

$$x \approx 60 \text{ feet}$$

Since $h = x \tan 36° \, 40'$, and $x \approx 60$,

$$h = 60 \,(.7445) \approx 45 \text{ feet.}$$ ▮

Many applications of trigonometry involve **bearing,** an important idea in navigation and surveying. Bearing is used to give directions. There are two common systems used to express bearing. When a single angle is given, such as 164°, bearing is measured in a clockwise direction from due north. Several typical bearings are shown in Figure 8.7.

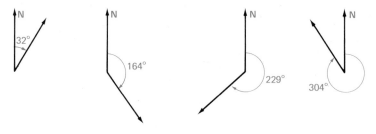

Figure 8.7

Example 5 Radar stations A and B are on an east-west line, 3.7 kilometers apart. Station A detects a plane at C on a bearing of 61°. Station B detects the same plane on a bearing of 331°. Find the distance from A to C.

Draw a sketch showing the given information, as in Figure 8.8. Angle C is a right angle, since angles CAB and CBA are complementary. The necessary distance, b, can be found by using cosine.

$$\cos 29° = \frac{b}{3.7}$$

$$3.7 \cos 29° = b$$
$$3.7(.8746) \approx b$$
$$b \approx 3.2 \text{ kilometers.}$$ ▮

The other common system for expressing bearing starts with a north-south line and uses an acute angle to show the direction, either east or west, from this line. Figure 8.9 shows several typical bearings using this system. The letter N or S always comes first, followed by an acute angle, and then E or W.

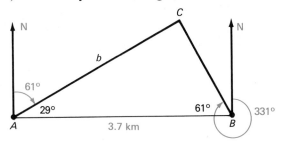

Figure 8.8

Example 6   The bearing from A to C is S 52° E. The bearing from A to B is N 84° E. The bearing from B to C is S 38° W. A plane flying at 250 kilometers per hour takes 2.4 hours to go from A to B. Find the distance from A to C.

Figure 8.10 shows a sketch of the given information. Since the bearing from A to B is 84°, angle ABE is $180° - 84° = 96°$. Thus, angle ABC is 46°. Also, angle BAC is $180° - (84° + 52°) = 44°$. Thus, angle C is 90°. We know that a plane flying at 250 kilometers per hour takes 2.4 hours to go from A to B. The distance from A to B is thus $2.4(250) = 600$ kilometers. We need to find b, the distance from A to C. We use sine. (We also could have used cosine.)

$$\sin 46° = \frac{b}{c}$$

$$\sin 46° = \frac{b}{600}$$

$$600 \sin 46° \approx b$$
$$600(.7193) \approx b$$
$$b = 430 \text{ kilometers.}$$

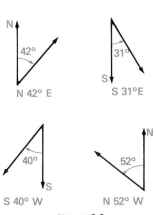

S 40° W   N 52° W

Figure 8.9

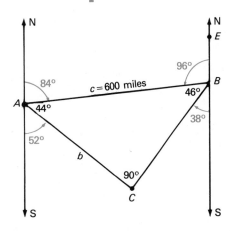

Figure 8.10

8.1 Exercises *Solve each of the following right triangles. Angle C is the right angle.*

1. $A = 28°$, $c = 17.4$ m

2. $B = 46°$, $c = 29.7$ m

3. $B = 73°$, $b = 128$ inches

4. $A = 61°$, $b = 39.2$ cm

5. $a = 76.4$ yards, $b = 39.3$ yards

6. $a = 958$ m, $b = 489$ m

7. $a = 18.9$ cm, $c = 46.3$ cm

8. $b = 219$ m, $c = 647$ m

9. $B = 39°$ $10'$, $c = .623$ m

10. $B = 82°$ $50'$, $c = 4.82$ cm

⊚ *Use a calculator to solve each of the following right triangles. Write answers with four significant digits.*

11. $A = 59°$ $44'$, $c = 18.74$ feet

12. $B = 38°$ $9'$, $b = 469.8$ m

13. $A = 47.62°$, $a = 39.46$ cm

14. $B = 61.74°$, $a = 976.9$ mm

15. $a = 327.4$ cm, $b = 481.1$ cm

16. $a = 15,690$ mm, $b = 21,940$ mm

Solve each of the following.

17. A 39.4 meter fire-truck ladder is leaning against a wall. Find the distance the ladder goes up the wall if it makes an angle of $42°$ $30'$ with the ground.

18. A swimming pool is 50.0 feet long and 4.0 feet deep at one end. If it is 12.0 feet deep at the other end, find the total distance along the bottom.

19. A guy wire 87.4 meters long is attached to the top of a tower that is 69.4 meters high. Find the angle that the wire makes with the ground.

20. Find the length of a guy wire that makes an angle of $42°$ $10'$ with the ground if the wire is attached to the top of a tower 79.6 meters high.

Work the following problems involving angles of elevation or depression.

21. Suppose the angle of elevation of the sun is $28°$ $10'$. Find the length of the shadow cast by a man 6.0 feet tall.

22. The shadow of a vertical tower is 58.2 meters long when the angle of elevation of the sun is $36°$ $20'$. Find the height of the tower.

23. Find the angle of elevation of the sun if a 53.9 foot flagpole casts a shadow 74.6 feet long.

24. The angle of depression from the top of a building to a point on the ground is $34°$ $50'$. How far is the point on the ground from the top of the building if the building is 368 meters high?

25. Priscilla drives her Peterbilt up a straight road inclined at an angle of $4°$ $10'$ with the horizontal. She starts at an elevation of 680 feet above sea level and drives 12,400 feet along the road. Find her final altitude.

26. The road into Death Valley is straight; it makes an angle of $4°$ $10'$ with the horizontal. Starting at sea level, the road descends to -121 feet. Find the distance it is necessary to travel along the road to reach bottom.

27. A tower stands on top of a hill. From a point on the ground 148 m from a point directly under the tower, the angle of elevation to the *bottom* of the tower is $18°$ $20'$. From the same point, the angle of elevation to the *top* of the tower is $34°$ $10'$. Find the height of the tower.

28. The angle of elevation from the top of an office building in New York City to the top of the World Trade Center is $68°$, while the angle of depression from the top of the office

building to the bottom of the Trade Center is 63°. The office building is 290 feet from the World Trade Center. Find the height of the World Trade Center.

29. Mt. Rogers, with an altitude of 5700 feet, is the highest point in Virginia. The angle of elevation from the top of Mt. Rogers to a plane flying overhead is 33°. The straight line distance from the mountaintop to the plane is 4600 feet. Find the altitude of the plane.

30. The highest point in Texas is Guadalupe Peak. The angle of depression from the top of this peak to a small miner's cabin at elevation 2000 feet is 26°. The cabin is 14,000 feet horizontally from a point directly under the top of the mountain. Find the altitude of the top of the mountain.

Find h in each of the following.

31.

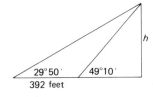

29° 50′   49° 10′
392 feet

32.

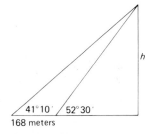

41° 10′   52° 30′
168 meters

33. The angle of elevation from a point on the ground to the top of a pyramid is 35° 30′. The angle of elevation from a point 135 feet further back to the top of the pyramid is 21° 10′. Find the height of the pyramid.

34. A lighthouse keeper is watching a boat approach directly to the lighthouse. When she first begins watching the boat, the angle of depression of the boat is 15° 50′. Just as the boat turns away from the lighthouse, the angle of depression is 35° 40′. If the height of the lighthouse is 68.7 meters, find the distance traveled by the boat as it approaches the lighthouse.

35. A television antenna is on top of the center of a house. The angle of elevation from a point 28.0 meters from the center of the house to the top of the antenna is 27° 10′, and the angle of elevation to the bottom of the antenna is 18° 10′. Find the height of the antenna.

36. The angle of elevation from Lone Pine to the top of Mt. Whitney is 10° 50′. If I drive 7.00 kilometers along a straight level road toward Mt. Whitney, I find the angle of elevation to be 22° 40′. Find the height of the top of Mt. Whitney above the level of the road.

In each of the following exercises, generalize problems from above by finding formulas for h in terms of k, A, and B. Assume A < B in Exercise 37, and A > B in Exercise 38.

37.

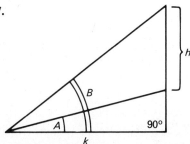

h

B

A   90°
k

38.

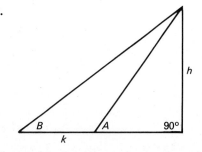

h

B   A   90°
k

Solve each of the following problems involving bearing.

39. A ship leaves port and sails on a bearing of 28° 10'. Another ship leaves the same port at the same time and sails on a bearing of 118° 10'. If the first ship sails at 20.0 miles per hour and the second sails at 24.0 miles per hour, find the distance between the two ships after five hours.

40. Radio direction finders are set up at points A and B, which are 2.00 miles apart on an east-west line. From A it is found that the bearing of the signal from a radio transmitter is 36° 20', while from B the bearing of the same signal is 306° 20'. Find the distance between the transmitter and B.

41. The bearing from Winston-Salem, North Carolina, to Danville, Virginia, is N 42° E. The bearing from Danville to Goldsboro, North Carolina, is S 48° E. A small plane traveling at 60 miles per hour takes 1 hour to go from Winston-Salem to Danville and 1.8 hours to go from Danville to Goldsboro. Find the distance from Winston-Salem to Goldsboro.

42. The bearing from Atlanta to Macon is S 27° E, while the bearing from Macon to Augusta is N 63° E. A plane traveling at 60 miles per hour needs 1¼ hours to go from Atlanta to Macon and 1¾ hours to go from Macon to Augusta. Find the distance from Atlanta to Augusta.

43. The airline distance from Philadelphia to Syracuse is 260 miles, on a bearing of 335°. The distance from Philadelphia to Cincinnati is 510 miles, on a bearing of 245°. Find the bearing from Cincinnati to Syracuse.

44. A ship travels 70 kilometers on a bearing of 27°, and then turns on a bearing of 117° for 180 kilometers. Find the distance of the end of the trip from the starting point.

45. A pendulum is m cm long. Suppose it is moved from its vertical position by an angle α ($0° \leq \alpha \leq 90°$). By how much has the end of the pendulum been raised vertically?

46. A woman is standing on a ship at sea h meters above the water. If the radius of the earth is r kilometers, find the distance she can see to the horizon.

Use a right triangle to find each of the following.

47. $\sin(\cos^{-1} 1/4)$

48. $\tan(\sin^{-1} 4/7)$

49. $\cos(\sin^{-1} 2/3)$

50. $\sin(\tan^{-1} 1/5)$

8.2 Oblique Triangles and the Law of Sines

The methods of solving triangles in the previous section apply only to right triangles. In the next few sections we generalize this work to include all triangles, not just right triangles. A triangle that is not a right triangle is called an **oblique triangle.**

One of the most useful of the formulas that apply to oblique triangles is given by the **law of sines.** To obtain this law, we start with a general oblique triangle such as the one shown in Figure 8.11. We construct the perpendicular from B to side AC. Let h be the length of this perpendicular. Let c be the hypotenuse of right triangle ADB, and let a be the hypotenuse of right triangle BDC. Then in triangle ADB $\sin A = \dfrac{h}{c}$ or $h = c \sin A$,

in triangle BDC $\sin C = \dfrac{h}{a}$ or $h = a \sin C$.

Since $h = c \sin A$ and $h = a \sin C$,

$$a \sin C = c \sin A$$

or, upon dividing both sides by $\sin A \sin C$,

$$\frac{a}{\sin A} = \frac{c}{\sin C}.$$

If we draw the perpendicular from C, and then from A, we get

$$\frac{a}{\sin A} = \frac{b}{\sin B} \quad \text{and} \quad \frac{b}{\sin B} = \frac{c}{\sin C}.$$

We have now proven the following theorem.

Theorem 8.1   (*The Law of Sines*) In any triangle ABC, with sides a, b, and c,

$$\frac{a}{\sin A} = \frac{b}{\sin B} \qquad \frac{a}{\sin A} = \frac{c}{\sin C} \quad \text{and} \quad \frac{b}{\sin B} = \frac{c}{\sin C}.$$

The three formulas of the law of sines are sometimes written as

$$\boxed{\frac{a}{\sin A} = \frac{b}{\sin B} = \frac{c}{\sin C}.}$$

Example 1 Solve triangle ABC if $A = 32° \; 00'$, $B = 81° \; 50'$, and $a = 42.9$ cm.
Start by drawing a triangle, roughly to scale, and labeling the given parts, as in Figure 8.12. Since we know A, B, and a, we use

$$\frac{a}{\sin A} = \frac{b}{\sin B}$$

to get

$$\frac{42.9}{\sin 32° \; 00'} = \frac{b}{\sin 81° \; 50'}.$$

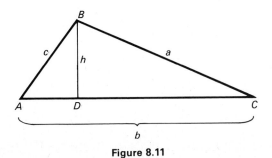

Figure 8.11

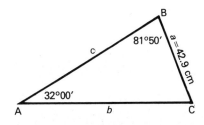

Figure 8.12

After multiplying both sides of the equation by sin 81° 50', we get

$$b = \frac{42.9 \sin 81° 50'}{\sin 32° 00'}.$$

$$b \approx \frac{42.9(.9899)}{.5299}$$

$$b \approx 80.1 \text{ centimeters.}$$

Use the fact that the sum of the angles of any triangle is 180° to find C.

$$A + B + C = 180°$$
$$C = 180° - A - B$$
$$= 180° - 32°00' - 81°50'$$
$$C = 66° \ 10'$$

Now we can use the law of sines again to find c. (Why shouldn't we use the Pythagorean theorem?) We have

$$\frac{a}{\sin A} = \frac{c}{\sin C}$$

$$\frac{42.9}{\sin 32° 00'} = \frac{c}{\sin 66° 10'}$$

$$c \approx 74.1 \text{ centimeters} \quad \blacksquare$$

Example 2   Solve triangle ABC if $C = 55° 40'$, $c = 8.94$ meters, and $b = 25.1$ meters.
Let us look first for angle B. We have

$$\frac{b}{\sin B} = \frac{c}{\sin C}$$

$$\frac{25.1}{\sin B} = \frac{8.94}{\sin 55° 40'}$$

$$\sin B = \frac{25.1 \sin 55° 40'}{8.94}$$

$$\sin B \approx \frac{25.1(.8258)}{8.94}$$

$$\sin B \approx 2.32$$

It is impossible to have $\sin B > 1$, so that the triangle described in the example cannot exist. See Figure 8.13. $\blacksquare$

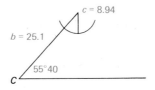

Figure 8.13

When any two angles and the length of a side of a triangle are given, the law of sines can be applied directly to solve the triangle. However, if only one angle and two sides are given, the triangle may not exist, as in Example 2, or there may be more than one triangle satisfying the given conditions. For example, suppose we know the measure of acute angle A of triangle ABC, the length of side a, and the length of side b. To show this information, we draw angle A having a terminal side of length b. Now we draw a side of length a opposite angle A. The chart in Figure 8.14 shows that there might be more than one possible outcome. This situation is called the **ambiguous case of the law of sines.**

Number of possible triangles	Sketch	Conditions necessary for case to hold
0	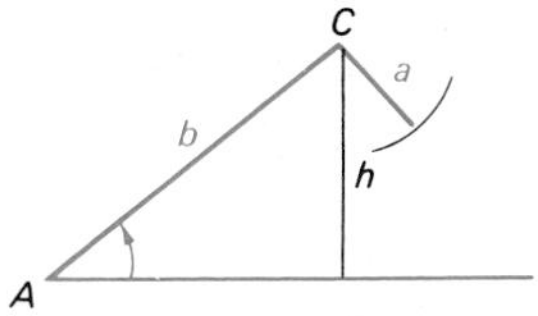	$a < h$ or $a < b \sin A$
1	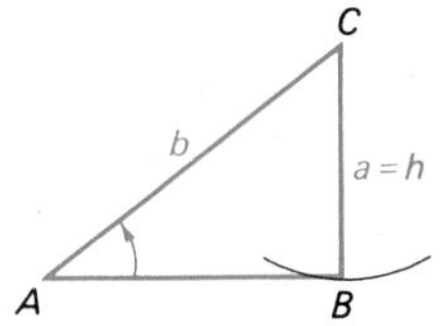	$a = h$ or $a = b \sin A$
1	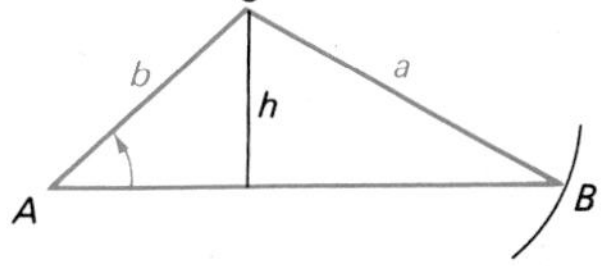	$a > b$ $a > h$
2	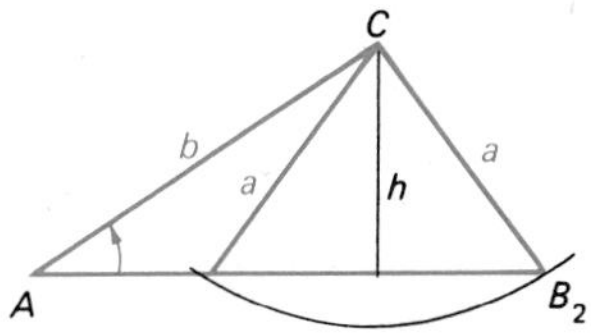	$b > a > h$ or $b > a > b \sin A$

Figure 8.14

If angle A is obtuse, there are two possible outcomes, as shown in the chart in Figure 8.15.

Number of possible triangles	Sketch	Conditions necessary for case to hold
0	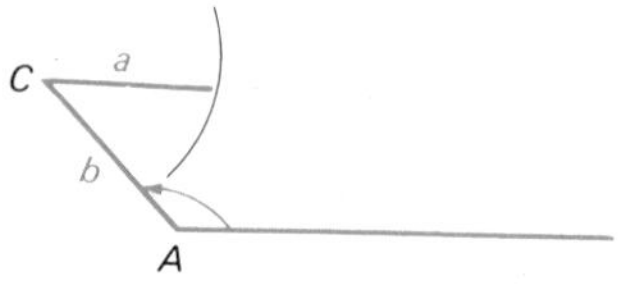	$a \le b$
1	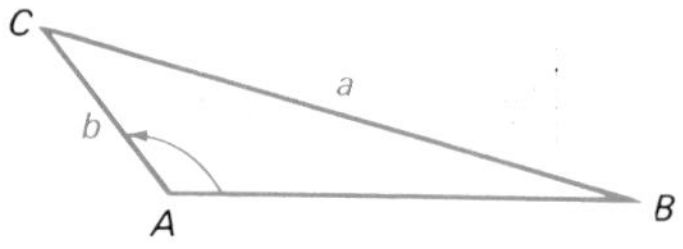	$a > b$

Figure 8.15

If we use the law of sines when solving a triangle and find that $\sin B$ is greater than 1, then we know there is no such triangle. (Why?) The case where we get two different triangles is illustrated in the next example.

Example 3   Solve triangle ABC if $A = 55° \ 20'$, $a = 22.8$, and $b = 24.9$.

To begin, let us use the law of sines to find angle B.

$$\frac{a}{\sin A} = \frac{b}{\sin B}$$

$$\frac{22.8}{\sin 55° \ 20'} = \frac{24.9}{\sin B}$$

$$\sin B = \frac{24.9 \sin 55° \ 20'}{22.8} \approx \frac{24.9(.8225)}{22.8}$$

$$\sin B \approx .8983$$

From Table 5, we find that one value of B is $B \approx 64°00'$. Since $\sin(180° - B) = \sin B$, another value of B is

$$B \approx 180° - 64°00' \approx 116°00'$$

To keep track of these two different values of B, let

$$B_1 \approx 116°00' \quad \text{and} \quad B_2 \approx 64°00'.$$

These two values of B may determine two triangles. To find out if they do, first find if there are two possible values for angle C. Since the sum of the angles of a triangle is 180°,

$$C_1 = 180° - (A + B_1)$$
$$= 180° - (55° \ 20' + 116° \ 00')$$
$$= 180° - 171° \ 20'$$
$$C_1 = 8° \ 40'$$

(If this result had been negative, we would have only one triangle.) Also,

$$C_2 = 180° - (55° \ 20' + 64° \ 00') = 60° \ 40'.$$

Since there are two values of C, we have two triangles, as shown in Figure 8.16.

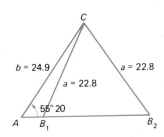

Figure 8.16

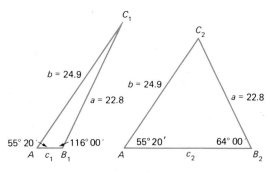

Figure 8.17

For simplicity, sketch the two triangles separately, as shown in Figure 8.17. Let us first solve triangle AB_1C_1.

Since

$$\frac{a}{\sin A} = \frac{c_1}{\sin C_1},$$

we have

$$\frac{22.8}{\sin 55° \ 20'} = \frac{c_1}{\sin 8° \ 40°}$$

$$c_1 = \frac{22.8 \sin 8° \ 40'}{\sin 55° \ 20'}$$

$$c_1 \approx 4.18.$$

Now we can solve triangle AB_2C_2. By the law of sines,

$$\frac{22.8}{\sin 55° \ 20'} = \frac{c_2}{\sin 60° \ 40'}$$

$$c_2 = \frac{22.8 \sin 60° \ 40'}{\sin 55° \ 20'}$$

$$c_2 \approx 24.2. \quad \blacksquare$$

The method we used to obtain the law of sines can also be used to obtain a useful formula for the area of a triangle. The standard formula for the area of a triangle is $K = \frac{1}{2}bh$, where K represents the area, b the base, and h the height. This formula cannot always be used, since h is often unknown. To find a more useful formula, refer to triangle ABC in Figure 8.18.

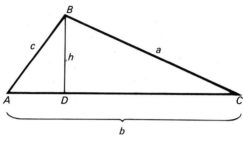

Figure 8.18

A perpendicular has been drawn from B to the base of the triangle. This perpendicular forms two smaller right triangles. Using triangle ABD, we get

$$\sin A = \frac{h}{c}, \quad \text{or} \quad h = c \sin A.$$

Substituting into the formula $K = \frac{1}{2}bh$, we get

$$K = \frac{1}{2} b(c \sin A)$$

$$K = \frac{1}{2} bc \sin A.$$

We can use any other pair of sides and the angle between them, as stated in the next theorem.

Theorem 8.2   The area of any triangle is given by half the product of the lengths of two sides and the sine of the angle between the two sides.

Example 4   Find the area of triangle MNP if $m = 29.7$ meters, $n = 53.9$ meters, and $P = 28° \, 40'$.

By Theorem 8.2, we have

$$K = \frac{1}{2} (29.7)(53.9) \sin 28° \, 40',$$

where K represents the area. Using a calculator or logarithms,

$$K \approx 384 \text{ square meters.}$$

8.2 Exercises   *Solve each of the following triangles that exist.*

1. $A = 51°$, $B = 46°$, $c = 14$ m
2. $B = 57°$, $C = 38°$, $a = 32$ cm
3. $A = 46° \ 30'$, $B = 52° \ 50'$, $b = 87.3$ mm
4. $B = 124° \ 10'$, $C = 18° \ 40'$, $c = 94.6$ m
5. $A = 68° \ 10'$, $b = 39.8$ feet, $a = 12.7$ feet
6. $C = 74° \ 00'$, $b = 69.3$ m, $c = 15.4$ m
7. $B = 20° \ 50'$, $C = 103° \ 10'$, $AC = 132$ feet
8. $A = 61° \ 20'$, $B = 65° \ 50'$, $AC = 675$ feet
   ◉ 9. $A = 32° \ 17'$, $B = 22° \ 42'$, $a = 798.2$ m
10. $B = 47° \ 51'$, $C = 122° \ 1'$, $c = 31.82$ m
11. $C = 25.14°$, $c = 948.4$ cm, $b = 252.8$ cm
12. $A = 39.43°$, $b = 20.03$ m, $a = 15.72$ m

Find the missing angles in each of the following triangles.

13. $B = 29° \ 40'$, $a = 39.6$ feet, $b = 28.4$ feet
14. $A = 52° \ 10'$, $b = 981$ cm, $a = 796$ cm
15. $A = 74° \ 20'$, $a = 859$ m, $b = 783$ m
16. $C = 82° \ 10'$, $a = 10.9$ km, $c = 7.62$ km
17. $A = 142° \ 10'$, $b = 5.43$ feet, $a = 7.29$ feet
18. $B = 113° \ 40'$, $a = 189$ m, $b = 243$ m
   ◉ 19. $A = 58.42°$, $a = 56.78$ m, $c = 24.55$ m
20. $C = 102.33°$, $a = 1.005$ cm, $c = 2.031$ cm

Solve each of the following triangles.

21. $A = 42° \ 30'$, $a = 15.6$ m, $b = 8.14$ m
22. $C = 52° \ 20'$, $a = 32.5$ yards, $c = 59.8$ yards
23. $B = 72° \ 10'$, $b = 78.3$ m, $c = 145$ m
24. $C = 29° \ 50'$, $a = 8.61$ m, $c = 5.21$ m
25. $B = 32° \ 50'$, $a = 7540$ cm, $b = 5180$ cm
26. $C = 22° \ 50'$, $b = 159$ mm, $c = 132$ mm
27. $B = 39° \ 40'$, $a = 29.8$ m, $b = 23.7$ m

28. $A = 51° \, 10'$, $c = 798$ cm, $a = 720$ cm

29. $A = 29° \, 47'$, $b = 292.7$ cm, $a = 289.6$ cm

30. $C = 58° \, 42'$, $c = 39.87$ feet, $a = 42.41$ feet

Solve each of the following exercises. Recall that bearing was discussed in Section 8.1.

31. To find the distance AB across a river, a distance $BC = 354$ meters is laid off on one side of the river. In triangle ABC, it is found that $B = 112° \, 10'$ and $C = 15° \, 20'$. Find AB.

32. To determine the distance RS across a deep canyon, Joanna lays off a distance $TR = 582$ yards. She then finds that in triangle RST, $T = 32° \, 50'$ and $R = 102° \, 20'$. Find RS.

33. Radio direction finders are placed at points A and B, which are 3.46 miles apart on an east-west line, with A west of B. From A the bearing of a certain radio transmitter is $47° \, 40'$, while from B the bearing is $302° \, 30'$. Find the distance between the transmitter and A.

34. A ship is sailing due north. Captain Odjakjian notices that the bearing of a lighthouse 12.5 kilometers distant is $38° \, 50'$. Later on, the captain notices that the bearing of the lighthouse has become $135° \, 50'$. How far did the ship travel between the two observations of the lighthouse?

35. A hill slopes at an angle of $12° \, 20'$ with the horizontal. The angle of elevation from the base of the hill to the top of a 457-foot tower at the top of the hill is $35° \, 50'$. Find the distance from the base of the hill to the base of the tower.

36. Mark notices that the bearing of a tree on the opposite bank of a river is $115° \, 20'$. Lisa is on the same bank as Mark but 428 meters away. She notices that the bearing of the tree is $45° \, 20'$. The river is flowing north between parallel banks. What is the distance across the river?

Find the area of each of the following triangles.

37. $A = 46° \, 30'$, $b = 12.7$ feet, $c = 8.90$ feet

38. $C = 67° \, 40'$, $b = 46.7$ m, $a = 38.2$ m

39. $B = 124° \, 30'$, $a = 30.4$ cm, $c = 28.4$ cm

40. $C = 142° \, 50'$, $a = 21.9$ m, $b = 24.6$ m

41. $A = 56° \, 49'$, $b = 32.68$ m, $c = 52.82$ m

42. $A = 34° \, 57'$, $b = 47.83$ m, $c = 28.65$ m

Prove that each of the following statements are true for any triangle ABC, with corresponding sides a, b, and c.

43. $\dfrac{a+b}{b} = \dfrac{\sin A + \sin B}{\sin B}$

44. $\dfrac{a-b}{a+b} = \dfrac{\sin A - \sin B}{\sin A + \sin B}$

45. $\dfrac{a+b}{c} = \dfrac{\cos \frac{1}{2}(A-B)}{\sin \frac{1}{2} C}$

46. $\dfrac{a - b}{c} = \dfrac{\sin \frac{1}{2}(A - B)}{\cos \frac{1}{2} C}$

47. In any triangle having sides a, b, and c, it must be true that $a + b > c$. Use this fact and the law of sines to show that $\sin A + \sin B > \sin (A + B)$ for any two angles A and B of a triangle.

48. Show that the area of a triangle having sides a, b, and c and corresponding angles A, B, and C is given by

$$\frac{a^2 \sin B \sin C}{2 \sin A}.$$

8.3 The Law of Cosines

If two sides and the angle between the two sides are given, the law of sines cannot be used to solve the triangle. (Try it.) Also, if all three of the sides of a triangle are given, the law of sines again cannot be used to find the unknown angles. For both these cases we need the law of cosines.

To obtain this law, we let ABC be any oblique triangle. We choose a coordinate system so that the origin is at vertex B and side BC is along the positive x-axis. See Figure 8.19.

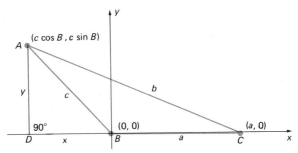

Figure 8.19

Let (x, y) be the coordinates of vertex A of the triangle. Verify that for angle B, whether obtuse or acute,

$$\sin B = \frac{y}{c} \qquad \text{and} \qquad \cos B = \frac{x}{c}.$$

(Here we assume x is negative if B is obtuse.) From these results,

$$y = c \sin B \qquad \text{and} \qquad x = c \cos B,$$

so that the coordinates of point A become

$$(c \cos B, c \sin B).$$

We know point C has coordinates $(a, 0)$ and AC has length b. By the distance formula

$$b = \sqrt{(c \cos B - a)^2 + (c \sin B)^2}.$$

Squaring both sides and simplifying gives

$$
\begin{aligned}
b^2 &= (c \cos B - a)^2 + (c \sin B)^2 \\
&= c^2 \cos^2 B - 2ac \cos B + a^2 + c^2 \sin^2 B \\
&= a^2 + c^2 (\cos^2 B + \sin^2 B) - 2ac \cos B \\
&= a^2 + c^2(1) - 2ac \cos B \\
b^2 &= a^2 + c^2 - 2ac \cos B
\end{aligned}
$$

This result is one form of the **law of cosines.** (If $B = 90°$, this result reduces down to the Pythagorean theorem.) In the work above, we could just as easily have placed A or C at the origin. This would have given the same result but one which is different in appearance. These various forms are summarized in the following theorem.

Theorem 8.3   (The Law of Cosines) In any triangle ABC, with sides a, b, and c,

$$
\begin{aligned}
a^2 &= b^2 + c^2 - 2bc \cos A \\
b^2 &= a^2 + c^2 - 2ac \cos B \\
c^2 &= a^2 + b^2 - 2ab \cos C.
\end{aligned}
$$

Example 1   Solve triangle ABC if $A = 42° 20'$, $b = 12.9$, and $c = 15.4$.
We can find a by using the law of cosines.

$$
\begin{aligned}
a^2 &= b^2 + c^2 - 2bc \cos A \\
a^2 &= (12.9)^2 + (15.4)^2 - 2(12.9)(15.4) \cos 42° 20' \\
a^2 &\approx 166.41 + 237.16 - (397.32)(.7392) \\
&\approx 403.57 - 293.70 \\
a^2 &\approx 109.87 \\
a &\approx 10.5.
\end{aligned}
$$

Now we know a, b, c, and A. We can use the law of sines to find B.

$$\frac{10.5}{\sin 42° 20'} = \frac{12.9}{\sin B}$$

$$\sin B = \frac{12.9 \sin 42° 20'}{10.5}$$

$$\sin B \approx .8274$$

From this result, $B \approx 55° 50'.$

Finally, we can find C.

$$C = 180° - A - B$$
$$C \approx 81° 50' \quad \blacksquare$$

Example 2   Solve triangle ABC if $C = 132°\ 40'$, $b = 259$, and $a = 423$.
We use the law of cosines $c^2 = a^2 + b^2 - 2ab \cos C$ to find c.

$$c^2 = a^2 + b^2 - 2ab \cos C$$
$$c^2 = (423)^2 + (259)^2 - 2(423)(259) \cos 132°\ 40'.$$

To find $\cos 132°\ 40'$, use reference angles. The reference angle for $132°\ 40'$ is $47°\ 20'$. Since $132°\ 40'$ is in quadrant II, $\cos 132°\ 40'$ will be negative.

$$\cos 132°\ 40' = -\cos 47°\ 20'$$
$$\cos 132°\ 40' = -0.6777$$

Now finish finding c.

$$c^2 \approx (423)^2 + (259)^2 - 2(423)(259)(-0.6777)$$
$$\approx 178{,}929 + 67{,}081 + 148{,}494$$
$$c^2 \approx 394{,}504$$

Take square roots to find that

$$c \approx 628.$$

Use the law of sines to complete the solution. Check that $A \approx 29°\ 40'$ and $B \approx 17°\ 40'$.   ▌

Example 3   Solve triangle ABC if $a = 9.47$, $b = 15.9$, and $c = 21.1$.
Again we use the law of cosines. It doesn't matter which angle we find first, so let us look for C. We have

$$c^2 = a^2 + b^2 - 2ab \cos C$$

or

$$\cos C = \frac{a^2 + b^2 - c^2}{2ab}.$$

Substituting the known values gives

$$\cos C = \frac{(9.47)^2 + (15.9)^2 - (21.1)^2}{2(9.47)(15.9)}$$

$$= \frac{-102.7191}{301.146}$$

$$\cos C \approx -.3411$$

From this last result,

$$C \approx 110°\ 00'.$$

(We know that C is obtuse since $\cos C < 0$.)
Now use the law of sines to find B. Verify that $B \approx 45°\ 00'$. Since $A = 180° - B - C$,

$$A \approx 25°\ 00'.\quad ▌$$

The law of cosines can be used to find a formula for the area of a triangle knowing only the lengths of the three sides of the triangle. This formula is given as the next theorem.

Theorem 8.4   (*Heron's Area Formula*). If a triangle has sides of lengths a, b, and c, and if

$$s = \frac{1}{2}(a + b + c),$$

then K, the area of the triangle, is given by

$$K = \sqrt{s(s - a)(s - b)(s - c)}.$$

A proof of this theorem is given as Exercises 41–42 below.

Example 4   Find the area of the triangle having sides of lengths $a = 29.7$ feet, $b = 42.3$ feet, and $c = 38.4$ feet.

To use Heron's area formula, first find s.

$$s = \frac{1}{2}(a + b + c)$$

$$s = \frac{1}{2}(29.7 + 42.3 + 38.4)$$

$$s = 55.2$$

The area is then given by

$$K = \sqrt{s(s - a)(s - b)(s - c)}$$
$$= \sqrt{55.2(55.2 - 29.7)(55.2 - 42.3)(55.2 - 38.4)}$$
$$K = \sqrt{55.2(25.5)(12.9)(16.8)}.$$
$$= \sqrt{305,055.07}$$
$$K \approx 552.$$

The area of the triangle is approximately 552 square feet.   ▌

8.3 Exercises   *Solve each of the following triangles.*

1. $A = 39° \ 50'$, $b = 6.74$ inches, $c = 5.92$ inches
2. $B = 35° \ 10'$, $a = 5.78$ yards, $c = 4.87$ yards
3. $C = 45° \ 40'$, $b = 8.94$ m, $a = 7.23$ m
4. $C = 72° \ 40'$, $a = 327$ feet, $b = 251$ feet
5. $B = 125° \ 30'$, $a = 8.91$ inches, $c = 6.42$ inches
6. $C = 142° \ 50'$, $a = 3.72$ miles, $b = 4.69$ miles
   ● 7. $C = 24° \ 47'$, $a = 251.4$ m, $b = 318.2$ m
8. $B = 52° \ 34'$, $a = 7.597$ km, $c = 6.978$ km

Find all the angles in each of the following triangles. Round answers to the nearest ten minutes in Exercises 9–12.

9. $a = 2$ feet, $b = 3$ feet, $c = 4$ feet

10. $a = 3$ m, $b = 4$ m, $c = 6$ m

11. $a = 9.3$ centimeters, $b = 5.7$ cm, $c = 8.2$ cm

12. $a = 189$ yards, $b = 214$ yards, $c = 325$ yards

⦿ **13.** $a = 1247$ m, $b = 876.2$ m, $c = 918.1$ m

14. $a = 298.2$ cm, $b = 421.4$ cm, $c = 324.8$ cm

Solve each of the following problems.

15. Points A and B are on opposite sides of Lake Yankee. From a third point C the angle between the lines of sight to A and B is 46° 20′. If AC is 350 meters long and BC is 286 meters long, find AB.

16. The sides of a parallelogram are 4.0 centimeters and 6.0 centimeters. One angle of the figure is 58° while another is 122°. Find the lengths of the diagonals of the figure.

17. Airports A and B are 450 kilometers apart, on an east-west line. Tom flies from A in a northeast direction to airport C. From C he flies 359 kilometers on a bearing of 128° 40′ to B. How far is C from A?

18. Pearl took a plane from A to B, a distance of 350 miles. Then her plane continued from B to C, a distance of 400 miles. Finally, she returned to A, a distance of 300 miles. If A and B are on an east-west line, find the bearing from A to C. (Assume C is north of the line through A and B.)

19. A hill slopes at an angle of 12° 30′ with the horizontal. From the base of the hill, the angle of inclination of the top of a 459-foot tower at the top of the hill is 35° 50′. How much rope would be required to reach from the top of the tower to the bottom of the hill?

20. A parallelogram has sides of length 25.9 cm and 32.5 cm. The longer diagonal has a length of 57.8 cm. Find the angle opposite the diagonal.

21. Two factories blow their whistles at 5 o'clock exactly. A man hears the two blasts at 3 seconds and 6 seconds after 5, respectively. The angle between his lines of sight to the two factories is 42° 10′. If sound travels 344 m per second, how far apart are the factories?

22. Two boats leave a dock together. They travel in straight line courses with the difference between the courses 54° 10′. One boat travels 36 km per hour, while the other goes 45 km per hour. How far apart will they be after 3 hours?

23. A plane flying a straight course observes a mountain at a bearing 24° 10′ to the right of its course. At that time, the plane is 7.92 km from the mountain. After flying awhile, the bearing to the mountain becomes 32° 40′. How far is the plane from the mountain when the second bearing is found?

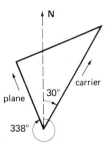

24. The aircraft carrier *Tallahassee* is traveling at sea on a steady course with a bearing of 30° at 32 miles per hour. Patrol planes on the carrier have enough fuel for 2.6 hours of flight when traveling at a speed of 520 miles per hour. One of the pilots takes off on a bearing of 338° and then turns and heads in a straight line, so as to be able to catch the carrier, landing on the deck at the exact instant that his fuel runs out. If the pilot left at 2 p.m., at what time did he turn to head for the carrier?

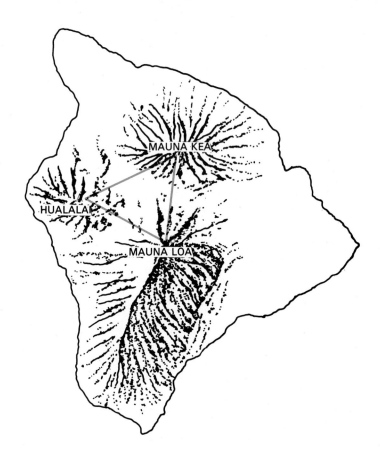

⊚ *To help predict eruptions from the volcano Mauna Loa on the island of Hawaii, scientists keep track of movement of the volcano by using a "super triangle" with vertices on the three volcanos shown on the map above. (For example, in a recent year Mauna Loa moved 6 inches north and northwest — a result of increasing internal pressure.) The following data have been rounded.*

25. $AB = 22.47928$ miles, $AC = 28.14276$ miles, $A = 58.56989°$; find BC.

26. $AB = 22.47928$ miles, $BC = 25.24983$ miles, $A = 58.56989°$; find B.

Find the area of each of the following triangles.

27. $a = 8.0$ feet, $b = 9.0$ feet, $c = 10.0$ feet

28. $a = 15$ cm, $b = 19$ cm, $c = 24$ cm

29. $a = 27$ m, $b = 40$ m, $c = 34$ m

30. $a = 150$ cm, $b = 170$ cm, $c = 183$ cm

31. $a = 25.4$ m, $b = 38.2$ m, $c = 19.8$ m

32. $a = 76.3$ cm, $b = 109$ cm, $c = 98.8$ cm

⊚ **33.** $a = 74.18$ feet, $b = 89.92$ feet, $c = 51.83$ feet

34. $a = 1.092$ km, $b = 1.145$ km, $c = 1.258$ km

35. Sam wants to paint a triangular region 75 by 68 by 85 meters. A can of paint covers 75 square meters of area. How many cans (to the next higher can) will he need?

36. How many cans would be needed if the region were 8.2 by 9.4 by 3.8 meters?

Use the fact that cos A = (b² + c² − a²)/(2bc) to show that each of the following is true.

37. $1 + \cos A = \dfrac{(b + c + a)(b + c - a)}{2bc}$

38. $1 - \cos A = \dfrac{(a - b + c)(a + b - c)}{2bc}$

39. $\cos \dfrac{A}{2} = \sqrt{\dfrac{s(s - a)}{bc}}$ $\left(\text{Recall: } \cos \dfrac{A}{2} = \sqrt{\dfrac{1 + \cos A}{2}}\right)$

40. $\sin \dfrac{A}{2} = \sqrt{\dfrac{(s - b)(s - c)}{bc}}$ $\left(\text{Recall: } \sin \dfrac{A}{2} = \sqrt{\dfrac{1 - \cos A}{2}}\right)$

41. The area of a triangle having sides b and c and angle A is given by Area $= \dfrac{1}{2} bc \sin A$. Show that this can be written as

$$\sqrt{\frac{1}{2} bc(1 + \cos A) \cdot \frac{1}{2} bc(1 - \cos A)}.$$

42. Use the results of Exercises 37–41 to prove Heron's Area Formula.

43. Let a and b be the equal sides of an isosceles triangle. Prove that $c^2 = 2a^2 (1 - \cos C)$.

44. Let point D on side AB of triangle ABC be such that CD bisects angle C. Show that $AD/DB = b/a$.

8.4 Vectors

We have learned so far in this chapter that we can find the measure of all six parts of a triangle, given at least one side and two other measures. In the rest of this chapter, we look at applications of this work to vectors. In this section, we introduce the basic ideas of vectors and then apply the law of sines and the law of cosines to vector problems.

A **vector** is a directed line segment, that is, a line segment pointing in a particular direction. A vector extending from an *initial point*, such as M, to a *terminal point*, such as N, is written in several different ways. When written by hand, the vector can be indicated by $\overrightarrow{MN}$. In textbooks, it is common to use bold type and write **MN**. Vector **MN** is not the same as **NM**, as shown in Figure 8.20.

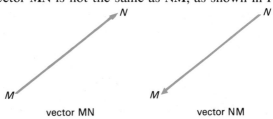

vector MN   vector NM

Figure 8.20

The length of a vector is called its **magnitude**; the magnitude of vector **MN** is written $|\textbf{MN}|$ or $|\overrightarrow{\textbf{MN}}|$. Two vectors having the same magnitude and the same direction are *equal*. Thus, a vector may be moved around at will, as long as its direction and magnitude are unchanged.

To completely describe many physical quantities, such as velocities, accelerations, or forces, we need both a magnitude and a direction. Quantities of this type are called **vector quantities**. We shall study vector quantities in more detail later.

To find the *sum* of two vectors **A** and **B**, which is written **A + B**, place the initial point of vector **B** at the terminal point of vector **A**, as shown in Figure 8.21. The vector with the same initial point as **A** and the same terminal point as **B** is the sum **A + B**. Notice that the sum of two vectors is again a vector.

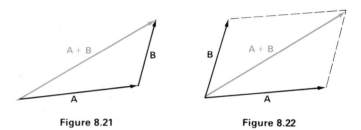

Figure 8.21   Figure 8.22

Another way to find the sum of two vectors is to use the **parallelogram rule**. Place vectors **A** and **B** so that their initial points coincide. Then complete a parallelogram which has **A** and **B** as two sides. The diagonal of the parallelogram with the same initial point as **A** and **B** is the vector sum **A + B**. See Figure 8.22.

As shown in Figure 8.22, vector **B + A** is the same as vector **A + B**, so that

$$\textbf{A} + \textbf{B} = \textbf{B} + \textbf{A}.$$

Thus, vector addition is commutative. The vector sum **A + B** is called the **resultant** of vectors **A** and **B**.

For every vector **v** there is a vector **−v**, which has the same magnitude as **v** but opposite direction. Vector **−v** is called the **opposite** of **v**. See Figure 8.23. The sum of **v** and **−v** has magnitude 0 and is called a **zero vector**. As with real numbers, if we wish to *subtract* vector **B** from vector **A**, we find the vector sum **A + (−B)**. See Figure 8.24

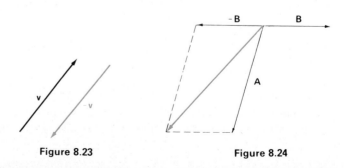

Figure 8.23   Figure 8.24

The **scalar product** of a real number (scalar) k and a vector $\mathbf{u}$ is the vector $k \cdot \mathbf{u}$ which has magnitude $|k|$ times the magnitude of $\mathbf{u}$. As shown in Figure 8.25, $k \cdot \mathbf{u}$ has the same direction as $\mathbf{u}$ if $k > 0$ and the opposite direction if $k < 0$.

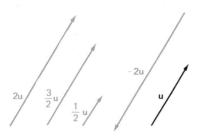

Figure 8.25

Example 1 Two forces of 15 and 22 grams act on a point in the plane. If the angle between the forces is 100°, find the magnitude of the resultant force.

As shown in Figure 8.26, we can form a parallelogram with the vectors representing the forces as adjacent sides. The angles of the parallelogram adjacent to angle P each measure 80°, and the opposite sides of the parallelogram are equal in length. The resultant force divides the parallelogram into two triangles. Now we can use the law of cosines to get

$$|\mathbf{v}|^2 = 15^2 + 22^2 - 2(15)(22) \cos 80°$$
$$\approx 225 + 484 - 115$$
$$|\mathbf{v}|^2 \approx 594,$$

so that, $|\mathbf{v}| \approx 24$ grams.

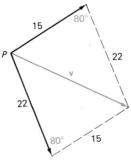

Figure 8.26

Let vector $\mathbf{u}$ be placed in a plane so that the initial point of the vector is at the origin, $(0, 0)$, and the endpoint is at the point (a, b). A vector with initial point at the origin is called a **position vector** or (sometimes) a **radius vector**. A position vector having endpoint at the point (a, b) is called the **vector** (a, b). For simplicity, the vector (a, b) is written as $\langle a, b \rangle$. The numbers a and b are called the **x-component** and **y-component,** respectively. Figure 8.27 shows the vector $\mathbf{u} = \langle a, b \rangle$. Note that

$$|\mathbf{u}| = \sqrt{a^2 + b^2}.$$

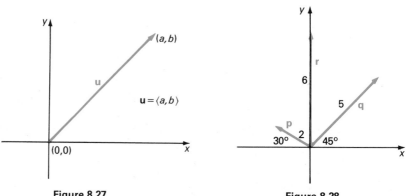

Figure 8.27   Figure 8.28

Example 2   Write each of the position vectors of Figure 8.28 in the form $\langle a, b \rangle$.

Vector **p** has length 2 and makes an angle of 30° with the negative x-axis. Thus, $\mathbf{p} = \langle -\sqrt{3}, 1 \rangle$.

Vector **q** has length 5 and makes an angle of 45° with the positive x-axis. Thus, $\mathbf{q} = \langle 5\sqrt{2}/2, 5\sqrt{2}/2 \rangle$.

Finally, $\mathbf{r} = \langle 0, 6 \rangle$.   ▌

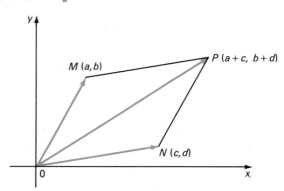

Figure 8.29

Let **OM** be given by $\langle a, b \rangle$, while **ON** is given by $\langle c, d \rangle$. Let **OP** be given by $\langle a + c, b + d \rangle$. Using facts from geometry, points O, N, M and P can be shown to form the vertices of a parallelogram. See Figure 8.29. Since a diagonal of this parallelogram gives the resultant of **OM** and **ON**, **OP** = **OM** + **ON,** and the resultant of $\langle a, b \rangle$ and $\langle c, d \rangle$ is given by $\langle a + c, b + d \rangle$. In the same way, for any real number k, we have $k \cdot \langle a, b \rangle = \langle ka, kb \rangle$. In summary,

$$\langle a, b \rangle + \langle c, d \rangle = \langle a + c, b + d \rangle$$
$$k \cdot \langle a, b \rangle = \langle ka, kb \rangle.$$

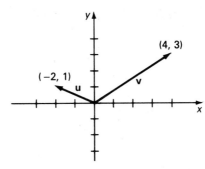

Figure 8.30

Example 3 Let $\mathbf{u} = \langle -2, 1 \rangle$ and $\mathbf{v} = \langle 4, 3 \rangle$. Find each of the following. See Figure 8.30.

(a) $\mathbf{u} + \mathbf{v} = \langle -2, 1 \rangle + \langle 4, 3 \rangle = \langle -2 + 4, 1 + 3 \rangle = \langle 2, 4 \rangle$

(b) $-2\mathbf{u} = -2 \cdot \langle -2, 1 \rangle = \langle -2(-2), -2(1) \rangle = \langle 4, -2 \rangle$

(c) $4\mathbf{u} + 3\mathbf{v} = 4 \cdot \langle -2, 1 \rangle + 3 \cdot \langle 4, 3 \rangle = \langle -8, 4 \rangle + \langle 12, 9 \rangle$
$= \langle -8 + 12, 4 + 9 \rangle = \langle 4, 13 \rangle$ ▌

The angle between the positive x-axis and a vector, measured in a counter-clockwise direction, is called the **direction angle** for the vector. In Figure 8.31, $\mathbf{u}$ has direction angle 60°, while $\mathbf{v}$ has direction angle 180°, and $\mathbf{w}$ has direction angle 280°.

In general, if $\mathbf{u}$ has direction angle θ and magnitude r; then

$$\mathbf{u} = \langle r \cos \theta, r \sin \theta \rangle.$$

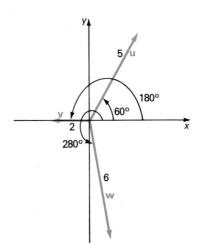

Figure 8.31

Example 4 Write the vectors from Figure 8.31 in the form $\langle a, b \rangle$.

Vector $\mathbf{u}$ in Figure 8.31 has a magnitude of 5 and direction angle 60°. Thus,

$$\mathbf{u} = \langle 5 \cos 60°, 5 \sin 60° \rangle = \left\langle 5 \cdot \frac{1}{2}, 5 \cdot \frac{\sqrt{3}}{2} \right\rangle = \left\langle \frac{5}{2}, \frac{5\sqrt{3}}{2} \right\rangle.$$

Also,

$$\mathbf{v} = \langle 2\cos 180°, 2\sin 180° \rangle = \langle 2(-1), 2(0) \rangle = \langle -2, 0 \rangle.$$

Finally, $\mathbf{w} = \langle 6\cos 280°, 6\sin 280° \rangle$
$$= \langle 6\cos 80°, -6\sin 80° \rangle.$$

(Here, we used reference angles.)

$$\approx \langle 6(.1736), -6(.9848) \rangle$$
$$\mathbf{w} \approx \langle 1.0416, -5.9088 \rangle. \quad \blacksquare$$

The next theorem gives the basic properties of vectors.

Theorem 8.5 Let a vector make an angle θ with the positive x-axis and have magnitude r. Then the x-component of the vector is

$$x = r\cos\theta,$$

and the y-component is

$$y = r\sin\theta.$$

Also, $\quad x^2 + y^2 = r^2, \quad$ and $\quad \theta = \tan^{-1}\dfrac{y}{x} \quad (x \neq 0).$

Example 5 Figure 8.32 shows vector $\mathbf{u} = \langle 3, -2 \rangle$. The magnitude of $\mathbf{u}$ is given by $\sqrt{3^2 + (-2)^2}$ $= \sqrt{13}$. To find the direction angle, first find angle θ'.

$$\theta' = \tan^{-1}\frac{-2}{3} \approx \tan^{-1}-0.6667,$$

so that $\qquad\qquad \theta' \approx -33° \; 40'.$

The direction angle is thus $\theta \approx 360° - 33° \; 40' = 326° \; 20'. \quad \blacksquare$

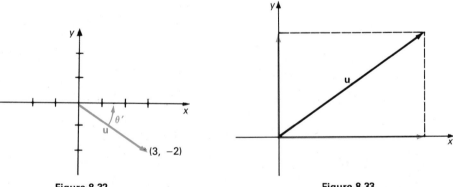

Figure 8.32   Figure 8.33

As shown in Figure 8.33, vector $\mathbf{u}$ can be thought of as the resultant of two vectors; one on the x-axis, having magnitude given by the absolute value of the x-component; and one on the y-axis, having magnitude given by the absolute value of the y-component.

This same process can be carried out for any vector **u.** Let $\mathbf{u} = \langle a, b \rangle$. Then
$$\mathbf{u} = \langle a, b \rangle = \langle a, 0 \rangle + \langle 0, b \rangle$$
$$= a \langle 1, 0 \rangle + b \langle 0, 1 \rangle.$$

The vector $\langle 1, 0 \rangle$ is called the **unit vector i,** while $\langle 0, 1 \rangle$ is the unit vector **j.** ("Unit vector" refers to the fact that the magnitude of both **i** and **j** is 1.) Thus, any vector $\mathbf{u} = \langle a, b \rangle$ may be written as

$$\mathbf{u} = a\mathbf{i} + b\mathbf{j}.$$

Using unit vectors, vector $\mathbf{u} = \langle 3, -2 \rangle$ can be written as

$$\mathbf{u} = 3\mathbf{i} - 2\mathbf{j}.$$

See Figure 8.34.

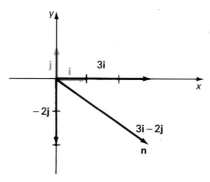

Figure 8.34

8.4 Exercises   *In Exercises 1–4 refer to the following vectors.*

Name all pairs of vectors

1. which appear to be equal.

2. which are opposites.

3. where the first is a scalar multiple of the other, with the scalar positive.

4. where the scalar is negative.

In Exercises 5–12 refer to the vectors pictured here.

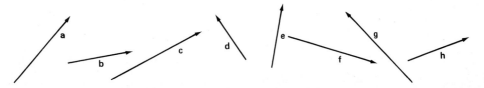

Draw a sketch to represent each of the following vectors.

5. $-\mathbf{b}$ **7.** $3\mathbf{a}$ **9.** $\mathbf{h} + \mathbf{g}$ **11.** $\mathbf{a} - \mathbf{c}$

6. $-\mathbf{g}$ **8.** $2\mathbf{h}$ **10.** $\mathbf{e} + \mathbf{f}$ **12.** $\mathbf{d} - \mathbf{e}$

Let $\mathbf{u} = \langle -2, 5 \rangle$, $\mathbf{v} = \langle 3, -2 \rangle$, and $\mathbf{w} = \langle -4, 6 \rangle$. Find each of the following vectors.

13. $\mathbf{u} + \mathbf{v}$ **14.** $\mathbf{u} - \mathbf{w}$ **15.** $6\mathbf{v} - 2\mathbf{u}$ **16.** $-3\mathbf{u} + 4\mathbf{w}$

In each of the following exercises, $\mathbf{v}$ has the given direction angle and magnitude. Find the x- and y-components of $\mathbf{v}$.

17. $\theta = 45°$, $|\mathbf{v}| = 20$ **21.** $\theta = 128° \, 30'$, $|\mathbf{v}| = 198$

18. $\theta = 75°$, $|\mathbf{v}| = 100$ **22.** $\theta = 146° \, 10'$, $|\mathbf{v}| = 238$

19. $\theta = 60° \, 10'$, $|\mathbf{v}| = 28.6$ **23.** $\theta = 251° \, 10'$, $|\mathbf{v}| = 69.1$

20. $\theta = 35° \, 50'$, $|\mathbf{v}| = 47.8$ **24.** $\theta = 302° \, 40'$, $|\mathbf{v}| = 7890$

Find the magnitude and direction angle for each of the following vectors.

25. $\langle 1, 1 \rangle$ **29.** $\langle 15, -8 \rangle$

26. $\langle -4, 4\sqrt{3} \rangle$ **30.** $\langle -7, 24 \rangle$

27. $\langle 8\sqrt{2}, -8\sqrt{2} \rangle$ **31.** $\langle -6, 0 \rangle$

28. $\langle \sqrt{3}, -1 \rangle$ **32.** $\langle 0, -12 \rangle$

Write each of the following vectors in the form $a\mathbf{i} + b\mathbf{j}$.

33. $\langle -5, 8 \rangle$ **34.** $\langle 6, -3 \rangle$ **35.** $\langle 2, 0 \rangle$ **36.** $\langle 0, -4 \rangle$

37. direction angle 45°, magnitude 8

38. direction angle 210°, magnitude 3

39. direction angle 115°, magnitude .6

40. direction angle 208°, magnitude .9

Let $\mathbf{u} = \langle a_1, b_1 \rangle$, $\mathbf{v} = \langle a_2, b_2 \rangle$, $\mathbf{w} = \langle a_3, b_3 \rangle$, and $\mathbf{0} = \langle 0, 0 \rangle$. Let k and m be any real numbers. Prove each of the following statements.

41. $\mathbf{u} + \mathbf{v} = \mathbf{v} + \mathbf{u}$ **44.** $k(\mathbf{u} + \mathbf{v}) = k\mathbf{u} + k\mathbf{v}$

42. $\mathbf{u} + (\mathbf{v} + \mathbf{w}) = (\mathbf{u} + \mathbf{v}) + \mathbf{w}$ **45.** $\mathbf{u} + \mathbf{0} = \mathbf{0}$

43. $-1(\mathbf{u}) = -\mathbf{u}$ **46.** $\mathbf{u} + (-\mathbf{u}) = \mathbf{0}$

Let $\mathbf{u} = a_1\mathbf{i} + b_1\mathbf{j}$ and $\mathbf{v} = a_2\mathbf{i} + b_2\mathbf{j}$. The dot product, *or* inner product, *of $\mathbf{u}$ and $\mathbf{v}$, written $\mathbf{u} \cdot \mathbf{v}$, is defined as*

$$\mathbf{u} \cdot \mathbf{v} = a_1 a_2 + b_1 b_2.$$

Find $\mathbf{u} \cdot \mathbf{v}$ for each of the following pairs of vectors.

47. $\mathbf{u} = 6\mathbf{i} - 2\mathbf{j}$, $\mathbf{v} = -3\mathbf{i} + 2\mathbf{j}$ **49.** $\mathbf{u} = \langle -6, 8 \rangle$ and $\mathbf{v} = \langle 3, -4 \rangle$

48. $\mathbf{u} = 3\mathbf{i} + 2\mathbf{j}$, $\mathbf{v} = -3\mathbf{i} + 7\mathbf{j}$ **50.** $\mathbf{u} = \langle 0, -2 \rangle$ and $\mathbf{v} = \langle -2, 6 \rangle$

51. Let α be the angle between the vectors $\mathbf{u}$ and $\mathbf{v}$, where $0° \leq \alpha \leq 180°$. Show that $\mathbf{u} \cdot \mathbf{v} = |\mathbf{u}| \cdot |\mathbf{v}| \cdot \cos \alpha$.

Use the result of Exercise 51 to find the angle between the following pairs of vectors.

52. $\mathbf{u} = \langle -2, 5 \rangle$ and $\mathbf{v} = \langle 3, -4 \rangle$

53. $\mathbf{u} = \langle 1, 8 \rangle$ and $\mathbf{v} = \langle 2, -5 \rangle$

54. $\mathbf{u} = \langle -6, -2 \rangle$ and $\mathbf{v} = \langle 3, -1 \rangle$

*Prove each of the following properties of the dot product. Assume that **u, v,** and **w** are vectors, and k is a nonzero real number.*

55. $\mathbf{u} \cdot \mathbf{v} = \mathbf{v} \cdot \mathbf{u}$

56. $\mathbf{u} \cdot \mathbf{u} = |\mathbf{u}|^2$

57. $\mathbf{u} \cdot (\mathbf{v} + \mathbf{w}) = \mathbf{u} \cdot \mathbf{v} + \mathbf{u} \cdot \mathbf{w}$

58. $(k \cdot \mathbf{u}) \cdot \mathbf{v} = k \cdot (\mathbf{u} \cdot \mathbf{v})$

59. If **u** and **v** are not **0**, and if $\mathbf{u} \cdot \mathbf{v} = 0$, then **u** and **v** are perpendicular.

60. If **u** and **v** are perpendicular, then $\mathbf{u} \cdot \mathbf{v} = 0$.

8.5 Applications of Vectors

Vectors are useful in solving problems which involve forces, velocities, or accelerations. In this section, we discuss some of the typical applications of vectors.

In the last section, we discussed methods for finding the resultant of two forces. If the resultant of two forces is **u,** then −**u** is called the *equilibrant* of the two forces. The **equilibrant** is the force necessary to counterbalance the joint action of the two forces.

Example 1 Find the magnitude of the equilibrant of forces of 48 and 60 grams acting on a point A, if the angle between the forces is 50°. Then find the angle between the equilibrant and the 48 gram force.

In Figure 8.35, the equilibrant is −**v.** The magnitude of **v,** and hence of −**v,** is found by using triangle ABC and the law of cosines.

$$|\mathbf{v}|^2 = 48^2 + 60^2 - 2(48)(60)\cos 130°$$
$$\approx 2304 + 3600 - 5760 \, (-.6428)$$
$$|\mathbf{v}|^2 \approx 9606.5,$$

or
$$|\mathbf{v}| \approx 98.$$

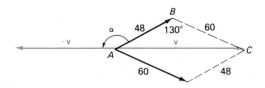

Figure 8.35

The angle we wish to find, labeled α in Figure 8.35, can be found by subtracting angle CAB from $180°$. Using the law of sines to find angle CAB, we have

$$\frac{98}{\sin 130°} = \frac{60}{\sin CAB}$$

$$\sin CAB \approx .4690$$

$$\text{angle } CAB \approx 28° \ 00'$$

Thus, $\alpha \approx 180° - 28° \ 00' = 152° \ 00'$. ▌

Example 2   Find the force required to pull a 50 pound weight up a ramp inclined at $20°$ to the horizontal.

In Figure 8.36 the vertical 50 pound force represents the force due to gravity. The vector **BC** represents the force with which the body pushes against the ramp, while the vector **AC** represents the force that would pull the body up the ramp. The angle between **AB** and **BC** is $20°$. Thus, in right triangle ABC,

$$\sin 20° = \frac{|\mathbf{AC}|}{50}$$

$$|\mathbf{AC}| = 50 \sin 20°$$

$$|\mathbf{AC}| \approx 17.1.$$

Thus, 17 pounds of force, to the nearest pound, will be required to pull the weight up the ramp. ▌

Problems involving bearing can also be worked with vectors, as shown in the next example.

Example 3   A ship leaves port on a bearing of $28°$ and travels 8.2 miles. The ship then turns due east and travels 4.3 miles. How far is the ship from port? What is its bearing from port?

In Figure 8.37 vectors **PA** and **AE** represent the ship's line of travel. We need to find the magnitude and bearing of **PE**. Triangle PNA is a right triangle, so that angle $NAP = 90° - 28° = 62°$. Then angle $PAE = 180° - 62° = 118°$. Using the law of cosines, we can find $|\mathbf{PE}|$, the magnitude of vector **PE**.

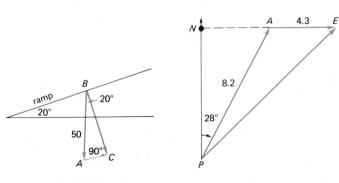

Figure 8.36   Figure 8.37

$$|\mathbf{PE}|^2 = 8.2^2 + 4.3^2 - 2(8.2)(4.3)\cos 118°$$
$$\approx 67.24 + 18.49 - 70.52(-.4695)$$
$$|\mathbf{PE}|^2 \approx 118.84$$

Therefore, $|\mathbf{PE}| \approx 10.9.$

To find the bearing of the ship from the port, we need to find angle *APE*. Using the law of sines, we have

$$\frac{4.3}{\sin APE} \approx \frac{10.9}{\sin 118°}$$

$$\sin APE \approx .3483$$

$$\text{angle } APE \approx 20° \ 20'.$$

The ship is 10.9 miles from port on a bearing of $28° + 20° \ 20' \approx 48° \ 20'$.   █

Example 4   A plane has a still-air speed of 190 miles per hour. It is headed on a bearing of 120°. A wind of 15 miles per hour is blowing from the north. Find the velocity vector for the airplane. Find the speed (the magnitude of the velocity vector). Find the bearing of the velocity vector.

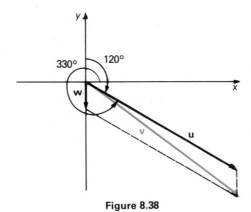

Figure 8.38

In Figure 8.38, vector **u** represents the original heading and still-air speed of the plane. Vector **w** represents the direction and speed of the wind. We need to find the resultant, vector **v.** We know the direction angle of vector **u** is 330°, while the direction angle for **w** is 270°. Thus,

$$\mathbf{u} = \langle 190 \cos 330°, \ 190 \sin 330° \rangle$$

$$= \langle 190 \left(\frac{\sqrt{3}}{2} \right), \ 190\left(-\frac{1}{2}\right) \rangle$$

$$\mathbf{u} \approx \langle 165, -95 \rangle.$$

Also, $\mathbf{w} = \langle 15 \cos 270°, \ 15 \sin 270° \rangle = \langle 0, -15 \rangle.$

Since $\mathbf{v} = \mathbf{u} + \mathbf{w},$ we have

$$\mathbf{v} \approx \langle 165, -95 \rangle + \langle 0, -15 \rangle = \langle 165, -110 \rangle.$$

The magnitude of **v** is

$$|\mathbf{v}| \approx \sqrt{165^2 + (-110)^2} = \sqrt{39,325} \approx 198.$$

Thus the actual speed of the plane is 198 miles per hour.

Given that θ is the direction angle of the vector **v**, then the x-component is given by $|\mathbf{v}| \cdot \cos\theta$. We know that the x-component of vector **v** is 165, and that $|\mathbf{v}| = 198$. Thus,

$$165 \approx 198 \cdot \cos\theta$$

$$\frac{165}{198} \approx \cos\theta$$

$$.8333 \approx \cos\theta$$

From this, results $\theta \approx 33° \ 30'$. However, from Figure 8.38, we find that θ is in quadrant IV. The direction angle of θ is

$$360° - 33°30' = 326°30'.$$

From the figure, the final bearing of the plane is $90° + 33°30' = 123°30'$. ▌

8.5 Exercises   *Solve each of the following problems.*

1. Two forces of 692 and 423 grams act on a point. The resultant force is 786 grams. Find the angle between the forces.

2. Two forces of 128 and 253 pounds act on a point. The equilibrant force is 320 pounds. Find the angle between the forces.

3. Find the force required to push a 100 gram box up a ramp inclined 10° with the horizontal.

4. Find the force required to keep a 3000 pound car parked on a hill which makes an angle of 15° with the horizontal.

5. A force of 25 kilograms is required to push an 80 kilogram lawn mower up a hill. What angle does the hill make with the horizontal?

6. A force of 500 pounds is required to pull a boat up a ramp inclined at 18° with the horizontal. How much does the boat weigh?

7. Two people are carrying a box. One person exerts a force of 150 kilograms at an angle of 62° with the horizontal. The other person exerts a force of 114 kilograms at an angle of 54°. Find the weight of the box.

8. A crate is supported by two ropes. One rope makes an angle of 46° 20′ with the horizontal and has a tension of 89.6 kilograms on it. The other rope is horizontal. Find the weight of the crate and the tension in the horizontal rope.

9. A force of 176 pounds makes an angle of 78° 50′ with a second force. The resultant of the two forces makes an angle of 41° 10′ with the first force. Find the magnitude of the second force and of the resultant.

10. A force of 28.7 kilograms makes an angle of 42° 10′ with a second force. The resultant of the two forces makes an angle of 32° 40′ with the first force. Find the magnitude of the second force and of the resultant.

11. Three forces acting at a point are in equilibrium. The forces are 980 kilograms, 760 kilograms, and 1220 kilograms. Find the angles between the directions of the forces. (Hint: arrange the forces to form the sides of a triangle.)

12. Starting at point A, a ship sails 18.5 kilometers on a bearing of 189°, then turns and sails 47.8 kilometers on a bearing of 317°. Find the distance of the ship from point A.

13. A plane flies 650 miles per hour at a bearing of 175°. A 25 mile per hour wind, bearing 86°, blows against the plane. Find the course of the plane.

14. A pilot wants to fly at a course of 74°. By flying due east, he finds that a 42 mile per hour wind, blowing from the south, puts him on course. Find the resulting speed that the plane flies.

15. The airline route from San Francisco to Honolulu is on a bearing of 233°. A jet flying at a still air speed of 450 miles per hour on that bearing runs into a wind blowing at 39 miles per hour from a direction 114°. Find the speed and direction that the plane flies.

16. The bearing of the Evergreen Ranch from Galt is 57° 40′. Harriet is flying there to visit her sister, a wrangler. She flies at a still-air speed of 168 miles per hour. A wind is blowing at 27.1 miles per hour from the south. Find her initial bearing so that she will end up in the right place.

Chapter 8   Review Exercises

Find the indicated parts in each of the following right triangles. Assume that the right angle is at C.

1. $A = 47° \ 20'$, $b = 39.6$ cm, find B and c

2. $A = 15° \ 20'$, $c = 301$ m, find B

3. $b = 68.6$ m, $c = 122.8$ m, find A and B

4. $A = 42° 10'$, $a = 689$ cm, find b and c

5. $B = 88°20'$, $b = 402$ feet, find a and c

6. When the angle of elevation of the sun is 15°50′, the shadow of a tower is 84.2 feet long. Find the height of the tower.

7. From the top of a cliff, the angle of depression to a river below is 32°10′. The river is 850 feet from a point directly below the top of the cliff. How high is the cliff?

8. From a point at the base of a mountain, the angle of elevation to the top is 21°10′. From a point 2000 feet back, the angle of elevation is 18°00′. Find the height of the mountain.

Find the indicated parts of each of the following triangles.

9. $A = 100°10'$, $B = 25°00'$, $a = 165$ m, find b

10. $A = 82°50'$, $C = 62°10'$, $b = 12.8$ cm, find a

11. $B = 39°50'$, $b = 268$ m, $a = 430$ m, find A

12. $C = 79°20'$, $c = 97.4$ mm, $a = 75.3$ mm, find A

13. $A = 25°10'$, $a = 6.92$ feet, $b = 4.82$ feet, find B

14. A ship is sailing east. At one point, the bearing of a submerged rock is 45°20′. After sailing 15.2 miles, the bearing of the rock has become 308°40′. Find the distance that the ship is then from the rock.

15. A hill makes an angle of 14°20′ with the horizontal. From the base of the hill, the angle of elevation to the top of a tree on top of the hill is 27°10′. The distance along the hill from the base to the tree is 212 feet. Find the height of the tree.

16. A surveyor reported the following data about a piece of property. "The property is triangular in shape, with dimensions as shown in the figure at the left." Use the law of sines to see if such a piece of property could exist.

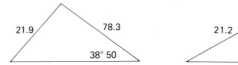

17. The surveyor tries again. "A second triangular piece of property has dimensions as shown in the figure at the right." This time it turns out that the surveyor did not consider every possible case. Use the law of sines to show why.

Find the indicated parts in each of the following triangles.

18. $A = 46°10′$, $b = 18.4$ m, $c = 19.2$ m, find a

19. $A = 129°40′$, $a = 127$ feet, $b = 69.8$ feet, find B

20. $C = 51°20′$, $c = 68.3$ m, $b = 58.2$ m, find B

21. $a = 86.1$ inches, $b = 253$ inches, $c = 241$ inches, find A

22. $a = 14.8$ m, $b = 19.7$ m, $c = 31.8$ m, find B

Find the area of each of the following triangles.

23. $a = 27.6$ cm, $b = 19.8$ cm, $C = 42°30′$

24. $b = 841$ m, $c = 716$ m, $A = 149°20′$

25. $a = 94.6$ yards, $b = 123$ yards, $c = 109$ yards

In Exercises 26–28, use the vectors shown here.

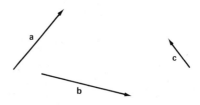

Find each of the following.

26. $\mathbf{a} + \mathbf{b}$ 27. $\mathbf{a} - \mathbf{b}$ 28. $\mathbf{a} + 3\mathbf{c}$

Suppose vector $\mathbf{v}$ *has the given direction angle and magnitude. Find the x- and y-components of* $\mathbf{v}$.

29. $\theta = 45°$, $|\mathbf{v}| = 2\sqrt{2}$ 30. $\theta = 210°$, $|\mathbf{v}| = 8$ 31. $\theta = 302°$, $|\mathbf{v}| = 25$

Find the magnitude and direction angles for each of the following vectors.

32. $\langle -6, 2 \rangle$

33. $\langle -6\sqrt{2}, 6\sqrt{2} \rangle$

34. $\langle 0, -2 \rangle$

35. $\langle \pi, 0 \rangle$

Write each of the following vectors in the form $a\mathbf{i} + b\mathbf{j}$.

36. $\langle 2, -1 \rangle$

37. $\langle -6, 3 \rangle$

38. direction angle 30°, magnitude 20

39. direction angle 162°, magnitude 5

Let $\mathbf{u}$ and $\mathbf{v}$ be as given. Find $\mathbf{u} \cdot \mathbf{v}$.

40. $\mathbf{u} = \langle 2, 6 \rangle$, $\mathbf{v} = \langle -3, 2 \rangle$

41. $\mathbf{u} = \langle 4, -5 \rangle$, $\mathbf{v} = \langle -2, 1 \rangle$

42. $\mathbf{u} = 5\mathbf{i}$, $\mathbf{v} = 2\mathbf{i} + 3\mathbf{j}$

43. $\mathbf{u} = -\mathbf{i} + 8\mathbf{j}$, $\mathbf{v} = 4\mathbf{i} + 3\mathbf{j}$

Find the angle between each of the following pairs of vectors.

44. $\mathbf{u} = 6\mathbf{i} + 2\mathbf{j}$, $\mathbf{v} = 3\mathbf{i} - 2\mathbf{j}$

45. $\mathbf{u} = 4\mathbf{i} - 3\mathbf{j}$, $\mathbf{v} = 2\mathbf{i} + \mathbf{j}$

46. $\mathbf{u} = \langle 2\sqrt{3}, 2 \rangle$, $\mathbf{v} = \langle 5, 5\sqrt{3} \rangle$

47. $\mathbf{u} = \langle 2\sqrt{2}, 2\sqrt{2} \rangle$, $\mathbf{v} = \langle -1, 1 \rangle$

Solve each of the following problems.

48. Forces of 475 and 586 grams act on an object. The angle between the forces is 78°20′. Find the magnitude of the resultant.

49. A force of 150 pounds acts at a right angle to a force of 225 pounds. Find the magnitude of the equilibrant and the angle it makes with the 150 pound force.

50. A force of 186 pounds just keeps a 2800 pound Toyota from rolling down a hill. What angle does the hill make with the horizontal?

51. A box of chickens is supported above the ground to keep the foxes out. The box hangs from two ropes. One makes an angle of 52°40′ with the horizontal. The tension in this rope is 89.6 kilograms. The second rope makes an angle of 82°30′ with the first rope, and has a tension of 61.7 kilograms. The box weighs 10 kilograms. Find the weight of the chickens. (Hint: add the *y*-components of each tension vector.)

52. A boat travels 15 kilometers per hour in still water. The boat is traveling across a large river, on a bearing of 130°. The current in the river, coming from the west, is at a speed of 7 kilometers per hour. Find the resulting speed of the boat and its resulting direction of travel.

53. A plane has a still-air speed of 520 miles per hour. The pilot wishes to fly on a bearing of 310°. A wind of 37 miles per hour is coming from a bearing of 212°. What direction should the pilot fly, and what will be her actual speed?

The following identities involve all six parts of a triangle, ABC, and are thus useful for checking answers. Prove each of these results.

54. *Newton's Formula* $\dfrac{a+b}{c} = \dfrac{\cos \frac{1}{2}(A-B)}{\sin \frac{1}{2}C}$

55. *Mollweide's Formula* $\dfrac{a-b}{c} = \dfrac{\sin \frac{1}{2}(A-B)}{\cos \frac{1}{2}C}$

The Law of Sines can be used to prove the identity for sin (A + B). Let ABC be any triangle, and go through the following steps.

56. Show that $c = a \cos B + b \cos A$.   (1)

57. Multiply the terms in (1) by the corresponding terms in the Law of Sines:

$$\frac{\sin C}{c} = \frac{\sin A}{a} = \frac{\sin B}{b}$$

58. Since $A + B + C = \pi$, we have $C = \pi - (A + B)$. Use the fact that $\sin (\pi - s) = \sin s$ to show that $\sin C = \sin (A + B)$.

59. Finally, obtain the identity for $\sin (A + B)$.

(This proof is only valid for values of A and B that might be angles of a triangle. Adjustments would have to be made to generalize this result for other angles. For more details, see the Mathematics Magazine, *vol. 35 (1962), p. 229.)*

The following exercises are taken with permission from a standard calculus book.

60. Let $\mathbf{v}_1 = \langle a_1, b_1 \rangle$ and $\mathbf{v}_2 = \langle a_2, b_2 \rangle$ be two nonzero vectors.

(a) Show that if $\mathbf{v}_1 = k\mathbf{v}_2$ for some scalar k, then $a_1 b_2 = a_2 b_1$.

(b) Show that if $a_1 b_2 = a_2 b_1$, then there exists a scalar k such that $\mathbf{v}_1 = k\mathbf{v}_2$.

61. Let $\mathbf{P}$ and $\mathbf{Q}$ be nonzero vectors. Prove that
(a) If $\mathbf{P}$ and $\mathbf{Q}$ are perpendicular, then $|\mathbf{P} + \mathbf{Q}|^2 = |\mathbf{P}|^2 + |\mathbf{Q}|^2$.
(b) If $|\mathbf{P} + \mathbf{Q}|^2 = |\mathbf{P}|^2 + |\mathbf{Q}|^2$, then $\mathbf{P}$ and $\mathbf{Q}$ are perpendicular.

62. Let A, B, C be the interior angles of a triangle in which no angle is a right angle. By calculating $\tan (A + B + C)$ and observing that $A + B + C = 180°$, show that the equation

$$\tan A + \tan B + \tan C = \tan A \tan B \tan C$$

must be satisfied.

Chapter 9

Systems of Equations and Inequalities

Many applications of mathematics require the simultaneous solution of a large number of equations or inequalities having many variables. In this chapter, we discuss methods of solving these systems of equations or inequalities.

9.1 Systems of Linear Equations in Two Variables

A set of equations is called a **system of equations**. The solution of a system is the set of all solutions that are true for *all* the equations of a system *at the same time*.

In this section, we solve systems of linear equations in *two* unknowns, commonly written

$$a_1x + b_1y = c_1$$
$$a_2x + b_2y = c_2,$$

where a_1, b_1, c_1, a_2, b_2, and c_2 are real numbers with a_1 or b_1 not zero and with a_2 or b_2 not zero.

The set of solutions of a linear equation in two variables is an infinite set of ordered pairs. The graph of such an equation is a straight line. The solution of a system of two such equations is found by locating the points (if any) where the two lines of the system cross. There are three possibilities for the solution of a system of two linear equations in two unknowns.

1. The graphs intersect in a single point. The coordinates of this point give the solution of the system. This is the most common case. (See Figure 9.1(a).)

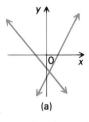

(a)

Figure 9.1

2. The graphs are distinct parallel lines. When this is the case, the equations are said to be **inconsistent**. That is, there is no solution common to both equations. (See Figure 9.1(b).)

3. The graphs are the same line. In this case, the equations are said to be **dependent** since any solution of one equation is also a solution of the other. (See Figure 9.1(c).)

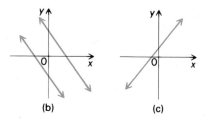

(b)   (c)

Figure 9.1

To solve a system of linear equations, use properties of algebra to change the system until a simpler equivalent system is obtained. An **equivalent system** is one having the same solution as the given system. There are three **transformations** that may be applied to a system to get a simpler, equivalent system:

Theorem 9.1   The following transformations of a linear system of equations produce an equivalent system.
(a) Exchanging any two equations of the system.
(b) Multiplying both sides of any equation of the system by any nonzero real number.
(c) Multiplying both sides of any equation of the system by a real number, and then adding the result to any other equation of the system.

We shall prove only part (c) of this theorem. We shall prove the theorem only for a system of two linear equations in two unknowns,

$$a_1x + b_1y = c_1 \tag{1}$$
$$a_2x + b_2y = c_2, \tag{2}$$

but the proof we give generalizes readily to equations with more variables.

Rewrite equation (1) as $a_1x + b_1y - c_1 = 0$, or, for simplicity, let $m = a_1x + b_1y - c_1$, so that (1) becomes $m = 0$. In the same way, write (2) as $n = 0$. Any solution of the original system will also be a solution of both $m = 0$ and $n = 0$. Form the new equation $km + n = 0$. Since both m and n become 0 when the numbers from the solution are substituted for x and y, the numbers from the solution must also make $km + n$ equal 0. Thus, a solution for the original system is also a solution for the transformed system

$$m = 0 \tag{3}$$
$$km + n = 0 \tag{4}$$

Suppose now that we start with the system made up of equations (3) and (4). Multiply both sides of the equation (3) by $-k$, obtaining (by part (b) of the theorem), the equivalent system

$$-km = 0 \tag{5}$$
$$km + n = 0. \tag{6}$$

A solution for this new system is made up of two real numbers. These real numbers may be substituted for x and y to make both $-km$ and $km + n$ equal zero. If $-km$ and $km + n$ both equal 0, then $(km + n) + (-km)$ must equal 0. Since $(km + n) + (-km) = n$, we must have $n = 0$. Thus, any solution for the system made up of equations (5) and (6) is also a solution for the system made up of the equations $m = 0$ and $n = 0$.

Example 1   Solve the system

$$3x - 4y = 1 \tag{7}$$
$$2x + 3y = 12. \tag{8}$$

We need to get a system of equations equivalent to the given system, but simpler. We do this by multiplying both sides of one equation by a real number and adding the result to the other equation so that we produce a new equation with only one variable. Start by multiplying both sides of equation (7) by 2, giving

$$6x - 8y = 2 \tag{9}$$
$$2x + 3y = 12. \tag{10}$$

This system is equivalent to the original system by Theorem 9.1(b). Now multiply both sides of equation (10) by -3, and add the result to equation (9), using Theorem 9.1(c).

$$(6x - 8y) + (-3)(2x + 3y) = 2 + (-3)(12)$$
$$6x - 8y - 6x - 9y = 2 - 36$$
$$-17y = -34$$
$$y = 2$$

We now have the equivalent system

$$y = 2$$
$$2x + 3y = 12$$

Substitute 2 for y in equation (10), giving

$$2x + 3(2) = 12$$
$$2x + 6 = 12$$
$$x = 3$$

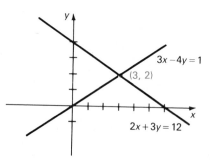

Figure 9.2

The solution of the original system is (3, 2). The graphs of both equations of the system are sketched in Figure 9.2. As the graph verifies, (3, 2) satisfies both equations of the system.   ▮

Since the solution shown in Example 1 results from the elimination of one variable from the system, it is called the **elimination method** for solving a system.

Example 2   Solve the system $3x - 2y = 4$ (11)

$$-6x + 4y = 7.$$ (12)

Multiply both sides of equation (11) by 2, and add to equation (12), giving

$$2(3x - 2y) + (-6x + 4y) = 2 \cdot 4 + 7$$
$$6x - 4y - 6x + 4y = 15$$
$$0 = 15$$

We now have the equivalent system

$$3x - 2y = 4$$
$$0 = 15$$

Since $0 = 15$ is never true, the system has no solution. As shown in Figure 9.3, this means that the graphs of the equation of the system never intersect.   ▮

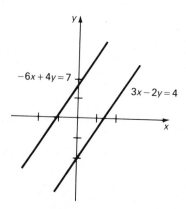

Figure 9.3

Example 3 Solve the system $8x - 2y = -4$ (13)

$$-4x + y = 2 \tag{14}$$

Multiply both sides of equation (14) by 2, and add the result to equation (13), to get the equivalent system

$$0 = 0$$

$$-4x + y = 2$$

The first equation, $0 = 0$, is always true, which means that both equations of the original system are really equivalent equations themselves. Thus, any ordered pair (r, s) that satisfies either equation will satisfy the system. If we replace x with r and y with s in equation (14), we get

$$-4r + s = 2,$$

or $s = 2 + 4r.$

The solution of the given system is thus the (infinite) set of ordered pairs of the form $(r,\ 2 + 4r)$. Typical ordered pairs belonging to the solution include: $(0, 2 + 4 \cdot 0) = (0, 2)$, $(-4, 2 + 4(-4)) = (-4, -14)$, $(3, 14)$, $(7, 30)$, and so on. As shown in Figure 9.4, both equations of the original system lead to the same graph, a straight line. ▌

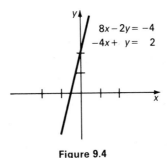

$8x - 2y = -4$
$-4x + y = 2$

Figure 9.4

The next example shows how an applied problem can be solved by a system of equations.

Example 4 For the fall algebra picnic the head of the picnic committee bought 10 hamburgers and 12 bags of french fries for $11.60. A later purchase of 4 hamburgers and 3 bags of fries cost $4.10. Find the cost of 1 hamburger and 1 bag of french fries.

From the information of the problem, we can set up a system of equations which we can then solve. To begin let

$$x = \text{cost of a hamburger}$$

$$y = \text{cost of a bag of fries.}$$

Since 10 hamburgers and 12 bags of fries cost $11.60, we have

$$10x + 12y = 11.60.$$

Also, $4x + 3y = 4.10.$

To solve this system we can first eliminate decimals if we multiply both sides of each equation by 100.

$$1000x + 1200y = 1160 \tag{15}$$
$$400x + 300y = 410 \tag{16}$$

Multiply both sides of equation (16) by $-5/2$, and add the result to equation (15), giving the equivalent system

$$450y = 135 \tag{17}$$
$$400x + 300y = 410 \tag{18}$$

From equation (17), check that $y = .3$. Use this result in equation (18) to find that $x = .80$, so that a hamburger costs $.80, or 80¢, and a bag of french fries costs $.30, or 30¢.   ▌

9.1 Exercises   *Solve each of the following systems.*

1. $x + y = 9$
    $2x - y = 0$

2. $2x + 7y = -8$
    $-2x + 3y = -12$

3. $3x + 2y = -6$
    $5x - 2y = -10$

4. $-6x + 2y = 8$
    $5x - 2y = -8$

5. $4x - 5y = 7$
    $4x + 5y = 17$

6. $2x + 7y = 31$
    $4x + 7y = 27$

7. $3x + 2y = 5$
    $6x + 4y = 8$

8. $9x - 5y = 1$
    $-18x + 10y = 1$

9. $2x - 3y = -7$
    $5x + 4y = 17$

10. $4x + 3y = -1$
    $2x + 5y = 3$

11. $5x + 7y = 6$
    $10x - 3y = 46$

12. $12x - 5y = 9$
    $3x - 8y = -18$

13. $6x + 7y = -2$
    $7x - 6y = 26$

14. $2x + 9y = 3$
    $5x + 7y = -8$

15. $\dfrac{x}{2} + \dfrac{y}{3} = 8$

    $\dfrac{2x}{3} + \dfrac{3y}{2} = 17$

16. $\dfrac{x}{5} + 3y = 31$

    $2x - \dfrac{y}{5} = 8$

17. $\dfrac{3x}{2} - \dfrac{y}{3} = 5$

    $\dfrac{5x}{2} + \dfrac{2y}{3} = 12$

18. $\dfrac{4x}{5} + \dfrac{y}{4} = -2$

    $\dfrac{x}{5} + \dfrac{y}{8} = 0$

⦿ 19. $.05x - .02y = -.18$
     $.04x + .06y = -.22$

20. $.08x + .03y = -.24$
$.04x - .01y = -.32$

21. $.6x + .3y = .087$
$.5x - .4y = .378$

22. $.7x - .5y = -.884$
$.1x + .3y = .13$

23. $1.9x - 4.8y = 11.2$
$-4.37x + 11.04y = -7.6$

24. $3.7x + 1.82y = -9.7$
$2.96x + 1.456y = 4.8$

25. $\dfrac{2}{x} + \dfrac{1}{y} = \dfrac{3}{2}$

$\dfrac{3}{x} - \dfrac{1}{y} = 1$

(Hint: let $\dfrac{1}{x} = t, \dfrac{1}{y} = u$.)

26. $\dfrac{1}{x} + \dfrac{3}{y} = \dfrac{16}{5}$

$\dfrac{5}{x} + \dfrac{4}{y} = 5$

27. $\dfrac{2}{x} + \dfrac{1}{y} = 11$

$\dfrac{3}{x} - \dfrac{5}{y} = 10$

28. $\dfrac{2}{x} + \dfrac{3}{y} = 18$

$\dfrac{4}{x} - \dfrac{5}{y} = -8$

29. $\dfrac{4}{x+2} - \dfrac{3}{y-1} = 1$

$\dfrac{1}{x+2} + \dfrac{2}{y-1} = 1$

30. $\dfrac{1}{x-3} + \dfrac{5}{y+2} = -6$

$\dfrac{-3}{x-3} + \dfrac{2}{y+2} = 1$

31. $2|x| + |y| = 6$
$3|x| - 2|y| = -5$

32. $-|x| + 6|y| = 2$
$5|x| - |y| = 19$

Write a system of two linear equations in two variables for each of the following, and then use the system to solve the problem.

33. Find values of a and b so that the line with equation $ax + by = 5$ goes through the points $(-2, 1)$ and $(-1, -2)$.

34. Find m and b so that the line $y = mx + b$ goes through $(4, 6)$ and $(-5, -3)$.

35. At the Sharp Ranch, 6 goats and 5 sheep sell for $305, while 2 goats and 9 sheep cost $285. Find the cost of 1 goat and 1 sheep.

36. Linda Ramirez is a building contractor. If she hires 7 day laborers and 2 concrete finishers, her payroll for the day is $346, while 1 day laborer and 5 concrete finishers cost $238. Find the daily-wage charge of each type of worker.

37. During summer vacation Hector and Ann earned a total of $1088. Hector worked 8 days less than Ann and earned $2 per day less. Find the number of days he worked and the daily wage he made if the total number of days worked by both was 72.

38. The perimeter of a rectangle is 42 centimeters. The larger side has a length of 7 centimeters more than the shorter side. Find the length of the longer side.

39. Thirty liters of a 50% alcohol solution are to be made by mixing 70% solution and 20% solution. How many liters of each solution should be used?

40. A merchant wishes to make one hundred pounds of a coffee blend that can be sold for $4 per pound. This blend is to be made by mixing coffee worth $6 a pound with coffee worth $3 a pound. How many pounds of each will be needed?

41. Ms. Kelley inherits $25,000. She deposits part at 8% annual interest and part at 10%. Her total annual income from these investments is $2300. How much is invested at each rate?

42. Chuck Sullivan earned $100,000 in a lottery. He invested part of the money at 10% and part at 12%. His total annual income from the two investments is $11,000. How much did he have invested at each rate?

43. Mr. Caminetti has some money invested at 8% and three times as much invested at 7%. His total annual income from the two investments is $1450. How much is invested at each rate?

44. A cash drawer contains only fives and twenties. There are eight more fives than twenties. The total value of the money is $215. How many of each type of bill are there?

45. How many gallons of milk (4.5% butterfat) must be mixed with 250 gallons of skim milk (0% butterfat) to get low-fat milk (2% butterfat)?

46. By boat Tom can go 72 miles upstream to a fishing hole in 4 hours. Returning, he needs only 3 hours. What is the speed of the current in the stream?

47. Two cars start together and travel in opposite directions. At the end of four hours, the cars are 656 kilometers apart. If one car travels 20 kilometers per hour faster than the other, find the speed of each car.

48. Two trains leave towns 192 kilometers apart, traveling toward one another. One train travels 40 kilometers per hour faster than the other. They pass one another two hours later. What is the speed of each train?

9.2 Systems of Linear Equations in More than Two Variables

In more advanced courses, it is shown that a linear equation in *three* variables such as

$$a_1x + b_1y + c_1z = d_1$$

has a graph in three-dimensional space which is a **plane**. Solutions of equations in three variables can be written as **ordered triples** (x, y, z). Thus, the solution of a system of three linear equations in three variables can be found by locating the points of intersection of three planes. As shown in Figure 9.5, there are four possibilities for the solution:

1. The three planes may meet at a single common point which gives the solution of the system. (See sketch (a).)

2. The three planes have the points of a line in common, so that the set of points which lie on the line make up the solution of the system. (See sketch (b).)

3. The planes may have no points in common so that there is no solution for the system. (See sketch (c).)

4. The three planes may coincide. (See sketch (d).)

Systems of linear equations in more than two unknowns can be solved using Theorem 9.1, as the next example shows.

Example 1   Solve the system

$$x + 3y + 2z = 1 \qquad (1)$$
$$2x + y - z = 2 \qquad (2)$$
$$x + y + z = 2 \qquad (3)$$

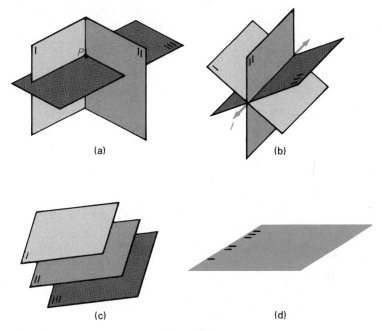

(a)

(b)

(c)

(d)

Figure 9.5

First, eliminate a variable from any pair of equations. Then eliminate the same variable from another pair of equations. Let us choose to eliminate x first. Multiply both sides of equation (1) by -2 and add the result to equation (2), giving the equivalent system

$$x + \quad 3y + 2z = 1 \tag{4}$$
$$-5y - 5z = 0 \tag{5}$$
$$x + \quad y + \quad z = 2. \tag{6}$$

Now eliminate x using equations (4) and (6). Multiply both sides of equation (6) by -1, and add the results to equation (4), giving

$$2y + \quad z = -1 \tag{7}$$
$$-5y - 5z = 0 \tag{8}$$
$$x + \quad y + \quad z = 2 \tag{9}$$

We can now use equations (7) and (8) and eliminate z. Multiply both sides of equation (7) by 5, and add the result to equation (8).

$$2y + z = -1 \tag{10}$$
$$5y \quad\quad = -5 \tag{11}$$
$$x + \quad y + z = 2 \tag{12}$$

From equation (11), $y = -1$. Replace y with -1 in equation (10), and find that $z = 1$. Finally, replace y with -1 and z with 1 in equation (12) to find that $x = 2$. The solution of the system is the ordered triple $(2, -1, 1)$.

In solving Example 1 above, we started by eliminating a variable from any pair of equations. Later on, we need more systematic methods of solving such systems. (The systematic methods we develop are necessary to permit computer solutions of systems of equations.) In the next example, we solve the same system of Example 1 by a more systematic method.

Example 2   Solve the system

$$x + 3y + 2z = 1 \tag{13}$$
$$2x + y - z = 2 \tag{14}$$
$$x + y + z = 2 \tag{15}$$

Since equation (13) has a coefficient of 1 for x, we leave it alone. (If the coefficient were, say, the nonzero number a, we could multiply both sides by $1/a$, or we could exchange the equation with another that did have a coefficient of 1 for x.)

Eliminate x in equation (14) by multiplying each term of equation (13) by -2 and adding the result to equation (14). This gives

$$-5y - 5z = 0. \tag{16}$$

Eliminate x in equation (15) by a similar process, to get

$$-2y - z = 1. \tag{17}$$

We now have the equivalent system

$$x + 3y + 2z = 1 \tag{13}$$
$$-5y - 5z = 0 \tag{16}$$
$$-2y - z = 1. \tag{17}$$

Now eliminate y in the last equation by multiplying both sides of equation (16) by $-2/5$, and adding the result to equation (17). This changes equation (17) into

$$z = 1. \tag{18}$$

We now have the equivalent system

$$x + 3y + 2z = 1 \tag{13}$$
$$-5y - 5z = 0 \tag{16}$$
$$z = 1. \tag{18}$$

This final equivalent system shows why this method is called **triangularization.**

From equation (18), we have $z = 1$. Substituting 1 for z in equation (16) gives $y = -1$. Finally, substituting -1 for y and 1 for z in equation (13) gives $x = 2$. The final solution of the system is thus $(2, -1, 1)$, as we saw before.   ▮

A system of equations will sometimes have more variables than equations. In this case, there can never be a single solution, and in fact there might be no solution at all. The next example shows how to handle these systems.

Example 3   Solve the system

$$x + 2y + z = 4 \tag{19}$$
$$3x - y - 4z = -9. \tag{20}$$

Eliminate x from equation (20) by multiplying both sides of equation (19) by -3 and adding it to equation (20).

$$x + 2y + z = 4 \tag{21}$$
$$-7y - 7z = -21 \tag{22}$$

Multiply both sides of equation (22) by $-1/7$, giving the simplified system

$$x + 2y + z = 4 \tag{23}$$
$$y + z = 3. \tag{24}$$

It is not possible to eliminate any more variables here—any attempt to do so would reintroduce x into the second equation. Instead, solve equation (24) for y. (We could have used z.)

$$y = 3 - z \tag{25}$$

Solve equation (23) for x:

$$x = 4 - 2y - z \tag{26}$$

Since $y = 3 - z$,

$$x = 4 - 2(3 - z) - z$$
$$= 4 - 6 + 2z - z$$
$$x = -2 + z$$

For any value of z that we might choose, y is found by the fact that $y = 3 - z$, and x from the fact that $x = -2 + z$. The solution can be written as the set of ordered triples $(-2 + z, 3 - z, z)$.

Typical values can be found by choosing values of z. For example, if z is 4, then $y = 3 - z = 3 - 4 = -1$, and $x = -2 + z = -2 + 4 = 2$, giving $(2, -1, 4)$. ▮

Had we solved equation (24) for z instead of y, the solution would have had a different form, but would lead to the same set of solutions. Our solution, $(-2 + z, 3 - z, z)$, is said to have z **arbitrary**.

In the system of equations given in Example 4 below, each equation has a constant of 0. By inspection, the ordered triple $(0, 0, 0)$ is a solution of the system. However, in this case, there is an infinite number of other solutions, as shown in Example 4. In general, the system

$$a_1 x + b_1 y + c_1 z = 0$$
$$a_2 x + b_2 y + c_2 z = 0$$
$$a_3 x + b_3 y + c_3 z = 0$$

is called a **homogeneous system** of three equations in three unknowns. The ordered triple $(0, 0, 0)$ is always a solution of a homogeneous system; this solution is the **trivial solution.**

Example 4   Solve the system

$$x + 2y + z = 0 \tag{27}$$
$$4x - y + z = 0 \tag{28}$$
$$-x - 2y - z = 0. \tag{29}$$

Equation (29) is a multiple of equation (27), so the system can be reduced to

$$x + 2y + z = 0 \tag{30}$$
$$4x - y + z = 0. \tag{31}$$

Eliminate z from this system by multiplying both sides of equation (30) by -1 and adding the result to equation (31). The result is the system

$$x + 2y + z = 0 \tag{32}$$
$$3x - 3y \quad = 0. \tag{33}$$

From equation (33), $x = y$.
  Substitute y for x in equation (32) to get

$$y + 2y + z = 0$$
$$3y + z = 0$$
$$z = -3y. \tag{34}$$

The final solution is made up of all ordered triples of the form $(y, y, -3y)$, where y is arbitrary. This same system could have been solved so that x is arbitrary or so that z is arbitrary. ▌

Applications of mathematics can produce a system of three linear equations in three variables, as the next example shows.

Example 5   A bank teller has a total of 70 bills, of five-, ten-, and twenty-dollar denominations. The number of fives is three times the number of tens, while the total value of the money is $960. Find the number of each type of bill that the teller has.
  Let x be the number of fives, y the number of tens, and z the number of twenties. From the information of the problem, we can produce the following system of equations.

$$x + y + z = 70 \tag{35}$$
$$x - 3y \quad = 0 \tag{36}$$
$$5x + 10y + 20z = 960 \tag{37}$$

To find the solution by triangularization, we first eliminate x from equation (36). Do this by multiplying each side of equation (35) by -1, and adding the results to equation (36). This gives the equivalent system

$$x + y + z = 70 \tag{35}$$
$$-4y - z = -70 \tag{38}$$
$$5x + 10y + 20z = 960. \tag{37}$$

Use a similar procedure to eliminate x from equation (37), getting

$$x + \quad y + \quad z = 70 \tag{35}$$
$$-4y - \quad z = -70 \tag{38}$$
$$5y + 15z = 610. \tag{39}$$

Eliminate y from equation (39) by multiplying both sides of equation (38) by 5/4 and adding the result to equation (39), getting the final equivalent system

$$x + \quad y + \quad z = 70 \tag{35}$$
$$-4y - \quad z = -70 \tag{38}$$
$$\frac{55}{4} z = \frac{1045}{2}. \tag{40}$$

From equation (40), we have $z = 38$. Substituting this result into equation (38) gives $y = 8$, and finally, from equation (35), $x = 24$. Thus, the teller had 24 fives, 8 tens, and 38 twenties. Check this result by going back to the words of the original problem. ▌

9.2   Exercises   *Solve each of the following systems of equations in three unknowns.*

1. $x + y + z = 2$
    $2x + y - z = 5$
    $x - y + z = -2$

2. $2x + y + z = 9$
    $-x - y + z = 1$
    $3x - y + z = 9$

3. $x + 3y + 4z = 14$
    $2x - 3y + 2z = 10$
    $3x - y + z = 9$

4. $4x - y + 3z = -2$
    $3x + 5y - z = 15$
    $-2x + y + 4z = 14$

5. $x + 2y + 3z = 8$
    $3x - y + 2z = 5$
    $-2x - 4y - 6z = 5$

6. $3x - 2y - 8z = 1$
    $9x - 6y - 24z = -2$
    $x - y + z = 1$

7. $x + 4y - z = 6$
    $2x - y + z = 3$
    $3x + 2y + 3z = 16$

8. $4x - 3y + z = 9$
    $3x + 2y - 2z = 4$
    $x - y + 3z = 5$

9. $5x + y - 3z = -6$
    $2x + 3y + z = 5$
    $-3x - 2y + 4z = 3$

10. $2x - 5y + 4z = -35$
    $5x + 3y - z = 1$
    $x + y + z = 1$

11. $x - 3y - 2z = -3$
    $3x + 2y - z = 12$
    $-x - y + 4z = 3$

12. $2x + 2y + 2z = 6$
    $3x - 3y - 4z = -1$
    $x + y + 3z = 11$

13. $4x + y + 3z = 5$
    $x + 4y \qquad = -1$
    $y + z = -3$

14. $3x - 2y - 4z = 1$
    $y + 2z = 4$
    $x - y \qquad = 1$

15. $\qquad 3y + 2z = 6$
    $x - y \qquad = 0$
    $4x \qquad + z = 8$

16. $x \qquad + 3z = 0$
    $2y - z = 9$
    $4x + y \qquad = -7$

17. $\dfrac{2}{x} + \dfrac{3}{y} - \dfrac{2}{z} = -1$

$\dfrac{8}{x} - \dfrac{12}{y} + \dfrac{5}{z} = 5$

$\dfrac{6}{x} + \dfrac{3}{y} - \dfrac{1}{z} = 1$

18. $-\dfrac{5}{x} + \dfrac{4}{y} + \dfrac{3}{z} = 2$

$\dfrac{10}{x} + \dfrac{3}{y} - \dfrac{6}{z} = 7$

$\dfrac{5}{x} + \dfrac{2}{y} - \dfrac{9}{z} = 6$

⦿ **19.** $1.2x + 3y - 4.8z = -5.28$

$-3x + 5.8y + 2.4z = -4.16$

$.7x - .5y + .1z = .75$

20. $-.6x + 2.5y - 3.2z = -1.25$

$1.1x + .4y + .8z = 1.22$

$-.3x - .7y - .4z = -.91$

21. $5.3x - 4.7y + 5.9z = 1.14$

$-2.5x + 3.2y - 1.4z = 7.22$

$2.25x - 2.88y + 1.26z = 4.88$

22. $7.77x - 8.61y + 4.2z = 15.96$

$11.6x - 4.9y + .8z = 12.4$

$3.7x - 4.1y + 2z = 7.6$

Solve each of the following systems in terms of an arbitrary variable.

23. $x - 2y + 3z = 6$
   $2x - y \quad = 5$

24. $3x + 4y - z = 8$
   $x \quad + 2z = 4$

25. $5x - 4y + z = 0$
   $x + y \quad = 0$
   $-10x + 8y - 2z = 0$

26. $2x + y - 3z = 0$
   $4x + 2y - 6z = 0$
   $x - y + z = 0$

27. $4x + y + z = 6$
   $y \quad = 2x$

28. $3x - 5y - 4z = 6$
   $3x \quad = z$

Solve each of the following systems of four linear equations with four variables.

29. $x + y + z + w = 4$
   $2x - y - z + w = 1$
   $-x + 4y - 2z + 3w = 4$
   $x - 5y + 3z - 2w = -3$

30. $3x - 2y + z - 3w = 0$
   $5x + y + 2z + w = 3$
   $x - 4y + z - 2w = -5$
   $4x + 3y - z + 3w = 2$

Solve each of the following systems by triangularization. Give the final equivalent system, as well as the solution of the system.

31. $2x - 3y + 2z = -2$
   $3x + y - z = -5$
   $x - y + 3z = 13$

32. $3x - 2y + z = 8$
   $2x + y - z = 1$
   $-3x + y + 2z = 3$

33. $x - y + z - w = 5$
   $x + 2y - z - w = 2$
   $2x - y + z = 6$
   $x - 3y - 2z + 2w = -9$

34. $x + 4y - z + w = 2$
   $2x - y + z - w = 7$
   $x - 5y + 3z + 2w = 6$
   $x - y + z - w = 4$

35. $2x - y + z = 0$
   $x + 2y - z = 0$
   $x - y + 2z = 0$

36. $x - 2y + z = 0$
   $2x + y - 3z = 0$
   $x + y + z = 0$

Write each of the following problems as a system of equations and then solve the system.

37. Find a, b, and c so that the graph of the equation $y = ax^2 + bx + c$ goes through the points $(2, 3)$, $(-1, 0)$, and $(-2, 2)$.

38. Find a, b, and c, so that the graph of the equation $y = ax^2 + bx + c$ goes through the points $(1, 0)$, $(0, -1)$, and $(-3, -16)$.

39. Find the values C, D, and F so that the points $(2, -6)$, $(6, -2)$, and $(-2, -2)$ lie on the circle with equation $x^2 + y^2 + Cx + Dy + F = 0$.

40. Find C, D, and F so that the points $(0, 9)$, $(-3, 0)$, and $(-6, 1)$ lie on the circle with equation $x^2 + y^2 + Cx + Dy + F = 0$.

41. The Rolling Rocks sell three kinds of tickets, "up close," "middle," and "farther back." "Up-close" tickets cost $2 more than "middle" tickets, while "middle" tickets cost $1 more than "farther-back" tickets. Twice the cost of an "up-close" ticket is $1 more than 3 times the cost of a "farther-back" seat. Find the price of each kind of ticket.

42. The perimeter of a triangle is 33 centimeters. The longest side is 3 centimeters longer than the medium side. The medium side is twice the shortest side. Find the length of each side of the triangle.

43. Marcia Odjakjian invests in three ways the $30,000 she won in a lottery. With part of the money, she buys a mutual fund, paying 9% per year. The second part, $2000 more than the first, is used to buy utility bonds paying 10% per year. The rest is invested in a tax-free 5% bond. The first year her investments bring a return of $2500. How much is invested at each rate?

44. Find three numbers whose sum is 50, if the first is 2 more than the second, and the third is two-thirds of the second.

45. The sum of three numbers is 15. The second number is the negative of one-sixth of the first number, while the third number is 3 more than the second. Find the three numbers.

46. A cashier has a total of 30 bills, made up of ones, fives, and twenties. The number of twenties is 9 more than the number of ones. The total value of the money is $351. How many of each type of bill are there?

47. A wine merchant wishes to get 300 liters of wine that sells for $2 per liter. He wishes to mix wines selling for $3, $1, and $1.50, respectively. He must use twice as much of the $1.50 wine as the $1 wine. How many liters of each should he use?

48. A glue company needs to make some glue that it can sell for $120 per barrel. It wants to use 150 barrels of glue worth $100 per barrel, along with some glue worth $150 per barrel, and glue worth $190 per barrel. It must use the same amounts of $150 and $190 glue. How much of the $150 and $190 glue will be needed? How many barrels of $120 glue will be produced?

9.3 The Substitution Method and Nonlinear Systems

An alternate method of solution for systems of equations that is useful in many practical problems is the **substitution method.** To solve systems of two equations, this method uses the following steps:

1. Solve one equation for one variable.

2. Substitute this result into the other equation of the system. Simplify to produce an equation in one variable.

3. Solve this equation.

4. Use the solution together with the original equation solved for one variable to find the complete solution of this system.

5. Check your solution in the original equations.

The next few examples show how this system works.

Example 1 Solve the system

$$2x - 5y = 15 \qquad (1)$$
$$x = 4y. \qquad (2)$$

From equation (2), we know that $x = 4y$. In equation (1), substitute $4y$ for x.

$$2x - 5y = 15$$
$$2(4y) - 5y = 15$$
$$8y - 5y = 15$$
$$3y = 15$$
$$y = 5$$

Since, from equation (2), $x = 4y$, we have $x = 4(5) = 20$. The solution of the given system is $(20, 5)$. ▌

Example 2 Use substitution to solve the system

$$2x + y + z = 4 \qquad (3)$$
$$x - 3y + 2z = -9 \qquad (4)$$
$$3x - y - z = -9. \qquad (5)$$

As one approach, solve equation (4) for x, getting

$$x = 3y - 2z - 9. \qquad (6)$$

Substitute this result for x in equation (3) and simplify as follows.

$$2x + y + z = 4 \qquad (3)$$
$$2(3y - 2z - 9) + y + z = 4$$
$$6y - 4z - 18 + y + z = 4$$
$$7y - 3z = 22 \qquad (7)$$

Now substitute $3y - 2z - 9$ for x in equation (5).

$$3x - y - z = -9 \qquad (5)$$
$$3(3y - 2z - 9) - y - z = -9$$
$$8y - 7z = 18 \qquad (8)$$

Solve equation (7) for y.

$$7y - 3z = 22 \qquad (7)$$
$$7y = 3z + 22$$
$$y = \frac{3z + 22}{7} \qquad (9)$$

Replace y with $(3z + 22)/7$ in equation (8).

$$8y - 7z = 18 \qquad (8)$$
$$8\left(\frac{3z + 22}{7}\right) - 7z = 18$$

Multiply both sides by 7, giving

$$8(3z + 22) - 49z = 126$$
$$24z + 176 - 49z = 126$$
$$-25z = -50$$
$$z = 2.$$

From equation (9), check that $y = 4$, and from equation (6), check that $x = -1$. The solution of the given system is $(-1, 4, 2)$. ▌

A system of equations in which at least one equation is *not* linear is called a **nonlinear system.** The substitution method works well for solving many such systems, as the next example shows.

Example 3 Solve the system

$$x^2 - y = 4 \tag{10}$$
$$x + y = -2 \tag{11}$$

Solve equation (11) for x, getting $x = -y - 2$. Substitute this for x in equation (10).

$$x^2 - y = 4 \tag{10}$$
$$(-y - 2)^2 - y = 4$$
$$y^2 + 4y + 4 - y = 4$$
$$y^2 + 3y = 0$$
$$y(y + 3) = 0$$
$$y = 0 \quad \text{or} \quad y + 3 = 0$$
$$y = 0 \quad \text{or} \quad y = -3$$

If $y = 0$, then from equation (11), we have $x = -2$. Also, if $y = -3$, then $x = 1$. The solutions of the given system are $(-2, 0)$, and $(1, -3)$. A graph of the system is shown in Figure 9.6. ▌

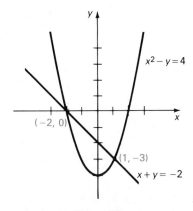

Figure 9.6

Some nonlinear systems are best solved with the elimination method presented earlier.

Example 4 Solve the system

$$x^2 + y^2 = 4 \tag{12}$$
$$2x^2 - y^2 = 8. \tag{13}$$

Multiply both sides of equation (12) by 1, and add the result to equation (13).

$$(x^2 + y^2) + (2x^2 - y^2) = 4 + 8$$
$$3x^2 = 12$$
$$x^2 = 4$$
$$x = 2 \quad \text{or} \quad x = -2$$

By substitution into equation (12), we can find y. If $x = 2$, then $y = 0$, and if $x = -2$, then $y = 0$. The solutions of the system are $(2, 0)$ and $(-2, 0)$, as shown in Figure 9.7. ▌

Some systems require a combination of the elimination method and substitution, as shown in the next example.

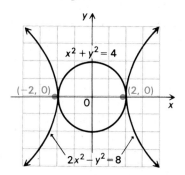

Figure 9.7

Example 5 Solve the system

$$x^2 + 3xy + y^2 = 22 \tag{14}$$
$$x^2 - xy + y^2 = 6. \tag{15}$$

Begin by multiplying both sides of equation (15) by -1, and adding the results to equation (14), giving

$$4xy = 16. \tag{16}$$

Now solve equation (16) for either x or y and substitute the result into one of the given equations. Let us solve for y.

$$y = \frac{4}{x} \quad (x \neq 0) \tag{17}$$

(Note that if $x = 0$ there is no value of y which satisfies the system.) Substituting for y in equation (15) and simplifying gives

$$x^2 - x\left(\frac{4}{x}\right) + \left(\frac{4}{x}\right)^2 = 6$$

$$x^2 - 4 + \frac{16}{x^2} = 6$$

$$x^4 - 4x^2 + 16 = 6x^2$$

$$x^4 - 10x^2 + 16 = 0$$

$$(x^2 - 2)(x^2 - 8) = 0$$

$$x^2 = 2 \quad \text{or} \quad x^2 = 8$$

$$x = \sqrt{2} \quad \text{or} \quad x = -\sqrt{2} \quad \text{or} \quad x = 2\sqrt{2} \quad \text{or} \quad x = -2\sqrt{2}.$$

Substitute these values of x into equation (17) to find the corresponding values for y.

$$\text{If } x = \sqrt{2}, \quad y = \frac{4}{\sqrt{2}} = 2\sqrt{2}.$$

$$\text{If } x = -\sqrt{2}, \quad y = -\frac{4}{\sqrt{2}} = -2\sqrt{2}.$$

$$\text{If } x = 2\sqrt{2}, \quad y = \frac{4}{2\sqrt{2}} = \sqrt{2}.$$

$$\text{If } x = -2\sqrt{2}, \quad y = -\frac{4}{2\sqrt{2}} = -\sqrt{2}.$$

The solutions of the system are $(\sqrt{2}, 2\sqrt{2})$, $(-\sqrt{2}, -2\sqrt{2})$, $(2\sqrt{2}, \sqrt{2})$ and $(-2\sqrt{2}, -\sqrt{2})$. ▮

9.3 Exercises   *Solve each of the following systems by the substitution method.*

1. $x - 5y = 8$
$x = 4y$

2. $6x - y = 5$
$y = 11x$

3. $4x - 5y = -11$
$2x + y = 5$

4. $-3x + 2y = 11$
$2x + 7y = 11$

5. $x - 2y + z = 3$
$3x + y - 2z = -1$
$x - 4y + z = 3$

6. $-2x + 5y + 3z = -6$
$4x - y - 2z = -6$
$3x + 4y - 2z = -14$

7. $y = x^2$
$x + y = 2$

8. $y = -x^2 + 2$
$x - y = 0$

9. $y = x^2 - 2x + 1$
$x - 3y = -1$

10. $y = x^2 + 6x + 9$
$x + 2y = -2$

11. $3x^2 + 2y^2 = 5$
$x - y = -2$

12. $x^2 + y^2 = 5$
$-3x + 4y = 2$

Solve the following systems by any method.

13. $x^2 + y^2 = 8$
$x^2 - y^2 = 0$

14. $x^2 + y^2 = 10$
$2x^2 - y^2 = 17$

15. $5x^2 - y^2 = 0$
$3x^2 + 4y^2 = 0$

16. $x^2 + y^2 = 4$
$2x^2 - 3y^2 = -12$

17. $2x^2 + 3y^2 = 5$
    $3x^2 - 4y^2 = -1$

18. $3x^2 + 5y^2 = 17$
    $2x^2 - 3y^2 = 5$

19. $3x^2 - 8y^2 = 76$
    $2x^2 + 5y^2 = 92$

20. $2x^2 + 9y^2 = 152$
    $5x^2 - 4y^2 = -44$

21. $5x^2 - y^2 = 9$
    $x^2 + y^2 = 45$

22. $x^2 + 3y^2 = 91$
    $2x^2 - y^2 = 119$

23. $2x^2 + 2y^2 = 20$
    $3x^2 + 3y^2 = 30$

24. $x^2 + y^2 = 4$
    $5x^2 + 5y^2 = 28$

25. $xy = 6$
    $x + y = 5$

26. $xy = -4$
    $2x + y = -7$

27. $xy = -15$
    $4x + 3y = 3$

28. $xy = 8$
    $3x + 2y = -16$

29. $2xy + 1 = 0$
    $x + 16y = 2$

30. $-5xy + 2 = 0$
    $x - 15y = 5$

31. $x^2 + 4y^2 = 25$
    $xy = 6$

32. $5x^2 - 2y^2 = 6$
    $xy = 2$

33. $x^2 + 2xy - y^2 = 14$
    $x^2 - y^2 = -16$

34. $3x^2 + xy + 3y^2 = 7$
    $x^2 + y^2 = 2$

35. $x^2 - xy + y^2 = 5$
    $2x^2 + xy - y^2 = 10$

36. $3x^2 + 2xy - y^2 = 9$
    $x^2 - xy + y^2 = 9$

37. $x^2 + 2xy - y^2 + y = 1$
    $3x + y = 6$

38. $x^2 - 4x + y + xy = -10$
    $2x - y = 10$

39. $y = 3^x$
    $y = 9^{2x}$

40. $y = 5^{3x}$
    $y = 125^{4x}$

41. $y = \log(x - 2)$
    $y = -1 + \log(8x + 4)$

42. $y = -1 + \log(18x + 10)$
    $y = \log(x + 5)$

Solve each of the following exercises by setting up a system of equations and then solving it.

43. The longest side of a right triangle is 13 meters in length. One of the other sides is 7 meters longer than the shortest side. Find the length of each of the two shorter sides of the triangle.

44. Does the straight line $3x - 2y = 9$ intersect the circle $x^2 + y^2 = 25$? (To find out, try to solve the system made up of these two equations.)

45. Do the parabola $y = x^2 + 2$ and the ellipse $2x^2 + y^2 - 4x - 4y = 0$ have any points in common?

46. For what value of b will the line $x + 2y = b$ touch the circle $x^2 + y^2 = 9$ in only one point?

47. For what values of a do the circle $x^2 + y^2 = 25$ and the ellipse $x^2/a^2 + y^2/25 = 1$ have exactly two points in common?

48. For what values of k do the parabolas $y = x^2 - 4$ and $y = -x^2 + k$ have exactly two points in common?

9.4 Matrices

Systems of equations, and in particular, systems of linear equations, occur in many practical situations. For this reason, several different methods for solving linear systems efficiently have been developed. Many of these methods depend on the computer. Computer solutions of linear systems almost always depend on the idea of a matrix. We shall discuss matrices themselves in this section and methods of using matrices to solve linear systems in the next section.

A **matrix** is a rectangular array of numbers. Each number in a matrix is an **element** of the matrix. Matrices are classified by their dimension or order, that is, by the number of rows and columns that they contain. The matrix

$$\begin{bmatrix} 2 & 7 & -5 \\ 3 & -6 & 0 \end{bmatrix}$$

has two rows and three columns. This matrix is said to be of dimension 2×3, or of order 2×3. In general, a matrix with m rows and n columns is of **dimension** $m \times n$ or **order** $m \times n$. The number of rows is always given first.

A matrix having the same number of rows as columns is called a **square matrix**. A matrix of only one row is a **row matrix**, while a matrix of only one column is a **column matrix**.

It is customary to use capital letters to name matrices. Subscript notation is used to name the elements of a matrix, as follows.

$$A = \begin{bmatrix} a_{11} & a_{12} & a_{13} & \cdots & a_{1n} \\ a_{21} & a_{22} & a_{23} & \cdots & a_{2n} \\ a_{31} & a_{32} & a_{33} & \cdots & a_{3n} \\ \cdot & \cdot & \cdot & & \cdot \\ \cdot & \cdot & \cdot & & \cdot \\ \cdot & \cdot & \cdot & & \cdot \\ a_{m1} & a_{m2} & a_{m3} & & a_{mn} \end{bmatrix}$$

Using this notation, the first row, first column element is denoted a_{11}; the second row, third column element is denoted a_{23}; and in general, the ith row, jth column element is denoted a_{ij}. As a shorthand notation, matrix A above is sometimes written as just $A = (a_{ij})$.

Two matrices are **equal** if they are of the same order and if each corresponding element, position by position, is equal. Using this definition, the matrices

$$\begin{bmatrix} 2 & 1 \\ 3 & -5 \end{bmatrix} \quad \text{and} \quad \begin{bmatrix} 1 & 2 \\ -5 & 3 \end{bmatrix}$$

are *not* equal (even though they contain the same elements and are of the same order), since the corresponding elements differ.

Example 1   From the definition of equality given above, the only way that the statement

$$\begin{bmatrix} 2 & 1 \\ p & q \end{bmatrix} = \begin{bmatrix} x & y \\ -1 & 0 \end{bmatrix}$$

can be true is if $2 = x$, $1 = y$, $p = -1$, and $q = 0$.   ▮

Example 2   The statement

$$\begin{bmatrix} x \\ y \end{bmatrix} = \begin{bmatrix} 1 \\ 4 \\ 0 \end{bmatrix}$$

can never be true, since the two matrices are of different order. (One is 2×1 and the other is 3×1.) ▌

To **add** two matrices of the same order, add corresponding elements. That is, for 2×2 matrices,

$$\begin{bmatrix} a_{11} & a_{12} \\ a_{21} & a_{22} \end{bmatrix} + \begin{bmatrix} b_{11} & b_{12} \\ b_{21} & b_{22} \end{bmatrix} = \begin{bmatrix} a_{11} + b_{11} & a_{12} + b_{12} \\ a_{21} + b_{21} & a_{22} + b_{22} \end{bmatrix}.$$

In general,

> Let $A = (a_{ij})$ and $B = (b_{ij})$ be two matrices of the same order. Then $A + B = (a_{ij}) + (b_{ij}) = (a_{ij} + b_{ij})$. **Only matrices of the same order can be added.**

Example 3   Find each of the following sums.

(a) $\begin{bmatrix} 5 & -6 \\ 8 & 9 \end{bmatrix} + \begin{bmatrix} -4 & 6 \\ 8 & -3 \end{bmatrix} = \begin{bmatrix} 5 + (-4) & -6 + 6 \\ 8 + 8 & 9 + (-3) \end{bmatrix}$

$$= \begin{bmatrix} 1 & 0 \\ 16 & 6 \end{bmatrix}$$

(b) $\begin{bmatrix} 2 \\ 5 \\ 8 \end{bmatrix} + \begin{bmatrix} -6 \\ 3 \\ 12 \end{bmatrix} = \begin{bmatrix} -4 \\ 8 \\ 20 \end{bmatrix}$

(c) The matrices

$$A = \begin{bmatrix} 5 & 8 \\ 6 & 2 \end{bmatrix} \quad \text{and} \quad B = \begin{bmatrix} 3 & 9 & 1 \\ 4 & 2 & 5 \end{bmatrix}$$

are of different orders. Therefore, the sum $A + B$ does not exist. ▌

A matrix containing only zero elements is called a **zero matrix**. For example, $[0 \quad 0 \quad 0]$ is the 1×3 zero matrix, while

$$\begin{bmatrix} 0 & 0 & 0 \\ 0 & 0 & 0 \end{bmatrix}$$

is the 2×3 zero matrix. We can have a zero matrix of any order. The matrix $A = (a_{ij})$ is a zero matrix if $a_{ij} = 0$ for every value of i and j.

In Chapter 1, we said that each real number has an additive inverse. That is, if a is a real number, we can find a real number $-a$ such that

$$a + (-a) = 0 \quad \text{and} \quad -a + a = 0.$$

What about matrices? If we are given the matrix

$$A = \begin{bmatrix} -5 & 2 & -1 \\ 3 & 4 & -6 \end{bmatrix},$$

can we find a matrix $-A$ such that

$$A + (-A) = 0 \quad \text{and} \quad -A + A = 0,$$

where 0 is the 2×3 zero matrix? To find matrix $-A$, we find the additive inverse of each element of A. (Remember, each element of A is a real number and, therefore, has an additive inverse.)

$$-A = \begin{bmatrix} 5 & -2 & 1 \\ -3 & -4 & 6 \end{bmatrix}$$

To check, first test that $A + (-A)$ equals 0.

$$A + (-A) = \begin{bmatrix} -5 & 2 & -1 \\ 3 & 4 & -6 \end{bmatrix} + \begin{bmatrix} 5 & -2 & 1 \\ -3 & -4 & 6 \end{bmatrix} = \begin{bmatrix} 0 & 0 & 0 \\ 0 & 0 & 0 \end{bmatrix}$$

Then test that $-A + A$ is also 0. Matrix $-A$ is called the **additive inverse**, or **negative,** of matrix A. Every matrix, no matter the order, has an additive inverse. In general terms, if $A = (a_{ij})$, then the additive inverse of A is $-A = (-a_{ij})$.

In Chapter 1, we said that to subtract the real number b from the real number a, written $a - b$, we add a and the additive inverse of b. That is,

$$a - b = a + (-b).$$

The same definition works for **subtraction** of matrices.

If $A = (a_{ij})$ and $B = (b_{ij})$ are two matrices of the same order, then
$$A - B = A + (-B) = (a_{ij}) + (-b_{ij}) = (a_{ij} - b_{ij}).$$

It can be shown that matrix addition (for matrices of the same order) satisfies the commutative, associative, closure, identity, and inverse properties. (See Exercises 41–45.)

Example 4   Find each of the following differences.

(a) $\begin{bmatrix} -5 & 6 \\ 2 & 4 \end{bmatrix} - \begin{bmatrix} -3 & 2 \\ 5 & -8 \end{bmatrix} = \begin{bmatrix} -5 & 6 \\ 2 & 4 \end{bmatrix} + \begin{bmatrix} 3 & -2 \\ -5 & 8 \end{bmatrix}$

(Here we found the additive inverse of each element in the second matrix.)

$$= \begin{bmatrix} -2 & 4 \\ -3 & 12 \end{bmatrix}$$

(b) $\begin{bmatrix} 8 & 6 & -4 \end{bmatrix} - \begin{bmatrix} 3 & 5 & -8 \end{bmatrix} = \begin{bmatrix} 5 & 1 & 4 \end{bmatrix}$

(c) The matrices

$$\begin{bmatrix} -2 & 5 \\ 0 & 1 \end{bmatrix} \quad \text{and} \quad \begin{bmatrix} 3 \\ 5 \end{bmatrix}$$

are of different orders and cannot be subtracted.   ▌

In work with matrices, a real number is called a **scalar** to distinguish it from a matrix. The product of a scalar k and a matrix X is the matrix kX, each of whose elements is k times the corresponding element of X. That is, for matrix $A = (a_{ij})$,

---

$$k \cdot A = k \cdot (a_{ij}) = (k \cdot a_{ij}).$$

Example 5   (a) $5\begin{bmatrix} 2 & -3 \\ 0 & 4 \end{bmatrix} = \begin{bmatrix} 10 & -15 \\ 0 & 20 \end{bmatrix}$

(b) $\dfrac{3}{4}\begin{bmatrix} 20 & 36 \\ 12 & -16 \end{bmatrix} = \begin{bmatrix} 15 & 27 \\ 9 & -12 \end{bmatrix}$ ▌

The proofs of the following properties of scalar multiplication are asked for in Exercises 50–53 below. Let A and B be matrices of the same order. Let c and d be real numbers. Then

$$(c + d)A = cA + dA$$
$$c(A + B) = cA + cB$$
$$cA = Ac$$
$$(cd)A = c(dA).$$

The definitions of addition, subtraction, and scalar multiplication seem intuitive – they "make sense." The definition of matrix multiplication, on the other hand, often seems artificial and contrived. However, matrix multiplication is defined as it is because this definition leads to useful results. Let us first find the product of

$$A = \begin{bmatrix} -3 & 4 & 2 \\ 5 & 0 & 4 \end{bmatrix} \quad \text{and} \quad B = \begin{bmatrix} -6 & 4 \\ 2 & 3 \\ 3 & -2 \end{bmatrix}.$$

First, locate *row* 1 of A and *column* 1 of B, shown shaded below.

$$A = \begin{bmatrix} -3 & 4 & 2 \\ 5 & 0 & 4 \end{bmatrix} \qquad B = \begin{bmatrix} -6 & 4 \\ 2 & 3 \\ 3 & -2 \end{bmatrix}$$

Multiply corresponding elements, and find the sum of the products.

$$(-3)(-6) + (4)(2) + (2)(3) = 32$$

This result is the element for row 1, column 1 of the product matrix.

Now use *row* 1 of A and *column* 2 of B (shown shaded below) to determine the element in row 1 and column 2 of the product matrix.

$$\begin{bmatrix} -3 & 4 & 2 \\ 5 & 0 & 4 \end{bmatrix} \qquad \begin{bmatrix} -6 & 4 \\ 2 & 3 \\ 3 & -2 \end{bmatrix}$$

Multiply corresponding elements:

$$(-3)(4) + (4)(3) + (2)(-2) = -4,$$

which is the row 1, column 2 element of the product matrix.

Next, use *row* 2 of A and *column* 1 of B; this will give the row 2, column 1 entry of the product matrix.

$$(5)(-6) + (0)(2) + (4)(3) = -18$$

Finally, use *row* 2 of A and *column* 2 of B to find the entry for row 2, column 2 of the product matrix.

$$(5)(4) + (0)(3) + (4)(-2) = 12$$

The product matrix can now be written.

$$\begin{bmatrix} -3 & 4 & 2 \\ 5 & 0 & 4 \end{bmatrix} \begin{bmatrix} -6 & 4 \\ 2 & 3 \\ 3 & -2 \end{bmatrix} = \begin{bmatrix} 32 & -4 \\ -18 & 12 \end{bmatrix}$$

As this example shows, the product of a 2×3 matrix and a 3×2 matrix is a 2×2 matrix.

In general, the **product** AB of an $m \times n$ matrix A and an $n \times p$ matrix B is found as follows. Multiply each element of the first row of A by the corresponding element of the first column of B. The sum of these n products is the first row, first column element of AB.

Also, the sum of the products found by multiplying the elements of the first row of A times the corresponding elements of the second column of B gives the first row, second column element of AB, and so on.

In general, to find the ith row, jth column element of AB, multiply each element in the ith row of A by the corresponding element in the jth column of B (note colored areas in matrices below). The sum of these products will give the element of row i, column j of AB.

$$A = \begin{bmatrix} a_{11} & a_{12} & a_{13} & \cdots & a_{1n} \\ a_{21} & a_{22} & a_{23} & \cdots & a_{2n} \\ \vdots \\ a_{i1} & a_{i2} & a_{i3} & \cdots & a_{in} \\ \vdots \\ a_{m1} & a_{m2} & a_{m3} & \cdots & a_{mn} \end{bmatrix} \qquad B = \begin{bmatrix} b_{11} & b_{12} & \cdots & b_{1j} & \cdots & b_{1p} \\ b_{21} & b_{22} & \cdots & b_{2j} & \cdots & b_{2p} \\ \vdots \\ b_{n1} & b_{n2} & \cdots & b_{nj} & \cdots & b_{np} \end{bmatrix}$$

To summarize:

Entry c_{ij} of the product matrix $C = AB$ is found as follows: $c_{ij} = a_{i1}b_{1j} + a_{i2}b_{2j} + \cdots + a_{in}b_{nj}$.

As this definition shows, matrix multiplication is defined only for two matrices A and B, where the number of columns of A is the same as the number of rows of B. The final product will have as many rows as A and as many columns as B.

Example 6   Suppose matrix A is 3×2, while matrix B is 2×4. Can the product AB be calculated? What is the order of the product? Can the product BA be calculated? What is the order of BA?

The following diagram helps us answer the questions about the product AB.

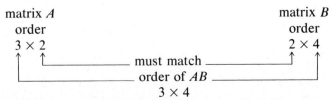

The product AB exists, since the two 2's are the same. The product has order 3×4.

Make a similar diagram for BA.

$$
\begin{array}{cc}
\text{matrix } B & \text{matrix } A \\
\text{order} & \text{order} \\
2 \times 4 & 3 \times 2
\end{array}
$$

different

The product BA does not exist.

Example 7   Find AB and BA, if possible, where

$$
A = \begin{bmatrix} 1 & -3 \\ 7 & 2 \end{bmatrix} \quad \text{and} \quad B = \begin{bmatrix} 1 & 0 & -1 & 2 \\ 3 & 1 & 4 & -1 \end{bmatrix}.
$$

Use the definition of matrix multiplication.

$$
AB = \begin{bmatrix} 1 & -3 \\ 7 & 2 \end{bmatrix}\begin{bmatrix} 1 & 0 & -1 & 2 \\ 3 & 1 & 4 & -1 \end{bmatrix}
$$

$$
= \begin{bmatrix} 1(1)+(-3)(3) & 1(0)+(-3)1 & 1(-1)+(-3)4 & 1(2)+(-3)(-1) \\ 7(1)+2(3) & 7(0)+2(1) & 7(-1)+2(4) & 7(2)+2(-1) \end{bmatrix}
$$

$$
= \begin{bmatrix} -8 & -3 & -13 & 5 \\ 13 & 2 & 1 & 12 \end{bmatrix}
$$

Since B is a 2×4 matrix, and A is a 2×2 matrix, we cannot find the product BA.

If $A = \begin{bmatrix} 1 & 3 \\ -2 & 5 \end{bmatrix}$ and $B = \begin{bmatrix} -2 & 7 \\ 0 & 2 \end{bmatrix}$, then we can use the definition of matrix multiplication to show that

$$
AB = \begin{bmatrix} -2 & 13 \\ 4 & -4 \end{bmatrix} \quad \text{and} \quad BA = \begin{bmatrix} -16 & 29 \\ -4 & 10 \end{bmatrix}.
$$

As this example shows, in general $AB \neq BA$. Thus, matrix multiplication is *not* commutative.

Matrix multiplication does, however, satisfy the associative and distributive properties: If A, B, and C are matrices such that all the following products and sums exist, then

$$
(AB)C = A(BC)
$$
$$
A(B + C) = AB + AC
$$
$$
(B + C)A = BA + CA.
$$

For proofs of these results for the special cases when A, B, and C are square matrices, see Exercises 46 and 47 below. The identity and inverse properties for matrix multiplication are discussed in a later section of this chapter.

9.4 Exercises   *Find the values of the variables in each of the following.*

1. $\begin{bmatrix} 2 & 1 \\ 4 & 8 \end{bmatrix} = \begin{bmatrix} x & 1 \\ y & z \end{bmatrix}$

2. $\begin{bmatrix} 2 & 5 & 6 \\ 1 & m & n \end{bmatrix} = \begin{bmatrix} z & y & w \\ 1 & 8 & -2 \end{bmatrix}$

3. $\begin{bmatrix} x+6 & y+2 \\ 8 & 3 \end{bmatrix} = \begin{bmatrix} -9 & 7 \\ 8 & k \end{bmatrix}$

4. $\begin{bmatrix} 9 & 7 \\ r & 0 \end{bmatrix} = \begin{bmatrix} m-3 & n+5 \\ 8 & 0 \end{bmatrix}$

5. $\begin{bmatrix} -7+z & 4r & 8s \\ 6p & 2 & 5 \end{bmatrix} + \begin{bmatrix} -9 & 8r & 3 \\ 2 & 5 & 4 \end{bmatrix} = \begin{bmatrix} 2 & 36 & 27 \\ 20 & 7 & 12a \end{bmatrix}$

6. $\begin{bmatrix} a+2 & 3z+1 & 5m \\ 4k & 0 & 3 \end{bmatrix} + \begin{bmatrix} 3a & 2z & 5m \\ 2k & 5 & 6 \end{bmatrix} = \begin{bmatrix} 10 & -14 & 80 \\ 10 & 5 & 9 \end{bmatrix}$

Perform each of the following operations, whenever possible.

7. $\begin{bmatrix} 6 & -9 & 2 \\ 4 & 1 & 3 \end{bmatrix} - \begin{bmatrix} -8 & 2 & 5 \\ 6 & -3 & 4 \end{bmatrix}$

8. $\begin{bmatrix} 9 & 4 \\ -8 & 2 \end{bmatrix} + \begin{bmatrix} -3 & 2 \\ -4 & 7 \end{bmatrix}$

9. $\begin{bmatrix} -6 & 8 \\ 0 & 0 \end{bmatrix} - \begin{bmatrix} 0 & 0 \\ -4 & -2 \end{bmatrix}$

10. $\begin{bmatrix} 1 & -4 \\ 2 & -3 \\ -8 & 4 \end{bmatrix} - \begin{bmatrix} -6 & 9 \\ -2 & 5 \\ -7 & -12 \end{bmatrix}$

11. $\begin{bmatrix} -8 & 4 & 0 \\ 2 & 5 & 0 \end{bmatrix} + \begin{bmatrix} 6 & 3 \\ 8 & 9 \end{bmatrix}$

12. $\begin{bmatrix} 2 \\ 3 \end{bmatrix} - \begin{bmatrix} 8 & 1 \\ 9 & 4 \end{bmatrix}$

13. $\begin{bmatrix} -4x+2y & -3x+y \\ 6x-3y & 2x-5y \end{bmatrix} + \begin{bmatrix} -8x+6y & 2x \\ 3y-5x & 6x+4y \end{bmatrix}$

14. $\begin{bmatrix} 4k-8y \\ 6z-3x \\ 2k+5a \\ -4m+2n \end{bmatrix} - \begin{bmatrix} 5k+6y \\ 2z+5x \\ 4k+6a \\ 4m-2n \end{bmatrix}$

15. When John inventoried his screw collection, he found that he had 7 flat-head long screws, 9 flat-head medium, 8 flat-head short, 2 round-head long, no round-head medium, and 6 round-head short. Write this information first as a 3 × 2 matrix and then as a 2 × 3 matrix.

16. At the grocery store, Miguel bought 4 quarts of milk, 2 loaves of bread, 4 chickens, and an apple. Mary bought 2 quarts of milk, a loaf of bread, 5 chickens, and 4 apples. Write this information first as a 2 × 4 matrix and then as a 4 × 2 matrix.

Let $A = \begin{bmatrix} -2 & 4 \\ 0 & 3 \end{bmatrix}$ and $B = \begin{bmatrix} -6 & 2 \\ 4 & 0 \end{bmatrix}$.

Find each of the following.

17. $2A$

18. $-3B$

19. $2A - B$

20. $-2A + 4B$

21. $-A + \dfrac{1}{2}B$

22. $\dfrac{3}{4}A - B$

Find each of the following matrix products, whenever possible.

23. $\begin{bmatrix} 1 & 2 \\ 3 & 4 \end{bmatrix}\begin{bmatrix} -1 \\ 7 \end{bmatrix}$

24. $\begin{bmatrix} 3 & -4 & 1 \\ 5 & 0 & 2 \end{bmatrix}\begin{bmatrix} -1 \\ 4 \\ 2 \end{bmatrix}$

25. $\begin{bmatrix} -1 & 2 & 0 \\ 0 & 3 & 2 \\ 0 & 1 & 4 \end{bmatrix}\begin{bmatrix} 2 & -1 & 2 \\ 0 & 2 & 1 \\ 3 & 0 & -1 \end{bmatrix}$

26. $\begin{bmatrix} -2 & -3 & -4 \\ 2 & -1 & 0 \\ 4 & -2 & 3 \end{bmatrix}\begin{bmatrix} 0 & 1 & 4 \\ 1 & 2 & -1 \\ 3 & 2 & -2 \end{bmatrix}$

27. $\begin{bmatrix} -2 & 1 & 4 \\ 0 & 1 & 2 \end{bmatrix}\begin{bmatrix} -2 & 1 & 0 \\ 0 & -2 & 0 \\ 4 & 1 & 2 \end{bmatrix}$

28. $\begin{bmatrix} -1 & 0 & 0 \\ 2 & 1 & 4 \end{bmatrix}\begin{bmatrix} 4 & -2 & 5 \\ 0 & 1 & 4 \\ 2 & -9 & 0 \end{bmatrix}$

29. $\begin{bmatrix} -3 & 0 & 2 & 1 \\ 4 & 0 & 2 & 6 \end{bmatrix}\begin{bmatrix} -4 & 2 \\ 0 & 1 \end{bmatrix}$

30. $\begin{bmatrix} -1 & 2 & 4 & 1 \\ 0 & 2 & -3 & 5 \end{bmatrix}\begin{bmatrix} 1 & 2 & 4 \\ -2 & 5 & 1 \end{bmatrix}$

31. $\begin{bmatrix} -2 & 4 & 6 \end{bmatrix}\begin{bmatrix} 3 \\ -2 \\ 1 \end{bmatrix}$

32. $\begin{bmatrix} 4 & 0 & 2 \end{bmatrix}\begin{bmatrix} -5 \\ 1 \\ 6 \end{bmatrix}$

33. $\begin{bmatrix} 3 \\ -2 \\ 1 \end{bmatrix}\begin{bmatrix} -2 & 4 & 6 \end{bmatrix}$

34. $\begin{bmatrix} -5 \\ 1 \\ 6 \end{bmatrix}\begin{bmatrix} 4 & 0 & 2 \end{bmatrix}$

35. The Bread Box, a small neighborhood bakery, sells four main items: sweet rolls, bread, cake, and pie. The amount of certain major ingredients required to make these items is given in matrix A.

$$A = \begin{array}{c} \\ \\ \\ \\ \\ \end{array} \begin{array}{ccccc} \text{eggs} & \text{flour*} & \text{sugar*} & \text{shortening*} & \text{milk*} \\ \left[\begin{array}{ccccc} 1 & 4 & \frac{1}{4} & \frac{1}{4} & 1 \\ 0 & 3 & 0 & \frac{1}{4} & 0 \\ 4 & 3 & 2 & 1 & 1 \\ 0 & 1 & 0 & \frac{1}{3} & 0 \end{array}\right] & \begin{array}{l} \text{rolls (dozen)} \\ \text{bread (loaves)} \\ \text{cake (1)} \\ \text{pie (1)} \end{array} \end{array}$$

The cost (in cents) for each ingredient when purchased in large lots and in small lots is given by matrix B.

$$B = \begin{array}{c} \\ \\ \\ \\ \\ \end{array} \begin{array}{ccc} & \text{cost} & \\ \text{large lot} & \text{small lot} & \\ \left[\begin{array}{cc} 5 & 5 \\ 8 & 10 \\ 10 & 12 \\ 12 & 15 \\ 5 & 6 \end{array}\right] & \begin{array}{l} \text{eggs} \\ \text{flour*} \\ \text{sugar*} \\ \text{shortening*} \\ \text{milk*} \end{array} \end{array}$$

*In cups.

(a) Use matrix multiplication to find a matrix representing the comparative costs per item under the two purchase options.

Suppose a day's orders consist of 20 dozen sweet rolls, 200 loaves of bread, 50 cakes, and 60 pies.

(b) Represent these orders as a 1×4 matrix and use matrix multiplication to write as a matrix the amount of each ingredient required to fill the day's orders.

(c) Use matrix multiplication to find a matrix representing the costs under the two purchase options to fill the day's orders.

Find each of the following products.

◉ **36.** $\begin{bmatrix} .8 & .4 \\ -.7 & -.22 \end{bmatrix}\begin{bmatrix} -.72 & -.8 \\ .4 & -.2 \end{bmatrix}$

37. $\begin{bmatrix} -.6 & .93 \\ .8 & .47 \end{bmatrix}\begin{bmatrix} .9 & .4 \\ .6 & -.8 \end{bmatrix}$

38. $\begin{bmatrix} -.42 & .6 \\ .9 & .3 \end{bmatrix}\begin{bmatrix} .1 & .8 \\ -.4 & .11 \end{bmatrix}$

39. $\begin{bmatrix} .8 & .72 & .44 \\ -.41 & .83 & .29 \\ -.77 & .61 & -.42 \end{bmatrix}\begin{bmatrix} -3 & .8 & -.4 \\ -7 & -.1 & -.2 \\ -1 & .3 & .9 \end{bmatrix}$

40. $\begin{bmatrix} .71 & -.22 & .88 \\ .62 & -.79 & .33 \\ .43 & -.11 & .19 \end{bmatrix}\begin{bmatrix} .08 & -.73 & -.07 \\ .04 & -.64 & .90 \\ .91 & 1.33 & -.22 \end{bmatrix}$

For the following exercises, let

$$A = \begin{bmatrix} a_{11} & a_{12} \\ a_{21} & a_{22} \end{bmatrix}, B = \begin{bmatrix} b_{11} & b_{12} \\ b_{21} & b_{22} \end{bmatrix}, \text{ and } C = \begin{bmatrix} c_{11} & c_{12} \\ c_{21} & c_{22} \end{bmatrix},$$

where all the elements are real numbers. Decide which of the following statements are true for these three matrices. If a statement is true, prove that it is true. If it is false, give a numerical example to show it false.

41. $A + B = B + A$ (commutative property)

42. $A + (B + C) = (A + B) + C$ (associative property)

43. $A + B$ is a 2×2 matrix   (closure property)

44. There exists a matrix 0 such that $A + 0 = A$ and $0 + A = A$.   (identity property)

45. There exists a matrix $-A$ such that $A + (-A) = 0$ and $-A + A = 0$.   (inverse property)

46. $(AB)C = A(BC)$ (associative property)

47. $A(B + C) = AB + AC$ (distributive property)

48. AB is a 2×2 matrix   (closure property)

49. $c(A + B) = cA + cB$ for any real number c

50. $(c + d)A = cA + dA$ for any real numbers c and d

51. $cA = Ac$

52. $(cd)A = c(dA)$

53. $(A + B)(A - B) = A^2 - B^2$ $(A^2 = AA)$

54. $(A + B)^2 = A^2 + 2AB + B^2$

9.5   Matrix Solution of Linear Systems

We solved linear systems of equations earlier in this chapter, and we discussed matrices in the last section. Now we shall see how to use matrix methods to solve a system of linear equations.

To begin, let

$$a_{11}x_1 + a_{12}x_2 + a_{13}x_3 + \cdots + a_{1n}x_n = b_1$$
$$a_{21}x_1 + a_{22}x_2 + a_{23}x_3 + \cdots + a_{2n}x_n = b_2$$
$$\vdots \qquad \vdots \qquad \vdots \qquad \qquad \vdots \qquad \vdots$$
$$a_{n1}x_1 + a_{n2}x_2 + a_{n3}x_3 + \cdots + a_{nn}x_n = b_n$$

be a system of n linear equations in n variables. All the necessary information about the system can be given by just the coefficients, the a_{ij}, and the constants, the b_i. To use this information, we form the $n \times (n+1)$ **augmented matrix** of the system:

$$\begin{bmatrix} a_{11} & a_{12} & a_{13} & \cdots & a_{1n} & b_1 \\ a_{21} & a_{22} & a_{23} & \cdots & a_{2n} & b_2 \\ \vdots & \vdots & \vdots & & \vdots & \vdots \\ a_{n1} & a_{n2} & a_{n3} & \cdots & a_{nn} & b_n \end{bmatrix}$$

(The bar, which is optional, is used merely to separate the coefficients from the constants.)

We operate with the rows of this augmented matrix just as one would with the equations of a system of equations. Since the augmented matrix is nothing more than a short form of the system, we can perform any transformation of the matrix which results in an equivalent system of equations. Operations which produce such transformations are given in the following theorem.

Theorem 9.2   For any augmented matrix of a system of linear equations, the following **row transformations** will result in the matrix of an equivalent system.
   (a) Any two rows may be interchanged.
   (b) The elements of any row may be multiplied by a nonzero real number.
   (c) Any row may be changed by adding to the elements of the row a real number times the elements of another row.

This theorem is just a restatement in matrix form of Theorem 9.1.

Example 1   Use Theorem 9.2 to solve the linear system

$$3x - 4y = 1$$
$$5x + 2y = 19.$$

Begin by forming the augmented matrix

$$\begin{bmatrix} 3 & -4 & | & 1 \\ 5 & 2 & | & 19 \end{bmatrix}.$$

Now use Theorem 9.2 and transform this augmented matrix into a matrix of the form

$$\begin{bmatrix} 1 & m & | & n \\ 0 & 1 & | & p \end{bmatrix}$$

which leads to a system that we can easily solve. The necessary row transformations are performed as follows.

It is best to work in columns, beginning in each column with the element which is to become 1. In our augmented matrix, we have 3 in the first row, first column position. To get 1 in this position, use Theorem 9.2(b) and multiply each entry in the first row by 1/3.

$$\begin{bmatrix} 1 & -4/3 & | & 1/3 \\ 5 & 2 & | & 19 \end{bmatrix}$$

To get 0 in the second row, first column, add to each element of the second row the result of multiplying -5 times the corresponding element of the first row, using Theorem 9.2(c).

$$\begin{bmatrix} 1 & -4/3 & | & 1/3 \\ 0 & 26/3 & | & 52/3 \end{bmatrix}$$

To get 1 in the second row, second column, multiply each element of the second row by 3/26, using Theorem 9.2(b).

$$\begin{bmatrix} 1 & -4/3 & | & 1/3 \\ 0 & 1 & | & 2 \end{bmatrix}$$

From this matrix, we get the system

$$x - \frac{4}{3}y = \frac{1}{3} \tag{1}$$

$$y = 2. \tag{2}$$

Substitute 2 for y in equation (1) to get $x = 3$. The final solution of the system is (3, 2). ▌

Example 2 Use matrix methods to solve the system

$$\begin{aligned} x - y + 5z &= -6 \\ 3x + 3y - z &= 10 \\ x + 3y + 2z &= 5. \end{aligned}$$

Begin by writing the augmented matrix of the linear system.

$$\begin{bmatrix} 1 & -1 & 5 & | & -6 \\ 3 & 3 & -1 & | & 10 \\ 1 & 3 & 2 & | & 5 \end{bmatrix}$$

We have 1 in row 1, column 1. The first thing we must do is get 0's in the rest of column 1. First, add to row 2 the results of multiplying each element of row 1 by -3.

$$\begin{bmatrix} 1 & -1 & 5 & -6 \\ 0 & 6 & -16 & 28 \\ 1 & 3 & 2 & 5 \end{bmatrix}$$

Now add to row 3 the results of multiplying each element of row 1 by -1.

$$\begin{bmatrix} 1 & -1 & 5 & -6 \\ 0 & 6 & -16 & 28 \\ 0 & 4 & -3 & 11 \end{bmatrix}$$

To get 1 in row 2, column 2, multiply each element of row 2 by 1/6.

$$\begin{bmatrix} 1 & -1 & 5 & -6 \\ 0 & 1 & -8/3 & 14/3 \\ 0 & 4 & -3 & 11 \end{bmatrix}$$

Next, we need to get 0 in row 3, column 2. To do this, add to row 3 the results of multiplying each element of row 2 by -4.

$$\begin{bmatrix} 1 & -1 & 5 & -6 \\ 0 & 1 & -8/3 & 14/3 \\ 0 & 0 & 23/3 & -23/3 \end{bmatrix}$$

Finally, multiply each element of the last row by 3/23 to get 1 in row 3, column 3.

$$\begin{bmatrix} 1 & -1 & 5 & -6 \\ 0 & 1 & -8/3 & 14/13 \\ 0 & 0 & 1 & -1 \end{bmatrix}$$

The **main diagonal** of this matrix is the diagonal where all elements are 1. Since each element below the main diagonal is 0, the matrix is written in **echelon** form.

The final matrix above produces the system of equations

$$x - y + 5z = -6 \tag{3}$$

$$y - \frac{8}{3}z = \frac{14}{3} \tag{4}$$

$$z = -1. \tag{5}$$

From equation (5), $z = -1$. Replace z with -1 in equation (4) to get $y = 2$. Finally, replace y with 2 and z with -1 in equation (3) to get $x = 1$. The final solution of the original system is written $(1, 2, -1)$. ▌

Example 3   Solve the system

$$x + y = 2$$
$$2x + 2y = 5.$$

Start with the augmented matrix.

$$\begin{bmatrix} 1 & 1 & 2 \\ 2 & 2 & 5 \end{bmatrix}$$

Next, add to row 2 the results of multiplying each element of row 1 by -2.

$$\begin{bmatrix} 1 & 1 & | & 2 \\ 0 & 0 & | & 1 \end{bmatrix}$$

This matrix gives the system of equations

$$x + y = 2$$
$$0 = 1,$$

a system with no solution. ▮

Example 4 Solve the system

$$x + y + 3z = 5$$
$$3x - 4y + z = 6.$$

The augmented matrix is

$$\begin{bmatrix} 1 & 1 & 3 & | & 5 \\ 3 & -4 & 1 & | & 6 \end{bmatrix}.$$

Get 0 in row 2, column 1.

$$\begin{bmatrix} 1 & 1 & 3 & | & 5 \\ 0 & -7 & -8 & | & -9 \end{bmatrix}$$

Now get 1 in row 2, column 2.

$$\begin{bmatrix} 1 & 1 & 3 & | & 5 \\ 0 & 1 & 8/7 & | & 9/7 \end{bmatrix}$$

We can't go any further since there are just two rows, so we write the system of equations.

$$x + y + 3z = 5 \qquad (6)$$
$$y + \frac{8}{7}z = \frac{9}{7} \qquad (7)$$

From equation (7), we can solve for y to get

$$y = -\frac{8}{7}z + \frac{9}{7}.$$

Substitute into equation (6) to get

$$x + \left(-\frac{8}{7}z + \frac{9}{7}\right) + 3z = 5$$

$$x = -\frac{13}{7}z + \frac{26}{7}.$$

Here z is the arbitrary variable; the solution can be written

$$\left(-\frac{13}{7}z + \frac{26}{7}, -\frac{8}{7}z + \frac{9}{7}, z\right). \qquad ▮$$

We can now summarize the cases that might come up when using matrix methods to solve a system of linear equations. When the matrix is written in echelon form:

1. If the number of rows having nonzero elements to the left of the vertical line is equal to the number of unknowns in the system, then the system has a single solution.

2. If the number of rows having nonzero elements to the left of the vertical line is less than the number of rows in the augmented matrix with nonzero elements, then the system has no solution.

   For example, the system that produced the matrix

$$\begin{bmatrix} 1 & -2 & 4 & | & 2 \\ 0 & 1 & 3 & | & -1 \\ 0 & 0 & 0 & | & 4 \end{bmatrix}$$

has no solution. Here 2 rows to the left of the vertical line have nonzero elements, but 3 rows in the entire matrix have nonzero elements.

3. If the number of rows of the matrix containing nonzero elements is less than the number of unknowns, then there is an infinite number of solutions for the system. This infinite number of solutions should be given in terms of an arbitrary variable.

The method of using matrices to solve a system of linear equations that was developed in this section is called the **Gaussian method**, after the mathematician K. F. Gauss (1777–1855).

9.5 Exercises *Write the augmented matrix for each of the following systems. Do not solve.*

1. $2x + 3y = 11$
   $x + 2y = 8$

2. $3x + 5y = -13$
   $2x + 3y = -9$

3. $x + 5y = 6$
   $y = 1$

4. $2x + 7y = 1$
   $5x = -15$

5. $2x + y + z = 3$
   $3x - 4y + 2z = -7$
   $x + y + z = 2$

6. $4x - 2y + 3z = 4$
   $3x + 5y + z = 7$
   $5x - y + 4z = 7$

7. $x + y = 2$
   $2y + z = -4$
   $z = 2$

8. $x = 6$
   $y + 2z = 2$
   $x - 3z = 6$

Write the system of equations associated with each of the following augmented matrices. Do not solve.

9. $\begin{bmatrix} 2 & 1 & | & 1 \\ 3 & -2 & | & -9 \end{bmatrix}$

10. $\begin{bmatrix} 1 & -5 & | & -18 \\ 6 & 2 & | & 20 \end{bmatrix}$

11. $\begin{bmatrix} 1 & 0 & 0 & | & 2 \\ 0 & 1 & 0 & | & 3 \\ 0 & 0 & 1 & | & -2 \end{bmatrix}$

12. $\begin{bmatrix} 1 & 0 & 1 & 4 \\ 0 & 1 & 0 & 2 \\ 0 & 0 & 1 & 3 \end{bmatrix}$

14. $\begin{bmatrix} 2 & 1 & 3 & 12 \\ 4 & -3 & 0 & 10 \\ 5 & 0 & -4 & -11 \end{bmatrix}$

13. $\begin{bmatrix} 3 & 2 & 1 & 1 \\ 0 & 2 & 4 & 22 \\ -1 & -2 & 3 & 15 \end{bmatrix}$

Use the Gaussian method to solve each of the following systems of equations.

15. $x + y = 5$
$x - y = -1$

16. $x + 2y = 5$
$2x + y = -2$

17. $x + y = -3$
$2x - 5y = -6$

18. $3x - 2y = 4$
$3x + y = -2$

19. $2x - 3y = 10$
$2x + 2y = 5$

20. $6x + y = 5$
$5x + y = 3$

21. $2x - 5y = 10$
$3x + y = 15$

22. $4x - y = 3$
$-2x + 3y = 1$

23. $x + y = -1$
$y + z = 4$
$x + z = 1$

24. $x - z = -3$
$y + z = 9$
$x + z = 7$

25. $x + y - z = 6$
$2x - y + z = -9$
$x - 2y + 3z = 1$

26. $x + 3y - 6z = 7$
$2x - y + z = 1$
$x + 2y + 2z = -1$

27. $-x + y = -1$
$y - z = 6$
$x + z = -1$

28. $x + y = 1$
$2x - z = 0$
$y + 2z = -2$

29. $2x - y + 3z = 0$
$x + 2y - z = 5$
$2y + z = 1$

30. $4x + 2y - 3z = 6$
$x - 4y + z = -4$
$-x + 2z = 2$

31. $x - 2y + z = 5$
$2x + y - z = 2$
$-2x + 4y - 2z = 2$

32. $3x + 5y - z = 0$
$4x - y + 2z = 1$
$-6x - 10y + 2z = 0$

33. $x + y + z = 6$
$2x - y - z = 3$

34. $5x - 3y + z = 1$
$2x + y - z = 4$

35. $x - 8y + z = 4$
$3x - y + 2z = -1$

36. $-3x + y - z = 8$
$2x + y + 4z = 0$

37. $x + 3y - z = 0$
$2y - z = 4$

38. $2x - y + 4z = 1$
$y + z = 3$

39. $3x + 2y - w = 0$
$2x + z + 2w = 5$
$x + 2y - z = -2$
$2x - y + z + w = 2$

40. $x + 3y - 2z - w = 9$
$4x + y + z + 2w = 2$
$-3x - y + z - w = -5$
$x - y - 3z - 2w = 2$

41. $x - y + 2z + w = 4$
$y + z = 3$
$z - w = 2$

42. $3x + y = 1$
$y - 4z + w = 0$
$z - 3w = -1$

⦿ **43.** $3.5x + 2.9y = 12.91$
$1.7x - 3.8y = -6.23$

44. $-4.3x + 1.1y = 10.1$
$\quad\;\; 4.8x - 2.7y = -17.31$

45. $9.1x + 2.3y - \quad z = -3.06$
$\quad\;\; 4.7x + \quad y - 3.8z = -21.15$
$\qquad\qquad 5.1y - 4.7z = -31.77$

46. $7.2x + 4.8y + \;\; 3.1z = -14.96$
$\qquad 3x - \quad y + 11.5z = -15.6$
$\quad\;\; 1.1x + 2.4y \qquad\qquad = -1.24$

Solve each of the following word problems.

47. A working couple earned a total of $2176. The wife earned $32 per day; the husband earned $4 per day less. Find the number of days each worked if the total number of days worked by both was 72.

48. Midtown Manufacturing Company makes two products, plastic plates and plastic cups. Both require time on two machines; plates: 1 hour on machine *A* and 2 hours on machine *B*, cups: 3 hours on machine *A* and 1 hour on machine *B*. Both machines operate 15 hours a day. How many of each product can be produced in a day under these conditions?

49. A company produces two models of bicycles, model 201 and model 301. Model 201 requires 2 hours of assembly time, and model 301 requires 3 hours of assembly time. The parts for model 201 cost $25 per bike; those for model 301 cost $30 per bike. If the company has a total of 34 hours of assembly time and $365 available per day for these two models, how many of each can be made in a day?

50. Juanita invests $10,000 in three ways. With one part, she buys mutual funds which offer a return of 8% per year. The second part, which amounts to twice the first, is used to buy government bonds at 9% per year. She puts the rest in the bank at 5% annual interest. The first year her investments bring a return of $830. How much did she invest each way?

51. To get the necessary funds for a planned expansion, a small company took out three loans totaling $25,000. The company was able to borrow some of the money at 8%. They borrowed $2000 more than one-half the amount of the 8% loan at 10%, and the rest at 9%. The total annual interest was $2220. How much did they borrow at each rate?

At rush hours, substantial traffic congestion is encountered at the traffic intersections shown in the figure.

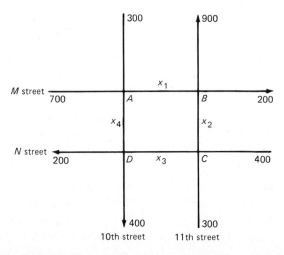

The city wishes to improve the signals at these corners so as to speed the flow of traffic. The traffic engineers first gather data. As the figure shows, 700 cars per hour come down M Street to intersection A; 300 cars per hour come to intersection A on 10th Street. A total of x_1 of these cars leave A on M Street, while x_4 cars leave A on 10th Street. The number of cars entering A must equal the number leaving, so that

$$x_1 + x_4 = 700 + 300$$

or

$$x_1 + x_4 = 1000.$$

For intersection B, x_1 cars enter B on M Street, and x_2 cars enter B on 11th Street. The figure shows that 900 cars leave B on 11th while 200 leave on M. We have

$$x_1 + x_2 = 900 + 200$$

$$x_1 + x_2 = 1100.$$

At intersection C, 400 cars enter on N Street, 300 on 11th Street, while x_2 leave on 11th Street and x_3 leave on N Street. This gives

$$x_2 + x_3 = 400 + 300$$

$$x_2 + x_3 = 700.$$

Finally, intersection D has x_3 cars entering at N and x_4 entering on 10th. There are 400 cars leaving D on 10th and 200 leaving on N.

52. Set up an equation for intersection D.

53. Use the four equations to set up an augmented matrix, and then use the Gaussian method to solve it.

54. Since you got a row of all zeros, the system of equations does not have a unique solution. Write three equations, corresponding to the three nonzero rows of the matrix. Solve each of the equations for x_4.

55. One of your equations should have been $x_4 = 1000 - x_1$. What is the largest possible value of x_1 so that x_4 is not negative?

56. Your second equation should have been $x_4 = x_2 - 100$. Find the smallest possible value of x_2 so that x_4 is not negative.

57. Find the largest possible values of x_3 and x_4 so that neither variable is negative.

58. Give the maximum possible values of x_1, x_2, x_3, and x_4 so that all the equations are satisfied and all variables are nonnegative.

Solve each of the following problems.

59. Three small boxes and 8 large boxes cost $13.30. If 6 small and 16 large boxes are purchased, the cost is $27.20. Find the cost of a small box and the cost of a large box.

60. The sum of three numbers is 20. One number is one more than another. Find the three numbers.

61. If three numbers are added, the result is -10. The second number, added to twice the third, gives 5. Find the three numbers.

62. If half of one number is added to another, the sum is twice a third number. The third number is half the second number. Find the three numbers.

9.6   Matrix Inverses

We have seen that the commutative, associative, closure, identity, and inverse properties hold for *addition* of matrices of the same order. Also, the associative and closure properties hold for *multiplication* of square matrices of the same order. There is no commutative property for multiplication, but the distributive property is valid for matrices of the proper order.

In this section we look at the two remaining properties, the identity and inverse properties for multiplication. Does the identity property hold? If it does hold, we must be able to find a matrix I such that

$$AI = A \qquad \text{and} \qquad IA = A$$

for any square matrix A. (Compare these products to the statement of the identity property for real numbers: $a \cdot 1 = a$ and $1 \cdot a = a$ for any real number a.) It turns out that for 2×2 matrices,

$$I = \begin{bmatrix} 1 & 0 \\ 0 & 1 \end{bmatrix}.$$

In general, for any value of n there is an $n \times n$ identity matrix having 1's down the diagonal and 0's elsewhere. That is, the **$n \times n$ identity matrix** is given by I_n, where

$$I_n = \begin{bmatrix} 1 & 0 & \cdots & 0 \\ 0 & 1 & \cdots & 0 \\ \cdot & & \cdot & & \cdot \\ \cdot & & \cdot & a_{ij} & \cdot \\ \cdot & & & & \cdot \\ 0 & 0 & \cdots & 1 \end{bmatrix}.$$

Here $a_{ij} = 1$ when $i = j$ (the diagonal elements) and $a_{ij} = 0$ otherwise.

For every nonzero real number a, there is a multiplicative inverse $1/a$ such that

$$a \cdot \frac{1}{a} = 1 \qquad \text{and} \qquad \frac{1}{a} \cdot a = 1.$$

(Recall: $1/a$ is also written a^{-1}.) In the rest of this section we study a method for finding a multiplicative inverse for any $n \times n$ matrix that has such an inverse. If A is an $n \times n$ matrix, then its **multiplicative inverse**, written A^{-1}, must satisfy both

$$AA^{-1} = I \qquad \text{and} \qquad A^{-1}A = I.$$

The inverse of a matrix, if it exists, can be found by use of the same row transformations that we used in the last section to solve a system of linear equations.

To obtain A^{-1} for any $n \times n$ matrix A for which A^{-1} exists, first form the augmented matrix $[A|I_n]$ where A is any $n \times n$ matrix and I_n is the $n \times n$ multiplicative identity matrix. We perform row operations on $[A|I_n]$ until we have an augmented matrix in the form $[I_n|B]$. The matrix B is the desired matrix A^{-1}. If it is not possible to get a matrix of the form $[I_n|B]$, then the inverse of matrix A does not exist.

A difficulty with this method is that it is not at all clear why the method produces the desired inverse. In fact, a proof of why the method works is given only in courses much more advanced than this. However, in any given case, it is always possible to show that the matrix B in $[I_n|B]$ is indeed A^{-1} by checking that $BA = I_n$ and $AB = I_n$.

Example 1 Let $A = \begin{bmatrix} 2 & 3 \\ 1 & -1 \end{bmatrix}$. Find A^{-1}.

Form the augmented matrix

$$[A|I_2] = \begin{bmatrix} 2 & 3 & | & 1 & 0 \\ 1 & -1 & | & 0 & 1 \end{bmatrix}.$$

Now perform row operations on $[A|I_2]$ until we obtain a new matrix of the form $[I_2|B]$, in which B is A^{-1}. Proceed as follows.

Step 1 Interchanging the first and second rows gives us a 1 in the upper left-hand corner:

$$\begin{bmatrix} 1 & -1 & | & 0 & 1 \\ 2 & 3 & | & 1 & 0 \end{bmatrix}.$$

Step 2 Adding to the second row the results of multiplying each element of row one by -2 gives

$$\begin{bmatrix} 1 & -1 & | & 0 & 1 \\ 0 & 5 & | & 1 & -2 \end{bmatrix}.$$

Step 3 Multiplying the second row by 1/5, we get a 1 for the second element in that row:

$$\begin{bmatrix} 1 & -1 & | & 0 & 1 \\ 0 & 1 & | & 1/5 & -2/5 \end{bmatrix}.$$

Step 4 Replacing the first row by the sum of the first row and the second row results in a 0 as the second element in the first row:

$$\begin{bmatrix} 1 & 0 & | & 1/5 & 3/5 \\ 0 & 1 & | & 1/5 & -2/5 \end{bmatrix}.$$

We have reached our goal, which was to transform $[A|I_2]$ into $[I_2|B]$. The transformation gives us

$$B = \begin{bmatrix} 1/5 & 3/5 \\ 1/5 & -2/5 \end{bmatrix}$$

which should equal A^{-1}. To check, multiply B times A. The result should be I.

$$BA = \begin{bmatrix} 1/5 & 3/5 \\ 1/5 & -2/5 \end{bmatrix} \begin{bmatrix} 2 & 3 \\ 1 & -1 \end{bmatrix} = \begin{bmatrix} 2/5 + 3/5 & 3/5 - 3/5 \\ 2/5 - 2/5 & 3/5 + 2/5 \end{bmatrix} = \begin{bmatrix} 1 & 0 \\ 0 & 1 \end{bmatrix} = I_2.$$

Also, it is necessary to verify that $AB = I_2$. Since it does,

$$A^{-1} = \begin{bmatrix} 1/5 & 3/5 \\ 1/5 & -2/5 \end{bmatrix}. \quad \blacksquare$$

Example 2   Find A^{-1} if $A = \begin{bmatrix} 1 & 0 & 1 \\ 2 & -2 & -1 \\ 3 & 0 & 0 \end{bmatrix}$.

Use row transformations as follows, going through as many steps as needed.

Step 1   Write as the augmented matrix $[A|I_3]$:

$$\begin{bmatrix} 1 & 0 & 1 & | & 1 & 0 & 0 \\ 2 & -2 & -1 & | & 0 & 1 & 0 \\ 3 & 0 & 0 & | & 0 & 0 & 1 \end{bmatrix}.$$

Step 2   Since 1 is already in the upper left-hand corner as necessary, begin by selecting the row operation which will result in a 0 for the first element in the second row. Add to each element in the second row the result of multiplying the first row by -2:

$$\begin{bmatrix} 1 & 0 & 1 & | & 1 & 0 & 0 \\ 0 & -2 & -3 & | & -2 & 1 & 0 \\ 3 & 0 & 0 & | & 0 & 0 & 1 \end{bmatrix}.$$

Step 3   To get 0 for the first element in the third row, add to the third row the results of multiplying each element of the first row by -3. This gives the new matrix

$$\begin{bmatrix} 1 & 0 & 1 & | & 1 & 0 & 0 \\ 0 & -2 & -3 & | & -2 & 1 & 0 \\ 0 & 0 & -3 & | & -3 & 0 & 1 \end{bmatrix}.$$

Step 4   To get 1 for the second element in the second row, multiply the second row by $-1/2$, obtaining the new matrix

$$\begin{bmatrix} 1 & 0 & 1 & | & 1 & 0 & 0 \\ 0 & 1 & 3/2 & | & 1 & -1/2 & 0 \\ 0 & 0 & -3 & | & -3 & 0 & 1 \end{bmatrix}.$$

Step 5   To get 1 for the third element in the third row, multiply the third row by $-1/3$, with the result

$$\begin{bmatrix} 1 & 0 & 1 & | & 1 & 0 & 0 \\ 0 & 1 & 3/2 & | & 1 & -1/2 & 0 \\ 0 & 0 & 1 & | & 1 & 0 & -1/3 \end{bmatrix}.$$

Step 6   To get 0 for the third element in the first row, add to the first row the results of multiplying each element in row three by -1:

$$\begin{bmatrix} 1 & 0 & 0 & | & 0 & 0 & 1/3 \\ 0 & 1 & 3/2 & | & 1 & -1/2 & 0 \\ 0 & 0 & 1 & | & 1 & 0 & -1/3 \end{bmatrix}.$$

Step 7   To get 0 for the third element in the second row, add to the second row the results of multiplying each element of row three by $-3/2$:

$$\begin{bmatrix} 1 & 0 & 0 & 0 & 0 & 1/3 \\ 0 & 1 & 0 & -1/2 & -1/2 & 1/2 \\ 0 & 0 & 1 & 1 & 0 & -1/3 \end{bmatrix}.$$

From the last transformation, we get the desired inverse:

$$A^{-1} = \begin{bmatrix} 0 & 0 & 1/3 \\ -1/2 & -1/2 & 1/2 \\ 1 & 0 & -1/3 \end{bmatrix}.$$

Confirm this by forming the products $A^{-1}A$, and AA^{-1}, which should equal I_3. ▌

We can see from the examples that the most efficient order of steps is to make the changes column by column from left to right, so that for each column the required 1 is the result of the first change. Next, perform the steps that obtain the zeros in that column. Then proceed to another column. Since it is tedious to find an inverse with paper and pencil, these same steps can be adapted for a computer program. A computer can produce the inverse of a large matrix in a few seconds.

Example 3   Find A^{-1} given $A = \begin{bmatrix} 2 & -4 \\ 1 & -2 \end{bmatrix}$.

Using row operations to transform the first column of the augmented matrix

$$\begin{bmatrix} 2 & -4 & | & 1 & 0 \\ 1 & -2 & | & 0 & 1 \end{bmatrix},$$

results in the following matrices:

$$\begin{bmatrix} 1 & -2 & | & 1/2 & 0 \\ 1 & -2 & | & 0 & 1 \end{bmatrix},$$

$$\begin{bmatrix} 1 & -2 & | & 1/2 & 0 \\ 0 & 0 & | & -1/2 & 1 \end{bmatrix}.$$

At this point, we wish to change the matrix so that the second row, second column element will be 1. Since that element is now 0, there is no way to complete the desired transformation. Thus, matrix A^{-1} does not exist. ▌

One application of matrix inverses comes in solving square linear systems of equations. (A square system has the same number of equations as variables.) For example, if we are given the linear system

$$a_{11}x + a_{12}y + a_{13}z = d_1$$
$$a_{21}x + a_{22}y + a_{23}z = d_2$$
$$a_{31}x + a_{32}y + a_{33}z = d_3,$$

we can use the definition of matrix multiplication to rewrite the system as

$$\begin{bmatrix} a_{11} & a_{12} & a_{13} \\ a_{21} & a_{22} & a_{23} \\ a_{31} & a_{32} & a_{33} \end{bmatrix} \cdot \begin{bmatrix} x \\ y \\ z \end{bmatrix} = \begin{bmatrix} d_1 \\ d_2 \\ d_3 \end{bmatrix}. \tag{1}$$

(To see this, multiply the matrices on the left.)

Let $A = \begin{bmatrix} a_{11} & a_{12} & a_{13} \\ a_{21} & a_{22} & a_{23} \\ a_{31} & a_{32} & a_{33} \end{bmatrix}$, $\quad X = \begin{bmatrix} x \\ y \\ z \end{bmatrix}$, $\quad$ and $B = \begin{bmatrix} d_1 \\ d_2 \\ d_3 \end{bmatrix}$,

so that the system given in (1) becomes

$$AX = B.$$

If we assume that A^{-1} exists, we can multiply both sides of $AX = B$ by A^{-1} to get

$$A^{-1}(AX) = A^{-1}B$$
$$(A^{-1}A)X = A^{-1}B$$
$$I_3 X = A^{-1}B$$
$$X = A^{-1}B.$$

Matrix $A^{-1}B$ gives the solution of the system.

Example 4 Use the method of matrix inverses to solve the system

$$2x - 3y = 4$$
$$x + 5y = 2.$$

To represent the system as a matrix equation, use one matrix for the coefficients, one for the variables, and one for the constants, as follows.

$$A = \begin{bmatrix} 2 & -3 \\ 1 & 5 \end{bmatrix}, \quad X = \begin{bmatrix} x \\ y \end{bmatrix} \quad \text{and} \quad B = \begin{bmatrix} 4 \\ 2 \end{bmatrix}$$

The system can then be written in matrix form as the equation $AX = B$, since

$$AX = \begin{bmatrix} 2 & -3 \\ 1 & 5 \end{bmatrix}\begin{bmatrix} x \\ y \end{bmatrix} = \begin{bmatrix} 2x - 3y \\ x + 5y \end{bmatrix} = \begin{bmatrix} 4 \\ 2 \end{bmatrix} = B.$$

To solve the system, first find A^{-1}. Use row transformations to verify that

$$A^{-1} = \begin{bmatrix} 5/13 & 3/13 \\ -1/13 & 2/13 \end{bmatrix}.$$

Next, find the product $A^{-1}B$.

$$A^{-1}B = \begin{bmatrix} 5/13 & 3/13 \\ -1/13 & 2/13 \end{bmatrix}\begin{bmatrix} 4 \\ 2 \end{bmatrix} = \begin{bmatrix} 2 \\ 0 \end{bmatrix}$$

Since $X = A^{-1}B$,

$$X = \begin{bmatrix} x \\ y \end{bmatrix} = \begin{bmatrix} 2 \\ 0 \end{bmatrix}.$$

Thus, the solution of the system is (2, 0). ▮

This method of using matrix inverses to solve systems of equations is useful when the inverse is already known or when several systems must be solved where the coefficients are the same and only the constants differ.

9.6 Exercises   *Decide whether the given matrices are inverses of each other.*

1. $\begin{bmatrix} 1 & -2 & -3 \\ 2 & -2 & -5 \\ -1 & 1 & 4 \end{bmatrix}$ and $\begin{bmatrix} -1 & 5/3 & 4/3 \\ -1 & 1/3 & -1/3 \\ 0 & 1/3 & 2/3 \end{bmatrix}$

2. $\begin{bmatrix} 1 & 2 & -1 \\ 2 & -1 & 3 \\ 3 & -2 & 3 \end{bmatrix}$ and $\begin{bmatrix} 3/10 & -2/5 & 1/2 \\ 3/10 & 3/5 & -1/2 \\ -1/10 & 4/5 & -1/2 \end{bmatrix}$

3. $\begin{bmatrix} 1 & 2 & -1 \\ 0 & 1 & 3 \\ 2 & 1 & -2 \end{bmatrix}$ and $\begin{bmatrix} 1 & 1 & 2 \\ 1 & 1 & 1 \\ 2 & 3 & 4 \end{bmatrix}$

4. $\begin{bmatrix} 2 & -1 & 4 \\ 0 & 5 & 0 \\ 3 & 2 & -1 \end{bmatrix}$ and $\begin{bmatrix} 1 & 0 & 1 \\ 6 & 4 & 2 \\ 1 & 1 & 0 \end{bmatrix}$

Use row operations to find the inverses of the following matrices if they exist.

5. $\begin{bmatrix} 1 & 5 \\ 2 & 0 \end{bmatrix}$

6. $\begin{bmatrix} 10 & 0 \\ 5 & 3 \end{bmatrix}$

7. $\begin{bmatrix} -6 & 4 \\ -3 & 2 \end{bmatrix}$

8. $\begin{bmatrix} -1 & 2 \\ 1 & -2 \end{bmatrix}$

9. $\begin{bmatrix} 1 & 2 & 3 \\ -3 & -2 & -1 \\ -1 & 0 & 1 \end{bmatrix}$

10. $\begin{bmatrix} 2 & 0 & 4 \\ 3 & 1 & 5 \\ -1 & 1 & -2 \end{bmatrix}$

11. $\begin{bmatrix} 2 & 1 & 3 \\ 7 & 4 & -2 \\ 0 & 1 & -1 \end{bmatrix}$

12. $\begin{bmatrix} -2 & -1 & -5 \\ 4 & 5 & 0 \\ 0 & 1 & 3 \end{bmatrix}$

13. $\begin{bmatrix} 1 & 1 & 0 & 2 \\ 2 & -1 & 1 & -1 \\ 3 & 3 & 2 & -2 \\ 1 & 2 & 1 & 0 \end{bmatrix}$

14. $\begin{bmatrix} 1 & -2 & 3 & 0 \\ 0 & 2 & -1 & 1 \\ -2 & 2 & 1 & 4 \\ 0 & 2 & -3 & 1 \end{bmatrix}$

⦿ 15. $\begin{bmatrix} .6 & .2 \\ .5 & .1 \end{bmatrix}$

16. $\begin{bmatrix} .8 & -.3 \\ .5 & -.2 \end{bmatrix}$

17. $\begin{bmatrix} -.4 & 1 & .2 \\ 0 & .6 & .8 \\ .3 & 0 & -.2 \end{bmatrix}$

18. $\begin{bmatrix} .8 & .2 & .1 \\ -.2 & 0 & .3 \\ 0 & 0 & .5 \end{bmatrix}$

Solve the matrix equation AX = B for X, given the following matrices.

19. $A = \begin{bmatrix} 1 & 0 & -1 \\ 2 & 1 & 1 \\ 3 & 2 & -1 \end{bmatrix}$ $B = \begin{bmatrix} 1 \\ 4 \\ 3 \end{bmatrix}$

20. $A = \begin{bmatrix} 2 & 3 & 1 \\ -3 & -4 & 0 \\ -1 & 2 & -2 \end{bmatrix}$ $B = \begin{bmatrix} 0 \\ 2 \\ -4 \end{bmatrix}$

Use the method of matrix inverses to solve each of the following systems. Some of the necessary inverses have been found in the text and exercises of this section.

21. $-x + y = 1$
$2x - y = 1$

22. $3x - y = 1$
$-5x + 2y = -1$

23. $2x - y = -8$
$3x + y = -2$

24. $x + 3y = -12$
$2x - y = 11$

25. $x + z = 3$
$2x - 2y - z = -2$
$3x = 3$

26. $4x + 3y + 3z = 11$
$-x - z = -4$
$-4x - 4y - 3z = -10$

27. $2x + y + 3z = 13$
$7x + 4y - 2z = -4$
$y - z = -3$

28. $2x + 4z = 14$
$3x + y + 5z = 19$
$-x + y - 2z = -7$

29. $x + y + 2w = 3$
$2x - y + z - w = 3$
$3x + 3y + 2z - 2w = 5$
$x + 2y + z = 3$

30. $x - 2y + 3z = -3$
$2y - z + w = 3$
$-2x + 2y + z + 4w = 7$
$2y - 3z + w = 5$

31. The Bread Box Bakery sells three types of cakes, each requiring the amounts of the basic ingredients shown in the following matrix.

	types of cake		
	I	II	III
flour (cups)	2	4	2
sugar (cups)	2	1	2
eggs	2	1	3

To fill its daily orders for the three kinds of cake, the bakery uses 72 cups of flour, 48 cups of sugar, and 60 eggs. How many daily orders for each type of cake does the bakery receive? (Let the order matrix be a 3×1 matrix X and solve a matrix equation for X.)

32. Give an example of two matrices A and B where $(AB)^{-1} \neq A^{-1}B^{-1}$.

33. Suppose A and B are matrices where A^{-1}, B^{-1}, and AB all exist. Show that $(AB)^{-1} = B^{-1}A^{-1}$.

34. Let $A = \begin{bmatrix} a & 0 \\ 0 & b \end{bmatrix}$. Under what conditions on a and b, does A^{-1} exist?

35. Derive a formula for the inverse of $\begin{bmatrix} a & b \\ c & d \end{bmatrix}$, where $ad - bc \neq 0$.

36. Let $A = \begin{bmatrix} a & 0 & 0 \\ 0 & b & 0 \\ 0 & 0 & c \end{bmatrix}$,

where a, b and c are nonzero real numbers. Find A^{-1}.

9.7 Determinants

Given any square matrix A, there is a unique real number associated with A — this real number is the **determinant** of the matrix. We define determinants in this section, look at their properties in the next, and then see how determinants can be used to solve a system of linear equations.

The determinant of a matrix A is written $|A|$. We shall first define $|A|$ for a 2×2 matrix:

If $A = \begin{bmatrix} a_{11} & a_{12} \\ a_{21} & a_{22} \end{bmatrix}$, then $|A| = \begin{vmatrix} a_{11} & a_{12} \\ a_{21} & a_{22} \end{vmatrix} = a_{11}\,a_{22} - a_{21}\,a_{12}.$

Example 1   Let $A = \begin{bmatrix} -3 & 4 \\ 6 & 8 \end{bmatrix}$. Find $|A|$.

Use the definition above:

$$|A| = \begin{vmatrix} -3 & 4 \\ 6 & 8 \end{vmatrix} = -3(8) - 6(4) = -48. \qquad \blacksquare$$

The determinant of a 3×3 matrix,

$$A = \begin{bmatrix} a_{11} & a_{12} & a_{13} \\ a_{21} & a_{22} & a_{23} \\ a_{31} & a_{32} & a_{33} \end{bmatrix},$$

is defined as

$$|A| = \begin{vmatrix} a_{11} & a_{12} & a_{13} \\ a_{21} & a_{22} & a_{23} \\ a_{31} & a_{32} & a_{33} \end{vmatrix} = \begin{aligned} &(a_{11}a_{22}a_{33} + a_{12}a_{23}a_{31} + a_{13}a_{21}a_{32}) \\ &-(a_{31}a_{22}a_{13} + a_{32}a_{23}a_{11} + a_{33}a_{21}a_{12}). \end{aligned}$$

We can rearrange terms on the right side of the equation and factor to get

$$\begin{vmatrix} a_{11} & a_{12} & a_{13} \\ a_{21} & a_{22} & a_{23} \\ a_{31} & a_{32} & a_{33} \end{vmatrix} = \begin{aligned} &a_{11}(a_{22}a_{33} - a_{32}a_{23}) - a_{21}(a_{12}a_{33} - a_{32}a_{13}) \\ &+ a_{31}(a_{12}a_{23} - a_{22}a_{13}). \end{aligned} \tag{1}$$

Each of the quantities in parentheses above represents a determinant of a 2×2 matrix that is the determinant of that part of the 3×3 matrix remaining when the row and column of the multiplier are eliminated. We can show this as follows.

$$a_{11}(a_{22}a_{33} - a_{32}a_{23}) \qquad \begin{bmatrix} a_{11} & a_{12} & a_{13} \\ a_{21} & a_{22} & a_{23} \\ a_{31} & a_{32} & a_{33} \end{bmatrix}$$

$$a_{21}(a_{12}a_{33} - a_{32}a_{13}) \qquad \begin{bmatrix} a_{11} & a_{12} & a_{13} \\ a_{21} & a_{22} & a_{23} \\ a_{31} & a_{32} & a_{33} \end{bmatrix}$$

$$a_{31}(a_{12}a_{23} - a_{22}a_{13}) \qquad \begin{bmatrix} a_{11} & a_{12} & a_{13} \\ a_{21} & a_{22} & a_{23} \\ a_{31} & a_{32} & a_{33} \end{bmatrix}$$

These determinants of 2×2 matrices are called **minors** of an element in the 3×3 matrix. The symbol M_{ij} represents the determinant of the matrix that results when row i and column j are eliminated. In the matrix above we have the following typical minors.

Element	Minor		Element	Minor
a_{11}	$M_{11} = \begin{vmatrix} a_{22} & a_{23} \\ a_{32} & a_{33} \end{vmatrix}$		a_{22}	$M_{22} = \begin{vmatrix} a_{11} & a_{13} \\ a_{31} & a_{33} \end{vmatrix}$
a_{21}	$M_{21} = \begin{vmatrix} a_{12} & a_{13} \\ a_{32} & a_{33} \end{vmatrix}$		a_{23}	$M_{23} = \begin{vmatrix} a_{11} & a_{12} \\ a_{31} & a_{32} \end{vmatrix}$
a_{31}	$M_{31} = \begin{vmatrix} a_{12} & a_{13} \\ a_{22} & a_{23} \end{vmatrix}$		a_{33}	$M_{33} = \begin{vmatrix} a_{11} & a_{12} \\ a_{21} & a_{22} \end{vmatrix}$

To find the determinant of a 3×3 or larger matrix, first choose any row or column. Then the minor of each element in that row or column must be multiplied by $+1$ or -1, depending on whether the sum of the row numbers and column numbers is even or odd. The product of a minor and the number $+1$ or -1 is called a **cofactor:**

Let M_{ij} be the minor for element a_{ij} in an $n \times n$ matrix. The *cofactor* of a_{ij}, written A_{ij}, is

$$A_{ij} = (-1)^{i+j} \cdot M_{ij}.$$

Finally, the determinant of a 3×3 or larger matrix is found by the following rule,

> Multiply each element in any row or column of the matrix by its cofactor. The sum of these products gives the determinant.

The process of forming this sum of products is called **expansion** about the given row or column. (See Exercise 35–36 below.)

Example 2   Evaluate $\begin{vmatrix} 2 & -3 & -2 \\ -1 & -4 & -3 \\ -1 & 0 & 2 \end{vmatrix}$.

Expand about the second column.

To find this determinant, first get the minors of each element in the second column.

$$M_{12} = \begin{vmatrix} -1 & -3 \\ -1 & 2 \end{vmatrix} = -1(2) - (-1)(-3) = -5$$

$$M_{22} = \begin{vmatrix} 2 & -2 \\ -1 & 2 \end{vmatrix} = 2(2) - (-1)(-2) = 2$$

$$M_{32} = \begin{vmatrix} 2 & -2 \\ -1 & -3 \end{vmatrix} = 2(-3) - (-1)(-2) = -8$$

Now find the cofactor for each of these minors.

$$A_{12} = (-1)^{1+2} \cdot M_{12} = (-1)^3 \cdot (-5) = (-1)(-5) = 5$$
$$A_{22} = (-1)^{2+2} \cdot M_{22} = (-1)^4 \cdot (2) = 1 \cdot 2 = 2$$
$$A_{32} = (-1)^{3+2} \cdot M_{32} = (-1)^5 \cdot (-8) = (-1)(-8) = 8$$

The determinant is found by multiplying each cofactor by its corresponding elements in the matrix and finding the sum of these products.

$$\begin{vmatrix} 2 & -3 & -2 \\ -1 & -4 & -3 \\ -1 & 0 & 2 \end{vmatrix} = a_{12} \cdot A_{12} + a_{22} \cdot A_{22} + a_{32} \cdot A_{32}$$
$$= -3(5) + (-4)(2) + (0)(8)$$
$$= -15 + (-8) + 0$$
$$= -23 \quad \blacksquare$$

We would get exactly the same answer by using any row or column of the determinant. One reason that column 2 was used here is that it contains a 0 element. Thus, it was not really necessary to calculate M_{32} and A_{32}, as we did above. One learns quickly that 0's are friends when working with determinants.

Instead of calculating $(-1)^{i+j}$ for a given element the following sign checkerboard can also be used.

$$\begin{array}{ccc} + & - & + \\ - & + & - \\ + & - & + \end{array}$$

The signs alternate for each row and column, beginning with $+$ in the first row, first column position. Thus, this array of signs can be reproduced as needed. If we expand about row 3, for example, the first minor would have a $+$ sign associated with it, the second minor a $-$ sign, and the third minor a $+$ sign. This array of signs can be extended in the same way for determinants of 4×4, 5×5, and larger matrices.

Example 3 Evaluate

$$\begin{vmatrix} -1 & -2 & 3 & 2 \\ 0 & 1 & 4 & -2 \\ 3 & -1 & 4 & 0 \\ 2 & 1 & 0 & 3 \end{vmatrix}.$$

Expand about the fourth row, and do the arithmetic that we are leaving out.

$$-2 \begin{vmatrix} -2 & 3 & 2 \\ 1 & 4 & -2 \\ -1 & 4 & 0 \end{vmatrix} + 1 \begin{vmatrix} -1 & 3 & 2 \\ 0 & 4 & -2 \\ 3 & 4 & 0 \end{vmatrix} - 0 \begin{vmatrix} -1 & -2 & 2 \\ 0 & 1 & -2 \\ 3 & -1 & 0 \end{vmatrix} + 3 \begin{vmatrix} -1 & -2 & 3 \\ 0 & 1 & 4 \\ 3 & -1 & 4 \end{vmatrix}$$
$$= -2(6) + 1(-50) - 0 + 3(-41)$$
$$= -185. \quad \blacksquare$$

9.7 Exercises *Find the value of each of the following determinants. All variables represent real numbers.*

1. $\begin{vmatrix} 5 & 8 \\ 2 & -4 \end{vmatrix}$

2. $\begin{vmatrix} -3 & 0 \\ 0 & 9 \end{vmatrix}$

3. $\begin{vmatrix} -1 & -2 \\ 5 & 3 \end{vmatrix}$

4. $\begin{vmatrix} 6 & -4 \\ 0 & -1 \end{vmatrix}$

5. $\begin{vmatrix} 9 & 3 \\ -3 & -1 \end{vmatrix}$

6. $\begin{vmatrix} 0 & 2 \\ 1 & 5 \end{vmatrix}$

7. $\begin{vmatrix} 3 & 4 \\ 5 & -2 \end{vmatrix}$

8. $\begin{vmatrix} -9 & 7 \\ 2 & 6 \end{vmatrix}$

9. $\begin{vmatrix} 0 & 4 \\ 4 & 0 \end{vmatrix}$

10. $\begin{vmatrix} 1 & 0 \\ 0 & 2 \end{vmatrix}$

11. $\begin{vmatrix} y & 2 \\ 8 & y \end{vmatrix}$

12. $\begin{vmatrix} 3 & 8 \\ m & n \end{vmatrix}$

13. $\begin{vmatrix} x & y \\ y & x \end{vmatrix}$

14. $\begin{vmatrix} 2m & 8n \\ 8n & 2m \end{vmatrix}$

Find the cofactor of each element in the second row for the following determinants.

15. $\begin{vmatrix} -2 & 0 & 1 \\ 3 & 2 & -1 \\ 1 & 0 & 2 \end{vmatrix}$

16. $\begin{vmatrix} 0 & -1 & 2 \\ 1 & 0 & 2 \\ 0 & -3 & 1 \end{vmatrix}$

17. $\begin{vmatrix} 1 & 2 & -1 \\ 2 & 3 & -2 \\ -1 & 4 & 1 \end{vmatrix}$

18. $\begin{vmatrix} 2 & -1 & 4 \\ 3 & 0 & 1 \\ -2 & 1 & 4 \end{vmatrix}$

Find the value of each of the following determinants. All variables represent real numbers.

19. $\begin{vmatrix} 1 & 0 & 0 \\ 0 & -1 & 0 \\ 1 & 0 & 1 \end{vmatrix}$

20. $\begin{vmatrix} -2 & 0 & 1 \\ 0 & 1 & 0 \\ 0 & 0 & -1 \end{vmatrix}$

21. $\begin{vmatrix} -2 & 0 & 0 \\ 4 & 0 & 1 \\ 3 & 4 & 2 \end{vmatrix}$

22. $\begin{vmatrix} 7 & -1 & 1 \\ 1 & -7 & 2 \\ -2 & 1 & 1 \end{vmatrix}$

23. $\begin{vmatrix} 1 & -2 & 3 \\ 0 & 0 & 0 \\ 1 & 10 & -12 \end{vmatrix}$

24. $\begin{vmatrix} 2 & 3 & 0 \\ 1 & 9 & 0 \\ -1 & -2 & 0 \end{vmatrix}$

25. $\begin{vmatrix} 3 & 3 & -1 \\ 2 & 6 & 0 \\ -6 & -6 & 2 \end{vmatrix}$

26. $\begin{vmatrix} 5 & -3 & 2 \\ -5 & 3 & -2 \\ 1 & 0 & 1 \end{vmatrix}$

27. $\begin{vmatrix} 3 & 2 & 0 \\ 0 & 1 & x \\ 2 & 0 & 0 \end{vmatrix}$

28. $\begin{vmatrix} 0 & 3 & y \\ 0 & 4 & 2 \\ 1 & 0 & 1 \end{vmatrix}$

29. $\begin{vmatrix} i & j & k \\ -1 & 2 & 4 \\ 3 & 0 & 5 \end{vmatrix}$

30. $\begin{vmatrix} i & j & k \\ 0 & -4 & 2 \\ -1 & 3 & 1 \end{vmatrix}$

31. $\begin{vmatrix} 4 & 0 & 0 & 2 \\ -1 & 0 & 3 & 0 \\ 2 & 4 & 0 & 1 \\ 0 & 0 & 1 & 2 \end{vmatrix}$

32. $\begin{vmatrix} -2 & 0 & 4 & 2 \\ 3 & 6 & 0 & 4 \\ 0 & 0 & 0 & 3 \\ 9 & 0 & 2 & -1 \end{vmatrix}$

33. $\begin{vmatrix} .4 & -.8 & .6 \\ .3 & .9 & .7 \\ 3.1 & 4.1 & -2.8 \end{vmatrix}$

34. $\begin{vmatrix} -.3 & -.1 & .9 \\ 2.5 & 4.9 & -3.2 \\ -.1 & .4 & .8 \end{vmatrix}$

Let $A = \begin{bmatrix} a_{11} & a_{12} & a_{13} \\ a_{21} & a_{22} & a_{23} \\ a_{31} & a_{32} & a_{33} \end{bmatrix}$.

35. Find $|A|$ by expansion about row 3. Show that your result is really equal to $|A|$ given in equation (1) of this section.

36. Do the same thing for column 3.

37. Suppose that every element in one row of matrix B is 0. Prove that $|B| = 0$.

Let $M = \begin{bmatrix} a_{11} & a_{12} \\ a_{21} & a_{22} \end{bmatrix}$.

38. Form a matrix N by exchanging the rows of M. Prove that $|M| = -|N|$.

39. Form matrix R by multiplying every element of row 1 of M by the real number k. Prove that $|R| = k \cdot |M|$.

40. Let matrix S be formed by adding to row 1 the result of multiplying each element of row 2 of M by the real number k. Show that $|M| = |S|$.

41. Let $Z = \begin{bmatrix} a_{11} & a_{12} & a_{13} \\ a_{11} & a_{12} & a_{13} \\ a_{31} & a_{32} & a_{33} \end{bmatrix}$, in which two rows are identical.

Show that $|Z| = 0$.

42. Suppose matrix Y has no zero elements. Prove that $|Y|$ can be 0.

Determinants can be used to find the area of a triangle given the coordinates of its vertices. Given a triangle PQR with vertices (x_1, y_1), (x_3, y_3), and (x_2, y_2), as shown in the following figure, we can introduce segments PM, RN, and QS perpendicular to the x-axis, forming trapezoids PMNR, NSQR, and PMSQ. Recall that the area of a trapezoid is given by half the sum of the parallel bases times the altitude. For example, the area of trapezoid

PMSQ equals $\dfrac{1}{2}(y_1 + y_3)(x_3 - x_1)$. The area of triangle PQR can be found by subtracting the area of PMSQ from the sum of the areas of PMNR and RNSQ. Thus, for the area A of triangle PQR, we have

$$A = \frac{1}{2}(x_3y_1 - x_1y_3 + x_2y_3 - x_3y_2 + x_1y_2 - x_2y_1).$$

By evaluating the determinant

$$\begin{vmatrix} x_1 & y_1 & 1 \\ x_2 & y_2 & 1 \\ x_3 & y_3 & 1 \end{vmatrix}$$

it can be shown that the area of the triangle is given by the absolute value of A, where

$$A = \frac{1}{2}\begin{vmatrix} x_1 & y_1 & 1 \\ x_2 & y_2 & 1 \\ x_3 & y_3 & 1 \end{vmatrix}.$$

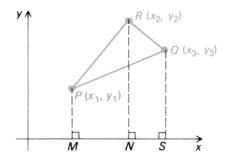

Use the formula given to find the area of the following triangles.

43. $P(0, 1)$, $Q(2, 0)$, $R(1, 3)$

44. $P(2, 5)$, $Q(-1, 3)$, $R(4, 0)$

45. $P(2, -2)$, $Q(0, 0)$, $R(-3, -4)$

46. $P(4, 7)$, $Q(5, -2)$, $R(1, 1)$

47. $P(3, 8)$, $Q(-1, 4)$, $R(0, 1)$

48. $P(-3, -1)$, $Q(4, 2)$, $R(3, -3)$

49. Prove that the straight line through the distinct points (x_1, y_1) and (x_2, y_2) has equation

$$\begin{vmatrix} x & y & 1 \\ x_1 & y_1 & 1 \\ x_2 & y_2 & 1 \end{vmatrix} = 0.$$

50. Use the result of Exercise 49 to show that three distinct points (x_1, y_1), (x_2, y_2) and (x_3, y_3) lie on a straight line if

$$\begin{vmatrix} x_1 & y_1 & 1 \\ x_2 & y_2 & 1 \\ x_3 & y_3 & 1 \end{vmatrix} = 0.$$

51. Show that the lines $a_1x + b_1y = c_1$ and $a_2x + b_2y = c_2$, when $c_1 \neq c_2$, are parallel if

$$\begin{vmatrix} a_1 & b_1 \\ a_2 & b_2 \end{vmatrix} = 0.$$

52. Prove that

$$\begin{vmatrix} 1 & 1 & 1 \\ a & b & c \\ a^2 & b^2 & c^2 \end{vmatrix} = (a - b)(b - c)(c - a).$$

9.8 Properties of Determinants

Some determinants can only be evaluated after much tedious calculation. The more calculation involved, the more chance for error. To evaluate a determinant of a 3×3 matrix, it is necessary to evaluate three different determinants of a 2×2 matrix and then combine them correctly. For a determinant of a 4×4 matrix, twelve determinants of 2×2 matrices must be found. In general, an $n \times n$ determinant requires that we find $n!/2$ different determinants of 2×2 matrices, where $n!$ represents the product $n(n - 1)(n - 2) \cdots 3 \cdot 2 \cdot 1$.

In this section we give several theorems which make it easier to calculate certain determinants. These theorems help us reduce a determinant to one which is easier to evaluate. The theorems are true for square matrices of any order, but we usually prove them only for determinants of 3×3 matrices.

Theorem 9.3 If every element in a row or column of matrix A is 0, then $|A| = 0$.

Example 1
$$\begin{vmatrix} -3 & 7 & 0 \\ 4 & 9 & 0 \\ -6 & 8 & 0 \end{vmatrix} = 0 \quad \blacksquare$$

To prove Theorem 9.3, expand the given determinant about the 0 row or column. Each term of this expansion would have a zero factor, so that the final determinant would be 0. For example,

$$\begin{vmatrix} a_{11} & a_{12} & a_{13} \\ 0 & 0 & 0 \\ a_{31} & a_{32} & a_{33} \end{vmatrix} = -0 \cdot \begin{vmatrix} a_{12} & a_{13} \\ a_{32} & a_{33} \end{vmatrix} + 0 \cdot \begin{vmatrix} a_{11} & a_{13} \\ a_{31} & a_{33} \end{vmatrix} - 0 \cdot \begin{vmatrix} a_{11} & a_{12} \\ a_{31} & a_{32} \end{vmatrix} = 0.$$

Theorem 9.4   If corresponding rows and columns of matrix A are interchanged to form the matrix B, then $|B| = |A|$.

Example 2   (a) Let $A = \begin{bmatrix} 2 & 1 \\ 3 & 4 \end{bmatrix}$. If we interchange the rows and columns of A, we get matrix B:

$$B = \begin{bmatrix} 2 & 3 \\ 1 & 4 \end{bmatrix}.$$

Check that $|A| = 5$ and $|B| = 5$, so that $|A| = |B|$.

(b) $\begin{vmatrix} 2 & 1 & 6 \\ 3 & 0 & 5 \\ -4 & 6 & 9 \end{vmatrix} = \begin{vmatrix} 2 & 3 & -4 \\ 1 & 0 & 6 \\ 6 & 5 & 9 \end{vmatrix}$ ▌

To prove Theorem 9.4, let

$$A = \begin{bmatrix} a_{11} & a_{12} & a_{13} \\ a_{21} & a_{22} & a_{23} \\ a_{31} & a_{32} & a_{33} \end{bmatrix} \quad \text{and} \quad B = \begin{bmatrix} a_{11} & a_{21} & a_{31} \\ a_{12} & a_{22} & a_{32} \\ a_{13} & a_{23} & a_{33} \end{bmatrix},$$

where B was obtained by interchanging the corresponding rows and columns of A. Find $|A|$ by expansion about row 1. Then find $|B|$ by expansion about column 1. You should find that $|A| = |B|$.

Theorem 9.5   If any two rows or columns of matrix A are interchanged to form matrix B, then $|B| = -|A|$.

Example 3   (a) Let $A = \begin{bmatrix} 2 & 5 \\ 3 & 4 \end{bmatrix}$. Exchange the two columns of A to get the matrix $B = \begin{bmatrix} 5 & 2 \\ 4 & 3 \end{bmatrix}$.

Check that $|A| = -7$ and $|B| = 7$, so that $|B| = -|A|$.

(b) $\begin{vmatrix} 2 & 1 & 6 \\ 3 & 0 & 5 \\ -4 & 6 & 9 \end{vmatrix} = - \begin{vmatrix} -4 & 6 & 9 \\ 3 & 0 & 5 \\ 2 & 1 & 6 \end{vmatrix}$.   ▌

Theorem 9.5 is proved by steps very similar to those used to prove Theorem 9.4. (See Exercise 29.)

Theorem 9.6   Suppose matrix B is formed by multiplying every element of a row or column of matrix A by the real number k. Then, $|B| = k \cdot |A|$.

Example 4   Let $A = \begin{bmatrix} 2 & -3 \\ 4 & 1 \end{bmatrix}$. Form the new matrix B by multiplying each element of the second row of A by -5:

$$B = \begin{bmatrix} 2 & -3 \\ 4(-5) & 1(-5) \end{bmatrix} = \begin{bmatrix} 2 & -3 \\ -20 & -5 \end{bmatrix}.$$

Check that $|B| = -5 \cdot |A|$.   ▌

The proof of Theorem 9.6 is given in Exercise 30 below.

Theorem 9.7   If two rows (or columns) of a matrix A are identical, then $|A| = 0$.

Example 5   Since two rows are identical, $\begin{vmatrix} -4 & 2 & 3 \\ 0 & 1 & 6 \\ -4 & 2 & 3 \end{vmatrix} = 0.$ ▌

Theorem 9.7 is proved using Theorem 9.5. According to Theorem 9.5, if two rows or columns of a matrix A are interchanged to form matrix B, then $|A| = -|B|$. If two rows of matrix A are identical and we interchange them, we still have matrix A. But by Theorem 9.5 we have $|A| = -|A|$. The only way this can happen is if $|A| = 0$.

The last theorem of this section is perhaps the most useful of all.

Theorem 9.8   If matrix B is obtained from matrix A by adding to the elements of a row or column of A the results of multiplying the real number k times the elements of a row or column of A, then $|B| = |A|$.

This theorem is proved in much the same way as the others in this section. (See Exercises 31–32 below.)

Example 6   Let $A = \begin{bmatrix} -3 & 5 \\ 1 & 2 \end{bmatrix}$. Add to the elements of the first row the results of multiplying the corresponding elements of the second row by 3. This gives a new matrix, B:

$$B = \begin{bmatrix} -3 + 1(3) & 5 + 2(3) \\ 1 & 2 \end{bmatrix} = \begin{bmatrix} 0 & 11 \\ 1 & 2 \end{bmatrix}.$$

Check that $|A| = |B|$. ▌

Example 7   Let $A = \begin{bmatrix} -2 & 4 & 1 \\ 2 & 1 & 5 \\ 3 & 0 & 2 \end{bmatrix}$. Obtain a new matrix by adding to the third column the results of multiplying each element of the first column by 3.

$$B = \begin{bmatrix} -2 & 4 & 1 + 3(-2) \\ 2 & 1 & 5 + 3(2) \\ 3 & 0 & 2 + 3(3) \end{bmatrix} = \begin{bmatrix} -2 & 4 & -5 \\ 2 & 1 & 11 \\ 3 & 0 & 11 \end{bmatrix}.$$

Check that $|A| = 37$ and $|B| = 37$, so that $|A| = |B|$. ▌

The following examples show how the properties of determinants can be used to simplify the calculation of determinants.

Example 8   Without expanding, show that the value of the following determinant is 0.

$$\begin{vmatrix} 2 & 5 & -1 \\ 1 & -15 & 3 \\ -2 & 10 & -2 \end{vmatrix}$$

Examining the columns of the array, we note that each element in the second column is -5 times the corresponding element in the third column. Thus, if we use Theorem 9.8 and add to the elements of the second column the results of multiplying the elements of the third column by 5, we have the equivalent determinant

$$\begin{vmatrix} 2 & 0 & -1 \\ 1 & 0 & 3 \\ -2 & 0 & -2 \end{vmatrix}.$$

By Theorem 9.3, the value of this determinant is 0. ▮

Example 9   Find $|A|$ if

$$|A| = \begin{vmatrix} 4 & 2 & 1 & 0 \\ -2 & 4 & -1 & 7 \\ -5 & 2 & 3 & 1 \\ 6 & 4 & -3 & 2 \end{vmatrix}.$$

Our goal is to change the first row (we could have selected any row or column) to a row in which every element but one is 0, using Theorem 9.8. To begin, add to the elements of the first column the results of multiplying the elements of the second column by -2.

$$\begin{vmatrix} 0 & 2 & 1 & 0 \\ -10 & 4 & -1 & 7 \\ -9 & 2 & 3 & 1 \\ -2 & 4 & -3 & 2 \end{vmatrix}.$$

Then replace the second column by the results we get when we add to the second column the results of multiplying the elements of column 3 by -2.

$$\begin{vmatrix} 0 & 0 & 1 & 0 \\ -10 & 6 & -1 & 7 \\ -9 & -4 & 3 & 1 \\ -2 & 10 & -3 & 2 \end{vmatrix}.$$

The first row has only one nonzero number, and so we expand about the first row.

$$|A| = +1 \begin{vmatrix} -10 & 6 & 7 \\ -9 & -4 & 1 \\ -2 & 10 & 2 \end{vmatrix}$$

Now let us try to change the third column to a column with two zeros.

Add to the elements of row 1 the results of multiplying row 2 by -7.
$$\begin{vmatrix} 53 & 34 & 0 \\ -9 & -4 & 1 \\ -2 & 10 & 2 \end{vmatrix}$$

Add to row 3 the results of multiplying row 2 by -2.
$$\begin{vmatrix} 53 & 34 & 0 \\ -9 & -4 & 1 \\ 16 & 18 & 0 \end{vmatrix}$$

Now expand about the third column to find the value of $|A|$.

$$|A| = -1 \begin{vmatrix} 53 & 34 \\ 16 & 18 \end{vmatrix} = -1(954 - 544) = -410 \quad ▮$$

Note that in applying Theorem 9.8 we worked with rows to get a column with only one nonzero number and with columns to get a row with one nonzero number.

9.8 Exercises *Tell why each of the following determinants has a value of 0. All variables represent real numbers.*

1. $\begin{vmatrix} 2 & 3 \\ 2 & 3 \end{vmatrix}$

2. $\begin{vmatrix} -5 & -5 \\ 6 & 6 \end{vmatrix}$

3. $\begin{vmatrix} 2 & 0 \\ 3 & 0 \end{vmatrix}$

4. $\begin{vmatrix} -8 & 0 \\ -6 & 0 \end{vmatrix}$

5. $\begin{vmatrix} -1 & 2 & 4 \\ 4 & -8 & -16 \\ 3 & 0 & 5 \end{vmatrix}$

6. $\begin{vmatrix} 1 & 0 & 0 \\ 1 & 0 & 1 \\ 3 & 0 & 0 \end{vmatrix}$

7. $\begin{vmatrix} m & 2 & 2m \\ 3n & 1 & 6n \\ 5p & 6 & 10p \end{vmatrix}$

8. $\begin{vmatrix} 7z & 8x & 2y \\ z & x & y \\ 7z & 7x & 7y \end{vmatrix}$

Use the appropriate theorems from this section to tell why each of the following is true. Do not evaluate the determinants. All variables represent real numbers.

9. $\begin{vmatrix} 2 & 1 & 6 \\ 3 & 0 & 2 \\ 4 & 1 & 8 \end{vmatrix} = \begin{vmatrix} 2 & 3 & 4 \\ 1 & 0 & 1 \\ 6 & 2 & 8 \end{vmatrix}$

10. $\begin{vmatrix} 4 & -2 \\ 3 & 8 \end{vmatrix} = \begin{vmatrix} 4 & 3 \\ -2 & 8 \end{vmatrix}$

11. $\begin{vmatrix} 2 & 6 \\ 3 & 5 \end{vmatrix} = - \begin{vmatrix} 3 & 5 \\ 2 & 6 \end{vmatrix}$

12. $\begin{vmatrix} -1 & 8 & 9 \\ 0 & 2 & 1 \\ 3 & 2 & 0 \end{vmatrix} = - \begin{vmatrix} 8 & -1 & 9 \\ 2 & 0 & 1 \\ 2 & 3 & 0 \end{vmatrix}$

13. $3 \begin{vmatrix} 6 & 0 & 2 \\ 4 & 1 & 3 \\ 2 & 8 & 6 \end{vmatrix} = \begin{vmatrix} 6 & 0 & 2 \\ 4 & 3 & 3 \\ 2 & 24 & 6 \end{vmatrix}$

14. $-\dfrac{1}{2} \begin{vmatrix} 5 & -8 & 2 \\ 3 & -6 & 9 \\ 2 & 4 & 4 \end{vmatrix} = \begin{vmatrix} 5 & 4 & 2 \\ 3 & 3 & 9 \\ 2 & -2 & 4 \end{vmatrix}$

15. $\begin{vmatrix} 3 & -4 \\ 2 & 5 \end{vmatrix} = \begin{vmatrix} 3 & -4 \\ 5 & 1 \end{vmatrix}$

16. $\begin{vmatrix} -1 & 6 \\ 3 & -5 \end{vmatrix} = \begin{vmatrix} -1 & 6 \\ 2 & 1 \end{vmatrix}$

17. $2 \begin{vmatrix} 4 & 2 & -1 \\ m & 2n & 3p \\ 5 & 1 & 0 \end{vmatrix} = \begin{vmatrix} 4 & 2 & -1 \\ 2m & 4n & 6p \\ 5 & 1 & 0 \end{vmatrix}$

18. $\begin{vmatrix} -4 & 2 & 1 \\ 3 & 0 & 5 \\ -1 & 4 & -2 \end{vmatrix} = \begin{vmatrix} -4 & 2 & 1 + (-4)k \\ 3 & 0 & 5 + 3k \\ -1 & 4 & -2 + (-1)k \end{vmatrix}$

Use Theorem 9.8 to find the value of each of the following determinants.

19. $\begin{vmatrix} 2 & 4 \\ 3 & 6 \end{vmatrix}$

20. $\begin{vmatrix} -5 & 10 \\ 6 & -12 \end{vmatrix}$

21. $\begin{vmatrix} 4 & 8 & 0 \\ -1 & -2 & 1 \\ 2 & 4 & 3 \end{vmatrix}$

22. $\begin{vmatrix} 6 & 8 & -12 \\ -1 & 0 & 2 \\ 4 & 0 & -8 \end{vmatrix}$

23. $\begin{vmatrix} 3 & 1 & 2 \\ 2 & 0 & 1 \\ 1 & 0 & -2 \end{vmatrix}$

24. $\begin{vmatrix} -2 & 2 & 3 \\ 0 & 2 & 1 \\ -1 & 4 & 0 \end{vmatrix}$

25. $\begin{vmatrix} -4 & 2 & 3 \\ 2 & 0 & 1 \\ 0 & 4 & 2 \end{vmatrix}$

26. $\begin{vmatrix} 6 & 3 & 2 \\ 1 & 0 & 2 \\ -1 & 4 & 1 \end{vmatrix}$

27. $\begin{vmatrix} 1 & 0 & 2 & 2 \\ 2 & 4 & 1 & -1 \\ 1 & -3 & 1 & 0 \\ 1 & 1 & 0 & 1 \end{vmatrix}$

28. $\begin{vmatrix} 2 & -1 & 1 & 0 \\ 1 & 1 & 0 & 1 \\ 0 & -1 & 1 & 1 \\ 1 & 2 & 1 & 2 \end{vmatrix}$

Let $A = \begin{bmatrix} a_{11} & a_{12} & a_{13} \\ a_{21} & a_{22} & a_{23} \\ a_{31} & a_{32} & a_{33} \end{bmatrix}$.

29. Obtain matrix B by exchanging columns 1 and 3 of matrix A. Show that $|A| = -|B|$.

30. Obtain matrix B by multiplying each element of row 3 of A by the real number k. Show that $|B| = k \cdot |A|$.

31. Obtain matrix B by adding to column 1 of matrix A the result of multiplying each element of column 2 of A by the real number k. Show that $|A| = |B|$.

32. Obtain matrix B by adding to row 1 of matrix A the result of multiplying each element of row 3 of A by the real number k. Show that $|A| = |B|$.

33. Let A and B be any 2×2 matrices. Show that $|AB| = |A| \cdot |B|$, where $|AB|$ is the determinant of matrix AB.

34. Let A be an $n \times n$ matrix. Suppose matrix B is found by multiplying every element of A by the real number k. Express $|B|$ in terms of $|A|$.

35. Show that

$$\begin{vmatrix} a_{11} & 0 & 0 & 0 \\ 0 & a_{22} & 0 & 0 \\ 0 & 0 & a_{33} & 0 \\ 0 & 0 & 0 & a_{44} \end{vmatrix} = a_{11}a_{22}a_{33}a_{44}.$$

36. Show that

$$\begin{vmatrix} a_{11} & a_{12} & a_{13} & a_{14} \\ a_{21} & a_{22} & a_{23} & a_{24} \\ 0 & 0 & a_{33} & a_{34} \\ 0 & 0 & a_{43} & a_{44} \end{vmatrix} = \begin{vmatrix} a_{11} & a_{12} \\ a_{21} & a_{22} \end{vmatrix} \cdot \begin{vmatrix} a_{33} & a_{34} \\ a_{43} & a_{44} \end{vmatrix}.$$

9.9 Cramer's Rule

We have now seen how to solve a system of n linear equations with n variables using the following methods: elimination, substitution, row transformations of matrices, and matrix inverses. These systems can also be solved with determinants, as we shall see in this section. The derivation of this method is a little messy, but the actual method itself is not too complicated to state. So bear with us through the following symbolism.

To see how determinants arise in solving a system, write the linear system

$$a_{11}x + a_{12}y = b_1$$
$$a_{21}x + a_{22}y = b_2,$$

where each equation has at least one nonzero coefficient. We shall solve this system using matrix methods, just as we did in Section 9.5. Begin by writing the augmented matrix

$$\left[\begin{array}{cc|c} a_{11} & a_{12} & b_1 \\ a_{21} & a_{22} & b_2 \end{array}\right].$$

Multiply each element of row 1 by $1/a_{11}$. (Here we assume $a_{11} \neq 0$—see Exercise 42 below.) This gives the matrix of an equivalent system:

$$\left[\begin{array}{cc|c} 1 & \dfrac{a_{12}}{a_{11}} & \dfrac{b_1}{a_{11}} \\ a_{21} & a_{22} & b_2 \end{array}\right]$$

Multiply each element of row 1 by $-a_{21}$, and add the result to the corresponding element of row 2.

$$\left[\begin{array}{cc|c} 1 & \dfrac{a_{12}}{a_{11}} & \dfrac{b_1}{a_{11}} \\ 0 & a_{22} - \dfrac{a_{21}a_{12}}{a_{11}} & b_2 - \dfrac{a_{21}b_1}{a_{11}} \end{array}\right]$$

Multiply each element of row 2 by a_{11}.

$$\begin{bmatrix} 1 & \dfrac{a_{12}}{a_{11}} & \bigg| & \dfrac{b_1}{a_{11}} \\ 0 & a_{11}\,a_{22} - a_{21}\,a_{12} & \bigg| & a_{11}\,b_2 - a_{21}\,b_1 \end{bmatrix}$$

This matrix leads to the system of equations

$$x + \frac{a_{12}}{a_{11}}\,y = \frac{b_1}{a_{11}}$$

$$(a_{11}\,a_{22} - a_{21}\,a_{12})y = a_{11}\,b_2 - a_{21}\,b_1.$$

From the second equation of this system,

$$y = \frac{a_{11}\,b_2 - a_{21}\,b_1}{a_{11}\,a_{22} - a_{21}\,a_{12}}.$$

Both the numerator and denominator here may be written as determinants.

$$y = \frac{\begin{vmatrix} a_{11} & b_1 \\ a_{21} & b_2 \end{vmatrix}}{\begin{vmatrix} a_{11} & a_{12} \\ a_{21} & a_{22} \end{vmatrix}} \tag{1}$$

By inserting this value of y into one of the original equations, we find that x can also be written with determinants.

$$x = \frac{\begin{vmatrix} b_1 & a_{12} \\ b_2 & a_{22} \end{vmatrix}}{\begin{vmatrix} a_{11} & a_{12} \\ a_{21} & a_{22} \end{vmatrix}} \tag{2}$$

The denominator of both x and y is just the determinant of the matrix of coefficients of the original system. This matrix is often denoted D, so that

$$D = \begin{bmatrix} a_{11} & a_{12} \\ a_{21} & a_{22} \end{bmatrix}.$$

In equation (1), the numerator is the determinant of a matrix obtained by replacing the coefficients of y in D with the respective constants: define D_y as

$$D_y = \begin{bmatrix} a_{11} & b_1 \\ a_{21} & b_2 \end{bmatrix}.$$

In the same way, from equation (2), define D_x as

$$D_x = \begin{bmatrix} b_1 & a_{12} \\ b_2 & a_{22} \end{bmatrix}.$$

With these new matrices, the solution of our given system is

$$x = \frac{|D_x|}{|D|} \quad \text{and} \quad y = \frac{|D_y|}{|D|}$$

The system has a single solution as long as $|D| \neq 0$. We have now proved much of the next theorem, called **Cramer's Rule.**

Theorem 9.9   Let $\begin{aligned} a_{11}x + a_{12}y &= b_1 \\ a_{21}x + a_{22}y &= b_2 \end{aligned}$

be a system of equations, where each equation has at least one nonzero coefficient. The system has a unique solution if $|D| \neq 0$; this solution is

$$x = \frac{|D_x|}{|D|} \quad \text{and} \quad y = \frac{|D_y|}{|D|}.$$

If $|D| = 0$, the system is dependent if $|D_x| = 0$ and $|D_y| = 0$; otherwise it is inconsistent.

(For proof of this last statement, see Exercises 41–42 below.)

Example 1   Use Cramer's Rule to solve the system

$$5x + 7y = -1$$
$$6x + 8y = 1.$$

To use Cramer's Rule, we need to evaluate $|D|$, $|D_x|$, and $|D_y|$.

$$|D| = \begin{vmatrix} 5 & 7 \\ 6 & 8 \end{vmatrix} = 5(8) - 6(7) = -2,$$

$$|D_x| = \begin{vmatrix} -1 & 7 \\ 1 & 8 \end{vmatrix} = (-1)(8) - (1)(7) = -15.$$

$$|D_y| = \begin{vmatrix} 5 & -1 \\ 6 & 1 \end{vmatrix} = 5(1) - (6)(-1) = 11.$$

By Cramer's Rule, $x = -15/-2$ and $y = 11/-2$. The solution is $(15/2, -11/2)$, as can be verified by substituting within the given system.   ▌

By much the same method we used above, Cramer's Rule can be generalized to systems of n linear equations with n variables. Assume these larger systems have equations written in the form

$$a_{11} x_1 + a_{12} x_2 + a_{13} x_3 + \cdots + a_{1n} x_n = b_1.$$

Define D as the $n \times n$ matrix of all coefficients. Define D_{x_1} as the matrix obtained from D by replacing the entries in column 1 of D with the constants of the system. Define D_{x_i} as the matrix obtained from D by replacing the entries in column i with the constants of the system. If $|D| \neq 0$, the unique solution of the system is given by

$$x_1 = \frac{|D_{x_1}|}{|D|}, \ x_2 = \frac{|D_{x_2}|}{|D|}, \ x_3 = \frac{|D_{x_3}|}{|D|}, \cdots, \ x_n = \frac{|D_{x_n}|}{|D|}.$$

Example 2   Use Cramer's Rule to solve the system

$$x + y - z + 2 = 0$$
$$2x - y + z + 5 = 0$$
$$x - 2y + 3z - 4 = 0.$$

To use Cramer's Rule, the system must be rewritten in the form

$$x + y - z = -2$$
$$2x - y + z = -5$$
$$x - 2y + 3z = 4.$$

The matrix of coefficients, D, is

$$D = \begin{bmatrix} 1 & 1 & -1 \\ 2 & -1 & 1 \\ 1 & -2 & 3 \end{bmatrix}.$$

To find D_x, replace the elements of the first column of D with the constants of the system. Find D_y and D_z in a similar way.

$$D_x = \begin{bmatrix} -2 & 1 & -1 \\ -5 & -1 & 1 \\ 4 & -2 & 3 \end{bmatrix}, \quad D_y = \begin{bmatrix} 1 & -2 & -1 \\ 2 & -5 & 1 \\ 1 & 4 & 3 \end{bmatrix}, \quad D_z = \begin{bmatrix} 1 & 1 & -2 \\ 2 & -1 & -5 \\ 1 & -2 & 4 \end{bmatrix}.$$

Now find the determinants of each of these matrices. Verify that

$$|D| = -3, |D_x| = 7, |D_y| = -22, \quad \text{and} \quad |D_z| = -21.$$

By Cramer's Rule,

$$x = \frac{|D_x|}{|D|} = \frac{7}{-3} = \frac{-7}{3}, y = \frac{|D_y|}{|D|} = \frac{-22}{-3} = \frac{22}{3}, \quad \text{and} \quad z = \frac{|D_z|}{|D|} = \frac{-21}{-3} = 7.$$

The solution of the system is $(-7/3, 22/3, 7)$. ▮

Example 3   Use Cramer's Rule to solve the system

$$2x - 3y + 4z = 10$$
$$6x - 9y + 12z = 24$$
$$x + 2y - 3z = 5.$$

Here $|D| = 0$. Also, $|D_x| = 6$. Since $|D| = 0$ and at least one of the other determinants is not zero, the system is inconsistent. (Had all the determinants been 0, the system would have been dependent.) ▮

We have now seen several different methods for solving systems of equations. In general, if a small system of linear equations must be solved by pencil and paper, substitution is the best method if the various equations can easily be solved in terms of each other. This happens rarely. The next choice, perhaps the best choice of all, is the elimination method. Some people like the Gaussian method, which is really just a systematic way of doing the elimination method. The Gaussian method is probably superior where four or more equations are involved. Cramer's Rule is seldom the method of choice simply because it involves more calculations than any other method.

9.9 Exercises   *Use Cramer's Rule to solve each of the following systems of linear equations.*

1. $x + y = 4$
$2x - y = 2$

2. $3x + 2y = -4$
$2x - y = -5$

3. $4x + 3y = -7$
$2x + 3y = -11$

4. $3x + 2y = -4$
$5x - y = 2$

5. $2x - 3y = -5$
$x + 5y = 17$

6. $x + 9y = -15$
$3x + 2y = 5$

7. $5x + 2y = 7$
$6x + y = 8$

8. $7x + 3y = 5$
$2x + 4y = 3$

9. $10x - 8y = 1$
$-15x + 12y = 4$

10. $8x - 6y = 10$
$20x - 15y = 6$

11. $4x - y + 3z = -3$
$3x + y + z = 0$
$2x - y + 4z = 0$

12. $5x + 2y + z = 15$
$2x - y + z = 9$
$4x + 3y + 2z = 13$

13. $2x - y + 4z = -2$
$3x + 2y - z = -3$
$x + 4y + 2z = 17$

14. $x + y + z = 4$
$2x - y + 3z = 4$
$4x + 2y - z = -15$

15. $4x - 3y + z = -1$
$5x + 7y + 2z = -2$
$3x - 5y - z = 1$

16. $2x - 3y + z = 8$
$-x - 5y + z = -4$
$3x - 5y + 2z = 12$

17. $x + 2y + 3z = 4$
$4x + 3y + 2z = 1$
$-x - 2y - 3z = 0$

18. $2x - y + 3z = 1$
$-2x + y - 3z = 2$
$5x - y + z = 2$

19. $x - 2y + 3z = 4$
$5x + 7y - z = 2$
$2x + 2y - 5z = 3$

20. $-3x - 2y - z = 4$
$4x + y + z = 5$
$3x - 2y + 2z = 1$

21. $2x + 3y = 13$
$2y - z = 5$
$x + 2z = 4$

22. $3x - z = -10$
$y + 4z = 8$
$x + 2z = -1$

23. $5x - y = -4$
$3x + 2z = 4$
$4y + 3z = 22$

24. $3x + 5y = -7$
$2x + 7z = 2$
$4y + 3z = -8$

25. $x + 2y = 10$
$3x + 4z = 7$
$-y - z = 1$

26. $5x - 2y = 3$
$4y + z = 8$
$x + 2z = 4$

27. $x + z = 0$
$y + 2z + w = 0$
$2x - w = 0$
$x + 2y + 3z = -2$

28. $x - y + z + w = 6$
$2y - w = -7$
$x - z = -1$
$y + w = 1$

⊙ **29.** $.4x - .6y = .4$
$.3x + .2y = -.22$

30. $-.5x + .4y = .43$
$.1x + .2y = .11$

31. $.4x - .2y + .3z = -.08$
$-.5x + .3y - .7z = .19$
$.8x - .7y + .1z = -.21$

32. $-.6x + .2y - .5z = -.16$
$.8x - .3y - .2z = -.48$
$.4x + .6y - .8z = -.8$

Use Cramer's Rule to solve each of the following.

33. The population of a town is 46,000; it is decreasing at the rate of 2500 per year. The population of a second town is 28,800; it is increasing at the rate of 1800 per year. In how many years will the towns have the same population?

34. One company offers a job with a starting salary of $14,300 and annual increases of $1200. A second company offers a starting salary of $11,300 and annual increases of $1500. After how many years will the salaries be the same?

35. A gold merchant has some 12-carat gold (12/24 pure gold), and some 22-carat gold (22/24 pure). How many grams of each should be mixed to get 25 grams of 15-carat gold?

36. A chemist has some 40% acid solution and some 60% solution. How many liters of each should be used to get 40 liters of a 45% solution?

37. How many pounds of tea worth $4.60 a pound should be mixed with 8 pounds of tea worth $6.50 a pound to get a mixture worth $5.20 a pound?

38. A solution of a drug with a strength of 5% is to be mixed with 15 milliliters of a 15% solution to get an 8% solution. How many milliliters of the 5% solution should be used?

39. The cashier at an amusement park has a total of $2480, made up of fives, tens, and twenties. The total number of bills is 290, and the value of the tens is $60 more than the value of the twenties. How many of each type of bill does the cashier have?

40. Ms. Levy invests $50,000 three ways—at 8%, $8\frac{1}{2}$%, and 11%. In total, she receives $4436.25 per year in interest. The interest from the 11% investment is $80 more than the interest on the 8% investment. Find the amount she has invested at each rate.

For the following two exercises, use the system of equations

$$a_1x + b_1y = c_1$$
$$a_2x + b_2y = c_2.$$

41. Assume $|D_x| = 0$ and $|D_y| = 0$. Show that if $c_1c_2 \neq 0$, then $|D| \neq 0$, and the equations are consistent.

42. Assume $|D| = 0, |D_x| = 0$, and $a_1a_2 \neq 0$. Show that $|D_y| = 0$.

9.10 Systems of Inequalities

We have seen that the solution of an inequality in two variables is usually an infinite set whose graph is one or more regions of the coordinate plane. The solution set of a system of inequalities, such as

$$x > 6 - 2y$$
$$x^2 < 2y$$

is the intersection of the solutions of its members. This intersection is found by graphing both inequalities on the same coordinate axes and identifying, by shading, the region common to both graphs.

Example 1 Graph the solution of the above system.

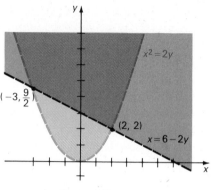

Figure 9.8

Figure 9.8 shows the graphs of both $x > 6 - 2y$ and $x^2 < 2y$. The methods of this chapter can be used to show that the graphs cross at $(2, 2)$ and $(-3, 9/2)$. The solution of the system is in the heavily shaded area. The points on the boundaries of $x > 6 - 2y$ and $x^2 < 2y$ do not belong to the graph of the solution. For this reason, the boundaries are dashed lines. ▮

Example 2 Graph the solution of the system

$$x^2 + y^2 \leq 9$$
$$\frac{x^2}{16} + \frac{y^2}{4} \geq 1.$$

The graph is found by graphing both inequalities on the same axes and shading the common region as shown in Figure 9.9. The graphs meet in four points, $(2\sqrt{15}/3, \ \sqrt{21}/3)$, $(2\sqrt{15}/3, \ -\sqrt{21}/3)$, $(-2\sqrt{15}/3, \ \sqrt{21}/3)$, and $(-2\sqrt{15}/3, -\sqrt{21}/3)$. ▮

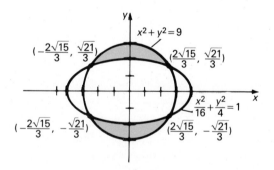

Figure 9.9

Example 3 Graph the solution of the system

$$|x| \leq 3$$
$$y \leq 0$$
$$y \geq |x| + 1.$$

The graph is shown in Figure 9.10. From the graph, we see that the solutions of $y \leq 0$ and $y \geq |x| + 1$ have no point in common, so that there is no solution for the system. ▌

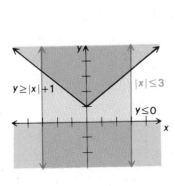

Figure 9.10

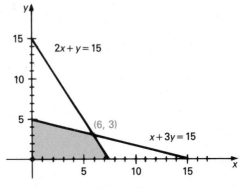

Figure 9.11

Example 4   Midtown Manufacturing Company makes plastic plates and cups, both of which require time on two machines. Plates require one hour on machine A and two hours on machine B. Cups require three hours on machine A and one hour on machine B. Suppose that the two machines, A and B, are operated for at most 15 hours per day. How many plates and cups can be made under those conditions?

Let x represent the number of plates, and y the number of cups produced in one day. Each plate requires one hour on machine A, while each cup requires three hours on this same machine. The total number of hours required on machine A is thus $x + 3y$. Since this machine operates for at most 15 hours per day,

$$x + 3y \leq 15.$$

In the same way, the total number of hours per day required on machine B is $2x + y$. It, too, operates at most 15 hours per day, so that

$$2x + y \leq 15.$$

Both x and y must be nonnegative integers (why?) so that

$$x \geq 0 \quad \text{and} \quad y \geq 0.$$

These four inequalities form the system

$$x + 3y \leq 15$$
$$2x + \ y \leq 15$$
$$x \geq 0$$
$$y \geq 0.$$

A graph of the solution of this system is shown in Figure 9.11. Any point in the shaded region satisfies all the conditions of the original problem. ▌

9.10 Exercises   *Graph the solution of each of the following systems of inequalities.*

1. $x + y \leq 4$
   $x - 2y \geq 6$

2. $2x + y > 2$
   $x - 3y < 6$

3. $4x + 3y < 12$
   $y + 4x > -4$

4. $3x + 5y \leq 15$
   $x - 3y \geq 9$

5. $x + 2y \leq 4$
   $y \geq x^2 - 1$

6. $4x - 3y \leq 12$
   $y \leq x^2$

7. $y \leq -x^2$
   $y \geq x^2 - 6$

8. $x^2 + y^2 \leq 9$
   $x \leq -y^2$

9. $x^2 - y^2 < 1$
   $-1 < y < 1$

10. $x^2 + y^2 \leq 36$
    $-4 \leq x \leq 4$

11. $2x^2 - y^2 > 4$
    $2y^2 - x^2 > 4$

12. $y \geq x^2 + 4x + 4$
    $y < -x^2$

13. $\dfrac{x^2}{16} + \dfrac{y^2}{9} \leq 1$

    $\dfrac{x^2}{4} - \dfrac{y^2}{16} \geq 1$

14. $y \geq (x-2)^2 + 3$
    $16x^2 + y^2 \leq 16$

15. $x + y \leq 4$
    $x - y \leq 5$
    $4x + y \leq -4$

16. $3x - 2y \geq 6$
    $x + y \leq -5$
    $y \leq 4$

17. $-2 < x < 3$
    $-1 \leq y \leq 5$
    $2x + y < 6$

18. $-2 < x < 2$
    $y > 1$
    $x - y > 0$

19. $2y + x \geq -5$
    $y \leq 3 + x$
    $x \leq 0$
    $y \leq 0$

20. $2x + 3y \leq 12$
    $2x + 3y > -6$
    $3x + y < 4$
    $x \geq 0$
    $y \geq 0$

21. $x^2/4 + y^2/9 > 1$
    $x^2 - y^2 \geq 1$
    $-4 \leq x \leq 4$

22. $2x - 3y < 6$
    $4x^2 + 9y^2 < 36$
    $x \geq -1$

23. $y \geq 3^x$
    $y \geq 2$

24. $y \leq (1/2)^x$
    $y \geq 4$

25. $|x| \geq 2$
    $|y| \geq 4$
    $y < x^2$

26. $|x| + 2 \geq 4$
    $|y| \leq 1$

    $\dfrac{x^2}{9} + \dfrac{y^2}{16} \leq 1$

27. $y \leq |x + 2|$

    $\dfrac{x^2}{16} - \dfrac{y^2}{9} \leq 1$

28. $y \leq \log x$
    $y \geq |x - 2|$

29. $y \geq |4 - x|$
    $y \geq |x|$

30. $|x + 2| < y$
    $|x| \leq 3$

Write a system of inequalities for each of the following and then graph the solution of the system.

31. A pizza company makes two kinds of pizza, basic and plain. Basic contains cheese and beef, while plain contains onions and beef. The company sells at least three units a day of basic, and at least two units of plain. The beef costs $5 per unit for basic, and $4 per unit for plain. They can spend no more than $50 per day on beef. Dough for basic is $2 per unit, while dough for plain is $1 per unit. The company can spend no more than $16 per day on dough.

32. A farmer raises only pigs and geese. She wants to raise no more than 16 animals, including no more than 12 geese. She spends $5 to raise a pig and $2 to raise a goose. She has available $50 for this purpose.

33. George takes vitamin pills. Each day he must have at least 16 units of vitamin A, 5 units of vitamin B_1, and 20 units of vitamin C. He can choose between red pills which contain 8 units of A, 1 of B_1, and 2 of C, and green pills which contain 2 units of A, 1 of B_1 and 7 of C.

34. Sue is on a diet and wishes to restrict herself to no more than 1600 calories per day. Her diet consists of foods chosen from three food groups: I, meats and dairy products; II, fruits and vegetables; III, breads and other starches. These three groups contain calories per serving as shown below.

Group	I	II	III
Calories	170	50	140

Sue wishes to include four servings daily from group I and more servings from group II than from the other groups combined.

35. A manufacturer of refrigerators must ship at least 100 refrigerators to its two West Coast warehouses. Each warehouse holds a maximum of 100 refrigerators. Warehouse A holds 25 refrigerators already, while warehouse B has 20 on hand. It costs $12 to ship a refrigerator to warehouse A and $10 to ship one to warehouse B. The total shipping cost is budgeted at a maximum of $1200.

36. The California Almond Growers have 2400 boxes of almonds to be shipped from their plant in Sacramento to Des Moines and San Antonio. The Des Moines market needs at least 1000 boxes, while the San Antonio market must have at least 800 boxes.

Chapter 9 Review Exercises

Use the elimination or substitution method to solve each of the following linear systems. Identify any dependent or inconsistent systems.

1. $3x - 5y = -18$
$2x + 7y = 19$

2. $6x + 5y = 53$
$4x - 3y = 29$

3. $\dfrac{2}{3}x - \dfrac{3}{4}y = 13$

$\dfrac{1}{2}x + \dfrac{2}{3}y = -5$

4. $3x + 7y = 10$
$18x + 42y = 50$

5. $\dfrac{1}{x} + \dfrac{1}{y} = \dfrac{7}{10}$

$\dfrac{3}{x} - \dfrac{5}{y} = \dfrac{1}{2}$

6. $.9x - .2y = .8$
$.3x + .7y = 4.1$

7. $2x - 3y + z = -5$
$x + 4y + 2z = 13$
$5x + 5y + 3z = 14$

8. $x - 3y = 12$
$2y + 5z = 1$
$4x + z = 25$

9. A student bought some candy bars, paying 25¢ each for some and 50¢ for others. The student bought a total of 22 bars, paying a total of $8.50. How many of each kind of bar did he buy?

10. Ink worth $25 a bottle is to be mixed with ink worth $18 per bottle to get 12 bottles of ink worth $20 each. How much of each type of ink should be used?

11. Donna Sharp wins $50,000 in a lottery. She invests part of the money at 6%, twice as much at 7%, with $10,000 more than the amount invested at 6% invested at 9%. Total annual interest is $3800. How much is invested at each rate?

12. The sum of three numbers is 23. The second number is 3 more than the first. The sum of the first and twice the third is 4. Find the three numbers.

Find solutions for the following systems in terms of an arbitrary variable.

13. $3x - 4y + z = 2$
$2x + y - 4z = 1$

14. $ax + by + cz = 5$
$dx + y = 1$

Solve each of the following systems.

15. $x^2 - 4y^2 = 19$
$x^2 + y^2 = 35$

16. $xy = 4$
$x - 6y = 2$

17. $x^2 + 2xy + y^2 = 4$
$x = 3y - 2$

18. $y = 5^{x+5}$
$y = 25^{3x}$

19. Do the circle $x^2 + y^2 = 144$ and the line $x + 2y = 8$ have any points in common? If so, what are they?

20. Find a value of b so that the straight line $3x - y = b$ touches the circle $x^2 + y^2 = 25$ in only one point.

Find the values of all variables in the following.

21. $\begin{bmatrix} 5 & x+2 \\ -6y & z \end{bmatrix} = \begin{bmatrix} a & 3x-1 \\ 5y & 9 \end{bmatrix}$

22. $\begin{bmatrix} 6+k & 2 & a+3 \\ -2+m & 3p & 2r \end{bmatrix} + \begin{bmatrix} 3-2k & 5 & 7 \\ 5 & 8p & 5r \end{bmatrix} = \begin{bmatrix} 5 & y & 6a \\ 2m & 11 & -35 \end{bmatrix}$

Perform each of the following operations whenever possible.

23. $\begin{bmatrix} 3 & -4 & 2 \\ 5 & -1 & 6 \end{bmatrix} + \begin{bmatrix} -3 & 2 & 5 \\ 1 & 0 & 4 \end{bmatrix}$

24. $\begin{bmatrix} 3 \\ 2 \\ 5 \end{bmatrix} - \begin{bmatrix} 8 \\ -4 \\ 6 \end{bmatrix} + \begin{bmatrix} 1 \\ 0 \\ 2 \end{bmatrix}$

25. $\begin{bmatrix} 2 & 5 & 8 \\ 1 & 9 & 2 \end{bmatrix} - \begin{bmatrix} 3 & 4 \\ 7 & 1 \end{bmatrix}$

26. $\begin{bmatrix} -3 & 4 \\ 2 & 8 \end{bmatrix}\begin{bmatrix} -1 & 0 \\ 2 & 5 \end{bmatrix}$

27. $\begin{bmatrix} 3 & 2 & -1 \\ 4 & 0 & 6 \end{bmatrix}\begin{bmatrix} -2 & 0 \\ 0 & 2 \\ 3 & 1 \end{bmatrix}$

28. $\begin{bmatrix} 1 & -2 & 4 & 2 \\ 0 & 1 & -1 & 8 \end{bmatrix}\begin{bmatrix} -1 \\ 2 \\ 0 \\ 1 \end{bmatrix}$

Use row operations to solve each of the following.

29. $2x + 3y = 10$
$-3x + y = 18$

30. $5x + 2y = -10$
$3x - 5y = -6$

31. $2x - y + 4z = -1$
$-3x + 5y - z = 5$
$2x + 3y + 2z = 3$

32. $5x - 8y + z = 1$
$3x - 2y + 4z = 3$
$10x - 16y + 2z = 3$

Find the inverse of each of the following matrices that have inverses.

33. $\begin{bmatrix} 2 & 1 \\ 5 & 3 \end{bmatrix}$

34. $\begin{bmatrix} -4 & 2 \\ 0 & 3 \end{bmatrix}$

35. $\begin{bmatrix} 2 & -1 & 0 \\ 1 & 0 & 1 \\ 1 & -2 & 0 \end{bmatrix}$

36. $\begin{bmatrix} 2 & 3 & 5 \\ -2 & -3 & -5 \\ 1 & 4 & 2 \end{bmatrix}$

Use the method of matrix inverses to solve each of the following.

37. $2x + y = 5$
$3x - 2y = 4$

38. $x + y + z = 1$
$2x - y = -2$
$3y + z = 2$

39. $x = -3$
$y + z = 6$
$2x - 3z = -9$

40. $3x - 2y + 4z = 1$
$4x + y - 5z = 2$
$-6x + 4y - 8z = -2$

Find each of the following determinants.

41. $\begin{vmatrix} -1 & 8 \\ 2 & 9 \end{vmatrix}$

42. $\begin{vmatrix} -2 & 4 \\ 0 & 3 \end{vmatrix}$

43. $\begin{vmatrix} -2 & 4 & 1 \\ 3 & 0 & 2 \\ -1 & 0 & 3 \end{vmatrix}$

44. $\begin{vmatrix} -1 & 2 & 3 \\ 4 & 0 & 3 \\ 5 & -1 & 2 \end{vmatrix}$

45. $\begin{vmatrix} -1 & 0 & 2 & -3 \\ 0 & 4 & 4 & -1 \\ -6 & 0 & 3 & -5 \\ 0 & -2 & 1 & 0 \end{vmatrix}$

Explain why each of the following statements is true.

46. $\begin{vmatrix} 8 & 9 & 2 \\ 0 & 0 & 0 \\ 3 & 1 & 4 \end{vmatrix} = 0$

47. $\begin{vmatrix} 4 & 6 \\ 3 & 5 \end{vmatrix} = \begin{vmatrix} 4 & 3 \\ 6 & 5 \end{vmatrix}$

48. $\begin{vmatrix} 8 & 2 \\ 4 & 3 \end{vmatrix} = 2 \begin{vmatrix} 4 & 1 \\ 4 & 3 \end{vmatrix}$

49. $\begin{vmatrix} 4 & 6 & 2 \\ -3 & 8 & -5 \\ 4 & 6 & 2 \end{vmatrix} = 0$

50. $\begin{vmatrix} 5 & -1 & 2 \\ 3 & -2 & 0 \\ -4 & 1 & 2 \end{vmatrix} = \begin{vmatrix} 5 & -1 & 2 \\ 8 & -3 & 2 \\ -4 & 1 & 2 \end{vmatrix}$

51. $\begin{vmatrix} 8 & 2 & -5 \\ -3 & 1 & 4 \\ 2 & 0 & 5 \end{vmatrix} = - \begin{vmatrix} 8 & -5 & 2 \\ -3 & 4 & 1 \\ 2 & 5 & 0 \end{vmatrix}$

Solve each of the following systems by Cramer's Rule. Identify any dependent or inconsistent systems.

52. $3x + y = -1$
$5x + 4y = 10$

53. $3x + 7y = 2$
$5x - y = -22$

54. $3x + 2y + z = 2$
$4x - y + 3z = -16$
$x + 3y - z = 12$

55. $5x - 2y - z = 8$
$-5x + 2y + z = -8$
$x - 4y - 2z = 0$

Graph the solution of each of the following systems of inequalities.

56. $x + y \le 6$
$2x - y \ge 3$

57. $x - 3y \ge 6$
$y^2 \le 16 - x^2$

58. $9x^2 + 16y^2 \ge 144$
$x^2 - y^2 \le 16$

59. A bakery makes both cakes and cookies. Each batch of cakes requires two hours in the oven and three hours in the decorating room. Each batch of cookies needs one and a half hours in the oven and two thirds of an hour in the decorating room. The oven is available no more than 16 hours a day, while the decorating room can be used no more than 12 hours per day. Set up a system of inequalities expressing this information, and then graph the system.

60. A candy company has 100 kilograms of chocolate-covered nuts and 125 kilograms of chocolate-covered raisins to be sold as two different mixtures. One mix will contain 1/2 nuts and 1/2 raisins, while the other mix will contain 1/3 nuts and 2/3 raisins. Set up a system of inequalities expressing this information, and then graph the system.

Chapter 10

Complex Numbers

10.1 The Complex Number System

So far in this book we have dealt only with real numbers. However, the set of real numbers is not large enough to include all the numbers that we need in algebra. For example, using real numbers alone, we cannot solve the equation $x^2 + 1 = 0$. (Try it.) Thus, we need a larger set of numbers. The basic element of this larger set of numbers is the number i, defined by

$$i = \sqrt{-1}.$$

We have defined i as the square root of -1, so that

$$i^2 = -1.$$

The square roots of other negative numbers can be found by the following definition. If $a > 0$, so that $-a$ is negative, then

$$\sqrt{-a} = i\sqrt{a}.$$

Example 1   (a) $\sqrt{-16} = i\sqrt{16}$

$$= 4i$$

(b) $\sqrt{-70} = i\sqrt{70}$ ▌

Products or quotients with square roots of negative numbers may be simplified using the fact that $\sqrt{-a} = i\sqrt{a}$, for positive numbers a. The next example shows how to do this.

Example 2   (a) $\sqrt{-7} \cdot \sqrt{-7} = i\sqrt{7} \cdot i\sqrt{7}$

$$= i^2 \cdot (\sqrt{7})^2$$

$$= (-1) \cdot (7)$$

$$= -7$$

(b) $\sqrt{-6} \cdot \sqrt{-10} = i\sqrt{6} \cdot i\sqrt{10}$

$$= i^2\sqrt{60}$$

$$= -1 \cdot 2\sqrt{15}$$

$$= -2\sqrt{15}$$

(c) $\dfrac{\sqrt{-20}}{\sqrt{-2}} = \dfrac{i\sqrt{20}}{i\sqrt{2}} = \sqrt{10}$

(d) $\dfrac{\sqrt{-48}}{\sqrt{24}} = \dfrac{i\sqrt{48}}{\sqrt{24}} = i\sqrt{2}$ ▌

When working with negative numbers under a radical sign, it is very important to use the definition $\sqrt{-a} = i\sqrt{a}$ before using any of the other rules for radicals. In particular, the rule $\sqrt{c} \cdot \sqrt{d} = \sqrt{cd}$ is valid only when c and d are *not* both negative.

The number $a + bi$ where a and b are real numbers is called a **complex number.** A nonzero real-number multiple of i, such as $8i$ or $-7i$, is called an **imaginary number.** If $b = 0$, the complex number $a + bi$ is of the form $a + 0i$, or just a, which is a real number. Therefore, both the real numbers and the imaginary numbers are subsets of the set of complex numbers. (See Figure 10.1.) A complex number written in the form $a + bi$ or $a + ib$ is in **standard form.** (The form $a + ib$ is used to simplify certain symbols, such as $i\sqrt{5}$, since $\sqrt{5}i$ is too easy to confuse with $\sqrt{5i}$.)

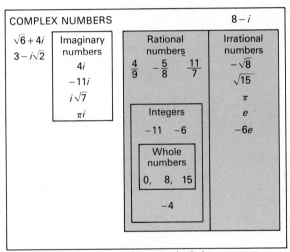

Real numbers are shaded.

Figure 10.1

Example 3 (a) $6 + 2i$ is a complex number but not an imaginary number or real number.
(b) $-\sqrt{2}$ is a complex number and a real number but not an imaginary number.
(c) $-5i$ is a complex number and an imaginary number but not a real number.   ▌

Example 4 The list below shows several numbers, along with the standard form of the number.

Number	Standard form
$6i$	$0 + 6i$
-9	$-9 + 0i$
0	$0 + 0i$
$9 - i$	$9 - i$

▌

Equality for complex numbers is defined as follows for real numbers a, b, c, and d,

$$a + bi = c + di \quad \text{if and only if} \quad a = c \text{ and } b = d.$$

The number a is called the **real part** of the complex number $a + bi$, while b (and *not bi*) is the **imaginary part**. The definition of equality for complex numbers can be rephrased by saying that two complex numbers are *equal* if and only if their real parts and imaginary parts are both equal.

Example 5 Solve $2 + mi = k + 3i$ for real numbers m and k.

By the definition of equality, $2 + mi = k + 3i$ if and only if $2 = k$ and $m = 3$. ▌

The **sum** of two complex numbers $a + bi$ and $c + di$ is defined as

$$(a + bi) + (c + di) = (a + c) + (b + d)i.$$

Example 6 (a) $(3 - 4i) + (-2 + 6i) = [3 + (-2)] + [-4 + 6]i$
$$= 1 + 2i$$
(b) $(-9 + 7i) + (3 - 15i) = -6 - 8i$ ▌

Since $(a + bi) + (0 + 0i) = a + bi$ for all complex numbers $a + bi$, the number $0 + 0i$ is called the **additive identity** for complex numbers. The sum of $a + bi$ and $-a - bi$ is $0 + 0i$, so that the number $-a - bi$ is called the **negative** or **additive inverse** of $a + bi$.

Using this definition of additive inverse, **subtraction** of the complex numbers $a + bi$ and $c + di$ is defined as follows:

$$(a + bi) - (c + di) = (a + bi) + (-c - di)$$

$$(a + bi) - (c + di) = (a - c) + (b - d)i.$$

Example 7 Subtract as indicated.

(a) $(-4 + 3i) - (6 - 7i) = (-4 + 3i) + (-6 + 7i)$
$$= -10 + 10i$$
(b) $(12 - 5i) - (8 - 3i) = 4 - 2i$ ▌

The **product** of two complex numbers $a + bi$ and $c + di$ is defined as

$$(a + bi)(c + di) = (ac - bd) + (ad + bc)i.$$

Because of the way we have defined addition and multiplication of complex numbers, the complex numbers satisfy the properties given in Chapter 1 for real numbers. Some of these properties are proved in this section and the next, and others are proved in the exercises.

The product of two complex numbers can be found without using the definition by using $i^2 = -1$ and multiplying as follows.

$$(a + bi)(c + di) = ac + adi + bic + bidi$$
$$= ac + adi + bci + bdi^2$$
$$= ac + (ad + bc)i + bd(-1)$$
$$(a + bi)(c + di) = (ac - bd) + (ad + bc)i$$

Example 8   Find each of the following products.

(a) $(2 - 3i)(3 + 4i) = 2(3) - 3i(3) + 2(4i) - 3i(4i)$

$$= 6 - 9i + 8i - 12i^2$$

$$= 6 - i - 12(-1)$$

$(2 - 3i)(3 + 4i) = 18 - i$

(b) $(5 - 4i)(7 - 2i) = 5(7) - 4i(7) + 5(-2i) - 4i(-2i)$

$$= 35 - 28i - 10i + 8i^2$$

$$= 35 - 38i + 8(-1)$$

$(5 - 4i)(7 - 2i) = 27 - 38i$

(c) i^{15}

We know that $i^2 = -1$. Therefore, $i^3 = i^2 \cdot i^1 = (-1) \cdot i = -i$. Furthermore, $i^4 = i^3 \cdot i = -i \cdot i = -i^2 = -(-1) = 1$. By writing i^{15} as a product involving a power of i^4, we can quickly simplify it. By properties of exponents.

$$i^{15} = i^{12} \cdot i^3 = (i^4)^3 \cdot i^3 = (1)^3(-i) = -i. \quad \blacksquare$$

Using methods similar to those of part (c) of this last example, we can construct a table of **powers of i:**

$i^1 = i$	$i^5 = i$	$i^9 = i$
$i^2 = -1$	$i^6 = -1$	$i^{10} = -1$
$i^3 = -i$	$i^7 = -i$	$i^{11} = -i$
$i^4 = 1$	$i^8 = 1$	$i^{12} = 1,$

and so on.
Since

$$(a + bi)(1 + 0i) = a \cdot 1 + a \cdot 0i + bi \cdot 1 + bi \cdot 0i$$

$$= a + bi,$$

$1 + 0i$ is called the **multiplicative identity** for complex numbers.

In the next section, we will discuss the multiplicative inverse of the complex number $a + bi$.

10.1 Exercises   *Add or subtract as indicated.*

1. $(3 + 2i) + (4 - 3i)$

2. $(4 - i) + (2 + 5i)$

3. $(6 - 4i) - (3 + 2i)$

4. $(5 - 2i) - (5 + 3i)$

5. $(2 - 5i) - (3 + 4i) - (-2 + i)$

6. $(-4 - i) - (2 + 3i) + (-4 + 5i)$

7. $-i - 2 - (3 - 4i) - (5 - 2i)$

8. $3 - (4 - i) - 4i + (-2 + 5i)$

Multiply as indicated.

9. $(2 + i)(3 - 2i)$

10. $(-2 + 3i)(4 - 2i)$

11. $(5 + 2i)(5 - 3i)$

12. $(-8 + i)(4 - 2i)$

13. $(-3 + 2i)^2$

14. $(2 + i)^2$

15. $(3 + i)(-3 - i)$

16. $(-5 - i)(5 + i)$

17. $(2 + 3i)(2 - 3i)$

18. $(6 - 4i)(6 + 4i)$

19. $(2 - 5i)(2 + 5i)$

20. $(-3 + i)(-3 - i)$

21. $(\sqrt{6} + i)(\sqrt{6} - i)$ **24.** $i(2 + 7i)(2 - 7i)$ **27.** $(4 + i)^4$

22. $(\sqrt{2} - 4i)(\sqrt{2} - 4i)$ **25.** $(3 + 5i)^3$ **28.** $(1 - i)^4$

23. $i(3 - 4i)(3 + 4i)$ **26.** $(2 - 3i)^3$

Simplify each of the following.

29. $\sqrt{-9}$ **35.** $\sqrt{-5} \cdot \sqrt{-5}$ **40.** $\dfrac{\sqrt{-190}}{\sqrt{-19}}$

30. $\sqrt{-25}$ **36.** $\sqrt{-20} \cdot \sqrt{-20}$

31. $-\sqrt{-400}$ **37.** $\sqrt{-8} \cdot \sqrt{-2}$ **41.** $\dfrac{\sqrt{-6} \cdot \sqrt{-2}}{\sqrt{3}}$

32. $-\sqrt{-225}$ **38.** $\sqrt{-27} \cdot \sqrt{-3}$

33. $\sqrt{-7}$ **39.** $\dfrac{\sqrt{-40}}{\sqrt{-10}}$ **42.** $\dfrac{\sqrt{-12} \cdot \sqrt{-6}}{\sqrt{8}}$

34. $\sqrt{-21}$

Find each of the following powers of i.

43. i^5 **46.** i^9 **49.** i^{20} **52.** i^{57}

44. i^6 **47.** i^{11} **50.** i^{25} **53.** $1/i^9$

45. i^8 **48.** i^{12} **51.** i^{43} **54.** $1/i^{12}$

Use the definition of equality for complex numbers to solve the following equations for real numbers a and b.

55. $a + bi = 23 + 5i$ **59.** $a + 3i = 5 + 3bi + 2a$

56. $a + bi = -2 + 4i$ **60.** $4a - 2bi + 7 = 3i + 3a + 5$

57. $a + bi = 18 - 3i$ **61.** $i(2b + 6) - 3 = 4(bi + a)$

58. $2 + bi = a - 4i$ **62.** $3i + 2(a - 1) = 4 + 2i(b + 3)$

Prove that the complex numbers $z_1 = a + bi$, $z_2 = c + di$, and $z_3 = e + fi$ satisfy each of the following properties.

63. commutative property for addition: $z_1 + z_2 = z_2 + z_1$

64. commutative property for multiplication: $z_1 z_2 = z_2 z_1$

65. associative property for addition: $(z_1 + z_2) + z_3 = z_1 + (z_2 + z_3)$

66. associative property for multiplication: $(z_1 z_2) z_3 = z_1 (z_2 z_3)$

67. distributive property: $z_1 (z_2 + z_3) = z_1 z_2 + z_1 z_3$

68. closure property of addition: $z_1 + z_2$ is a complex number

69. closure property of multiplication: $z_1 z_2$ is a complex number

Let $f(z) = 8z - z^2$. Find each of the following.

70. $f(2 + i)$ **71.** $f(4 - 3i)$ **72.** $f(-6i)$

Find all complex numbers $a + bi$ such that the square $(a + bi)^2$ is

73. real

74. imaginary

75. Show that $\dfrac{\sqrt{2}}{2} + \dfrac{\sqrt{2}}{2}i$ is a square root of i.

76. Show that $\dfrac{\sqrt{3}}{2} - \dfrac{1}{2}i$ is a cube root of i.

10.2   Division and Graphing of Complex Numbers

To find the multiplicative inverse of $a + bi$, when $a \neq 0$ or $b \neq 0$, we start with $1/(a + bi)$. We want $1/(a + bi)$ to be written in standard form for complex numbers. Since

$$(a + bi)(a - bi) = a^2 + b^2,$$

multiply numerator and denominator of $1/(a + bi)$ by $a - bi$ to get:

$$\frac{1}{a + bi} \cdot \frac{a - bi}{a - bi} = \frac{1(a - bi)}{(a + bi)(a - bi)}$$

$$= \frac{a - bi}{a^2 - b^2 i^2}$$

$$= \frac{a - bi}{a^2 + b^2}$$

$$\frac{1}{a + bi} = \frac{a}{a^2 + b^2} - \frac{b}{a^2 + b^2}i.$$

Thus, the **multiplicative inverse** of $a + bi$, in standard form, is

$$\frac{a}{a^2 + b^2} - \frac{b}{a^2 + b^2}i.$$

The number **$a - bi$** is called the **conjugate** of $a + bi$.

Example 1   Find the multiplicative inverse of $2 - 3i$.

We could use the formula given above to find this inverse. However, this formula is hard to remember, so it is best to go back to the basics and multiply numerator and denominator of $1/(2 - 3i)$ by the conjugate of $2 - 3i$, or $2 + 3i$:

$$\frac{1}{2 - 3i} = \frac{1 \cdot (2 + 3i)}{(2 - 3i)(2 + 3i)}$$

$$= \frac{2 + 3i}{4 - 6i + 6i - 9i^2}$$

$$= \frac{2 + 3i}{4 - 9(-1)}$$

$$= \frac{2 + 3i}{13}$$

$$\frac{1}{2 - 3i} = \frac{2}{13} + \frac{3}{13}i$$

To check that this is correct, multiply $2 - 3i$ by its inverse to see that the product is 1. ▌

The conjugate of the divisor is used to find the **quotient** of two complex numbers, as shown in the next example.

Example 2 (a) $\dfrac{3 + 2i}{5 - i} = \dfrac{(3 + 2i)(5 + i)}{(5 - i)(5 + i)}$ Multiply by the conjugate of $5 - i$.

$$= \frac{15 + 3i + 10i + 2i^2}{25 - i^2}$$

$$= \frac{13 + 13i}{26}$$

$$= \frac{1}{2} + \frac{1}{2}i$$

To check this answer, show that

$$(5 - i)\left(\frac{1}{2} + \frac{1}{2}i\right) = 3 + 2i.$$

(b) $\dfrac{3}{i} = \dfrac{3(-i)}{i(-i)}$ ($-i$ is the conjugate of i)

$$= \frac{-3i}{-i^2}$$

$$= \frac{-3i}{1} \qquad (-i^2 = -(-1) = 1)$$

$$= -3i \qquad (0 - 3i \text{ in standard form}) \quad \blacksquare$$

We can prove several useful properties of conjugates of complex numbers. In working with complex numbers and their conjugates, we let $z = a + bi$, and $\bar{z} = a - bi$, the conjugate of z. For example if $z = 5 + 3i$, then $\bar{z} = 5 - 3i$.

Theorem 10.1   For any complex numbers c and d,

(a) $c \cdot \bar{c}$ is a real number.   (d) $\overline{c + d} = \bar{c} + \bar{d}$.

(b) $c + \bar{c}$ is a real number.   (e) $\overline{cd} = \bar{c} \cdot \bar{d}$.

(c) If c is a real number, then $\bar{c} = c$.   (f) $\overline{c^n} = (\bar{c})^n$ for every positive integer n.

Properties (d) and (e) can be extended to more than two complex numbers. We have already seen that (a) is true, since if $c = a + bi$,

$$(a + bi)(a - bi) = a^2 + b^2.$$

Example 3   Prove part (d) of Theorem 10.1.

To show that (d) is true, let $c = a + bi$ and $d = m + ni$. Then $c + d = (a + m) + (b + n)i$. By definition,

$$\bar{c} = a - bi$$
$$\bar{d} = m - ni$$
$$\overline{c + d} = (a + m) - (b + n)i.$$

Then we have, $(a - bi) + (m - ni) = (a + m) - (b + n)i,$

or $\qquad \bar{c} \quad + \quad \bar{d} \quad = \overline{c + d}. \quad \blacksquare$

The proofs of the remaining properties are left for the exercises.

We cannot graph a complex number, such as $2 - 3i$, on the Cartesian coordinate system we have used up to now. To graph a complex number, we must modify this coordinate system. One way is to let the horizontal axis represent the **real axis** and the vertical axis represent the **imaginary axis**. Then complex numbers can be graphed as shown by the examples in Figure 10.2. This coordinate system is called the **complex plane**.

Each complex number graphed in this way determines a unique directed line segment, the segment from the origin to the point representing the complex number. Recall from Chapter 8 that such directed line segments (like **OP** of Figure 10.2) are called vectors.

We know that the sum of the two complex numbers $4 + i$ and $1 + 3i$ is $5 + 4i$. Graphically, the sum of two complex numbers is represented by the vector which is the resultant of the vectors corresponding to the two numbers. An example of this is shown in Figure 10.3.

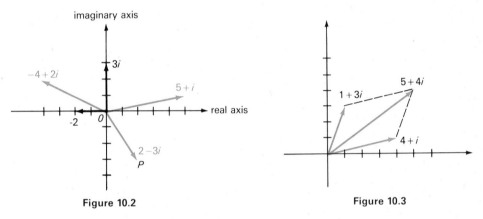

Figure 10.2   Figure 10.3

Example 4 Find the resultant of $6 - 2i$ and $-4 - 3i$. Graph both complex numbers and their resultant.

The resultant is found by adding the two numbers.

$$(6 - 2i) + (-4 - 3i) = 2 - 5i$$

The graphs are shown in Figure 10.4.

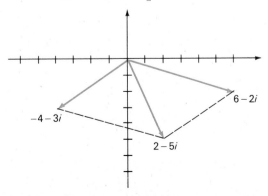

Figure 10.4

Figure 10.5 shows the graph of the complex number $3 - 4i$. The length of the vector associated with $3 - 4i$ is found (by the Pythagorean theorem) to be

$$\sqrt{3^2 + 4^2} = \sqrt{25} = 5.$$

This number is called the absolute value or length or modulus of $3 - 4i$. In general, the **absolute value** or **length** or **modulus** of the complex number $a + bi$, written $|a + bi|$, is $\sqrt{a^2 + b^2}$.

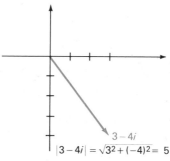

$|3 - 4i| = \sqrt{3^2 + (-4)^2} = 5$

Figure 10.5

Example 5 (a) $|-5 + 6i| = \sqrt{(-5)^2 + 6^2} = \sqrt{61}$.

(b) $|-2i| = \sqrt{0^2 + (-2)^2} = 2$

(c) $|25| = \sqrt{25^2 + 0^2} = 25$ ▮

When we graph a complex number such as $2 - 3i$, we associate the number $2 - 3i$ with a point on a plane. We can also think of this point as the point with co-ordinates $(2, -3)$. Thus, we sometimes represent complex numbers as ordered pairs of real numbers.

Example 6 Write the following complex numbers as ordered pairs.

(a) $-2 - 5i$ can be written as $(-2, -5)$

(b) $3i$ can be written as $(0, 3)$

(c) -12 can be written as $(-12, 0)$ ▮

We know that the real numbers correspond to the points on a line, which allows us to order the real numbers according to their relative positions on the line. Because the complex numbers correspond to points on a plane, there is no way to order them.

10.2 Exercises *Find the multiplicative inverse of each of the following.*

1. i

2. $2i$

3. $-4i$

4. $-3i/2$

5. $1 + i$

6. $3 - 4i$

7. $5 - 12i$

8. $-2 + 5i$

Divide as indicated.

9. $\dfrac{1+i}{1-i}$ **11.** $\dfrac{4-3i}{4+3i}$ **13.** $\dfrac{4+i}{6+2i}$ **15.** $\dfrac{5-2i}{6-i}$

10. $\dfrac{2-i}{2+i}$ **12.** $\dfrac{5+6i}{5-6i}$ **14.** $\dfrac{3-2i}{5+3i}$ **16.** $\dfrac{3-4i}{2-5i}$

Perform the indicated operations and write your answers in standard form.

17. $\dfrac{2+i}{3-i} \cdot \dfrac{5+2i}{1+i}$ **21.** $\dfrac{5-i}{3+i} + \dfrac{2+7i}{3+i}$ **24.** $\dfrac{4-i}{3+4i} - \dfrac{3+2i}{3-4i}$

18. $\dfrac{1-i}{2+i} \cdot \dfrac{4+3i}{1+i}$ **22.** $\dfrac{4-3i}{2+5i} + \dfrac{8-i}{2+5i}$ **25.** $\dfrac{6+3i}{1-i} - \dfrac{2-i}{4+i}$

19. $\dfrac{6+2i}{5-i} \cdot \dfrac{1-3i}{2+6i}$ **23.** $\dfrac{6+2i}{1+3i} + \dfrac{2-i}{1-3i}$ **26.** $\dfrac{2-3i}{2+i} + \dfrac{6+i}{3+5i}$

20. $\dfrac{5-3i}{1+2i} \cdot \dfrac{2-4i}{1+i}$

Find each of the following.

27. $|2-5i|$ **29.** $|8-4i|$ **31.** $|-4i|$ **33.** $|23|$

28. $|7+3i|$ **30.** $|-2-i|$ **32.** $|6i|$ **34.** $|-5|$

Graph the following complex numbers.

35. $-2+3i$ **37.** $2-2\sqrt{3}i$ **39.** $-4i$ **41.** -8

36. $-4+5i$ **38.** $4\sqrt{2}+4\sqrt{2}i$ **40.** $3i$ **42.** 2

Find the resultant of each of the following pairs of complex numbers.

43. $2-3i,\ -1+4i$ **46.** $8-5i,\ -6+3i$ **49.** $7+6i,\ 3i$

44. $-4-5i,\ 2+i$ **47.** $2+6i,\ -2i$ **50.** $-5-8i,\ -1$

45. $-5+6i,\ 3-4i$ **48.** $4-2i,\ 5$

Prove the following properties for any complex numbers c and d.

51. $c + \bar{c}$ is a real number.

52. If c is a real number, then $\bar{c} = c$.

53. $\overline{cd} = \bar{c} \cdot \bar{d}$

54. $\overline{c^n} = (\bar{c})^n$ for every positive integer n

55. $|cd| = |c| \cdot |d|$

56. $\dfrac{|c|}{|d|} = \left|\dfrac{c}{d}\right|$

57. $|c| = \sqrt{c \cdot \bar{c}}$

58. $|c| = 0$ if and only if $c = 0$

Find and graph all complex numbers c satisfying the following conditions.

59. $|c| = 1$

60. $|c| > 1$

61. The real part of c is 1.

62. The imaginary part of c is 1.

63. The real and imaginary parts of c are equal.

64. The real part of c equals c itself.

10.3 Complex Solutions of Equations

In Section 10.1, we mentioned that the complex numbers satisfy many of the properties of real numbers. Therefore, we can extend many theorems about real numbers to complex numbers. In particular, the Quadratic Formula holds for complex numbers. We now permit coefficients of the quadratic equation $ax^2 + bx + c = 0$ to be complex numbers and not just real numbers.

Theorem 10.2 (*Quadratic Formula*)   The solutions of the quadratic equation $ax^2 + bx + c = 0$, for complex numbers a, b, and c, are

$$x = \frac{-b \pm \sqrt{b^2 - 4ac}}{2a}.$$

Example 1 Solve $2x^2 = x - 4$.

To find the values of a, b, and c, first rewrite the equation as $2x^2 - x + 4 = 0$. Then $a = 2$, $b = -1$, and $c = 4$. By the Quadratic Formula,

$$x = \frac{1 \pm \sqrt{1 - 32}}{4}$$

$$x = \frac{1 \pm \sqrt{-31}}{4}$$

$$x = \frac{1 \pm i\sqrt{31}}{4}.$$

The two solutions are complex conjugates of each other. █

Example 2 Solve $2ix^2 - x + 3i = 0$.

Here $a = 2i$, $b = -1$, and $c = 3i$. Use the Quadratic Formula.

$$x = \frac{-(-1) \pm \sqrt{(-1)^2 - 4(2i)(3i)}}{2(2i)}$$

$$= \frac{1 \pm \sqrt{1 + 24}}{4i}$$

$$x = \frac{1 \pm 5}{4i}$$

One solution is $\dfrac{1 + 5}{4i} = \dfrac{6}{4i} = \dfrac{3}{2i} = \dfrac{3 \cdot i}{(2i)i} = -\dfrac{3i}{2}.$

The second solution is $\dfrac{1 - 5}{4i} = \dfrac{-4}{4i} = -\dfrac{1}{i} = -\dfrac{1 \cdot i}{i \cdot i} = i.$ █

The following property from Chapter 2 also holds for complex numbers.

Theorem 10.3 (*Zero-Factor Property*)   The product of two complex numbers a and b is zero if and only if $a = 0$ or $b = 0$.

One use of the Zero-Factor Property is to write an equation given the solutions. For example, to find an equation which has the complex numbers c and d as solutions, work as follows.

$$x = c \qquad \text{or} \qquad x = d$$
$$x - c = 0 \qquad\qquad x - d = 0$$
$$(x - c)(x - d) = 0$$
$$x^2 - (c + d)x + cd = 0$$

If $d = \bar{c}$, the conjugate of c, then $c + d$ and cd are real numbers and the equation has real coefficients.

Example 3   Write an equation which has solutions $2 + 3i$ and $2 - 3i$.
The equation can be written as the product

$$[x - (2 + 3i)][x - (2 - 3i)] = 0.$$

From the work shown above,

$$x^2 - (2 + 3i + 2 - 3i)x + (2 + 3i)(2 - 3i) = 0$$
$$x^2 - 4x + 13 = 0. \quad \blacksquare$$

Example 4   Write an equation which has solutions 1, 2, and i.
By an extension of the Zero-Factor Property,

$$x = 1 \qquad \text{or} \qquad x = 2 \qquad \text{or} \qquad x = i$$
$$x - 1 = 0 \qquad \text{or} \qquad x - 2 = 0 \qquad \text{or} \qquad x - i = 0$$
$$(x - 1)(x - 2)(x - i) = 0.$$

Multiplying the three factors together gives the equation

$$x^3 - (3 + i)x^2 + (2 + 3i)x - 2i = 0. \quad \blacksquare$$

10.3 Exercises

Use the Quadratic Formula to solve the following equations.

1. $x^2 - 6x + 25 = 0$
2. $x^2 + 2x + 5 = 0$
3. $3x^2 + 2x + 4 = 0$
4. $5x^2 + 3x + 1 = 0$
5. $p^2 - \sqrt{2}p + 1 = 0$
6. $k^2 + \sqrt{3}k + 2 = 0$

7. $\sqrt{2}p^2 - 3p + 2\sqrt{2} = 0$
8. $\sqrt{6}m^2 - 2m + \sqrt{6} = 0$
9. $x^2 + ix + 1 = 0$
10. $3m^2 - 2m + i = 0$
11. $ip^2 - 2p + i = 0$
12. $2ix^2 - 3x + 3i = 0$

13. $(1 + i)x^2 - x + (1 - i) = 0$
14. $(2 + i)r^2 - 3r + (2 - i) = 0$
15. $-iy^2 + 2y - 3i = 0$
16. $4k^2 - ik + 5 = 0$
17. $2x^2 + 3ix - 4 = 0$
18. $(1 + 2i)m^2 + 3m - (1 - 2i) = 0$

Solve each of the following equations by factoring first and then using the Quadratic Formula.

19. $x^3 - 1 = 0$
20. $x^3 + 1 = 0$

21. $x^3 + 64 = 0$
22. $x^3 - 64 = 0$

23. $x^3 + 27 = 0$
24. $x^3 - 27 = 0$

For each of the following, find an equation which has the given solutions.

25. $2 + i$, $2 - i$
26. $3 - i$, $3 + i$

27. $1 + 2i$, $1 - 2i$
28. $2 - 5i$, $2 + 5i$

29. $-1, 2, -i$
30. $-3, 1, 2i$

31. Prove that the sum of the solutions of $ax^2 + bx + c = 0$ is $-b/a$.

32. Prove that the product of the solutions of $ax^2 + bx + c = 0$ is c/a.

10.4   Trigonometric Form of Complex Numbers

Figure 10.6 shows a complex number $x + yi$ which determines a vector **OP**. Let r $(r > 0)$ represent the radius vector **OP**, and let θ be the smallest positive angle (measured in a counterclockwise direction) between the positive real axis and **OP**. Point P can be located uniquely if we know r and θ. Therefore, r and θ can be used as coordinates of P. We call (r, θ) the **polar coordinates** of point P. The following relationships between r, θ, x, and y can be verified from Figure 10.6.

$$x = r \cos \theta \qquad r = \sqrt{x^2 + y^2}$$

$$y = r \sin \theta \qquad \theta = \tan^{-1} \frac{y}{x}$$

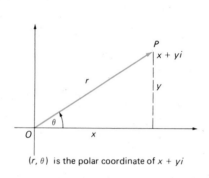

(r, θ) is the polar coordinate of $x + yi$

Figure 10.6

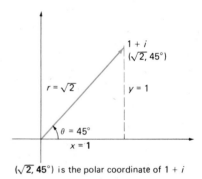

$(\sqrt{2}, 45°)$ is the polar coordinate of $1 + i$

Figure 10.7

Example 1   Find the polar coordinates of the complex number $1 + i$.
      Here $x = 1$ and $y = 1$. Thus, $r = \sqrt{1^2 + 1^2} = \sqrt{2}$, and $\theta = \tan^{-1} 1/1 = \tan^{-1} 1$ $= 45°$. (Angle θ is not 225° because the complex number lies in quadrant I.) Hence the polar coordinates of $1 + i$ are $(\sqrt{2}, 45°)$, as shown in Figure 10.7. ▌

    We know $x = r \cos \theta$ and $y = r \sin \theta$. These facts can be used to rewrite $x + yi$.

$$x + yi = r \cos \theta + (r \sin \theta)i$$

or $\qquad\qquad\qquad x + yi = r(\cos \theta + i \sin \theta)$

The expression $r(\cos \theta + i \sin \theta)$ is called the **trigonometric form** of the complex number $x + yi$. The radius vector r, which is the absolute value of $x + yi$, is also called the **modulus** of $x + yi$. Angle θ is called the **argument** of $x + yi$.
    Using the work from Example 1 above, we can express $1 + i$ in trigonometric form as

$$1 + i = \sqrt{2}(\cos 45° + i \sin 45°).$$

Example 2   Express $2(\cos 300° + i \sin 300°)$ as a complex number in standard form.
    We know $\cos 300° = 1/2$, while $\sin 300° = -\sqrt{3}/2$. Hence

$$2(\cos 300° + i \sin 300°) = 2\left(\frac{1}{2} - \frac{\sqrt{3}}{2} i\right)$$

$$= 1 - \sqrt{3} \; i. \quad \blacksquare$$

Example 3   Express the following complex numbers in trigonometric form.

(a) $-\sqrt{3} + i$

Since $x = -\sqrt{3}$ and $y = 1$, we have

$$r = \sqrt{x^2 + y^2} = \sqrt{3 + 1} = 2,$$

$$\tan \theta = \frac{y}{x} = \frac{1}{-\sqrt{3}} = -\frac{\sqrt{3}}{3}.$$

As shown in Figure 10.8, θ is in quadrant II, so that $\theta = 150°$. In trigono-metric form,

$$x + yi = r(\cos \theta + i \sin \theta)$$

$$-\sqrt{3} + i = 2(\cos 150° + i \sin 150°).$$

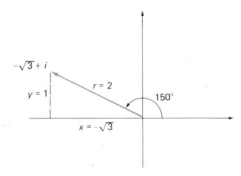

Figure 10.8

(b) $-2 - 2i$

First find r and θ.

$$r = \sqrt{x^2 + y^2} = \sqrt{4 + 4} = 2\sqrt{2}$$

$$\tan \theta = \frac{y}{x} = \frac{-2}{-2} = 1$$

Since θ is in quadrant III, $\theta = 225°$. Thus, the trigonometric form of $-2 - 2i$ is

$$2\sqrt{2}(\cos 225° + i \sin 225°). \quad \blacksquare$$

We showed how to find the product of two complex numbers in Section 10.1. For example,

$$(1 + i\sqrt{3})(-2\sqrt{3} + 2i) = -2\sqrt{3} + 2i - 2i(3) + 2i^2\sqrt{3}$$

$$= -2\sqrt{3} + 2i - 6i - 2\sqrt{3}$$

$$(1 + i\sqrt{3})(-2\sqrt{3} + 2i) = -4\sqrt{3} - 4i$$

We can obtain this same product by converting the complex numbers $1 + \sqrt{3}i$ and $-2\sqrt{3} + 2i$ to trigonometric form and then multiplying.

$$1 + \sqrt{3}i = 2(\cos 60° + i \sin 60°)$$

and

$$-2\sqrt{3} + 2i = 4(\cos 150° + i \sin 150°)$$

If we now multiply the trigonometric forms together and use the trigonometric identities for the cosine and the sine of the sum of two angles, we have

$$[2(\cos 60° + i \sin 60°)][4(\cos 150° + i \sin 150°)]$$
$$= 2 \cdot 4(\cos 60° \cdot \cos 150° + i \sin 60° \cdot \cos 150°$$
$$+ i \cos 60° \cdot \sin 150° + i^2 \sin 60° \cdot \sin 150°)$$
$$= 8[(\cos 60° \cdot \cos 150° - \sin 60° \cdot \sin 150°)$$
$$+ i(\sin 60° \cdot \cos 150° + \cos 60° \cdot \sin 150°)]$$
$$= 8[\cos(60° + 150°) + i \sin (60° + 150°)]$$
$$= 8(\cos 210° + i \sin 210°).$$

The modulus of the product, 8, is the *product* of the moduli of the factors, $2 \cdot 4$, and the argument of the product, 210°, is the *sum* of the arguments of the factors, $60° + 150°$. In general,

Theorem 10.4   If $r_1(\cos \theta_1 + i \sin \theta_1)$ and $r_2(\cos \theta_2 + i \sin \theta_2)$ are any two complex numbers written in trigonometric form, then

$$[r_1(\cos \theta_1 + i \sin \theta_1)][r_2(\cos \theta_2 + i \sin \theta_2)] = r_1 r_2[\cos (\theta_1 + \theta_2) + i \sin (\theta_1 + \theta_2)].$$

Example 4   Find the product of $3(\cos 45° + i \sin 45°)$ and $2(\cos 135° + i \sin 135°)$.
Using Theorem 10.4,

$$[3(\cos 45° + i \sin 45°)][2(\cos 135° + i \sin 135°)]$$
$$= 3 \cdot 2[\cos (45° + 135°) + i \sin (45° + 135°)]$$
$$= 6(\cos 180° + i \sin 180°),$$

which can be expressed as $6(-1 + i \cdot 0) = 6(-1) = -6$. Thus, the two complex numbers of this example are complex factors of -6.   ▮

Now let's consider the quotient of two complex numbers. The quotient of $1 + \sqrt{3}i$ and $-2\sqrt{3} + 2i$ is

$$\frac{1 + \sqrt{3}i}{-2\sqrt{3} + 2i} = \frac{(1 + \sqrt{3}i)(-2\sqrt{3} - 2i)}{(-2\sqrt{3} + 2i)(-2\sqrt{3} - 2i)} = \frac{-2\sqrt{3} - 2i - 6i - 2\sqrt{3}i^2}{12 - 4i^2}$$

$$= \frac{-8i}{16}$$

$$\frac{1 + \sqrt{3}i}{-2\sqrt{3} + 2i} = -\frac{1}{2}i.$$

If we write $1 + \sqrt{3}i, -2\sqrt{3} + 2i$, and $-\dfrac{1}{2}i$ in trigonometric form, we have

$$1 + \sqrt{3}i = 2(\cos 60° + i \sin 60°)$$
$$-2\sqrt{3} + 2i = 4(\cos 150° + i \sin 150°)$$
$$-\frac{1}{2}i = \frac{1}{2}[(\cos - 90° + i \sin - 90°)].$$

The modulus of the quotient, $1/2$, is the quotient of the two moduli, 2 and 4. The argument of the quotient, $-90°$, is the difference of the two arguments, $60° - 150° = -90°$. It is certainly easier to express the quotient of two complex numbers in trigonometric form than in standard form. Generalizing from this example leads to the following theorem.

Theorem 10.5 If $r_1(\cos \theta_1 + i \sin \theta_1)$ and $r_2(\cos \theta_2 + i \sin \theta_2)$ are complex numbers, where $r_2(\cos \theta_2 + i \sin \theta_2) \neq 0$, then

$$\frac{r_1(\cos \theta_1 + i \sin \theta_1)}{r_2(\cos \theta_2 + i \sin \theta_2)} = \frac{r_1}{r_2}[\cos (\theta_1 - \theta_2) + i \sin (\theta_1 - \theta_2)].$$

Example 5 Find the quotient of $10[\cos(-60°) + i \sin(-60°)]$ and $5(\cos 150° + i \sin 150°)$. Write the result in standard form.
    By Theorem 10.5,

$$\frac{10[\cos(-60°) + i \sin(-60°)]}{5(\cos 150° + i \sin 150°)}$$

$$= \frac{10}{5}[\cos(-60° - 150°) + i \sin(-60° - 150°)]$$

$$= \frac{10}{5}[\cos(-210°) + i \sin(-210°)].$$

Since angles of $-210°$ and $150°$ are coterminal, we may replace $-210°$ with $150°$ to get

$$\frac{10[\cos(-60°) + i \sin(-60°)]}{5(\cos 150° + i \sin 150°)} = 2(\cos 150° + i \sin 150°).$$

Because $\cos 150° = -\sqrt{3}/2$ and $\sin 150° = 1/2$,

$$2(\cos 150° + i \sin 150°) = 2\left(\frac{-\sqrt{3}}{2} + i \cdot \frac{1}{2}\right)$$

$$= -\sqrt{3} + i.$$

The quotient in standard form is $-\sqrt{3} + i$. ▌

Example 6   Note the use of polar coordinates in the following example, taken with permission from *Calculus and Analytic Geometry,* fifth edition, by George Thomas and Ross Finney (Addison-Wesley, 1979).

Karl von Frisch has advanced the following theory about how bees communicate information about newly discovered sources of food. A scout returning to the hive from a flower bed gives away samples of the food and then, if the bed is more than about a hundred yards away, performs a dance to show where the flowers are. The bee runs straight ahead for a centimeter or so, waggling from side to side, and circles back to the starting place. The bee then repeats the straight run, circling back in the opposite direction (See Figure 10.9.) The dance continues this way in regular alternation. Exceptionally excited bees have been observed to dance for more than three and a half hours.

If the dance is performed inside, it is performed on the vertical wall of a honeycomb, with gravity substituting for the sun's position. A vertical straight run means that the food is in the direction of the sun. A run 30° to the right of vertical means that the food is 30° to the right of the sun, and so on. Distance (more accurately, the amount of energy required to reach the food) is communicated by the duration of the straight-run portions of the dance. Straight runs lasting three seconds each are typical for distances of about a half-mile from the hive. Straight runs that last five seconds each mean about two miles.

The waggle dance of a scout bee.

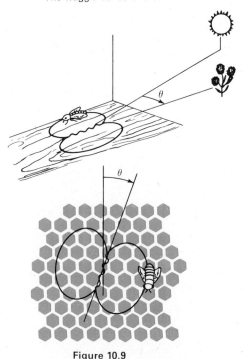

Figure 10.9

George B. Thomas, Jr./Ross L. Finney, *Calculus and Analytic Geometry,* 5/E, © 1979, Addison-Wesley, Reading, Massachusetts. (Pp. 462, 463.) Reprinted with permission.

10.4 Exercises   *Find the polar coordinates of the following complex numbers.*

1. $2 - 2i$ **4.** -2 **7.** $1 + i\sqrt{3}$

2. $-1 - i$ **5.** $\sqrt{3} + i$ **8.** $-2 + 2i\sqrt{3}$

3. $3i$ **6.** $-\sqrt{2} - i\sqrt{2}$

Express in standard form the complex numbers whose polar coordinates are given below.

9. $(2, 45°)$ **11.** $(1, 135°)$ **13.** $(3, 90°)$ **15.** $(1, -30°)$

10. $(3, 60°)$ **12.** $(2, 300°)$ **14.** $(2, 180°)$ **16.** $(4, -60°)$

Express the following as complex numbers in standard form.

17. $2(\cos 45° + i \sin 45°)$ **21.** $4(\cos 240° + i \sin 240°)$

18. $4(\cos 60° + i \sin 60°)$ **22.** $2(\cos 330° + i \sin 330°)$

19. $10(\cos 90° + i \sin 90°)$ **23.** $(\cos 30° + i \sin 30°)$

20. $8(\cos 270° + i \sin 270°)$ **24.** $3(\cos 150° + i \sin 150°)$

Express the following complex numbers in trigonometric form.

25. $3 - 3i$ **29.** $-5 - 5i$

26. $1 + i\sqrt{3}$ **30.** $-\sqrt{2} + i\sqrt{2}$

27. $\sqrt{3} - i$ **31.** $-5i$

28. $4\sqrt{3} + 4i$ **32.** -4

Find each of the following products. Write the result in standard form.

33. $[2(\cos 30° + i \sin 30°)][3(\cos 60° + i \sin 60°)]$

34. $[3(\cos 60° + i \sin 60°)][4(\cos 150° + i \sin 150°)]$

35. $[2(\cos 135° + i \sin 135°)][2(\cos 225° + i \sin 225°)]$

36. $[6(\cos 240° + i \sin 240°)][8(\cos 300° + i \sin 300°)]$

37. $[4(\cos 60° + i \sin 60°)][6(\cos 330° + i \sin 330°)]$

38. $[8(\cos 210° + i \sin 210°)][2(\cos 330° + i \sin 330°)]$

39. $[5(\cos 90° + i \sin 90°)][3(\cos 45° + i \sin 45°)]$

40. $[6(\cos 120° + i \sin 120°)][5(\cos -30° + i \sin -30°)]$

Find the following quotients. Write the results in standard form.

41. $\dfrac{3(\cos 60° + i \sin 60°)}{(\cos 30° + i \sin 30°)}$ **45.** $\dfrac{8}{\sqrt{3} + i}$

42. $\dfrac{9(\cos 135° + i \sin 135°)}{3(\cos 45° + i \sin 45°)}$ **46.** $\dfrac{2i}{-1 - i\sqrt{3}}$

43. $\dfrac{16(\cos 300° + i \sin 300°)}{8(\cos 60° + i \sin 60°)}$ **47.** $\dfrac{-i}{1 + i}$

44. $\dfrac{24(\cos 150° + i \sin 150°)}{2(\cos 30° + i \sin 30°)}$ **48.** $\dfrac{1}{2 - 2i}$

49. Prove Theorem 10.4.

50. Prove Theorem 10.5.

10.5   De Moivre's Theorem and nth Roots

We can use the results of Theorem 10.4 to find the square of a complex number. For example, the square of $r(\cos \theta + i \sin \theta)$ is found by multiplying the number by itself.

$$[r(\cos \theta + i \sin \theta)]^2 = [r(\cos \theta + i \sin \theta)][r(\cos \theta + i \sin \theta)]$$
$$= r \cdot r[\cos (\theta + \theta) + i \sin (\theta + \theta)]$$
$$[r(\cos \theta + i \sin \theta)]^2 = r^2(\cos 2\theta + i \sin 2\theta).$$

In the same way, we can show

$$[r(\cos \theta + i \sin \theta)]^3 = r^3(\cos 3\theta + i \sin 3\theta).$$

These results suggest the plausibility of the following theorem.

Theorem 10.6   (*De Moivre's Theorem*)   If $r(\cos \theta + i \sin \theta)$ is a complex number expressed in trigonometric form and if n is any positive integer, then

$$[r(\cos \theta + i \sin \theta)]^n = r^n(\cos n\theta + i \sin n\theta).$$

De Moivre's Theorem can be proved by the method of mathematical induction, which is discussed in Chapter 12.

Example 1   Find $(1 + i\sqrt{3})^8$.

We can use De Moivre's theorem if we first convert $1 + i\sqrt{3}$ into trigonometric form.

$$1 + i\sqrt{3} = 2(\cos 60° + i \sin 60°)$$

Now we can apply De Moivre's theorem.

$$(1 + i\sqrt{3})^8 = [2(\cos 60° + i \sin 60°)]^8$$
$$= 2^8[\cos (8 \cdot 60°) + i \sin (8 \cdot 60°)]$$
$$= 256(\cos 480° + i \sin 480°)$$
$$= 256(\cos 120° + i \sin 120°)$$
$$= 256\left(-\frac{1}{2} + i \frac{\sqrt{3}}{2}\right)$$
$$(1 + i\sqrt{3})^8 = -128 + 128\sqrt{3}i \quad \blacksquare$$

The complex number $a + bi$ is an **nth root** of the complex number $x + yi$ if

$$(a + bi)^n = x + yi.$$

We can use De Moivre's theorem to find nth roots of complex numbers. For example, to find the cube roots of the complex number $8(\cos 135° + i \sin 135°)$, we look for a complex number, say $r(\cos \alpha + i \sin \alpha)$, that will satisfy

$$[r(\cos \alpha + i \sin \alpha)]^3 = 8(\cos 135° + i \sin 135°).$$

By De Moivre's theorem, this equation becomes

$$r^3(\cos 3\alpha + i \sin 3\alpha) = 8(\cos 135° + i \sin 135°).$$

One way to satisfy this equation is to set $r^3 = 8$ and

$$\cos 3\alpha + i \sin 3\alpha = \cos 135° + i \sin 135°.$$

The first condition implies that $r = 2$, and the second implies

$$\cos 3\alpha = \cos 135° \quad \text{and} \quad \sin 3\alpha = \sin 135°$$

or $$\cos 3\alpha = \frac{-\sqrt{2}}{2} \quad \text{and} \quad \sin 3\alpha = \frac{\sqrt{2}}{2}.$$

This last pair of equations can be satisfied if and only if

$$3\alpha = 135° + 360° \cdot k, \qquad k \text{ any integer,}$$

or $$\alpha = \frac{135° + 360° \cdot k}{3}, \qquad k \text{ any integer.}$$

If $k = 0$, $$\alpha = \frac{135° + 0}{3} = 45°.$$

For $k = 1$, $$\alpha = \frac{135° + 360°}{3} = \frac{495°}{3} = 165°.$$

When $k = 2$, $$\alpha = \frac{135° + 720°}{3} = \frac{855°}{3} = 285°.$$

In the same way, we get $\alpha = 405°$ when $k = 3$. But $\sin 405° = \sin 45°$ and $\cos 405° = \cos 45°$. Hence, we get all of the cube roots (3 of them) by letting $k = 0, 1,$ and 2. When $k = 0$ we get the root

$$2(\cos 45° + i \sin 45°).$$

When $k = 1$ we have $2(\cos 165° + i \sin 165°)$, and when $k = 2$ we have $2(\cos 285° + i \sin 285°)$. These are the three cube roots of $8(\cos 135° + i \sin 135°)$.

We generalize this result in the following theorem. The proof is a generalization of the discussion above.

Theorem 10.7   If *n* is any positive integer and *r* is a positive real number, then the complex number $r(\cos \theta + i \sin \theta)$ has exactly *n* distinct *n*th roots, given by

$$r^{1/n}(\cos \alpha + i \sin \alpha),$$

where $$\alpha = \frac{\theta + 360° \cdot k}{n}, \qquad k = 0, 1, 2, \ldots, n - 1.$$

Example 2   Find all 4th roots of $-8 + 8\sqrt{3}i$.

First write $-8 + 8\sqrt{3}i$ in trigonometric form as

$$-8 + 8\sqrt{3}i = 16(\cos 120° + i \sin 120°).$$

Here $r = 16$ and $\theta = 120°$. The 4th roots of this number have modulus $16^{1/4} = 2$ and arguments given as follows.

If $k = 0$, $\dfrac{120° + 360° \cdot 0}{4} = 30°$.   If $k = 2$, $\dfrac{120° + 360° \cdot 2}{4} = 210°$.

If $k = 1$, $\dfrac{120° + 360° \cdot 1}{4} = 120°$.   If $k = 3$, $\dfrac{120° + 360° \cdot 3}{4} = 300°$.

Using these angles, we can write the 4th roots as

$$2(\cos 30° + i \sin 30°)$$
$$2(\cos 120° + i \sin 120°)$$
$$2(\cos 210° + i \sin 210°)$$
$$2(\cos 300° + i \sin 300°).$$

In standard form the four roots are $\sqrt{3} + i, -1 + \sqrt{3}i, -\sqrt{3} - i$, and $1 - \sqrt{3}i$.

Example 3   Find all 5th roots of 1.

Write 1 in trigonometric form as

$$1 = 1 + 0i = 1(\cos 0° + i \sin 0°).$$

The modulus of the 5th roots is $1^{1/5} = 1$, while the arguments are given by

$$\frac{0° + 360° \cdot k}{5}, \qquad k = 0, 1, 2, 3, \text{ or } 4.$$

Using these arguments we can write the 5th roots as

$1(\cos 0° + i \sin 0°)$	$1(\cos 216° + i \sin 216°)$
$1(\cos 72° + i \sin 72°)$	$1(\cos 288° + i \sin 288°).$
$1(\cos 144° + i \sin 144°)$	

Note that the first of these roots equals 1, but the others cannot easily be expressed in standard form. The five 5th roots all lie on a unit circle and are equally spaced around it, as shown in Figure 10.10.

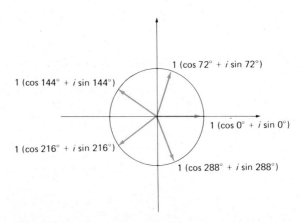

Figure 10.10

10.5 Exercises *Find the following powers. Write the result in standard form.*

1. $[2(\cos 60° + i \sin 60°)]^3$

2. $[3(\cos 120° + i \sin 120°)]^4$

3. $(\cos 45° + i \sin 45°)^8$

4. $[2(\cos 120° + i \sin 120°)]^3$

5. $(\sqrt{3} + i)^5$

6. $(2\sqrt{2} - 2i\sqrt{2})^6$

7. $(2 - 2i\sqrt{3})^4$

8. $\left(\dfrac{\sqrt{2}}{2} - \dfrac{\sqrt{2}}{2}i\right)^8$

9. $(-2 - 2i)^5$

10. $(-1 + i)^7$

⊙ 11. $(-.4283 + .5172i)^4$

12. $(1.87615 - 1.42213i)^3$

Find and graph all cube roots of the following complex numbers.

13. 1

14. i

15. $-8i$

16. $27i$

17. -64

18. 27

19. $-2\sqrt{3} + 2i$

20. $\sqrt{3} - i$

⊙ *Find the following roots.*

21. cube roots of $1.832 + 4.761i$

22. square roots of $11.489i$

23. fourth roots of 259.86

24. fourth roots of -38.476

Find and graph all the following roots of 1.

25. 2nd   26. 4th   27. 6th   28. 8th

Find and graph all the following roots of i.

29. 2nd   30. 4th

Find all solutions of the following equations.

31. $x^3 - 1 = 0$

32. $x^4 + i = 0$

33. $x^3 - 8 = 0$

34. $x^3 + 27 = 0$

35. $x^4 + 1 = 0$

36. $x^4 + 16 = 0$

⊙ 37. $x^3 - 7.60 = 0$

38. $x^4 + 11.83 = 0$

Let $z = a + bi$. Solve the following equations for z.

39. $z^2 = 1 + i$

40. $z^2 = -\sqrt{2} + i\sqrt{2}$

41. $z^2 = 3 - 3i$

42. $z^2 = -\sqrt{3} - 1$

43. Let α be an *n*th root of 1 (that is, $\alpha^n = 1$). Show that $\alpha^{n-1} + \alpha^{n-2} + \cdots + \alpha + 1 = 0$.
(Hint: divide $\alpha^n - 1$ by $\alpha - 1$.)

Chapter 10   Review Exercises

Simplify each of the following.

1. $(1 - i) - (3 + 4i) + 2i$

2. $(2 - 5i) + (9 - 10i) - 3$

3. $(6 - 5i) + (2 + 7i) - (3 - 2i)$

4. $(4 - 2i) - (6 + 5i) - (3 - i)$

5. $(3 + 5i)(8 - i)$

6. $(4 - i)(5 + 2i)$

7. $(2 + 6i)^2$

8. $(6 - 3i)^2$

9. $(1 - i)^3$

10. $(2 + i)^3$

11. i^{17}

12. i^{52}

13. $\dfrac{6 + 2i}{3 - i}$

14. $\dfrac{2 - 5i}{1 + i}$

15. $\dfrac{2 + i}{1 - 5i} \cdot \dfrac{1 + i}{3 - i}$

16. $\dfrac{4 + 3i}{1 - i} \cdot \dfrac{2 - 3i}{2 + i}$

17. $\dfrac{8 - i}{2 + i} + \dfrac{3 + 2i}{4i}$

18. $\dfrac{6 + 3i}{1 + i} + \dfrac{1 - i}{2 + 2i}$

19. $\sqrt{-12}$

20. $\sqrt{-18}$

21. $|3 + 6i|$

22. $|5i|$

23. $|-2|$

Solve each of the following equations.

24. $a + 2i = 3 - bi$

25. $4 - 6i = a + 5 - bi + i$

26. $2a - 3bi + 5 = i - 3a + 5i$

27. $2i + 2(a - 2) = -1 + i(b - 3)$

Find the resultant of each of the following pairs of complex numbers.

28. $7 + 3i$ and $-2 + i$

29. $2 - 4i$ and $-1 - 2i$

Graph each of the following complex numbers.

30. $-4 + 2i$

31. $5i$

32. -4

Solve the following equations.

33. $2x^2 - 4x + 3 = 0$

34. $y^2 + 5y + 1 = 0$

35. $2m^2 + \sqrt{3}m + 1 = 0$

36. $\sqrt{5}p^2 + 2m + \sqrt{5} = 0$

37. $x^3 - 8 = 0$

38. $x^3 + 8 = 0$

Find an equation which has the given solutions.

39. $2 + i, 2 - i$

40. $3 - 2i, 3 + 2i$

41. $4i, -4i, 3$

42. $2, -5, i + 1$

Complete the following chart.

	standard form	polar coordinates	trigonometric form
43.	$-2 + 2i$	_____	_____
44.	_____	$(3, 90°)$	_____
45.	_____	_____	$2(\cos 315° + i \sin 315°)$

Perform the indicated operations and write your answers in standard form.

46. $3(\cos 135° + i \sin 135°) \cdot 2(\cos 105° + i \sin 105°)$

47. $5(\cos 90° + i \sin 90°) \cdot 6(\cos 180° + i \sin 180°)$

48. $\dfrac{4(\cos 270° + i \sin 270°)}{2(\cos 90° + i \sin 90°)}$

49. $\dfrac{2(\cos 60° + i \sin 60°)}{8(\cos 300° + i \sin 300°)}$

50. $(2 - 2i)^5$

51. $(\sqrt{3} + i)^3$

52. $(\cos 20° + i \sin 20°)^3$

53. $(\cos 100° + i \sin 100°)^6$

54. Find the cube roots of $1 - i$.

55. Find the fifth roots of $-2 + 2i$.

56. Find the fourth roots of $\sqrt{3} + i$.

The following exercises are taken with permission from a standard calculus book.

Solve each of the following equations for the real numbers x and y.

57. $(3 + 4i)^2 - 2(x - iy) = x + iy$

58. $\left(\dfrac{1 + i}{1 - i}\right)^2 + \dfrac{1}{x + iy} = 1 + i$

59. $(3 - 2i)(x + iy) = 2(x - 2iy) + 2i - 1$

Let R(z), I(z) denote respectively the real and imaginary parts of z. Show that

60. $z + \bar{z} = 2R(z)$

61. $z - \bar{z} = 2iI(z)$

62. $|R(z)| \le |z|$

63. $|z_1 + z_2|^2 = |z_1|^2 + |z_2|^2 + 2R(z_1\bar{z}_2)$

64. $|z_1 + z_2| \le |z_1| + |z_2|$

65. Find all pairs (x_0, y_0) that are both polar and rectangular coordinates for the same point.

66. A regular pentagon is inscribed in a circle with center at the origin and radius 3. One vertex is on the positive x-axis. Write the polar coordinates of all the vertices.

67. Show that the distance between the points with polar coordinates (r_1, θ_1) and (r_2, θ_2) is
$$\sqrt{r_1^2 + r_2^2 - 2r_1r_2 \cos (\theta_1 - \theta_2)}$$

68. Use the results of the previous exercise to find an equation in polar coordinates of the circle with center $(2, \pi/3)$ and radius 3.

Exercises 57–64: George B. Thomas, Jr./Ross L. Finney, *Calculus and Analytic Geometry,* 5/E, © 1979, Addison-Wesley, Reading, Massachusetts. (Pp. 832, 838.) Reprinted with permission. Exercises 65–68: Reproduced from *Calculus,* by Leonard Gillman and Robert H. McDowell, 2nd Edition, by permission of W. W. Norton & Company, Inc. Copyright © 1978, 1973 by W. W. Norton & Company, Inc.

Zeros of
Polynomials

A **polynomial function of degree n** is defined as a function of the form

$$P(x) = a_n x^n + a_{n-1} x^{n-1} + \ldots + a_1 x + a_0,$$

where all the a's are complex numbers and $a_n \neq 0$. (We use $P(x)$ instead of $f(x)$ to show that we are working with **polynomial** functions.) The number a_n is the **leading coefficient.** If all the coefficients are 0, the polynomial is 0 and is called the **zero polynomial.** The zero polynomial has no degree. However, a polynomial of the form $P(x) = a_0$, for a complex number $a_0 \neq 0$, has degree 0.

A complex number c is a **zero** of a polynomial $P(x)$ in case $P(c) = 0$. The number c is also a **root** or **solution** of the equation $P(x) = 0$. We shall discuss methods of finding zeros of polynomials in this chapter.

11.1 Polynomial Division

To find the quotient of two polynomials, we use a **division algorithm** which is very similar to that used for dividing whole numbers. (An algorithm is an orderly procedure for working a problem.)

Example 1   Divide $4m^3 - 8m^2 + 4m + 6$ by $2m - 1$.
Work as follows.

$$
\begin{array}{r}
2m^2 - 3m + \frac{1}{2} \\
2m - 1\overline{)4m^3 - 8m^2 + 4m + 6} \\
\underline{4m^3 - 2m^2} \\
-6m^2 + 4m \\
\underline{-6m^2 + 3m} \\
m + 6 \\
\underline{m - \frac{1}{2}} \\
\frac{13}{2}
\end{array}
$$

Hence, $\dfrac{4m^3 - 8m^2 + 4m + 6}{2m - 1} = 2m^2 - 3m + \dfrac{1}{2} + \dfrac{13/2}{2m - 1}$

or $4m^3 - 8m^2 + 4m + 6 = (2m - 1)\left(2m^2 - 3m + \dfrac{1}{2}\right) + \dfrac{13}{2}.$

At the first step in dividing these polynomials, we subtracted $4m^3 - 2m^2$ from $4m^3 - 8m^2 + 4m + 6$. The result, $-6m^2 + 4m + 6$, should be written under the line. However, it is customary to save work and "bring down" only the $4m$, the only term needed for the next step.   ▮

A polynomial such as $3x^3 - 2x^2 - 150$ has a missing term, the term where the variable is x. When dividing a polynomial with a missing term, it is necessary to allow for that term, as shown below.

Example 2

$$
\begin{array}{r}
3x^2 + 10x\ + 40 \\
x - 4\overline{\smash{)}3x^3 -\ \ 2x^2\qquad\quad - 150} \\
\underline{3x^3 - 12x^2} \\
10x^2 \\
\underline{10x^2 - 40x} \\
40x - 150 \\
\underline{40x - 160} \\
10
\end{array}
$$

The result of this division can be written as

$$\frac{3x^3 - 2x^2 - 150}{x - 4} = 3x^2 + 10x + 40 + \frac{10}{x - 4}$$

or $3x^3 - 2x^2 - 150 = (x - 4)(3x^2 + 10x + 40) + 10.$ ▮

The following theorem generalizes the division process we have illustrated above.

Theorem 11.1   (*Division Algorithm*)   If $P(x)$ and $S(x)$ are polynomials, then there exist unique polynomials $Q(x)$ and $R(x)$ such that

$$P(x) = S(x) \cdot Q(x) + R(x),$$

and $R(x) = 0$ or $R(x)$ is of degree less than $S(x)$.

The polynomial $Q(x)$ of Theorem 11.1 is called the **quotient polynomial** or the **quotient,** while $R(x)$ is the **remainder polynomial** or the **remainder.**

The division algorithm applies to the polynomials of Examples 1 and 2. In Example 1, we had

$$\frac{4m^3 - 8m^2 + 4m + 6}{2m - 1} = 2m^2 - 3m + \frac{1}{2} + \frac{13/2}{2m - 1}$$

from which we can see

$$4m^3 - 8m^2 + 4m + 6 = (2m - 1)\left(2m^2 - 3m + \frac{1}{2}\right) + \frac{13}{2}.$$

$$\underset{P(x)}{} \quad = \underset{S(x)}{} \cdot \underset{Q(x)}{} \underset{+R(x).}{}$$

We often need to divide a polynomial by a first-degree binomial of the form $x + k$, where the coefficient of x is 1. We can develop a shortcut for this type of division problem. To illustrate, we will rework Example 2. To simplify the division process, we can omit all variables and write only coefficients. We use 0 to represent the coefficient of any missing variables. Since the coefficient of x in the division is always 1 in problems of this type, we can omit it too. These omissions simplify the problem as follows.

$$
\begin{array}{r}
3 \quad 10 \quad 40 \\
-4\,|\,\overline{3 - 2 \quad\; 0 - 150} \\
\underline{3 - 12} \\
10 \\
\underline{10 - 40} \\
40 - 150 \\
\underline{40 - 160} \\
10
\end{array}
$$

The numbers in color are repetitions of the numbers directly above, and can be omitted.

$$
\begin{array}{r}
3 \quad 10 \quad 40 \\
-4\,|\,\overline{3 - 2 \quad\; 0 - 150} \\
\underline{- 12} \\
10 \\
\underline{- 40} \\
40 - 150 \\
\underline{- 160} \\
10
\end{array}
$$

The entire problem can now be condensed, with the top row of numbers omitted, since it duplicates the bottom row.

$$
\begin{array}{r}
-4\,|\,\overline{3 - 2 \quad\;\; 0 - 150} \\
\underline{- 12 - 40 - 160} \\
3 \quad 10 \quad 40 \quad\;\; 10
\end{array}
$$

We obtained the bottom row by subtracting -12, -40, and -160 from the corresponding terms above. For reasons that will become clear in the discussion of Theorem 11.2 below, we change the -4 at the left to 4, which also changes the sign of the numbers in the second row, and then add. Doing this, we have

$$
\begin{array}{r}
4\,|\,\overline{3 - 2 \quad\;\; 0 - 150} \\
\underline{12 \quad 40 \quad 160} \\
3 \quad 10 \quad 40 \quad\;\; 10
\end{array}
$$

This abbreviated process is called **synthetic division.**

Example 3   Use synthetic division to divide $5m^3 - 6m^2 - 28m - 2$ by $m + 2$.

We begin by writing

$$-2\overline{\smash{\big)}5 - 6 - 28 - 2}$$

Note that we have changed the 2 to -2. To begin, we bring down the 5.

$$-2\overline{\smash{\big)}5 - 6 - 28 - 2}$$
$$\underline{}$$
$$5$$

Now, multiply -2 by 5 to get -10, and add it to the -6 in the first row. The result is -16.

$$-2\overline{\smash{\big)}5 - 6 - 28 - 2}$$
$$\underline{- 10}$$
$$5 - 16$$

Next, we have $(-2)(-16) = 32$. We add this to the -28 in the first row.

$$-2\overline{\smash{\big)}5 - 6 - 28 - 2}$$
$$\underline{- 10 \quad 32}$$
$$5 - 16 \quad 4$$

Since $(-2)(4) = -8$, we have

$$-2\overline{\smash{\big)}5 - 6 - 28 - 2}$$
$$\underline{- 10 \quad 32 - 8}$$
$$5 - 16 \quad 4 - 10$$

The coefficients of the quotient are read directly from the bottom row. The degree of the quotient will always be one less than the degree of the polynomial to be divided. Therefore,

$$\frac{5m^3 - 6m^2 - 28m - 2}{m + 2} = 5m^2 - 16m + 4 + \frac{-10}{m + 2}.$$ ▮

The division algorithm says that if we divide $P(x)$ by $x - k$, then

$$P(x) = (x - k) \cdot Q(x) + r,$$

for some polynomial $Q(x)$ and complex number r. This equality is true for all complex values of x, so that it is true for $x = k$. Thus

$$P(k) = (k - k) \cdot Q(k) + r$$
$$P(k) = r.$$

We have now proved the following theorem.

Theorem 11.2   (*Remainder Theorem*)   If the polynomial $P(x)$ is divided by $x - k$, then the remainder is equal to $P(k)$.

For example, we found in Example 2 above that

$$P(x) = 3x^3 - 2x^2 - 150$$

can be written as

$$P(x) = (x - 4)(3x^2 + 10x + 40) + 10.$$

To find $P(4)$, replace x with 4.

$$P(4) = (4 - 4)(3 \cdot 4^2 + 10 \cdot 4 + 40) + 10$$
$$= 0(3 \cdot 4^2 + 10 \cdot 4 + 40) + 10$$
$$P(4) = 10$$

Thus, instead of replacing x with 4 in $P(x) = 3x^3 - 2x^2 - 150$, we need only divide $P(x)$ by $x - 4$, with $P(4)$ equal to the remainder we get.

In general, instead of evaluating $P(k)$ by substituting k for x in the polynomial $P(x)$, we could find $P(k)$ by dividing $P(x)$ by $x - k$. Then $P(k)$ equals the remainder obtained in the division.

Example 4   Let $P(x) = -x^4 + 3x^2 - 4x - 5$. Find $P(-2)$.
Use the remainder theorem and synthetic division.

$$
\begin{array}{r|rrrrr}
-2 & -1 & 0 & 3 & -4 & -5 \\
   &   & 2 & -4 & 2 & 4 \\
\hline
   & -1 & 2 & -1 & -2 & -1
\end{array}
$$

Therefore, $P(-2) = -1$, the remainder when $P(x)$ is divided by $x - (-2)$ or $x + 2$. ▍

By the remainder theorem, if $P(k) = 0$, then $x - k$ is a factor of $P(x)$, and conversely, if $x - k$ is a factor of $P(x)$, then $P(k)$ must equal 0. Thus, we have proved the following theorem.

Theorem 11.3   (*Factor Theorem*)   The polynomial $x - k$ is a factor of the polynomial $P(x)$ if and only if $P(k) = 0$. That is,

$$P(k) = 0 \text{ if and only if } P(x) = (x - k) \cdot Q(x),$$
for some polynomial $Q(x)$.

Example 5   Is $x - 3$ a factor of $P(x) = 2x^3 - 4x^2 + 5x - 3$?
By the factor theorem, $x - 3$ will be a factor of $P(x)$ only if $P(3) = 0$. Use synthetic division and the remainder theorem to decide.

$$
\begin{array}{r|rrrr}
3 & 2 & -4 & 5 & -3 \\
  &   & 6 & 6 & 33 \\
\hline
  & 2 & 2 & 11 & 30
\end{array}
$$

The remainder is 30, and not 0, so that $x - 3$ is not a factor of $P(x)$. ▍

Example 6   Is $x - i$ a factor of $P(x) = x^4 - x^3 - x^2 - x - 2$?
Use synthetic division to find out.

$$
\begin{array}{r|rrrrr}
i & 1 & -1 & -1 & -1 & -2 \\
  &   & i & -1-i & 1-2i & 2 \\
\hline
  & 1 & -1+i & -2-i & -2i & 0
\end{array}
$$

The remainder is 0. Thus $P(i) = 0$, and so $x - i$ is a factor of $P(x)$. Also, $x = i$ is a root of the equation $x^4 - x^3 - x^2 - x - 2 = 0$. (Can you find the other three?) █

By the results above, any time we have a zero of $P(x)$, we also have found a factor of $P(x)$. That is, if k is a zero of $P(x)$, then $x - k$ is a factor of $P(x)$, and conversely.

Example 7   Find a polynomial having zeros $4, -3$, and 2.
Let $P(x)$ be the polynomial having the three zeros. By the factor theorem, $P(x)$ must have factors $x - 4$, $x + 3$, and $x - 2$. Thus, one polynomial with the desired zeros is

$$P(x) = (x - 4)(x + 3)(x - 2)$$
$$P(x) = x^3 - 3x^2 - 10x + 24.$$

This polynomial is not the only possible one — in fact, we could obtain an infinite number of such polynomials by multiplying $P(x)$ above by an infinite number of distinct nonzero polynomials. █

11.1 Exercises   *Perform the following divisions. Find $Q(x)$ and $R(x)$ for each one.*

1. $\dfrac{2x^3 - 11x^2 + 19x - 10}{2x - 5}$

2. $\dfrac{3p^3 - 11p^2 + 5p + 3}{3p + 1}$

3. $\dfrac{x^4 + 2x^3 + 2x^2 - 2x - 3}{x^2 - 1}$

4. $\dfrac{2y^5 + y^3 - 2y^2 - 1}{2y^2 + 1}$

5. $\dfrac{4z^5 - 4z^2 - 5z + 3}{2z^2 + z + 1}$

6. $\dfrac{12z^4 - 25z^3 + 35z^2 - 26z + 10}{4z^2 - 3z + 5}$

Use synthetic division to perform the following divisions. Find $Q(x)$ and r for each one.

7. $\dfrac{p^4 - 3p^3 - 5p^2 + 2p - 16}{p + 2}$

8. $\dfrac{3x^3 - 11x^2 - 20x + 3}{x - 5}$

9. $\dfrac{4m^3 - 3m - 2}{m + 1}$

10. $\dfrac{3q^3 - 4q + 2}{q - 1}$

11. $\dfrac{x^5 + 3x^4 + 2x^3 + 2x^2 + 3x + 1}{x + 2}$

12. $\dfrac{m^6 - 3m^4 + 2m^3 - 6m^2 - 5m + 3}{m + 2}$

Use synthetic division to decide whether or not the given number is a zero of the given polynomial.

13. 2; $P(x) = x^2 + 2x - 8$

14. -1; $P(m) = m^2 + 4m - 5$

15. 2; $P(g) = g^3 - 3g^2 + 4g - 4$

16. -3; $P(m) = m^3 + 2m^2 - m + 6$

17. $1 - i$; $P(y) = y^2 - 2y + 2$

18. $3 - 2i$; $P(r) = r^2 - 6r + 13$

19. $2 + i$; $P(k) = k^2 + 3k + 4$

20. $1 - 2i$; $P(z) = z^2 - 3z + 5$

21. i; $P(x) = x^3 + 2ix^2 + 2x + i$

22. $-i$; $P(p) = p^3 - ip^2 + 3p + 5i$

23. $1 + i$; $P(p) = p^3 + 3p^2 - p + 1$

24. $2 - i$; $P(r) = 2r^3 - r^2 + 3r - 5$

Use the Remainder Theorem to find P(k) for the following.

25. $k = 5$; $P(x) = -x^2 + 2x + 7$

26. $k = -3$; $P(x) = 3x^2 + 8x + 5$

27. $k = 3$; $P(x) = x^2 - 4x + 5$

28. $k = -2$; $P(x) = x^2 + 5x + 6$

29. $k = 2 + i$; $P(x) = x^2 - 5x + 1$

30. $k = 3 - 2i$; $P(x) = x^2 - x + 3$

31. $k = 1 - i$; $P(x) = x^3 + x^2 - x + 1$

32. $k = 2 - 3i$; $P(x) = x^3 + 2x^2 + x - 5$

Use the Factor Theorem to find the value of c that makes the second polynomial a factor of the first.

33. $4x^2 + 2x - c$; $x - 3$

34. $-3x^2 + cx + 2$; $x + 2$

35. $3x^3 - 12x^2 - 11x + c$; $x - 5$

36. $4x^3 + 6x^2 - 5x + c$; $x + 2$

37. $2x^4 + 5x^3 - 2x^2 + cx + 3$; $x + 3$

38. $5x^4 + 16x^3 - 15x^2 + cx + 16$; $x + 4$

Find a polynomial of lowest degree having the following zeros.

39. $-1, 2, -5$

40. $-4, 6, 3$

41. $\sqrt{2}, -\sqrt{2}, 3$

42. $-\sqrt{5}, \sqrt{5}, -1$

43. $\dfrac{1 + \sqrt{11}}{2}, \dfrac{1 - \sqrt{11}}{2}, -2, 3$

44. $\dfrac{2 - \sqrt{7}}{3}, \dfrac{2 + \sqrt{7}}{3}, 4, 2$

⊙ *To evaluate $P(x) = x^3 - 4x^2 + 2x - 5$ for particular values of x, we replace x with the necessary value. To simplify such evaluation with calculators or computers, we can use **nested multiplication**. Write P(x) as*

$$P(x) = x^3 - 4x^2 + 2x - 5$$
$$= x(x^2 - 4x + 2) - 5$$
$$P(x) = x(x(x - 4) + 2) - 5$$

Use this last form to evaluate P(x) for

45. $x = 2$

46. $x = -3$

47. $x = -.08$

48. $x = .47$

49. Show that $P(x) = 2x^4 + 4x^2 + 1$ can have no factor $x - k$ where k is a real number.

50. Show that $P(x) = -x^4 - 5x^2 - 3$ can have no factor $x - k$ where k is a real number.

51. Show that $x - c$ is a factor of $x^n - c^n$ for all positive integers n.

52. Show that $x + c$ is a factor of $x^n + c^n$ for all odd positive integers n.

53. Let $P(x)$ be a polynomial having a zero of c. Let a be a number "close" to c. Write $P(x)$ as $(x - a) \cdot Q(x) + r$. Find the following approximation for c:

$$c \approx a - \frac{P(a)}{Q(a)}.$$

⊙ *Use the result of Exercise 53 along with the given value of a to find an approximation to the nearest hundredth of a zero for the following polynomials.*

54. $P(x) = x^3 + 7x^2 - 2x - 14$; $a = -1.4$

55. $P(x) = x^3 + 4x^2 - 5x - 5$; $a = 1.5$

56. $P(x) = 2x^3 + 3x^2 - 22x - 33$; $a = 3.2$

11.2   Complex Zeros of Polynomials

We have seen that if a polynomial $P(x)$ can be divided with remainder 0 by $x - k$, then $P(k) = 0$, and conversely. The next theorem says that every polynomial function of degree greater than or equal to 1 has a zero, meaning every such polynomial can be factored.

Theorem 11.4   (*Fundamental Theorem of Algebra*)   If $P(x)$ is a polynomial of degree n, where $n \geq 1$, then there exists at least one complex number k such that $P(k) = 0$.

This theorem was first proved by the mathematician Gauss in his doctoral thesis is 1799, when he was 22. Although many proofs of his result have been given over the years, none of them involve only algebra and trigonometry. Hence, no proof is included here. From the fundamental theorem and the factor theorem, we have the following result.

Theorem 11.5   If $P(x)$ is a polynomial of degree n, where $n \geq 1$, then there exists a complex number k and a polynomial $Q(x)$ such that

$$P(x) = (x - k) \cdot Q(x).$$

We could use the Factor Theorem and the Fundamental Theorem to factor the polynomial $Q(x)$ of Theorem 11.5. If we continue this process a total of n times, we get the result of the next theorem.

Theorem 11.6   If $P(x)$ is a polynomial of degree n, where $n \geq 1$, then there exist n complex numbers $k_1, k_2, k_3, \ldots, k_n$, which need not be distinct, such that

$$P(x) = a(x - k_1)(x - k_2) \cdots (x - k_n),$$

where a is the leading coefficient of $P(x)$.

Using this result, we can prove that a polynomial of degree n, where $n \geq 1$, has at most n distinct zeros. To prove this, we use an **indirect proof.** To prove a statement indirectly, we assume that the opposite of the statement is true. We then show that if we assume the opposite statement to be true, we are led to a false conclusion. Here we wish to prove that a polynomial of degree $n \geq 1$ has at most n distinct zeros, so we begin by assuming the opposite — that the polynomial has *more* than n distinct zeros.

Let us assume that a polynomial $P(x)$ of degree n has $n + 1$ distinct zeros. Use Theorem 11.6 to rewrite $P(x)$ as

$$P(x) = a(x - k_1)(x - k_2) \cdots (x - k_n). \tag{1}$$

From this form of the polynomial, n of the zeros are the numbers $k_1, k_2, k_3, \ldots, k_n$. (These n zeros may or may not be distinct.) We have assumed that $P(x)$ has $n + 1$ distinct zeros, so there must be another zero, say k, that is not in the list $k_1, k_2, k_3, \ldots, k_n$. Since k is a zero,

$$P(k) = 0.$$

From equation (1), replacing x with k gives

$$P(k) = a(k - k_1)(k - k_2) \cdots (k - k_n)$$

or

$$0 = a(k - k_1)(k - k_2) \cdots (k - k_n). \qquad (2)$$

Since $k \neq k_1$, $k \neq k_2$, . . ., $k \neq k_n$, we have $k - k_1 \neq 0$, $k - k_2 \neq 0$, . . ., $k - k_n \neq 0$, so that the right side of equation (2) is made up of the product of all nonzero factors. Since the product of nonzero factors cannot equal 0, we have a contradiction.

This contradiction shows that our original assumption is false. We have now proved the following result.

Theorem 11.7   If $P(x)$ is a polynomial of degree n, where $n \geq 1$, then there exist at most n distinct zeros of $P(x)$.

The theorem says that there exist *at most n* distinct zeros. For example, the polynomial $P(x) = x^3 + 3x^2 + 3x + 1 = (x + 1)^3$ is of degree $n = 3$, but has only the one zero -1. Actually the zero -1 occurs three times since there are three factors of $x + 1$. We sometimes refer to this as a **zero of multiplicity 3.**

Example 1   Find a polynomial $P(x)$ of degree 3 which satisfies the following conditions.
   (a) Zeros of -1, 2, and 4; and $P(1) = 3$.

From these three zeros, we know that $x + 1$, $x - 2$, and $x - 4$ must be factors of $P(x)$. Since $P(x)$ is to be of degree 3, these are the only possible factors, by Theorem 11.7. By Theorem 11.6, $P(x)$ has the form

$$P(x) = a (x + 1)(x - 2)(x - 4).$$

Since $P(1) = 3$,

$$P(1) = a(1 + 1)(1 - 2)(1 - 4) = 3$$

$$a(2)(-1)(-3) = 3$$

$$6a = 3$$

$$a = \frac{1}{2}.$$

Thus,

$$P(x) = \frac{1}{2}(x + 1)(x - 2)(x - 4)$$

or

$$P(x) = \frac{1}{2}x^3 - \frac{5}{2}x^2 + x + 4.$$

   (b) -2 is a root of multiplicity 3, and $P(-1) = 4$.
      We know that $P(x)$ has the form

$$P(x) = a(x + 2)(x + 2)(x + 2)$$

$$= a(x + 2)^3.$$

Since $P(-1) = 4$, we have

$$P(-1) = a(-1 + 2)^3 = 4$$

or

$$a(1)^3 = 4$$

$$a = 4.$$

Therefore, $P(x) = 4(x + 2)^3 = 4x^3 + 24x^2 + 48x + 32.$ ∎

Using the remainder theorem, we can show that both $2 + i$ and $2 - i$ are zeros of $P(x) = x^3 - x^2 - 7x + 15$. It is not just coincidence that both $2 + i$ and its conjugate $2 - i$ are zeros of this polynomial. We can prove that if $a + bi$ is a zero of a polynomial function with real coefficients, then so is $a - bi$.

To see this, we use some of the properties of complex conjugates. Let $z = a + bi$, and write $\bar{z}$ for the conjugate of z, $\bar{z} = a - bi$. Now consider the polynomial having real coefficients

$$P(x) = a_n x^n + a_{n-1} x^{n-1} + \cdots + a_1 x + a_0,$$

where $a_n \neq 0$. If $z = a + bi$ is a zero of $P(x)$, then

$$P(z) = a_n z^n + a_{n-1} z^{n-1} + \cdots + a_1 z + a_0 = 0.$$

If we take the conjugate of both sides of this last equation, we have

$$\overline{a_n z^n + a_{n-1} z^{n-1} + \cdots + a_1 z + a_0} = \overline{0}.$$

This becomes

$$\overline{a_n z^n} + \overline{a_{n-1} z^{n-1}} + \cdots + \overline{a_1 z} + \overline{a_0} = \overline{0}.$$

or

$$\overline{a_n} \overline{z_n} + \overline{a_{n-1}} \overline{z^{n-1}} + \cdots + \overline{a_1} \overline{z} + \overline{a_0} = 0$$

Here we have used generalizations of the properties $\overline{c + d} = \bar{c} + \bar{d}$ and $\overline{cd} = \bar{c} \cdot \bar{d}$; we now use the fact that for any real number a, $\bar{a} = a$, to get

$$a_n (\bar{z})^n + a_{n-1} (\bar{z})^{n-1} + \cdots + a_1 (\bar{z}) + a_0 = 0.$$

Hence, $\bar{z}$ is also a zero of $P(x)$, and we have proved the following result.

Theorem 11.8 If $P(x)$ is a polynomial having real coefficients and if $a + bi$ is a zero of $P(x)$, where a and b are real numbers, then $a - bi$ is also a zero of $P(x)$.

The requirement that the polynomial have real coefficients is very important. For example, $P(x) = x - (1 + i)$ has $1 + i$ as a zero, but the conjugate, $1 - i$, is not a zero.

Example 2 Find a polynomial of lowest degree having real coefficients and zeros 3 and $2 + i$.

By Theorem 11.8, the number $2 - i$ must also be a zero. Thus, there must be at least three zeros, 3, $2 + i$, and $2 - i$. By the factor theorem there must then be three factors, $x - 3$, $x - (2 + i)$, and $x - (2 - i)$. A polynomial of lowest degree is

$$P(x) = (x - 3)[x - (2 + i)][x - (2 - i)]$$
$$= (x - 3)(x - 2 - i)(x - 2 + i)$$
$$P(x) = x^3 - 7x^2 + 17x - 15.$$

There are other polynomials, such as $3(x^3 - 7x^2 + 17x - 15)$ or $\sqrt{5}(x^3 - 7x^2 + 17x - 15)$, that satisfy the given conditions as to zeros. The information on zeros given in the statement of the example is not enough for us to find a single value of the leading coefficient.

Theorem 11.8 is important in helping predict the number of real zeros of a polynomial with real coefficients. A polynomial with real coefficients of odd degree n, where $n \geq 1$, must have at least one real zero (since we have just seen that zeros of the form $a + bi$, where $b \neq 0$, occur in pairs). On the other hand, a polynomial with real coefficients of even degree n, where $n \geq 2$, need have no real zeros, but may have up to n real zeros.

Example 3 Find all zeros of $x^4 - 7x^3 + 18x^2 - 22x + 12$, given that $x = 1 - i$ is a zero.

Since $x = 1 - i$ is a zero, we know by Theorem 11.8 that the conjugate $x = 1 + i$ is also a zero. Thus, we should first divide the original polynomial by $1 - i$ and then divide the quotient by $1 + i$, as follows.

$$
\begin{array}{r|rrrrr}
1 - i & 1 & -7 & 18 & -22 & 12 \\
& & 1 - i & -7 + 5i & 16 - 6i & -12 \\
\hline
& 1 & -6 - i & 11 + 5i & -6 - 6i & 0 \\
\end{array}
$$

$$
\begin{array}{r|rrrr}
1 + i & 1 & -6 - i & 11 + 5i & -6 - 6i \\
& & 1 + i & -5 - 5i & 6 + 6i \\
\hline
& 1 & -5 & 6 & 0 \\
\end{array}
$$

Now find the zeros of the quadratic polynomial $x^2 - 5x + 6$. By factoring, the zeros are 2 and 3, so that the four zeros of $x^4 - 7x^3 + 18x^2 - 22x + 12$ are $1 - i$, $1 + i$, 2, and 3. ▌

11.2 Exercises *For each of the following, find a polynomial of degree 3 with real coefficients that satisfies the given conditions.*

1. zeros of $-3, -1$, and 4; and $P(2) = 5$

2. zeros of $1, -1$, and 0; and $P(2) = -3$

3. -2 is a zero of multiplicity $2, -3$ is a zero; and $P(1) = 4$

4. 5 is a zero of multiplicity $2, -1$ is a zero; and $P(2) = 3$

5. zeros of 3 and i; and $P(2) = 50$.

6. zeros of -2 and $-i$, and $P(-3) = 30$

For each of the following, find a polynomial of lowest degree with real coefficients having the given zeros.

7. $5 + i$ and $5 - i$

8. $3 - 2i$ and $3 + 2i$

9. $2, 1 - i$, and $1 + i$

10. $-3, 2 - i$, and $2 + i$

11. $1 + \sqrt{2}, 1 - \sqrt{2}$, and 1

12. $1 - \sqrt{3}, 1 + \sqrt{3}$, and -2

13. $2 + i, 2 - i, 3$, and -1

14. $3 + 2i, 3 - 2i, -1$, and 2

15. 2 and $3 + i$

16. -1 and $4 - 2i$

17. $1 - \sqrt{2}$, $1 + \sqrt{2}$, and $1 - i$

18. $2 + \sqrt{3}$, $2 - \sqrt{3}$, and $2 + 3i$

19. $2 - i$, $3 + 2i$

20. $5 + i$, $4 - i$

For each of the following polynomials, one zero is given. Find all others.

21. $P(x) = x^3 - x^2 - 4x - 6$; $x = 3$

22. $P(x) = x^3 - 5x^2 + 17x - 13$; $x = 1$

23. $P(x) = x^3 + x^2 - 4x - 24$; $x = -2 + 2i$

24. $P(x) = x^3 + x^2 - 20x - 50$; $x = -3 + i$

25. $P(x) = 2x^3 - 2x^2 - x - 6$; $x = 2$

26. $P(x) = 2x^3 - 5x^2 + 6x - 2$; $x = 1 + i$

27. $P(x) = x^4 - 3x^3 + 6x^2 + 2x - 60$; $x = 1 + 3i$

28. $P(x) = x^4 - 6x^3 - x^2 + 86x + 170$; $x = 5 + 3i$

29. $P(x) = x^4 - 6x^3 + 15x^2 - 18x + 10$; $x = 2 + i$

30. $P(x) = x^4 + 8x^3 + 26x^2 + 72x + 153$; $x = -3i$

31. Show that 2 is a zero of multiplicity 3 of $P(x) = x^5 - 6x^4 + 13x^3 - 14x^2 + 12x - 8$, and find all other complex zeros. Then write $P(x)$ in factored form.

32. Show that 1 is a zero of multiplicity 4 of $P(x) = x^6 - 8x^5 + 27x^4 - 48x^3 + 47x^2 - 24x + 5$, and find all other complex zeros. Then write $P(x)$ in factored form.

33. Show that every polynomial of degree 3 with real coefficients has at least one real root.

34. Show that every polynomial with real coefficients of degree n, where n is an odd positive integer, has at least one real root.

35. Show that it is not possible for a polynomial of degree 3 with real coefficients to have zeros of 1, 2, and $1 + i$.

36. Show that the zeros of $P(x) = x^3 + ix^2 - (7 - i)x + (6 - 6i)$ are $1 - i$, 2, and -3. Why does Theorem 11.8 not apply?

37. Show that the equation

$$\frac{1}{x - 3} + \frac{2}{x + 3} - \frac{6}{x^2 - 9} = 0$$

has no solution. Why doesn't this contradict the fundamental theorem of algebra?

38. Show that if

$$P(x) = a_n x^n + a_{n-1}x^{n-1} + \cdots + a_1 x + a_0$$

has $n + 1$ distinct zeros, then each a_i must equal 0.

39. Show that $P(x) = 0$ and $Q(x) = 0$ have exactly the same solutions (with the same multiplicity) if and only if $P(x) = c \cdot Q(x)$ for some complex number c.

40. Let $P(x)$ and $Q(x)$ be polynomials each of which has c as a zero. Show that $x - c$ is a factor of the remainder when $P(x)$ is divided by $Q(x)$.

11.3   Rational Zeros of Polynomials

We know by the fundamental theorem of algebra that every polynomial of degree 1 or more has a zero. However, the fundamental theorem merely asserts that such a zero exists. It gives no help at all in identifying zeros. For second-degree polynomials we can use the quadratic formula. Similar but more complicated formulas exist for finding zeros of third- and fourth-degree polynomial functions. It was proved by the Norwegian mathematician Niels Henrik Abel (1802–29), at age 22, that it is not possible to produce a formula that will find zeros of fifth-degree or higher polynomials.

In practice, however, it is usually enough to find only rational zeros and decimal approximations of any irrational zeros. In this section we develop a necessary condition for a rational number to be a zero of a polynomial function having rational coefficients. In the next section we discuss approximations of irrational zeros.

The next theorem gives a useful test for determining whether or not a given rational number is a possible zero of a polynomial $P(x)$ having integer coefficients.

Theorem 11.9   Let $P(x) = a_n x^n + a_{n-1} x^{n-1} + \cdots + a_1 x + a_0$ $(a_n \neq 0)$ be a polynomial with integer coefficients. If p/q is a rational number written in lowest terms with the property that $P(p/q) = 0$, then p is a factor of a_0 and q is a factor of a_n.

Since p/q is a zero of $P(x)$, replace x with p/q to get

$$a_n(p/q)^n + a_{n-1}(p/q)^{n-1} + \cdots + a_1(p/q) + a_0 = 0,$$

which can also be written as

$$a_n(p^n/q^n) + a_{n-1}(p^{n-1}/q^{n-1}) + \cdots + a_1(p/q) + a_0 = 0.$$

Multiply both sides of this last result by q^n and add $-a_0 q^n$ to both sides.

$$a_n p^n + a_{n-1} p^{n-1} q + \cdots + a_1 p q^{n-1} = -a_0 q^n.$$

Factoring out p gives

$$p(a_n p^{n-1} + a_{n-1} p^{n-2} q + \cdots + a_1 q^{n-1}) = -a_0 q^n.$$

By this last result, p must be a factor of $-a_0 q^n$. (Why?) Since we have assumed that p/q is written in lowest terms, p and q have no common factor other than 1. Hence, p is not a factor of q^n. Thus we must conclude that p is a factor of a_0. In a similar way we can show that q is a factor of a_n.

Example 1   Find all rational zeros of $P(x) = 2x^4 - 11x^3 + 14x^2 - 11x + 12$.

If p/q is to be a rational zero of $P(x)$, we know by Theorem 11.9 that p must be a factor of $a_0 = 12$ and q must be a factor of $a_4 = 2$. Hence, p must be $\pm 1, \pm 2, \pm 3, \pm 4, \pm 6,$ or ± 12, while q must be ± 1 or ± 2. From this we see that any rational zero of $P(x)$ will come from the list

$$\pm 1, \quad \pm 1/2, \quad \pm 2, \quad \pm 3, \quad \pm 3/2, \quad \pm 4, \quad \pm 6, \quad \text{or} \quad \pm 12.$$

Though we are not sure that any of these numbers are zeros, if $P(x)$ has any rational zeros at all, they will be in the list above. We can check these proposed zeros by synthetic division. By trial and error we find that $x = 4$ is a zero.

$$4\underline{\big|2 \quad -11 \quad 14 \quad -11 \quad 12}$$
$$\quad 8 \quad -12 \quad 8 \quad -12$$
$$\overline{2 \quad -3 \quad 2 \quad -3 \quad 0}$$

As a fringe benefit of this calculation, we now only need to look for zeros of the simpler polynomial $Q(x) = 2x^3 - 3x^2 + 2x - 3$. By Theorem 11.9 any rational zero of $Q(x)$ will have a numerator of ± 3 or ± 1 with a denominator of ± 1 or ± 2. Hence, any rational zeros of $Q(x)$ will come from the list

$$\pm 3, \quad \pm 3/2, \quad \pm 1, \quad \pm 1/2.$$

Again we use synthetic division and trial and error to find that $x = 3/2$ is a zero.

$$3/2\underline{\big|2 \quad -3 \quad 2 \quad -3}$$
$$\quad 3 \quad 0 \quad 3$$
$$\overline{2 \quad 0 \quad 2 \quad 0}$$

The quotient is $2x^2 + 2$, which, by the quadratic formula, has i and $-i$ as zeros. They are, however, imaginary zeros. The rational zeros of the polynomial function

$$P(x) = 2x^4 - 11x^3 + 14x^2 - 11x + 12$$

are 4 and 3/2. ▮

To find any rational zeros of a polynomial with rational coefficients, first multiply the polynomial by a number that will clear it of all fractional coefficients. Then use Theorem 11.9.

11.3 Exercises   *Find all rational zeros of the following polynomials.*

1. $P(x) = x^3 - 2x^2 - 13x - 10$

2. $P(x) = x^3 + 5x^2 + 2x - 8$

3. $P(x) = x^3 + 6x^2 - x - 30$

4. $P(x) = x^3 - x^2 - 10x - 8$

5. $P(x) = x^3 + 9x^2 - 14x - 24$

6. $P(x) = x^3 + 3x^2 - 4x - 12$

7. $P(x) = x^4 + 9x^3 + 21x^2 - x - 30$

8. $P(x) = x^4 + 4x^3 - 7x^2 - 34x - 24$

9. $P(x) = 6x^3 + 17x^2 - 31x - 12$

10. $P(x) = 15x^3 + 61x^2 + 2x - 8$

11. $P(x) = 12x^3 + 20x^2 - x - 6$

12. $P(x) = 12x^3 + 40x^2 + 41x + 12$

13. $P(x) = 2x^3 + 7x^2 + 12x - 8$

14. $P(x) = 2x^3 + 20x^2 + 68x - 40$

15. $P(x) = x^4 + 4x^3 + 3x^2 - 10x + 50$

16. $P(x) = x^4 - 2x^3 + x^2 + 18$

17. $P(x) = x^4 + 2x^3 - 13x^2 - 38x - 24$

18. $P(x) = 6x^4 + x^3 - 7x^2 - x + 1$

19. $P(x) = 3x^4 + 4x^3 - x^2 + 4x - 4$

20. $P(x) = x^4 + 8x^3 + 16x^2 - 8x - 17$

21. $P(x) = x^5 + 3x^4 - 5x^3 - 11x^2 + 12$

22. $P(x) = 4x^5 + 4x^4 - 37x^3 - 37x^2 + 9x + 9$

23. $P(x) = x^3 - \dfrac{4}{3}x^2 - \dfrac{13}{3}x - 2$

24. $P(x) = x^3 + x^2 - \dfrac{16}{9}x + \dfrac{4}{9}$

27. $P(x) = \dfrac{1}{3}x^5 + x^4 - \dfrac{5}{3}x^3 - \dfrac{11}{3}x^2 + 4$

25. $P(x) = x^4 + \dfrac{1}{4}x^3 + \dfrac{11}{4}x^2 + x - 5$

28. $P(x) = x^5 + x^4 - \dfrac{37}{4}x^2 + \dfrac{9}{4}x + \dfrac{9}{4}$

26. $P(x) = \dfrac{10}{7}x^4 - x^3 - 7x^2 + 5x - \dfrac{5}{7}$

29. Show that $P(x) = x^2 - 2$ has no rational zeros, so that $\sqrt{2}$ must be irrational.

30. Show that $P(x) = x^2 - 5$ has no rational zeros, so that $\sqrt{5}$ must be irrational.

31. Show that $P(x) = x^4 + 5x^2 + 4$ has no rational zeros.

32. Show that $P(x) = x^5 - 3x^3 + 5$ has no rational zeros.

11.4   Approximate Zeros of Polynomials

We know that every polynomial function of degree 1 or more has a zero. However, we do not know whether or not the function has real zeros. Even if it does have real zeros, we often have no way to find them. In this section we look into methods of approximating any real zeros a polynomial function may have. These methods work well using a computer or a calculator.

Much of our work in locating real zeros uses the following result, which follows from the fact that graphs of polynomial functions are unbroken curves, with no gaps or sudden jumps.

Theorem 11.10   If $P(x)$ is a polynomial function with real coefficients, and a and b are real numbers such that $a < b$ and such that $P(a)$ and $P(b)$ are opposite in sign, then there exists a real number c, $a < c < b$, such that $P(c) = 0$.

The next theorem gives a good method for narrowing the search for real zeros.

Theorem 11.11   If $P(x) = a_n x^n + a_{n-1} x^{n-1} + \cdots + a_1 x + a_0$ is a polynomial of degree $n \geq 1$ with real coefficients and $a_n > 0$, and if $P(x)$ is divided synthetically by $x - c$, then

(a) if $c > 0$ and all numbers in the bottom row of the synthetic division are nonnegative, then c is larger than or equal to any zero of $P(x)$.

(b) if $c < 0$ and the numbers in the bottom row of the synthetic division alternate in sign (with 0 considered positive or negative, as needed), then c is less than or equal to any zero of $P(x)$.

⦿ **Example 1**   Approximate the real zeros of $P(x) = x^4 - 6x^3 + 8x^2 + 2x - 1$.

Let us begin to look for zeros by trying $c = -2$. To do this, we divide $P(x)$ by $x + 2$.

$$
\begin{array}{r|rrrrr}
-2 & 1 & -6 & 8 & 2 & -1 \\
   &   & -2 & 16 & -48 & 92 \\
\hline
   & 1 & -8 & 24 & -46 & 91 \\
\end{array}
$$

The leading coefficient is positive and the numbers in the bottom row alternate in sign. Since $-2 < 0$, we know by Theorem 11.11(b) that $x = -2$ is less than or equal to any zero of $P(x)$. If we divide $P(x)$ by $x + 1$, we get

$$
\begin{array}{r|rrrrr}
-1 & 1 & -6 & 8 & 2 & -1 \\
   &   & -1 & 7 & -15 & 13 \\
\hline
   & 1 & -7 & 15 & -13 & 12 \\
\end{array}
$$

By this result, $x = -1$ is also less than or equal to any real zero of $P(x)$. Note that $P(-1) = 12 > 0$, while $P(0) = -1 < 0$. Hence, there is at least one real number zero between $x = -1$ and $x = 0$ (by Theorem 11.10).

Let us try $c = -.5$. If we divide $P(x)$ by $x + .5$, we have

$$
\begin{array}{r|rrrrr}
-.5 & 1 & -6 & 8 & 2 & -1 \\
    &   & -.5 & 3.25 & -5.625 & 1.8125 \\
\hline
    & 1 & -6.5 & 11.25 & -3.625 & .8125 \\
\end{array}
$$

Since $P(-.5) > 0$ and $P(0) < 0$, the real number zero is between $-.5$ and 0. Now try $c = -.4$.

$$
\begin{array}{r|rrrrr}
-.4 & 1 & -6 & 8 & 2 & -1 \\
    &   & -.4 & 2.56 & -4.224 & .8896 \\
\hline
    & 1 & -6.4 & 10.56 & -2.224 & -.1104 \\
\end{array}
$$

Note that $P(-.5) > 0$, while $P(-.4) < 0$. Since $P(-.4)$ is closer to zero than $P(-.5)$, we are probably safe in saying that, to one decimal place of accuracy, one real number zero of $P(x)$ is $x = -.4$. We can get further decimal places of accuracy by continuing this process. In the same way, we can show that $P(x)$ has three more real zeros. To one decimal place of accuracy these three other zeros are .3, 2.4, and 3.7. ▌

Descartes' rule of signs, stated in the next theorem, gives a useful, practical test for finding the number of positive or negative real zeros of a given polynomial.

Theorem 11.12 (*Descartes' Rule of Signs*) Let $P(x)$ be a polynomial with real number coefficients.
  (a) The number of positive real zeros of $P(x)$ is either equal to the number of variations in sign occurring in the coefficients of $P(x)$, or else is less than the number of variations by a positive even integer.
  (b) The number of negative real zeros of $P(x)$ either equals the number of variations in sign of $P(-x)$, or else is less than the number of variations by a positive even integer.

For the purposes of this theorem, $(x-1)^4$ is said to have four positive zeros, each equal to 1. The polynomial of Example 1

$$P(x) = x^4 - 6x^3 + 8x^2 + 2x - 1,$$

has three variations in sign:

$$+ x^4 - 6x^3 + 8x^2 + 2x - 1.$$
$$\quad 1 \qquad 2 \qquad\qquad 3$$

Thus, by Descartes' rule of signs, $P(x)$ has either 3 or $3 - 2 = 1$ positive real zeros. We found in Example 1 that $P(x)$ has three positive real zeros. Since $P(x)$ is of degree 4 and has 3 positive real zeros, we know it must have 1 negative real zero, which corresponds to the result above. We could also verify this with part (b) of Descartes' rule of signs. Note that

$$P(-x) = (-x)^4 - 6(-x)^3 + 8(-x)^2 + 2(-x) - 1$$
$$= x^4 + 6x^3 + 8x^2 - 2x - 1$$

has only one variation in sign. Hence, $P(x)$ has only one negative real zero, which again corresponds to our result from above.

Example 2 Find the number of positive and negative real zeros of

$$Q(x) = x^5 + 5x^4 + 3x^2 + 2x + 1.$$

The polynomial $Q(x)$ has no variations in sign and hence has no positive real zeros. Here

$$Q(-x) = -x^5 + 5x^4 + 3x^2 - 2x + 1,$$

which has three variations in sign. Hence, $Q(x)$ has either 3 or 1 negative real zeros. ▌

11.4 Exercises *Use Theorem 11.10 to show that the following polynomials have a real zero between the numbers given.*

1. $P(x) = x^3 + 3x^2 - 2x - 6$; 1 and 2
2. $P(x) = x^3 + x^2 - 5x - 5$; 2 and 3
3. $P(x) = 2x^3 - 8x^2 + x + 16$; 2 and 2.5
4. $P(x) = 3x^3 + 7x^2 - 4$; 1/2 and 1

5. $P(x) = 2x^4 - 4x^2 + 3x - 6$; 2 and 1.5
6. $P(x) = x^4 - 4x^3 - x + 1$; 1 and .3
7. $P(x) = -3x^4 - x^3 + 2x^2 + 4$; 1 and 1.2
8. $P(x) = x^5 + 2x^4 + x^3 + 3$; -1.3 and -2

Use Theorem 11.11 to show that the real zeros of each of the following polynomials satisfy the given conditions.

9. $P(x) = x^4 - x^3 + 3x^2 - 8x + 8$; no real zeros greater than 2
10. $P(x) = 2x^5 - x^4 + 2x^3 - 2x^2 + 4x - 4$; no real zero greater than 1
11. $P(x) = x^4 + x^3 - x^2 + 3$; no real zero less than -2
12. $P(x) = x^5 + 2x^3 - 2x^2 + 5x + 5$; no real zero less than -1
13. $P(x) = 3x^4 + 2x^3 - 4x^2 + x - 1$; no real zero greater than 1
14. $P(x) = 3x^4 + 2x^3 - 4x^2 + x - 1$; no real zero less than -2
15. $P(x) = x^5 - 3x^3 + x + 2$; no real zero greater than 2
16. $P(x) = x^5 - 3x^3 + x + 2$; no real zero less than -3

◉ *For each of the following polynomials, (a) use Theorem 11.12 to find the number of positive and negative real zeros. (See Example 2.) (b) Find all real zeros. Approximate each zero as a decimal to the nearest tenth.*

17. $P(x) = x^3 + 3x^2 - 2x - 6$

18. $P(x) = x^3 + x^2 - 5x - 5$

19. $P(x) = x^3 - 4x^2 - 5x + 14$

20. $P(x) = x^3 + 9x^2 + 34x + 13$

21. $P(x) = x^3 + 6x - 13$

22. $P(x) = x^3 - 3x^2 + 4x - 5$

23. $P(x) = x^4 - 8x^3 + 17x^2 - 2x - 14$

24. $P(x) = x^4 - 4x^3 - x^2 + 8x - 2$

◉ *The following polynomials have zeros in the given intervals. Approximate these zeros to the nearest hundredth.*

25. $P(x) = x^4 + x^3 - 6x^2 - 20x - 16$, [3.2, 3.3] and [−1.4, −1.1]

26. $P(x) = x^4 - 2x^3 - 2x^2 - 18x + 5$, [.2, .4] and [3.7, 3.8]

27. $P(x) = x^4 - 4x^3 - 20x^2 + 32x + 12$; [−4, −3], [−1, 0], [1, 2], and [6, 7]

28. $P(x) = x^4 - 4x^3 - 44x^2 + 160x - 80$; [−7, −6], [0, 1], [2, 3], and [7, 8]

29. Suppose a polynomial $P(x)$ has only rational zeros. Show how to express $P(x)$ with only rational coefficients; with only irrational coefficients.

30. Let $P(x) = x^n + a_{n-1}x^{n-1} + a_{n-2}x^{n-2} + \cdots + a_1x + a_0$. Let m be the largest of the absolute values of the a's. Show that all real zeros of $P(x)$ are no greater than $m + 1$.

Chapter 11 Review Exercises

For each of the following divisions, find $Q(x)$ and $R(x)$.

1. $\dfrac{4x^3 - 2x^2 + 3x + 5}{2x - 1}$

2. $\dfrac{3x^3 + 5x^2 - 5x + 2}{3x + 2}$

3. $\dfrac{x^4 - 3x^2 + 5x - 1}{x^2 + 2}$

4. $\dfrac{2x^4 - x^3 + x^2 + 5x}{2x^2 - x}$

Use synthetic division to find $Q(x)$ and r for each of the following.

5. $\dfrac{2x^3 + 3x^2 - 4x + 1}{x - 1}$

6. $\dfrac{4x^3 + 3x^2 + 3x + 5}{x - 5}$

7. $\dfrac{2x^3 - 4x + 6}{x - 2}$

8. $\dfrac{3x^4 - x^2 + x - 1}{x + 1}$

Use synthetic division to find $P(2)$ for each of the following.

9. $P(x) = x^3 + 3x^2 - 5x + 1$

10. $P(x) = 2x^3 - 4x^2 + 3x - 10$

11. $P(x) = 5x^4 - 12x^2 + 2x - 8$

12. $P(x) = x^5 - 3x^2 + 2x - 4$

Find a polynomial of lowest degree having the following zeros.

13. −1, 4, 7

14. 8, 2, 3

15. $-\sqrt{7}, \sqrt{7}, 2, -1$

16. $1 + \sqrt{5}, 1 - \sqrt{5}, -4, 1$

17. Is −1 a zero of $P(x) = 2x^4 + x^3 - 4x^2 + 3x + 1$?

18. Is −2 a zero of $P(x) = 2x^4 + x^3 - 4x^2 + 3x + 1$?

19. Is $x + 1$ a factor of $P(x) = x^3 + 2x^2 + 3x - 1$?

20. Is $x + 1$ a factor of $P(x) = 2x^3 - x^2 + x + 4$?

21. Find a polynomial of degree 3 with -2, 1, and 4 as zeros, and $P(2) = 16$.

22. Find a polynomial of degree 4 with $1, -1$, and $3i$ as zeros, and $P(2) = 39$.

23. Find a lowest-degree polynomial with real coefficients having zeros $2, -2$, and $-i$.

24. Find a lowest-degree polynomial with real coefficients having zeros of $2, -3$, and $5i$.

25. Find the polynomial of lowest degree with real coefficients having -3 and $1 - i$ as zeros.

26. Find all zeros of $P(x) = x^4 - 3x^3 - 8x^2 + 22x - 24$, given that $1 - i$ is a zero.

27. Find all zeros of $P(x) = x^4 - 6x^3 + 14x^2 - 24x + 40$, given that $3 + i$ is a zero.

28. Find all zeros of $P(x) = x^4 + x^3 - x^2 + x - 2$, given that 1 is a zero.

Find all rational zeros of the following.

29. $P(x) = 2x^3 - 9x^2 - 6x + 5$

30. $P(x) = 3x^3 - 10x^2 - 27x + 10$

31. $P(x) = x^3 - \dfrac{17}{6}x^2 - \dfrac{13}{3}x - \dfrac{4}{3}$

32. $P(x) = 8x^4 - 14x^3 - 29x^2 - 4x + 3$

33. $P(x) = -x^4 + 2x^3 - 3x^2 + 11x - 7$

34. $P(x) = x^5 - 3x^4 - 5x^3 + 15x^2 + 4x - 12$

35. Use a polynomial to show that $\sqrt{11}$ is irrational.

36. Show that $P(x) = x^3 - 9x^2 + 2x - 5$ has no rational zeros.

Show that the following polynomials have real zeros satisfying the given conditions.

37. $P(x) = 3x^3 - 8x^2 + x + 2$, zero in $[-1, 0]$ and $[2, 3]$

38. $P(x) = 4x^3 - 37x^2 + 50x + 60$, zero in $[2, 3]$ and $[7, 8]$

39. $P(x) = x^3 + 2x^2 - 22x - 8$, zero in $[-1, 0]$ and $[-6, -5]$

40. $P(x) = 2x^4 - x^3 - 21x^2 + 51x - 36$ has no real zero greater than 4

41. $P(x) = 6x^4 + 13x^3 - 11x^2 - 3x + 5$ has no zero greater than 1 or less than -3

◉ *Approximate the real zeros of each of the following as a decimal to the nearest tenth.*

42. $P(x) = 2x^3 - 11x^2 - 2x + 2$

43. $P(x) = x^4 - 4x^3 - 5x^2 + 14x - 15$

44. (a) Find the number of positive and negative zeros of $P(x) = x^3 + 3x^2 - 4x - 2$

   (b) Show that $P(x)$ has a zero between -4 and -3. Approximate this zero to the nearest tenth.

Chapter 12

Further Topics in Algebra

12.1 Mathematical Induction

Many results in mathematics are claimed to be true for any positive integer. Any of these results could be checked for $n = 1$, $n = 2$, $n = 3$, and so on, but since the set of positive integers is infinite it would be impossible to check every possible case. For example, let S_n represent the statement that the sum of the first n positive integers is $n(n + 1)/2$, or

$$S_n: 1 + 2 + 3 + \ldots + n = \frac{n(n + 1)}{2}.$$

We can easily check the truth of this statement for the first few values of n:

If $n = 1$, S_1 is $1 = \dfrac{1(1 + 1)}{2}$ true.

If $n = 2$, S_2 is $1 + 2 = \dfrac{2(2 + 1)}{2}$ true.

If $n = 3$, S_3 is $1 + 2 + 3 = \dfrac{3(3 + 1)}{2}$ true.

If $n = 4$, S_4 is $1 + 2 + 3 + 4 = \dfrac{4(4 + 1)}{2}$ true.

We could continue in this way as long as we wanted, but we could still never prove that S_n is true for *every* positive integer value of n. To prove that such statements are true for every positive integer value of n, we can often use the **Principle of Mathematical Induction,** which states

> Let S_n be a statement concerning the positive integer n. Suppose that
> (a) S_1 is true
> (b) If S_n is true for the positive integer k, then S_n is also true for the integer $k + 1$. (That is, the truth of S_k implies the truth of S_{k+1}.)
> Then S_n is true for every positive integer value of n.

A proof by mathematical induction can be explained as follows. By (a) above, the statement is true when $n = 1$. By (b) above, the fact that the statement is true for $n = 1$ implies that it is true for $n = 1 + 1 = 2$. Using (b) again, it is thus true for $2 + 1 = 3$, for $3 + 1 = 4$, for $4 + 1 = 5$, and so on. By continuing in this way, the statement must be true for *every* positive integer, no matter how large.

Two separate steps are required for a proof by mathematical induction:

(1) Prove that the statement is true for $n = 1$.

(2) Assume that S_n is true for the positive integer k. Show that this implies that S_n is also true for the positive integer $k + 1$.

In the next example we use mathematical induction to prove the statement S_n mentioned at the beginning of this section.

Example 1   Let S_n represent the statement

$$1 + 2 + 3 + \ldots + n = \frac{n(n + 1)}{2}.$$

Prove that S_n is true for every positive integer n.

The proof by mathematical induction is as follows.

Step 1   Show that the statement is true when $n = 1$. If $n = 1$, S_1 becomes

$$1 = \frac{1(1 + 1)}{2}$$

which is true.

Step 2   Assume that S_n is true for the statement $n = k$. That is, assume that

$$1 + 2 + 3 + \ldots + k = \frac{k(k + 1)}{2}$$

is true. Show that this implies the truth of S_{k+1}, where S_{k+1} is the statement

$$1 + 2 + 3 + \ldots + k + (k + 1) = \frac{(k + 1)[(k + 1) + 1]}{2}.$$

We have assumed that

$$1 + 2 + 3 + \ldots + k = \frac{k(k + 1)}{2}.$$

By adding $k + 1$ to both sides of the known equation, we have

$$1 + 2 + 3 + \cdots + k + (k + 1) = \frac{k(k + 1)}{2} + (k + 1)$$

Then, factoring on the right gives

$$= (k + 1)\left(\frac{k}{2} + 1\right)$$

$$= (k + 1)\left(\frac{k + 2}{2}\right)$$

$$1 + 2 + 3 + \cdots + (k + 1) = \frac{(k + 1)[(k + 1) + 1]}{2}.$$

This final result is the statement we wished to establish for $n = k + 1$, so that the truth of S_k implies the truth of S_{k+1}.

The two steps required for a proof by mathematical induction have now been completed, so that our statement S_n is true for every positive integer value of n. ▌

Example 2   Prove: if x is a real number between 0 and 1, then for every positive integer n,

$$0 < x^n < 1.$$

Here S_1 is: if $0 < x < 1$, then $0 < x^1 < 1$, which is true. Assume now that S_k is true:

$$\text{if } 0 < x < 1, \text{ then } 0 < x^k < 1.$$

We must now show that this implies the truth of S_{k+1}. Multiply all members of $0 < x^k < 1$ by x to get

$$x \cdot 0 < x \cdot x^k < x \cdot 1.$$

(Here we use the fact that $0 < x$.) Simplify to get

$$0 < x^{k+1} < x.$$

We know that $x < 1$. Thus,

$$x^{k+1} < x < 1,$$

and $$0 < x^{k+1} < 1.$$

By this work, the truth of S_k implies the truth of S_{k+1}, so that the given statement is true for every positive integer n. ▌

Some statements S_n are not true for the first few values of n, but are true for all values of n that are at least equal to some fixed integer j. The following slightly generalized form of the Principle of Mathematical Induction takes care of these cases.

Let S_n be a statement concerning the positive integer n. Let j be a fixed positive integer. Suppose that
   (a) S_j is true
   (b) If S_n is true for the positive integer k, where $k \geq j$, then S_n is also true for the positive integer $k + 1$.
Then S_n is true for all positive integers n, where $n \geq j$.

Example 3   Let S_n represent the statement

$$2^n > 2n + 1.$$

Show that S_n is true for all values of n such that $n \geq 3$.

(Check that S_n is *false* for $n = 1$ and $n = 2$.) As before, our proof requires two steps.

Step 1   Show that S_n is true for $n = 3$. If $n = 3$, S_n is

$$2^3 > 2 \cdot 3 + 1$$

or $$8 > 7$$

which is true.

Step 2   Assume that S_n is true for some positive integer k, where $k \geq 3$. That is, assume the truth of

$$S_k: 2^k > 2k + 1.$$

We must now show that the truth of S_k implies the truth of S_{k+1}, or

$$S_{k+1}: 2^{k+1} > 2(k + 1) + 1.$$

Our assumption is that $2^k > 2k + 1$. Multiply both sides by 2, obtaining

$$2 \cdot 2^k > 2(2k + 1)$$

or $$2^{k+1} > 4k + 2.$$

Rewrite $4k + 2$ as $2(k + 1) + 2k$, giving

$$2^{k+1} > 2(k + 1) + 2k. \tag{1}$$

Since k is a positive integer,

$$2k > 1. \tag{2}$$

Adding $2(k + 1)$ to both sides of inequality (2) gives

$$2(k + 1) + 2k > 2(k + 1) + 1. \tag{3}$$

From inequalities (1) and (3),

$$2^{k+1} > 2(k + 1) + 2k > 2(k + 1) + 1$$

or $$2^{k+1} > 2(k + 1) + 1.$$

Thus, the truth of S_k implies the truth of S_{k+1}, and this, together with the fact that S_3 is true, shows that S_n is true for every positive integer value of n greater than or equal to 3.   ▌

Example 4   There is a flaw in the following "proof." See if you can spot it.

Prove: In every set of n dogs, if at least one is male, then they are all male.

S_1 is obviously true: in a set of one dog, if one is male then all are male. Assume that S_k is true. Let us show that S_{k+1} is true. Suppose

$$\{D_1, D_2, \ldots, D_k, D_{k+1}\}$$

is any set of $k + 1$ dogs, and suppose that one of them is male; say D_1 is male (if it happens that the male was D_2 or D_6, or whatever, just rearrange them so that D_1 is a male). Thus $\{D_1, D_2, \ldots, D_k\}$ is a set of k dogs and one of them is a male,

Adapted from *Algebra and Trigonometry with Analytic Geometry* by Arthur B. Simon. Copyright © 1979 by W. H. Freeman and Company. Reprinted by permission.

so *all* are males, because S_k is assumed true. But this means that $\{D_2, D_3, \ldots, D_k, D_{k+1}\}$ is now a set of k dogs (we left D_1 out) and one is male (in fact, $D_2, \ldots, D_k$ are males) so they *all* are, including D_{k+1}. Thus, all $k + 1$ dogs are male. This completes our induction argument. (The error appears as a footnote* on the following page.) █

Arguments with exactly the same fallacy as in Example 4 have appeared again and again in mathematics. The particular example used here is taken with permission from *Algebra and Trigonometry with Analytic Geometry* by Arthur B. Simon (W. H. Freeman and Company, 1979).

12.1 Exercises   *Write out in full and verify each of the statements S_1, S_2, S_3, S_4, and S_5 for each of the following. Then use mathematical induction to prove that each of the given statements is true for every positive integer n.*

1. $2 + 4 + 6 + \cdots + 2n = n(n + 1)$

2. $1 + 3 + 5 + \cdots + (2n - 1) = n^2$

Use the method of mathematical induction to prove that each of the following statements is true for every positive integer n.

3. $2 + 4 + 8 + \cdots + 2^n = 2^{n+1} - 2$

4. $1^2 + 2^2 + 3^2 + \cdots + n^2 = \dfrac{n(n + 1)(2n + 1)}{6}$

5. $1^3 + 2^3 + 3^3 + \cdots + n^3 = \dfrac{n^2(n + 1)^2}{4}$

6. $3 + 3^2 + 3^3 + \cdots + 3^n = \dfrac{3(3^n - 1)}{2}$

7. $5 \cdot 6 + 5 \cdot 6^2 + 5 \cdot 6^3 + \cdots + 5 \cdot 6^n = 6(6^n - 1)$

8. $\dfrac{1}{1 \cdot 2} + \dfrac{1}{2 \cdot 3} + \dfrac{1}{3 \cdot 4} + \cdots + \dfrac{1}{n(n + 1)} = \dfrac{n}{n + 1}$

9. $\dfrac{1}{1 \cdot 4} + \dfrac{1}{4 \cdot 7} + \dfrac{1}{7 \cdot 10} + \cdots + \dfrac{1}{(3n - 2)(3n + 1)} = \dfrac{n}{3n + 1}$

10. $\dfrac{1}{2} + \dfrac{1}{2^2} + \dfrac{1}{2^3} + \cdots + \dfrac{1}{2^n} = 1 - \dfrac{1}{2^n}$

11. $1 \cdot 2 + 2 \cdot 3 + 3 \cdot 4 + \ldots + n(n + 1) = \dfrac{n(n + 1)(n + 2)}{3}$

12. $1 \cdot 4 + 2 \cdot 9 + 3 \cdot 16 + \ldots + n(n + 1)^2 = \dfrac{n(n + 1)(n + 2)(3n + 5)}{12}$

13. $x^{2n} + x^{2n-1}y + \cdots + xy^{2n-1} + y^{2n} = \dfrac{x^{2n+1} - y^{2n+1}}{x - y}$

14. $x^{2n-1} + x^{2n-2}y + \cdots + xy^{2n-2} + y^{2n-1} = \dfrac{x^{2n} - y^{2n}}{x - y}$

15. $(a^m)^n = a^{mn}$ (Assume a and m are constant.)

16. $(ab)^n = a^n b^n$ (Assume a and b are constant.)

17. $2^n > 2n$ if $n \geq 3$

18. $3^n > 2n + 1$, if $n \geq 2$

19. $3n^3 + 6n$ is divisible by 9

20. $n^2 + n$ is divisible by 2

21. $3^{2n} - 1$ is divisible by 8

22. If $a > 1$, then $a^n > 1$

23. If $a > 1$, then $a^n > a^{n-1}$

24. If $0 < a < 1$, then $a^n < a^{n-1}$

25. $2^n > n^2$, for $n \geq 4$

26. $n! > 2^n$, where $n! = n(n-1)(n-2) \cdots (3)(2)(1)$

27. $4^n > n^4$, for $n \geq 7$

28. $(1 + x)^n \geq 1 + nx$ for every $n > 1$ and fixed $x \geq -1$

29. $\sin(\theta + n\pi) = (-1)^n \cdot \sin \theta$

30. $|\sin nx| \leq n|\sin x|$

31. $[r(\cos \theta + i \sin \theta)]^n = r^n(\cos n\theta + i \sin n\theta)$ (De Moivre's Theorem)

32. What is wrong with the following "proof" by mathematical induction?

Prove: Any natural number equals the next natural number.
    To begin, we assume the statement true for some natural number k:

$$k = k + 1.$$

We must now show that the statement is true for $n = k + 1$. If we add 1 to both sides, we have

$$k + 1 = k + 1 + 1$$
$$k + 1 = k + 2.$$

Hence, if the statement is true for $n = k$, it is also true for $n = k + 1$. Thus, the theorem is proved.

33. In the country of Pango, the government prints only three-glok banknotes and five-glok notes. Prove that any purchase of 8 gloks or more can be paid for with only three-glok notes and five-glok notes. (Hint: Consider two cases: k gloks being paid with only three-glok notes, and k gloks requiring at least one five-glok note.)

34. Suppose that n straight lines (with $n \geq 2$) are drawn in a plane, where no two lines are parallel and no three lines pass through the same point. Show that the number of points of intersection of the lines is $(n^2 - n)/2$.

35. The series of sketches below starts with an equilateral triangle having sides of length 1. In the following steps, equilateral triangles are constructed on each side of the preceding figure. The lengths of the sides of these new triangles is 1/3 the length of the sides of the preceding triangles. Develop a formula for the number of sides of the nth figure. Use mathematical induction to prove your answer.

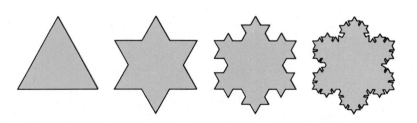

---

*Answer to the question posed in Example 4: The deduction that S_k implies S_{k+1} is correct whenever $k \geq 2$. However, *it does not hold for* $k = 1$; that is, the argument fails to prove that if S_1 is true, then S_2 is also true.

36. Find the perimeter of the nth figure in Exercise 35.

37. Show that the area of the nth figure in Exercise 35 is

$$\sqrt{3}\left[\frac{2}{5} - \frac{3}{20}\left(\frac{4}{9}\right)^{n-1}\right].$$

38. A pile of n rings, each smaller than the one below it, is on a peg. Two other pegs are attached to a board with this peg. In the game called the *Tower of Hanoi* puzzle, all the rings must be moved to a different peg, with only one ring moved at a time, and with no ring ever placed on top of a smaller ring. Find the least number of moves that would be required. Prove your result with mathematical induction.

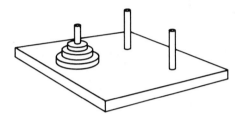

12.2 The Binomial Theorem

In this section, we look at a method of expanding the binomial expression $(x + y)^n$. We begin by listing expansions of $(x + y)^n$ for various positive integer values of n. For example,

$$(x + y)^1 = x + y$$
$$(x + y)^2 = x^2 + 2xy + y^2$$
$$(x + y)^3 = x^3 + 3x^2y + 3xy^2 + y^3$$
$$(x + y)^4 = x^4 + 4x^3y + 6x^2y^2 + 4xy^3 + y^4$$
$$(x + y)^5 = x^5 + 5x^4y + 10x^3y^2 + 10x^2y^3 + 5xy^4 + y^5$$

and so on. By studying these results, we can find a pattern. Let us try to write down this pattern so that we can write a general expression for $(x + y)^n$.

First, notice that each expression begins with x raised to the same power as the binomial itself. That is, the expansion of $(x + y)^1$ has a first term of x^1, $(x + y)^2$ has a first term of x^2, $(x + y)^3$ has a first term of x^3, and so on. Also, the last term in each expansion is y to the same power as the binomial. We can see that the expression of $(x + y)^n$ should begin with the term x^n and end with the term y^n.

Also, the exponents on x decrease by one in each term after the first, while the exponents on y, beginning with y in the second term, increase by one in each succeeding term. Thus, the *variables* in the expansion of $(x + y)^n$ have the following pattern.

$$x^n, \quad x^{n-1}y, \quad x^{n-2}y^2, \quad x^{n-3}y^3, \quad \ldots, \quad xy^{n-1}, \quad y^n$$

From this pattern, we note that the sum of the exponents on x and y in each term is n. For example, in the third term in the list above, the variable is $x^{n-2}y^2$, and the sum of the exponents is $n - 2 + 2 = n$.

Now examine the pattern for the *coefficients* in the terms of the expansions shown above. Writing the coefficients alone in a triangular pattern gives

$$
\begin{array}{ccccccccccccc}
 & & & & & 1 & & 1 & & & & & \\
 & & & & 1 & & 2 & & 1 & & & & \\
 & & & 1 & & 3 & & 3 & & 1 & & & \\
 & & 1 & & 4 & & 6 & & 4 & & 1 & & \\
 & 1 & & 5 & & 10 & & 10 & & 5 & & 1 &
\end{array}
$$

With the coefficients arranged in this way it can be seen that each number in the triangle is the sum of the two numbers directly above it (one to the right and one to the left.) For example, in the fourth row from the top, 1 is the sum of 1, the only number above it, 4 is the sum of 1 and 3, 6 is the sum of 3 and 3, and so on. This triangular array of numbers is called **Pascal's Triangle**, in honor of the famous seventeenth-century mathematician Blaise Pascal, one of the first to use it extensively.

To get the coefficients for $(x + y)^6$, include a sixth row on the array of numbers given above. By adding adjacent numbers the sixth row is found to be

$$1 \quad 6 \quad 15 \quad 20 \quad 15 \quad 6 \quad 1.$$

Using these coefficients the expansion of $(x + y)^6$ is

$$(x + y)^6 = x^6 + 6x^5y + 15x^4y^2 + 20x^3y^3 + 15x^2y^4 + 6xy^5 + y^6.$$

Although it is possible to use Pascal's Triangle to find the coefficients of $(x + y)^n$ for any positive integer value of n, this becomes impractical for large values of n due to the very large numbers involved. A more efficient way of finding these coefficients uses the notation $n!$ (read "n-factorial"), which you may recall. By definition,

$$n! = n(n - 1)(n - 2) \cdots (3)(2)(1),$$

for any positive integer n. For example, $5! = 5 \cdot 4 \cdot 3 \cdot 2 \cdot 1 = 120$, $7! = 7 \cdot 6 \cdot 5 \cdot 4 \cdot 3 \cdot 2 \cdot 1 = 5040$, $2! = 2 \cdot 1 = 2$, and so on. To simplify certain formulas later on, $0!$ is defined as

$$0! = 1.$$

Now let us look at the coefficients of the expression

$$(x + y)^5 = x^5 + 5x^4y + 10x^3y^2 + 10x^2y^3 + 5xy^4 + y^5.$$

The coefficient on the second term, $5x^4y$, is 5, and the exponents on the variables are 4 and 1. Note that

$$5 = \frac{5!}{4!1!}.$$

The coefficient on the third term is 10, with exponents of 3 and 2, and

$$10 = \frac{5!}{3!2!}.$$

The last term (the sixth term) can be written as $y^5 = 1x^0y^5$, with coefficient 1, and exponents of 0 and 5. Since $0! = 1$, check that

$$1 = \frac{5!}{0!5!}.$$

In general, the coefficient for the term of the expansion of $(x + y)^n$ in which the variable part is $x^r y^{n-r}$ (where $r \le n$) will be

$$\frac{n!}{r!(n - r)!}.$$

This number, called a **binomial coefficient,** is often symbolized $\binom{n}{r}$, (read "n above r") so that

$$\binom{n}{r} = \frac{n!}{r!(n - r)!}.$$

Example 1   (a) $\displaystyle \binom{6}{2} = \frac{6!}{2!(6 - 2)!}$

$$= \frac{6!}{2!4!}$$

$$= \frac{6 \cdot 5 \cdot 4 \cdot 3 \cdot 2 \cdot 1}{2 \cdot 1 \cdot 4 \cdot 3 \cdot 2 \cdot 1}$$

$$= 15$$

(b) $\displaystyle \binom{8}{0} = \frac{8!}{0!(8 - 0)!} = \frac{8!}{0!8!} = \frac{8!}{1 \cdot 8!} = 1$

(c) $\displaystyle \binom{10}{10} = \frac{10!}{10!(10 - 10)!} = \frac{10!}{10!0!} = 1$ ▌

Using binomial coefficients, we have the following binomial theorem, which gives the expansion of $(x + y)^n$ for any positive integer value of n.

Theorem 12.1   (*Binomial Theorem*) For any positive integer n, and any complex numbers x and y,

$$(x + y)^n = x^n + \binom{n}{n-1}x^{n-1}y + \binom{n}{n-2}x^{n-2}y^2$$

$$+ \binom{n}{n-3}x^{n-3}y^3 + \cdots + \binom{n}{n-r}x^{n-r}y^r + \cdots + \binom{n}{1}xy^{n-1} + y^n \qquad (1)$$

The binomial theorem is proved by mathematical induction. Let S_n be statement (1) above. Begin by verifying S_n for $n = 1$.

$$S_1: \quad (x + y)^1 = x^1 + y^1,$$

which is true.

Now assume that S_n is true for the positive integer k. Statement S_k becomes (using the definition of the binomial coefficient.)

$$S_k: \quad (x + y)^k = x^k + \frac{k!}{1!(k-1)!} x^{k-1}y + \frac{k!}{2!(k-2)!} x^{k-2}y^2$$

$$+ \cdots + \frac{k!}{(k-1)!1!} xy^{k-1} + y^k. \tag{2}$$

Multiply both sides of equation (2) by $x + y$.

$$(x + y)^k \cdot (x + y) = x(x + y)^k + y(x + y)^k$$

$$= \left[x \cdot x^k + \frac{k!}{1!(k-1)!} x^k y + \frac{k!}{2!(k-2)!} x^{k-1}y^2 \right.$$

$$\left. + \cdots + \frac{k!}{(k-1)!1!} x^2 y^{k-1} + xy^k \right]$$

$$+ \left[x^k \cdot y + \frac{k!}{1!(k-1)!} x^{k-1}y^2 + \cdots \right.$$

$$\left. + \frac{k!}{(k-1)!1!} xy^k + y \cdot y^k \right].$$

Rearrange terms to get

$$(x + y)^{k+1} = x^{k+1} + \left[\frac{k!}{1!(k-1)!} + 1 \right] x^k y +$$

$$\left[\frac{k!}{2!(k-2)!} + \frac{k!}{1!(k-1)!} \right] x^{k-1}y^2 + \cdots +$$

$$\left[1 + \frac{k!}{(k-1)!1!} \right] xy^k + y^{k+1}. \tag{3}$$

The first expression in brackets in equation (3) simplifies to $\binom{k+1}{1}$. The second becomes $\binom{k+1}{2}$, the last $\binom{k+1}{k}$, and so on. The result of equation (3) is just equation (2) with every k replaced by $k + 1$. Thus, the truth of S_n when $n = k$ implies the truth of S_n for $n = k + 1$, proving the theorem by mathematical induction.

Example 2   Write out the binomial expansion of $(x + y)^9$.
Using the binomial theorem,

$$(x + y)^9 = x^9 + \binom{9}{8}x^8 y + \binom{9}{7}x^7 y^2 + \binom{9}{6}x^6 y^3 + \binom{9}{5}x^5 y^4$$

$$+ \binom{9}{4}x^4 y^5 + \binom{9}{3}x^3 y^6 + \binom{9}{2}x^2 y^7 + \binom{9}{1}xy^8 + y^9.$$

Now evaluate each of the binomial coefficients.

$$= x^9 + \frac{9!}{1!8!}x^8y + \frac{9!}{2!7!}x^7y^2 + \frac{9!}{3!6!}x^6y^3 + \frac{9!}{4!5!}x^5y^4$$

$$+ \frac{9!}{5!4!}x^4y^5 + \frac{9!}{6!3!}x^3y^6 + \frac{9!}{7!2!}x^2y^7 + \frac{9!}{8!1!}xy^8 + y^9$$

$$= x^9 + 9x^8y + 36x^7y^2 + 84x^6y^3 + 126x^5y^4 + 126x^4y^5$$

$$+ 84x^3y^6 + 36x^2y^7 + 9xy^8 + y^9 \quad \blacksquare$$

Example 3   Expand $\left(a - \frac{b}{2}\right)^5$.

Again we use the binomial theorem. Let $x = a$, $y = -\frac{b}{2}$, and $n = 5$.

$$\left(a - \frac{b}{2}\right)^5 = a^5 + \binom{5}{4}a^4\left(-\frac{b}{2}\right) + \binom{5}{3}a^3\left(-\frac{b}{2}\right)^2 + \binom{5}{2}a^2\left(-\frac{b}{2}\right)^3$$

$$+ \binom{5}{1}a\left(-\frac{b}{2}\right)^4 + \left(-\frac{b}{2}\right)^5$$

$$= a^5 + 5a^4\left(-\frac{b}{2}\right) + 10a^3\left(-\frac{b}{2}\right)^2 + 10a^2\left(-\frac{b}{2}\right)^3$$

$$+ 5a\left(-\frac{b}{2}\right)^4 + \left(-\frac{b}{2}\right)^5$$

$$= a^5 - \frac{5}{2}a^4b + \frac{5}{2}a^3b^2 - \frac{5}{4}a^2b^3 + \frac{5}{16}ab^4 - \frac{1}{32}b^5 \quad \blacksquare$$

Example 4   Expand $\left(\frac{3}{m^2} - 2\sqrt{m}\right)^4$. (Assume $m > 0$.)

Use the binomial theorem.

$$\left(\frac{3}{m^2} - 2\sqrt{m}\right)^4 = \left(\frac{3}{m^2}\right)^4 + \binom{4}{1}\left(\frac{3}{m^2}\right)^3(-2\sqrt{m})^1 + \binom{4}{2}\left(\frac{3}{m^2}\right)^2(-2\sqrt{m})^2$$

$$+ \binom{4}{3}\left(\frac{3}{m^2}\right)^1(-2\sqrt{m})^3 + (-2\sqrt{m})^4$$

$$= \frac{81}{m^8} + 4\left(\frac{27}{m^6}\right)(-2m^{1/2}) + 6\left(\frac{9}{m^4}\right)(4m)$$

$$+ 4\left(\frac{3}{m^2}\right)(-8m^{3/2}) + 16m^2$$

Here we used the fact that $\sqrt{m} = m^{1/2}$. Finally,

$$\left(\frac{3}{m^2} - 2\sqrt{m}\right)^4 = \frac{81}{m^8} - \frac{216}{m^{11/2}} + \frac{216}{m^3} - \frac{96}{m^{1/2}} + 16m^2 \quad \blacksquare$$

We can also write any single term of a binomial expansion. For example, to find the tenth term of $(x + y)^n$, where $n \geq 9$, first notice that in the tenth term we have y raised to the ninth power (since y has the power 1 in the second term, the power 2 in the third term, and so on). Since the exponents on x and y in any term must have a sum of n, the exponent on x in the tenth term is $n - 9$. Thus, the tenth term of the expansion is

$$\binom{n}{n-9} x^{n-9} y^9 = \frac{n!}{(n-9)!9!} x^{n-9} y^9.$$

This same idea can be used to obtain the result given in the following theorem.

Theorem 12.2   The rth term of the binomial expansion of $(x + y)^n$, where $n \geq r - 1$, is

$$\binom{n}{n-(r-1)} x^{n-(r-1)} y^{r-1}.$$

Example 5   Find the seventh term of $(a + 2b)^{10}$.

In the seventh term $2b$ has an exponent of 6, while a has an exponent of $10 - 6$, or 4. The seventh term is thus

$$\binom{10}{4} a^4 (2b)^6 = 210 a^4 (64 b^6)$$

$$= 13{,}440 a^4 b^6. \quad \blacksquare$$

12.2 Exercises   *Write out the binomial expansion for each of the following.*

1. $(x + y)^6$
2. $(m + n)^4$
3. $(p - q)^5$
4. $(a - b)^7$
5. $(r^2 + s)^5$
6. $(m + n^2)^4$

7. $(p + 2q)^4$
8. $(3r - s)^6$
9. $\left(\dfrac{m}{2} - 1\right)^6$
10. $\left(3 + \dfrac{y}{3}\right)^5$

11. $\left(2p + \dfrac{q}{3}\right)^4$
12. $\left(\dfrac{r}{6} - \dfrac{m}{2}\right)^3$
13. $(m^{-2} + m^2)^4$

14. $\left(\sqrt{x} + \dfrac{4}{\sqrt{x}}\right)^5$
15. $(p^{2/3} - 5p^{4/3})^5$
16. $(3y^{3/2} + 5y^{1/2})^4$

Write only the first four terms in each of the following expansions.

17. $(x + 6)^{21}$
18. $(y - 8)^{17}$
19. $(3m^{-2} + 5m^{-4})^9$
20. $\left(\dfrac{8}{k^2} + 6k\right)^{17}$

For each of the following write the indicated term of the binomial expansion.

21. 5th term of $(m - 2p)^{12}$
22. 4th term of $(3x + y)^6$
23. 9th term of $(2m + n)^{10}$
24. 7th term of $(3r - 5s)^{12}$
25. 17th term of $(p^2 + q)^{20}$
26. 10th term of $(2x^2 + y)^{14}$

27. 8th term of $(x^3 + 2y)^{14}$

28. 13th term of $(a + 2b^3)^{12}$

29. Find the middle term of $(3x^7 + 2y^3)^8$

30. Find the two middle terms of $(-2m^{-1} + 3n^{-2})^{11}$.

Use the binomial expansion to evaluate each of the following to three decimal places.

31. $(1.01)^{10}$ (Hint: $1.01 = 1 + .01$)

32. $(0.99)^{15}$ (Hint: $0.99 = 1 - 0.01$)

33. $(1.99)^8$

34. $(2.99)^3$

35. $(3.02)^6$

36. $(1.01)^9$

● *In calculus, it is shown that*

$$(1 + x)^n = 1 + nx + \frac{n(n-1)}{2!}x^2 + \frac{n(n-1)(n-2)}{3!}x^3 + \cdots$$

for any real number n (not just positive integer values) and any real number x where $|x| < 1$. This result, a generalized binomial theorem, may be used to find approximate values of powers and roots. For example,

$$\sqrt[4]{630} = (625 + 5)^{1/4} = \left[625\left(1 + \frac{5}{625}\right)\right]^{1/4} = 625^{1/4}\left(1 + \frac{5}{625}\right)^{1/4}$$

37. Use the result above to approximate $(1 + 5/625)^{1/4}$ to the nearest thousandth. Then approximate $\sqrt[4]{630}$.

38. Approximate $\sqrt[3]{9.42}$, using this method.

39. Approximate $(1.02)^{-3}$.

40. Approximate $1/(1.04)^5$.

41. In the formula above, let $n = -1$ and find $(1 + x)^{-1}$.

42. Find the first four terms when you divide $1 + x$ into 1. Compare with the results of Exercise 41.

43. Work out the first four terms in the expansion of $(1 + 3)^{1/2}$ using $x = 3$ and $n = 1/2$ in the formula above. Do you get a result close to $(1 + 3)^{1/2} = 4^{1/2} = 2$? Why not?

44. Use the result above to show that for small values of x, $\sqrt{1 + x} \approx 1 + \frac{1}{2}x$.

Prove that each of the following properties of factorial notation are true for any positive integer n.

45. $n(n - 1)! = n!$

46. $\dfrac{n!}{n(n - 1)} = (n - 2)!$

Find all values of n for which

47. $(n + 2)! = 56 \cdot n!$

48. $(n - 4)! = n - 4$

12.3 Sequences

A **sequence** is an ordered list of real numbers, such as

$$3, 5, 7, 9, 11, \ldots$$

Each number in the list is called a **term** of the sequence. In this sequence the first term, written a_1, is $a_1 = 3$. Also, $a_2 = 5$, $a_3 = 7$, $a_4 = 9$, and so on.

If a sequence has no last term, it is called **infinite**, but otherwise it is **finite**. The sequence of positive even integers,

$$2, 4, 6, 8, 10, 12, 14, \ldots$$

is infinite, while the sequence of days in June,

$$1, 2, 3, 4, 5, 6, \ldots, 29, 30,$$

is finite.

It is common to specify the terms of a sequence by giving the **general** or **nth term** of the sequence, written a_n. In this way, any particular term may be found.

Example 1   Find the first five terms for the sequence having general term

$$a_n = \frac{n+1}{n+2}.$$

Replace n, in turn, by 1, 2, 3, 4, and 5, to get

$$a_1 = \frac{2}{3}, \quad a_2 = \frac{3}{4}, \quad a_3 = \frac{4}{5}, \quad a_4 = \frac{5}{6}, \quad \text{and} \quad a_5 = \frac{6}{7}. \quad \blacksquare$$

Example 2   Find a_{100} for the sequences having the following general terms.

(a) $a_n = (-1)^n(2n)$

Replace n with 100.

$$a_{100} = (-1)^{100}(2 \cdot 100) = 200$$

(b) $a_n = \frac{(-1)^{n+1} \cdot 5n}{7n - 4}$

We have $a_{100} = \dfrac{(-1)^{101} \cdot 5(100)}{7(100) - 4} = \dfrac{-500}{696} = -\dfrac{125}{174}. \quad \blacksquare$

Sometimes the terms of a sequence are defined by reference to the preceding terms. The following is an example.

Example 3   The **Fibonacci sequence**, which occurs again and again in mathematics, is defined as follows.

$$f_1 = 1, \; f_2 = 1, \quad \text{and} \quad f_n = f_{n-1} + f_{n-2} \qquad \text{for } n \geq 3.$$

That is, each term from the third term on is the sum of the two preceding terms. For example,

$$f_3 = f_2 + f_1 = 1 + 1 = 2$$
$$f_4 = f_3 + f_2 = 2 + 1 = 3$$
$$f_5 = f_4 + f_3 = 3 + 2 = 5,$$

and so on. This sequence is defined with a **recursive** definition—each term is defined in terms of previous terms of the sequence. The first twelve terms of the Fibonacci sequence are

$$1, 1, 2, 3, 5, 8, 13, 21, 34, 55, 89, 144. \quad \blacksquare$$

Example 4   Define a sequence as follows:

$$b_1 = 6, \, b_2 = 5, \, b_3 = 2, \text{ and } b_n = 2 \cdot b_{n-1} - 3 \cdot b_{n-3} \quad \text{for } n \geq 4.$$

Find each of the following terms of the sequence.

(a) $b_4 = 2 \cdot b_3 - 3 \cdot b_1$

$\qquad = 2(2) - 3(6) = 4 - 18 = -14.$

(b) $b_5 = 2 \cdot b_4 - 3 \cdot b_2 = 2(-14) - 3(5) = -28 - 15 = -43.$ $\blacksquare$

Suppose a sequence has terms $a_1, \, a_2, \, a_3, \, a_4, \, \ldots$. Then S_n is defined as the sum of the first n terms of the sequence.

$$S_n = a_1 + a_2 + a_3 + \cdots + a_n.$$

The sum S_n is called the **nth partial sum** of the sequence. The sequence

$$S_1, \, S_2, \, S_3, \, S_4, \, \ldots, \, S_n, \, \ldots$$

is the **sequence of partial sums.**

Example 5   For the sequence

$$1, \frac{1}{2}, \frac{1}{4}, \frac{1}{8}, \frac{1}{16}, \frac{1}{32}, \ldots$$

we have

$$S_1 = 1$$

$$S_2 = 1 + \frac{1}{2} = \frac{3}{2}$$

$$S_3 = 1 + \frac{1}{2} + \frac{1}{4} = \frac{7}{4}$$

$$S_4 = 1 + \frac{1}{2} + \frac{1}{4} + \frac{1}{8} = \frac{15}{8}$$

$$S_5 = \frac{31}{16},$$

$$S_6 = \frac{63}{32},$$

and so on. Here the sequence

$$1, \frac{3}{2}, \frac{7}{4}, \frac{15}{8}, \frac{31}{16}, \frac{63}{32}, \ldots$$

is the sequence of partial sums. In calculus, you will see that sequences of this type may approach a specific value as n gets larger and larger. $\blacksquare$

Since partial sums do come up again and again, a special shorthand notation has been developed to simplify their writing. The symbol Σ, the Greek letter sigma, is used for sums. For example,

$$\sum_{i=1}^{n} a_i$$

represents the sum

$$\sum_{i=1}^{n} a_i = a_1 + a_2 + a_3 + \cdots + a_n.$$

Example 6   Find the sum $\displaystyle\sum_{i=1}^{6} (4i - 3)$.

To evaluate this sum, replace i in $4i - 3$ first by 1, then 2, then 3, until finally i is replaced with 6. That is,

$$\sum_{i=1}^{6} (4i - 3) = (4 \cdot 1 - 3) + (4 \cdot 2 - 3) + (4 \cdot 3 - 3)$$

$$+ (4 \cdot 4 - 3) + (4 \cdot 5 - 3) + (4 \cdot 6 - 3)$$

$$= 1 + 5 + 9 + 13 + 17 + 21$$

$$= 66. \quad \blacksquare$$

Here i is called the **index of summation.** Do not confuse this use of i with the use of i to represent an imaginary number.

Example 7   Evaluate each of the following sums.

(a) $\displaystyle\sum_{i=1}^{4} i^2(i + 1) = 1^2(1 + 1) + 2^2(2 + 1) + 3^2(3 + 1) + 4^2(4 + 1)$

$$= 1 \cdot 2 + 4 \cdot 3 + 9 \cdot 4 + 16 \cdot 5$$

$$= 2 + 12 + 36 + 80$$

$$= 130.$$

(b) $\displaystyle\sum_{i=3}^{6} \frac{i + 1}{i - 2} = \frac{3 + 1}{3 - 2} + \frac{4 + 1}{4 - 2} + \frac{5 + 1}{5 - 2} + \frac{6 + 1}{6 - 2}$

$$= \frac{4}{1} + \frac{5}{2} + \frac{6}{3} + \frac{7}{4}$$

$$= \frac{41}{4}. \quad \blacksquare$$

In the next few sections, we develop formulas that can be used to evaluate some of the sums without finding each term in the sequence. Summation notation has many useful properties, as given in the following theorem.

Theorem 12.3   Let n be a positive integer. Let a_i and b_i represent real numbers for $i = 1, 2, 3,$ . . ., n. Let c be any real number. Then

(a) $\displaystyle\sum_{i=1}^{n} c = n \cdot c$ (b) $\displaystyle\sum_{i=1}^{n} (a_i + b_i) = \sum_{i=1}^{n} a_i + \sum_{i=1}^{n} b_i$ (c) $\displaystyle\sum_{i=1}^{n} ca_i = c \cdot \sum_{i=1}^{n} a_i$

To prove part (a) of the theorem, use the definition of summation to write

$$\sum_{i=1}^{n} a_i = a_1 + a_2 + a_3 + \cdots + a_n.$$

If each a_i is equal to the constant c, we get

$$\sum_{i=1}^{n} c = c + c + c + \cdots + c,$$

where c appears n times in the sum. That is,

$$\sum_{i=1}^{n} c = (1 + 1 + 1 + \cdots + 1)c = nc.$$

For proofs of parts (b) and (c) of the theorem, see Exercises 53–55 below.

12.3 Exercises   *Write the first five terms in each of the following sequences.*

1. $a_n = 6n + 4$

2. $a_n = 3n - 2$

3. $a_n = 2^{-n+1}$

4. $a_n = 3^{-n-1}$

5. $a_n = (-1)^{n+1}$

6. $a_n = (-1)^n(n + 2)$

7. $a_n = \dfrac{2n}{n + 3}$

8. $a_n = \dfrac{-4}{n + 5}$

9. $a_n = \dfrac{8n - 4}{2n + 1}$

10. $a_n = \dfrac{-3n + 6}{n + 1}$

11. $a_n = (-2)^n(n)$

12. $a_n = (-1/2)^n(n^{-1})$

13. $a_n = \dfrac{n^2 + 1}{n^2 + 2}$

14. $a_n = \dfrac{(-1)^{n-1}(n + 1)}{n + 2}$

15. $a_n = x^n$

16. $a_n = n \cdot x^{-n}$

17. a_n is the nth prime number

18. b_n is the number of positive integers that divide into n

19. k_n is the sum of the first n positive integers

20. r_n is the sum of the cubes of the first n positive integers

Find the first ten terms for the sequences defined as follows.

21. $a_1 = 4$, $a_n = a_{n-1} + 5$, for $n > 1$

22. $a_1 = -3$, $a_n = a_{n-1} + 2$, for $n > 1$

23. $a_1 = -9$, $a_2 = -5$, $a_n = a_{n-2} + 4$, for $n > 2$

24. $a_1 = -1$, $a_2 = 3$, $a_n = a_{n-2} - 10$, for $n > 2$

25. $a_1 = 2$, $a_n = 2 \cdot a_{n-1}$, for $n > 1$

26. $a_1 = 3$, $a_n = -2 \cdot a_{n-1}$, for $n > 1$

27. $a_1 = 1$, $a_n = n \cdot \sin\left(\pi \cdot a_{n-1} + \dfrac{\pi}{2}\right)$, for $n > 1$

28. $a_1 = 1$, $a_n = n \cdot \cos(\pi \cdot a_{n-1})$, for $n > 1$

Find each of the following terms in the Fibonacci sequence.

29. f_{18}, given that $f_{16} = 987$ and $f_{17} = 1597$

30. f_{22}, given that $f_{20} = 6765$ and $f_{21} = 10{,}946$

Evaluate each of the following sums.

31. $\displaystyle\sum_{i=1}^{5} (2i + 1)$

32. $\displaystyle\sum_{i=1}^{6} (3i - 2)$

33. $\displaystyle\sum_{i=1}^{5} (i + 1)^{-1}$

34. $\displaystyle\sum_{i=1}^{4} i^{i}$

35. $\displaystyle\sum_{i=1}^{3} i^{-i}$

36. $\displaystyle\sum_{i=1}^{4} (i + 1)^{2}$

37. $\displaystyle\sum_{i=1}^{6} (-1)^{i} \cdot i$

38. $\displaystyle\sum_{i=1}^{7} (-1)^{i+1} \cdot i^{2}$

39. $\displaystyle\sum_{i=3}^{7} i/2$

40. $\displaystyle\sum_{i=5}^{9} (i + 1)/3$

41. $\displaystyle\sum_{i=5}^{8} (i^{2} + 1)/2$

42. $\displaystyle\sum_{i=3}^{5} (i + 3)/i$

43. $\displaystyle\sum_{i=0}^{4} 2^{i}$

44. $\displaystyle\sum_{i=0}^{4} 3^{-i}$

45. $\displaystyle\sum_{i=1}^{6} i \cdot 10^{-i}$

Write out each of the following.

46. $\displaystyle\sum_{i=3}^{7} x^{-i}$

47. $\displaystyle\sum_{i=1}^{5} i \cdot x^{i}$

48. $\displaystyle\sum_{i=1}^{5} i^{2}/x^{i}$

● *For each of the following sequences whose general term is given, find the first ten partial sums, $S_1, S_2, S_3, \ldots, S_{10}$. Decide on a number, if any, that these partial sums seem to be approaching.*

49. $a_n = 2 \cdot \left(\dfrac{1}{3}\right)^{n}$

50. $a_n = \left(\dfrac{3}{4}\right)^{n}$

51. $a_n = \left(\dfrac{5}{3}\right)^{n}$

52. $a_n = \left(\dfrac{3}{2}\right)^{n}$

Use the definition of summation and prove each of the following, for n (a positive integer), a_i and b_i (real numbers for $i = 1, 2, 3, \ldots, n$) and c (any real number).

53. $\displaystyle\sum_{i=1}^{n} (a_i + b_i) = \sum_{i=1}^{n} a_i + \sum_{i=1}^{n} b_i$

54. $\displaystyle\sum_{i=1}^{n} ca_i = c \cdot \sum_{i=1}^{n} a_i$

55. Prove all three parts of Theorem 12.3 by mathematical induction.

56. Is it true that $\sum_{i=1}^{n} a_i^2 = \left[\sum_{i=1}^{n} a_i\right]^2$?

57. In statistics, the **standard deviation** for a group of n numbers $x_1, x_2, x_3, \ldots x_n$, is sometimes defined as

$$\sqrt{\frac{\sum_{i=1}^{n} (x_i - \bar{x})^2}{n}}$$

where $\bar{x}$ (the *mean* of the number) is defined as

$$\bar{x} = \frac{\sum_{i=1}^{n} x_i}{n}$$

Show that the standard deviation is also equal to

$$\frac{1}{n} \cdot \sqrt{n \cdot \sum x_i^2 - \left(\sum_{i=1}^{n} x_i\right)^2}.$$

The text above gave a recursive definition for the Fibonacci sequence. An alternate definition is as follows: the nth term, f_n, is

$$f_n = \frac{\sqrt{5}}{5}\left[\left(\frac{1 + \sqrt{5}}{2}\right)^n - \left(\frac{1 - \sqrt{5}}{2}\right)^n\right].$$

Use this result to find each of the following terms of the Fibonacci sequence.

58. f_2 **59.** f_4 **60.** f_5

● **61.** Let $a_n = \left(1 + \frac{1}{n}\right)^n$. Find the first twelve terms of this sequence. Also find a_{50}, a_{100}, and a_{1000}. (As n gets larger and larger, the terms of this sequence approach the number e, which we discussed in Chapter 5.)

● **62.** It is shown in more advanced courses that

$$\frac{\pi}{4} = 4\left(\frac{1}{5} - \frac{1}{3 \cdot 5^3} + \frac{1}{5 \cdot 5^5} - \frac{1}{7 \cdot 5^7} + \cdots\right) - \left(\frac{1}{239} - \frac{1}{3 \cdot 239^3} + \cdots\right).$$

Use the terms shown here to find π correct to five decimal places.

12.4 Arithmetic Sequences

A sequence in which each term after the first is obtained by adding a fixed number, called the **common difference,** to the previous term is called an **arithmetic sequence** (or arithmetic progression). Thus, the sequence

$$5, 9, 13, 17, 21, \ldots$$

is an arithmetic sequence since each term after the first is obtained by adding 4 to the previous term. That is,

$$9 = 5 + 4$$
$$13 = 9 + 4$$
$$17 = 13 + 4$$
$$21 = 17 + 4,$$

and so on. Here 4 is the common difference.

Example 1   Find the common difference, d, for the arithmetic sequence

$$-9, -12, -15, -18, -21, \ldots$$

Since we know that this sequence is arithmetic, we can find d by choosing any two adjacent terms and subtracting the first from the second. If we choose -15 and -18 here, we have $d = -18 - (-15) = -3$.

If we had chosen -9 and -12, we would have found $d = -12 - (-9) = -3$, the same result.   ▌

Example 2   Write the first five terms for each of the following arithmetic sequences.

(a) The first term is 7, and each succeeding term is found by adding -3 to the preceding term.

Here $a_1 = 7$
$$a_2 = 7 + (-3) = 4$$
$$a_3 = 4 + (-3) = 1$$
$$a_4 = 1 + (-3) = -2$$
$$a_5 = -2 + (-3) = -5.$$

(b) $a_1 = -12, d = 5$

We have $a_1 = -12$
$$a_2 = -12 + d = -12 + 5 = -7$$
$$a_3 = -7 + d = -7 + 5 = -2$$
$$a_4 = -2 + d = -2 + 5 = 3$$
$$a_5 = 3 + d = 3 + 5 = 8.$$ ▌

In general, if a_1 is the first term of an arithmetic sequence and d is the common difference, then the terms of the sequence are given by

$$a_1 = a_1$$
$$a_2 = a_1 + d$$
$$a_3 = a_2 + d = a_1 + d + d = a_1 + 2d$$
$$a_4 = a_3 + d = a_1 + 2d + d = a_1 + 3d$$
$$a_5 = a_1 + 4d$$
$$a_6 = a_1 + 5d,$$

and, by this pattern,

$$a_n = a_1 + (n - 1)d.$$

Example 3   Find a_{13} and a_n for the arithmetic sequence

$$-3, 1, 5, 9, \ldots .$$

Here $a_1 = -3$ and $d = 4$. (We found d by the method of Example 1.) Now substitute 13 for n in the formula above.

$$a_{13} = a_1 + (13 - 1)d$$
$$a_{13} = -3 + (12)4$$
$$a_{13} = -3 + 48$$
$$a_{13} = 45.$$

To find a_n, substitute values for a_1 and d.

$$a_n = -3 + (n - 1) \cdot 4$$
$$a_n = -3 + 4n - 4$$
$$a_n = 4n - 7 \quad \blacksquare$$

Example 4   Find a_{18} and a_n for the arithmetic sequence having $a_2 = 9$ and $a_3 = 15$.
Here $d = a_3 - a_2 = 15 - 9 = 6$. Since $a_2 = a_1 + d$, we have

$$9 = a_1 + 6$$
$$a_1 = 3.$$

Thus,

$$a_{18} = 3 + (18 - 1) \cdot 6$$
$$a_{18} = 105$$

and

$$a_n = 3 + (n - 1) \cdot 6$$
$$a_n = 6n - 3. \quad \blacksquare$$

Example 5   Suppose that an arithmetic sequence has $a_8 = -16$ and $a_{16} = -40$. Find a_1.
We know that $a_8 = a_1 + (8 - 1)d$. Therefore, $-16 = a_1 + 7d$ or $a_1 = -16 - 7d$. Similarly, we find that $-40 = a_1 + 15d$ or $a_1 = -40 - 15d$. From these two equations we have $-16 - 7d = -40 - 15d$ or $d = -3$. Since $-16 = a_1 + 7d$, we have $a_1 = 5$. $\quad \blacksquare$

Given a_1 and d we can find the sum of the first n terms of an arithmetic sequence. To begin, write the sum of the first n terms as follows.

$$S_n = a_1 + [a_1 + d] + [a_1 + 2d] + \cdots + [a_1 + (n - 1)d]$$

Next, write this same sum in reversed order.

$$S_n = [a_1 + (n - 1)d] + [a_1 + (n - 2)d] + \cdots + [a_1 + d] + a_1$$

Now add the respective sides of these two equations.

$$S_n + S_n = (a_1 + [a_1 + (n - 1)d]) + ([a_1 + d] + [a_1 + (n - 2)d]) + \cdots$$
$$+ ([a_1 + (n - 1)d] + a_1)$$

From this,

$$2S_n = [2a_1 + (n - 1)d] + [2a_1 + (n - 1)d] + \cdots + [2a_1 + (n - 1)d].$$

Since there are n of the $[2a_1 + (n-1)d]$ terms on the right,

$$2S_n = n[2a_1 + (n-1)d]$$

$$S_n = \frac{n}{2}[2a_1 + (n-1)d].$$

Since $a_n = a_1 + (n-1)d$, we also have $S_n = \frac{n}{2}[a_1 + a_1 + (n-1)d]$, or

$$S_n = \frac{n}{2}(a_1 + a_n).$$

The following theorem summarizes our work with arithmetic sequences.

Theorem 12.4   If an arithmetic sequence has first term a_1 and common difference d, then
  (a) the nth term, a_n, is given by

$$a_n = a_1 + (n-1)d.$$

  (b) the sum of the first n terms, S_n, is given by

$$S_n = \frac{n}{2}(a_1 + a_n)$$

or $$S_n = \frac{n}{2}[2a_1 + (n-1)d].$$

The first formula of part (b) of the theorem is used when we know the first and last term, otherwise the second formula is used.

Example 6   (a) Find S_{12} for the arithmetic sequence $-9, -5, -1, 3, 7, \ldots$ ..
      Here $a_1 = -9$ and $d = 4$. Thus

$$a_{12} = -9 + (12 - 1) \cdot 4$$
$$= -9 + 44$$
$$a_{12} = 35.$$

Thus, $$S_{12} = \frac{12}{2}(-9 + 35)$$

$$= 6(26)$$
$$S_{12} = 156.$$

  (b) Find the sum of the first 60 positive integers.
      Here $n = 60$, $a_1 = 1$, and $a_{60} = 60$.

$$S_{60} = \frac{60}{2}(1 + 60) = 30 \cdot 61 = 1830. \quad \blacksquare$$

Example 7   The sum of the first 17 terms of an arithmetic sequence is 187. If $a_{17} = -13$, find a_1 and d.
      We can use the formula for S_n developed above in order to find a_1.

$$187 = \frac{17}{2}(a_1 - 13)$$

$$374 = 17(a_1 - 13)$$

$$22 = a_1 - 13$$

$$a_1 = 35.$$

We know $a_{17} = a_1 + (17 - 1)d$. Hence,

$$-13 = 35 + 16d$$

$$-48 = 16d$$

$$d = -3. \quad \blacksquare$$

Example 8   Find each of the following sums.

(a) $\sum\limits_{i=1}^{10} (4i + 8)$

This sum represents the sum of the first ten terms of the airthmetic sequence having

$$a_1 = 4 \cdot 1 + 8 = 12,$$

$$n = 10.$$

and

$$a_n = a_{10} = 4 \cdot 10 + 8 = 48.$$

Thus,

$$\sum\limits_{i=1}^{10} (4i + 8) = S_{10} = \frac{10}{2}(12 + 48)$$

$$= 5(60)$$

$$= 300.$$

(b) $\sum\limits_{i=1}^{15} (9 - i) = S_{15} = \frac{15}{2}[8 + (-6)]$

$$= \frac{15}{2}[2]$$

$$= 15. \quad \blacksquare$$

12.4 Exercises   *Write the terms of the arithmetic sequences satisfying each of the following conditions.*

1. $a_1 = 4$, $d = 2$, $n = 5$

2. $a_1 = 6$, $d = 8$, $n = 4$

3. $a_2 = 9$, $d = -2$, $n = 4$

4. $a_3 = 7$, $d = -4$, $n = 4$

5. $a_1 = 4 - \sqrt{5}$, $a_2 = 4$, $n = 5$

6. $a_1 = -8$, $a_2 = -8 + \sqrt{7}$, $n = 5$

For each of the following arithmetic sequences, find d and a_n.

7. 12, 17, 22, 27, 32, 37, . . .

8. 8, 17, 26, 35, 44, 53, . . .

9. 18, 15, 12, 9, 6, . . .

10. 30, 24, 18, 12, . . .

11. $-6 + \sqrt{2}, -6 + 2\sqrt{2}, -6 + 3\sqrt{2}, \ldots$

12. $4 - \sqrt{11}, 5 - \sqrt{11}, 6 - \sqrt{11}, \ldots$

13. $x, x + m, x + 2m, x + 3m, x + 4m, \ldots$

14. $k + p, k + 2p, k + 3p, k + 4p, \ldots$

15. $2z + m, 2z, 2z - m, 2z - 2m, 2z - 3m, \ldots$

16. $3r - 4z, 3r - 3z, 3r - 2z, 3r - z, 3r, 3r + z, \ldots$

Find a_8 and a_n for each of the following arithmetic sequences.

17. $a_1 = 5, d = 2$

18. $a_1 = -3, d = -4$

19. $a_3 = 2, d = 1$

20. $a_4 = 5, d = -2$

21. $a_1 = 8, a_2 = 6$

22. $a_1 = 6, a_2 = 3$

23. $a_1 = 12, a_3 = 6$

24. $a_2 = 5, a_4 = 1$

25. $a_5 = 4.2, a_6 = 4.5$

26. $a_3 = -9.5, a_4 = -10.6$

27. $a_1 = x, a_2 = x + 3$

28. $a_2 = y + 1, d = -3$

29. $a_6 = 2m, a_7 = 3m$

30. $a_5 = 4p + 1, a_7 = 6p + 7$

Find the sum of the first ten terms for each of the following arithmetic sequences.

31. $a_1 = 8, d = 3$

32. $a_1 = 2, d = 6$

33. $a_3 = 5, a_4 = 8$

34. $a_2 = 9, a_4 = 13$

35. $5, 9, 13, \ldots$

36. $8, 6, 4, \ldots$

⊙ 37. $a_1 = 9.428, d = -1.723$

38. $a_1 = -3.119, d = 2.422$

39. $a_4 = 2.556, a_5 = 3.004$

40. $a_7 = 11.192, a_9 = 4.812$

Evaluate each of the following sums.

41. $\sum_{i=1}^{3} (i + 4)$

42. $\sum_{i=1}^{5} (i - 8)$

43. $\sum_{i=1}^{10} (2i + 3)$

44. $\sum_{i=1}^{15} (5i - 9)$

45. $\sum_{i=1}^{12} (-5 - 8i)$

46. $\sum_{i=1}^{19} (-3 - 4i)$

47. $\sum_{i=1}^{1000} i$

48. $\sum_{i=1}^{2000} i$

49. $\sum_{i=6}^{15} (4i - 2)$

50. $\sum_{i=9}^{20} (8i + 3)$

51. $\sum_{i=7}^{12} (6 - 2i)$

52. $\sum_{i=4}^{17} (-3 - 5i)$

Find a_1 for each of the following arithmetic sequences.

53. $a_9 = 47, a_{15} = 77$

54. $a_{10} = 50, a_{20} = 110$

55. $a_{15} = 168, a_{16} = 180$

56. $a_{10} = -54, a_{17} = -89$

Find a_1 for each of the following arithmetic sequences.

57. $S_{20} = 1090$, $a_{20} = 102$ **58.** $S_{31} = 5580$, $a_{31} = 360$

59. Find the sum of all the integers from 51 to 71.

60. Find the sum of all the integers from -8 to 30.

61. Find the sum of the first n positive integers.

62. Find the sum of the first n odd positive integers.

63. If a clock strikes the proper number of bongs each hour on the hour, how many bongs will it bong in a month of 30 days?

64. A stack of telephone poles has 30 in the bottom row, 29 in the next, and so on, with one pole in the top row. How many poles are in the stack?

65. A sky diver falls 10 meters during the first second, 20 meters during the second, 30 meters during the third, and so on. How many meters will the diver fall during the tenth second? During the first ten seconds?

66. Deepwell Drilling Company charges a flat $500 set-up charge, plus $5 for the first foot of well drilled, $6 for the second, $7 for the third, and so on. Find the total charge for a 70-foot well.

67. An object falling under the force of gravity falls about 16 feet the first second, 48 feet during the second, 80 feet during the third, and so on. How far would the object fall during the eighth second? What is the total distance the object would fall in eight seconds?

68. The population of a city was 49,000 five years ago. Each year, the zoning commission permits an increase of 580 in the population of the city. What will the population be five years from now?

69. The sum of four terms in an arithmetic sequence is 66. The sum of the squares of the terms is 1214. Find the terms.

70. The sum of five terms of an arithmetic sequence is 5. If the product of the first and second is added to the product of the fourth and fifth, the result is 326. Find the terms.

71. A super slide of uniform slope is to be built on a level piece of land. There are to be twenty equally spaced supports, with the longest support 15 m in length, and the shortest 2 m in length. Find the total length of all the supports.

72. How much material would be needed for the rungs of a ladder of 31 rungs, if the rungs taper from 18 inches to 28 inches? Assume that the lengths of the rungs form the terms of an arithmetic sequence.

73. Find all arithmetic sequences $a_1, a_2, a_3, \ldots$, such that $a_1^2, a_2^2, a_3^2, \ldots$, is also an arithmetic sequence.

74. Suppose that $a_1, a_2, a_3, \ldots$ and $b_1, b_2, b_3, \ldots$ are each arithmetic sequences. Let $d_n = a_n + c \cdot b_n$, for any real number c and every positive integer n. Show that $d_1, d_2, d_3, \ldots$ is an arithmetic sequence.

Explain why each of the following sequences is arithmetic.

75. log 2, log 4, log 8, log 16, log 32, . . .   **76.** log 12, log 36, log 108, log 324, . . .

Prove each of the following results from Theorem 12.4 by mathematical induction.

77. $a_n = a_1 + (n - 1)d$ **78.** $S_n = \dfrac{n}{2}(a_1 + a_n)$

12.5 Geometric Sequences

A **geometric sequence** (or geometric progression) is a sequence in which each term after the first is obtained by multiplying the preceding term by a constant nonzero real number, called the **common ratio.** Thus,

$$2, 8, 32, 128, \ldots$$

is a geometric sequence whose first term is 2 and whose common ratio is 4.

If the common ratio of a geometric sequence is r, then by the definition of a geometric sequence

$$a_{n+1} = r \cdot a_n,$$

for every positive integer n. Therefore, $r = a_{n+1}/a_n$, so that the common ratio can be found by choosing any term except the first and dividing it by the preceding term.

In the geometric sequence

$$2, 8, 32, 128, \ldots$$

$r = 8/2 = 4$. Notice that

$$8 = 2 \cdot 4$$
$$32 = 8 \cdot 4 = (2 \cdot 4) \cdot 4 = 2 \cdot 4^2$$
$$128 = 32 \cdot 4 = (2 \cdot 4^2) \cdot 4 = 2 \cdot 4^3.$$

To generalize this, assume that a geometric sequence has first term a_1 and common ratio r. The second term can be written as $a_2 = a_1 r$, the third as $a_3 = a_2 r = (a_1 r)r = a_1 r^2$, and so on. Thus, in general, the nth term of a geometric sequence is given by

$$a_n = a_1 r^{n-1}.$$

Example 1 Find a_5 and a_n for each of the following geometric sequences.

(a) 4, 12, 36, 108, . . .

In this sequence, $a_1 = 4$. To find r, choose any term except the first and divide it by the preceding term. Here

$$r = 36/12 = 3.$$

Thus,

$$a_n = a_1 r^{n-1}$$
$$a_5 = 4 \cdot (3)^{5-1}$$
$$= 4 \cdot 3^4$$
$$a_5 = 324.$$

Also,

$$a_n = 4 \cdot 3^{n-1}.$$

(b) 64, 32, 16, 8, . . .

Here $r = 8/16 = 1/2$, and $a_1 = 64$. Thus,

$$a_5 = 64(1/2)^{5-1}$$
$$= 64(1/16)$$
$$a_5 = 4.$$

Also,

$$a_n = 64(1/2)^{n-1}. \quad \blacksquare$$

Example 2   Suppose that the third term of a geometric sequence is 20 and the sixth term is 160. Find the first term a_1 and the common ratio r.

Use the formula for the nth term of a geometric sequence.

$$\text{for } n = 3, \qquad a_3 = a_1 r^2 = 20;$$
$$\text{for } n = 6, \qquad a_6 = a_1 r^5 = 160.$$

Since $a_1 r^2 = 20$, then $a_1 = 20/r^2$. Substituting this in the second equation gives

$$a_1 r^5 = 160$$
$$(20/r^2)r^5 = 160$$
$$20r^3 = 160$$
$$r^3 = 8$$
$$r = 2.$$

Since $a_1 r^2 = 20$ and $r = 2$, we end up with $a_1 = 5$. (We assume throughout this chapter that all terms of sequences are real numbers.) ▌

In applications of geometric sequences, it is often necessary to know the nth partial sum for the sequence. To find a formula for this partial sum, S_n, the sum of the first n terms of a geometric sequence, start with

$$S_n = a_1 + a_2 + a_3 + \cdots + a_n,$$

which can also be written as

$$S_n = a_1 + a_1 r + a_1 r^2 + \cdots + a_1 r^{n-1}. \tag{1}$$

If $r = 1$, we have $S_n = na_1$, which is a correct formula for this case. If $r \neq 1$, we can multiply both sides of (1) by r, obtaining

$$rS_n = a_1 r + a_1 r^2 + a_1 r^3 + \cdots + a_1 r^n. \tag{2}$$

If we subtract (2) from (1), we have

$$S_n - rS_n = a_1 - a_1 r^n$$

or

$$S_n(1 - r) = a_1(1 - r^n),$$

which finally gives

$$S_n = \frac{a_1(1 - r^n)}{1 - r} \qquad (r \neq 1).$$

The following theorem summarizes our work so far with geometric sequences.

Theorem 12.5   If a geometric sequence has first term a_1 and common ratio r, then
(a) the nth term of the sequence, a_n, is

$$a_n = a_1 r^{n-1},$$

(b) the sum of the first n terms, the nth partial sum S_n, is

$$S_n = \frac{a_1(1 - r^n)}{1 - r} \qquad (r \neq 1).$$

Example 3 (a) Find S_5 for the geometric sequence

$$3, 6, 12, 24, 48.$$

Here $a_1 = 3$ and $r = 2$. Thus,

$$S_5 = \frac{3(1 - 2^5)}{1 - 2}$$

$$= \frac{3(1 - 32)}{-1}$$

$$= \frac{3(-31)}{-1}$$

$$S_5 = 93.$$

(b) Find S_4 for the sequence

$$10, 2, \frac{2}{5}, \ldots$$

Here $a_1 = 10$, $r = 1/5$, and $n = 4$. Using the formula for S_n,

$$S_4 = \frac{10\left[1 - \left(\frac{1}{5}\right)^4\right]}{1 - \frac{1}{5}}$$

$$S_4 = \frac{10\left[1 - \frac{1}{625}\right]}{\frac{4}{5}}$$

$$S_4 = 10\left(\frac{624}{625}\right) \cdot \frac{5}{4}$$

$$S_4 = \frac{312}{25}. \quad \blacksquare$$

Example 4 Find each of the following sums.

(a) $\displaystyle\sum_{i=1}^{6} 2 \cdot 3^i.$

This sum is the sum of the first six terms of a geometric sequence having $a_1 = 2 \cdot 3^1 = 6$ and $r = 3$. Thus,

$$\sum_{i=1}^{6} 2 \cdot 3^i = S_6 = \frac{6(1 - 3^6)}{1 - 3}$$

$$= \frac{6(1 - 729)}{-2}$$

$$= \frac{6(-728)}{-2}$$

$$= 2184.$$

(b) $\displaystyle\sum_{i=1}^{5} \left(\frac{3}{4}\right)^i = S_5 = \dfrac{\dfrac{3}{4}\left[1 - \left(\dfrac{3}{4}\right)^5\right]}{1 - \dfrac{3}{4}}$

$\qquad = \dfrac{\dfrac{3}{4}\left[1 - \dfrac{243}{1024}\right]}{\dfrac{1}{4}}$

$\qquad = 3\left[\dfrac{781}{1024}\right]$

$\qquad = \dfrac{2343}{1024}.$ ▮

12.5 Exercises

Write the terms of the geometric sequences that satisfy each of the following conditions.

1. $a_1 = 2$, $r = 3$, $n = 4$

2. $a_1 = 4$, $r = 2$, $n = 5$

3. $a_1 = 1/2$, $r = 4$, $n = 4$

4. $a_1 = 2/3$, $r = 6$, $n = 3$

5. $a_1 = -2$, $r = -3$, $n = 4$

6. $a_1 = -4$, $r = 2$, $n = 5$

7. $a_3 = 6$, $a_4 = 12$, $n = 5$

8. $a_2 = 9$, $a_3 = 3$, $n = 4$

Find a_5 and a_n for each of the following geometric sequences.

9. $a_1 = 4$, $r = 3$

10. $a_1 = 8$, $r = 4$

11. $a_1 = -3$, $r = -5$

12. $a_1 = -4$, $r = -2$

13. $a_2 = 3$, $r = 2$

14. $a_3 = 6$, $r = 3$

15. $a_4 = 64$, $r = -4$

16. $a_4 = 81$, $r = -3$

For each of the following sequences that are geometric, find r and a_n.

17. 6, 12, 24, 48, . . .

18. 4, 16, 64, 256, . . .

19. 3/4, 3/2, 3, 6, 12, . . .

20. 5/6, 5/3, 10/3, 20/3, 40/3, . . .

21. 18, 20, 24, 32, 48, . . .

22. $-7, -5, -3, -1, 1, 3, . . .$

23. $a_3 = 9$, $r = 2$

24. $a_5 = 6$, $r = 1/2$

25. $a_3 = -2$, $r = 3$

26. $a_2 = 5$, $r = 1/2$

Find the sum of the first five terms for each of the following geometric sequences.

27. 3, 6, 12, 24, . . .

28. 5, 20, 80, 320, . . .

29. 12, -6, 3, $-3/2$, . . .

30. 18, -3, 1/2, $-1/12$, . . .

⊙ **31.** $a_1 = 8.423$, $r = 2.859$

32. $a_1 = -3.772$, $r = -1.553$

33. $a_1 = -5$, $r = .2033$

34. $a_1 = 4$, $r = -.8765$

Find each of the following sums.

35. $\displaystyle\sum_{i=1}^{4} 2^i$

36. $\displaystyle\sum_{i=1}^{6} 3^i$

37. $\displaystyle\sum_{i=1}^{8} 64(1/2)^i$

38. $\displaystyle\sum_{i=1}^{6} 81(2/3)^i$

39. $\displaystyle\sum_{i=1}^{4} (2/5)^i$

40. $\displaystyle\sum_{i=1}^{4} (-3/4)^i$

41. $\displaystyle\sum_{i=1}^{4} 6(3/2)^i$

42. $\displaystyle\sum_{i=1}^{5} 9(5/3)^i$

43. $\displaystyle\sum_{i=3}^{6} 2^i$ **44.** $\displaystyle\sum_{i=4}^{7} 3^i$ **45.** $\displaystyle\sum_{i=1}^{4} 5(3/5)^{i-1}$ **46.** $\displaystyle\sum_{i=1}^{5} 256(-3/4)^{i-1}$

◉ **47.** Suppose you could save $1 on January 1, $2 on January 2, $4 on January 3, and so on. What amount would you save on January 31? What would be the total amount of your savings during January? (Hint: $2^{31} = 2,147,483,648$.)

48. Richkand Oil has a well which produced $4,000,000 of income its first year. Each year thereafter, the well produced half as much income as the previous year. What is the total amount of income produced by the well in six years?

49. The final step in processing a black and white photographic print is to immerse the print in a chemical called "fixer." The print is then washed in running water. Under certain conditions, 98% of the fixer in a print will be removed with 15 minutes of washing. How much of the original fixer would be left after one hour of washing?

50. A sequence of equilateral triangles is constructed. The first triangle has sides 2 m in length. To get the second triangle, midpoints of the sides of the original triangle are connected. What is the length of the side of the eighth such triangle?

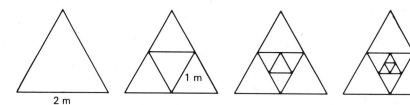

51. A scientist has a vat containing 100 liters of a pure chemical. Twenty liters are drained and replaced with water. After complete mixing, twenty liters of the mixture is drained and replaced with water. What will be the strength of the mixture after nine such drainings?

52. The half-life of a radioactive substance is the time it takes for half the substance to decay. Suppose the half-life of a substance is 3 years, and that 10^{15} molecules of the substance are present initially. How many molecules will be present after 15 years?

53. Each year a machine loses 20% of the value it had at the beginning of the year. Find the value of a machine at the end of 6 years if it cost $100,000 new.

54. A bicycle wheel rotates 400 times in one minute. If the rider removes his or her feet from the pedals, the wheel will start to slow down. Each minute, it will rotate only 3/4 as many times as in the preceeding minute. How many times will the wheel rotate in the fifth minute after the rider's feet were removed from the pedals?

55. A piece of paper is .008 inch thick. Suppose the paper is folded in half, so that its thickness doubles, for 12 times in a row. How thick would the final stack of paper be?

56. Fruit-and-vegetable dealer Marcia Odjakjian paid 10c per pound for 10,000 pounds of onions. Each week the price she charges increases by .1c per pound, while the onions lose 5% of their weight. If she sells the onions after six weeks, did she make or lose money? How much?

57. Find three numbers x, y, and z that are consecutive terms of both an arithmetic sequence and a geometric sequence.

58. Let $a_1, a_2, a_3, \ldots$ and $b_1, b_2, b_3, \ldots$ be geometric sequences. Let $d_n = c \cdot a_n \cdot b_n$ for any real number c and every positive integer n. Show that $d_1, d_2, d_3, \ldots$ is a geometric sequence.

Find a_1 and r for each of the following geometric sequences.

59. $a_2 = 6, \ a_6 = 486$

60. $a_3 = -12, \ a_6 = 96$

61. $a_2 = 64, \ a_8 = 1$

62. $a_2 = 100, \ a_5 = .1$

Explain why the following sequences are geometric.

63. log 6, log 36, log 1296, log 1,679,616, . . .

64. log 2, log 4, log 16, log 256, . . .

Prove each of the following results from Theorem 12.5 by mathematical induction.

65. $a_n = a_1 \cdot r^{n-1}$

66. $S_n = \dfrac{a_1(1 - r^n)}{1 - r}$

12.6 Sums of Infinite Geometric Sequences

In the last section we found that the nth partial sum of the geometric sequence having first term a_1 and common ratio r is given by

$$S_n = \sum_{i=1}^{n} a_i = \frac{a_1(1 - r^n)}{1 - r}.$$

Let us now look at the infinite geometric sequence

$$2, 1, \frac{1}{2}, \frac{1}{4}, \frac{1}{8}, \frac{1}{16}, \frac{1}{32}, \ldots$$

The first term of this sequence is $a_1 = 2$, and the common ratio is $r = 1/2$. Using the formula above or direct calculation, we can find the first few partial sums for this sequence, giving the following sequence of partial sums:

$$S_1 = 2, \quad S_2 = 3, \quad S_3 = \frac{7}{2}, \quad S_4 = \frac{15}{4}, \quad S_5 = \frac{31}{8}, \quad S_6 = \frac{63}{16},$$

and so on.

These partial sums seem to be getting closer and closer to the number 4. In fact, by selecting a value of n large enough, we can make S_n as close as we might wish to 4. This is expressed as

$$\lim_{n \to \infty} S_n = 4.$$

(Read: "the limit of S_n as n increases without bound is 4.") For no value of n is $S_n = 4$. However, if n is large enough, then S_n is as close to 4 as we might wish.*

---

*These phrases "large enough" and "as close as we wish" are not nearly precise enough for mathematicians; much of a standard calculus course is devoted to making them more precise.

Since $$\lim_{n \to \infty} S_n = 4,$$

the number 4 is called the **sum** of the infinite geometric sequence

$$2, 1, \frac{1}{2}, \frac{1}{4}, \ldots$$

and $$2 + 1 + \frac{1}{2} + \frac{1}{4} + \frac{1}{8} + \cdots = 4.$$

Example 1 Find $1 + \frac{1}{3} + \frac{1}{9} + \frac{1}{27} + \ldots$.

Here we use the formula for the sum of the first n terms of a geometric sequence to get the sequence of partial sums

$$S_1 = 1, \quad S_2 = \frac{4}{3}, \quad S_3 = \frac{13}{9}, \quad S_4 = \frac{40}{27},$$

and so on. In general, if $a_1 = 1$ and $r = 1/3$, we have

$$S_n = \frac{1\left[1 - \left(\frac{1}{3}\right)^n\right]}{1 - \frac{1}{3}}.$$

The following chart shows the value of $(1/3)^n$ for larger and larger values of n.

n	1	10	100	200
$\left(\frac{1}{3}\right)^n$	$\frac{1}{3}$	.0000169	1.9×10^{-48}	3.76×10^{-96}

As the chart suggests, $(1/3)^n$ gets closer and closer to 0 as n gets larger and larger. This is written

$$\lim_{n \to \infty} \left(\frac{1}{3}\right)^n = 0.$$

Thus, it seems reasonable that

$$\lim_{n \to \infty} S_n = \frac{1(1 - 0)}{1 - \frac{1}{3}} = \frac{1}{\frac{2}{3}} = \frac{3}{2}.$$

Hence, $$1 + \frac{1}{3} + \frac{1}{9} + \frac{1}{27} + \cdots = \frac{3}{2}. \quad \blacksquare$$

In general, if a geometric sequence has a first term a_1 and a common ratio r, then

$$S_n = \frac{a_1(1 - r^n)}{1 - r}.$$

for every positive integer n. If $-1 < r < 1$, then

$$\lim_{n \to \infty} r^n = 0.$$

and

$$\lim_{n \to \infty} S_n = \frac{a_1(1 - 0)}{1 - r} \quad \text{for } -1 < r < 1$$

$$\lim_{n \to \infty} S_n = \frac{a_1}{1 - r} \quad \text{for } -1 < r < 1$$

This quotient, $a_1/(1 - r)$, is called the **sum of the infinite geometric sequence** with first term a_1 and common ratio r, where $-1 < r < 1$. The limit

$$\lim_{n \to \infty} S_n$$

is often expressed as S_∞ or $\sum_{i=1}^{\infty} a_i$, so that

$$S_\infty = \sum_{i=1}^{\infty} a_i = \lim_{n \to \infty} S_n = \frac{a_1}{1 - r}, \qquad -1 < r < 1.$$

Example 2   (a) Find the sum

$$-\frac{3}{4} + \frac{3}{8} - \frac{3}{16} + \frac{3}{32} - \frac{3}{64} + \cdots.$$

Here $a_1 = -3/4$. To find r, divide any two adjacent terms. For example,

$$r = \frac{-\dfrac{3}{16}}{\dfrac{3}{8}} = -\frac{1}{2}.$$

Since $-1 < r < 1$, the formula of this section applies, and

$$S_\infty = \frac{a_1}{1 - r}$$

$$= \frac{-\dfrac{3}{4}}{1 - \left(-\dfrac{1}{2}\right)}$$

$$S_\infty = -\frac{1}{2}.$$

(b) $\displaystyle \sum_{i=1}^{\infty} \left(\frac{3}{5}\right)^i = \frac{\dfrac{3}{5}}{1 - \dfrac{3}{5}}$

$$= \frac{3}{2} \quad \blacksquare$$

12.6 Exercises *Find r for each of the following infinite geometric sequences. Identify any whose sums would exist.*

1. 9, 18, 36, 72, 144, . . .

2. 3, 9, 27, 81, . . .

3. 10, 100, 1000, 10,000, . . .

4. −8, −4, −2, −1, −1/2, . . .

5. 12, 6, 3, 3/2, . . .

6. −8, −16, −32, −64, . . .

7. 1, 1.1, 1.21, 1.331, . . .

8. −1, 1.2, −1.44, 1.728, . . .

9. 1, −.9, .81, −.729, . . .

10. 1, .7, .49, .343, . . .

Find each of the following sums which exist by using the formula of this section where it applies.

11. $16 + 4 + 1 + \cdots$

12. $81 + 27 + 9 + 3 + 1 + \cdots$

13. $100 + 10 + 1 + \cdots$

14. $128 + 64 + 32 + \cdots$

15. $90 + 30 + 10 + \cdots$

16. $25 + 5 + 1 + \cdots$

17. $256 - 128 + 64 - 32 + \cdots$

18. $120 - 60 + 30 - 15 + \cdots$

19. $\dfrac{3}{4} + \dfrac{3}{8} + \dfrac{3}{16} + \cdots$

20. $\dfrac{4}{5} + \dfrac{2}{5} + \dfrac{1}{5} + \cdots$

21. $\dfrac{1}{3} - \dfrac{2}{9} + \dfrac{4}{27} - \dfrac{8}{81} + \cdots$

22. $1 + \dfrac{1}{1.01} + \dfrac{1}{(1.01)^2} + \cdots$

23. $\dfrac{1}{36} + \dfrac{1}{30} + \dfrac{1}{25} + \cdots$

24. $1 + \dfrac{1}{2^2} + \dfrac{1}{2^4} + \cdots$

25. $\displaystyle\sum_{i=1}^{\infty} (1/4)^i$

26. $\displaystyle\sum_{i=1}^{\infty} (9/10)^i$

27. $\displaystyle\sum_{i=1}^{\infty} (1.2)^i$

28. $\displaystyle\sum_{i=1}^{\infty} (1.001)^i$

29. $\displaystyle\sum_{i=1}^{\infty} (-1/4)^i$

30. $\displaystyle\sum_{i=1}^{\infty} (.3)^i$

31. $\displaystyle\sum_{i=1}^{\infty} 1/5^i$

32. $\displaystyle\sum_{i=1}^{\infty} (-1/2)^i$

33. $\displaystyle\sum_{i=1}^{\infty} 10^{-i}$

34. $\displaystyle\sum_{i=1}^{\infty} 4^{-i}$

Express each of the following repeating decimals in the form p/q, where p and q are integers. (Hint: $0.55555 \ldots = .5 + .05 + .005 + .0005 + \ldots$)

35. $0.55555 \ldots$

36. $0.33333 \ldots$

37. $0.121212 \ldots$

38. $0.858585 \ldots$

39. $0.313131 \ldots$

40. $0.909090 \ldots$

41. $0.508508508 \ldots$

42. $0.613613613 \ldots$

43. $0.3455555 \ldots$

44. $0.5688888 \ldots$

45. Mitzi drops a ball from a height of 10 meters and notices that on each bounce the ball returns to about 3/4 of its previous height. About how far will the ball travel before it comes to rest? (Hint: consider the sum of two sequences.)

46. A sugar factory receives an order for 1000 units of sugar. The production manager thus orders production of 1000 units of sugar. He forgets, however, that the production of sugar requires some sugar (to prime the machines, for example), and so he ends up with only 900 units of sugar. He then orders an additional 100 units, and receives only 90 units. A further order for 10 units produces 9 units. Finally seeing he is wrong, the manager decides to try mathematics. He views the production process as an infinite geometric progression with $a_1 = 1000$ and $r = .1$. Using this, find the number of units of sugar that he should have ordered originally.

47. After a person pedaling a bicycle removes his or her feet from the pedals, the wheel rotates 400 times the first minute. As it continues to slow down, each minute it rotates only 3/4 as many times as in the previous minute. How many times will the wheel rotate before coming to a complete stop?

48. A pendulum bob swings through an arc 40 cm long on its first swing. Each swing thereafter, it swings only 80% as far as on the previous swing. How far will it swing altogether before coming to a complete stop?

49. A sequence of equilateral triangles is constructed. The first triangle has sides 2 m in length. To get the second triangle, midpoints of the sides of the original triangle are connected. (See Exercise 50 of Section 12.5.) If this process could be continued indefinitely, what would be the total perimeter of all the triangles?

50. What would be the total area of all the triangles of Exercise 49, disregarding the overlapping?

12.7 Counting: Permutations and Combinations

If there are 3 roads from Albany to Baker and 2 roads from Baker to Creswich, in how many ways can we travel from Albany to Creswich by way of Baker? For each of the 3 roads from Albany to Baker, there are 2 different roads from Baker to Creswich. Hence, there are $3 \cdot 2 = 6$ different ways to make the trip, as shown in the **tree diagram** of Figure 12.1.

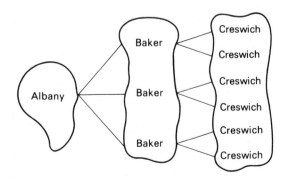

Figure 12.1

This example illustrates the following property of counting.

Successive Events Property

If one event can occur in *m* ways and a second event can occur in *n* ways, then both events can occur in *mn* ways, provided the outcome of the first event does not influence the outcome of the second.

The successive events property can be extended to any number of events, provided the outcome of no one event influences the outcome of another.

Example 1   Maxwell's Restaurant offers 3 salads, 5 main dishes, and 2 desserts. Use the successive events property to find the number of different meals that can be selected.

We have three events, selecting a salad, selecting a main dish, and selecting a dessert. The outcome of no one event influences the outcome of another. The first event can occur in 3 ways, the second event can occur in 5 ways, and the third event can occur in 2 ways, so there are

$$3 \cdot 5 \cdot 2 = 30 \text{ different meals.}$$

Example 2   David Krause has 5 different history books which he wishes to arrange on his desk. How many different arrangements are possible?

We have five events, selecting a book for the first space, selecting a book for the second space, and so on. Here the outcome of the first event *does* influence the outcome of the other events (since one book has already been chosen). However, we can say that for the second space the student has only 4 choices, for the third space 3 choices, and so on, so that the outcome of any one event no longer influences the outcome of another. Now we can use the successive events property to find that there are

$$5 \cdot 4 \cdot 3 \cdot 2 \cdot 1 = 120 \text{ different arrangements.}$$

Earlier in this chapter, we wrote products of this type with factorial notation. The product $5 \cdot 4 \cdot 3 \cdot 2 \cdot 1$ was written 5! ("5-factorial"). For example, if the person of Example 2 had 7 books, instead of 5, he could arrange them in

$$7! = 7 \cdot 6 \cdot 5 \cdot 4 \cdot 3 \cdot 2 \cdot 1 = 5040$$

different ways. Recall also that we defined 0! = 1.

Example 3   Suppose David wishes to place only 3 of the 5 history books on his desk. How many arrangements of 3 books are possible?

He again has 5 ways to fill the first space, 4 ways to fill the second space, and 3 ways to fill the third. Since he wants to use only 3 books, there are only 3 spaces to be filled (3 events) instead of 5. Thus there are

$$5 \cdot 4 \cdot 3 = 60 \text{ arrangements.}$$

The number 60 in the example above is called the number of permutations of 5 things taken 3 at a time, written $P(5, 3) = 60$. In Example 2 we found the number of ways of arranging 5 elements from a set of 5 elements, written $P(5, 5) = 120$.

In general, a **permutation** of n elements taken r at a time is the number of ways we can *arrange* r elements from a set of n elements. Generalizing from these examples and the successive events property, we have the following theorems.

Theorem 12.6   If $P(n, n)$ denotes the number of permutations of n elements taken n at a time, then

$$P(n, n) = n!$$

Theorem 12.7   If $P(n, r)$ denotes the number of permutations of n elements taken r at a time, then

$$P(n, r) = \frac{n!}{(n - r)!}$$

As illustrated by Example 2, Theorem 12.6 is a direct result of the successive events property. To prove Theorem 12.7, we note that

$$P(n, r) = n(n - 1)(n - 2) \cdots (n - r + 1)$$

$$= \frac{n(n - 1)(n - 2) \cdots (n - r + 1)(n - r) \cdots (2)(1)}{(n - r)(n - r - 1) \cdots (2)(1)}$$

$$= \frac{n!}{(n - r)!}$$

Example 4   Suppose 8 people enter a swimming meet. In how many ways could the gold, silver, and bronze prizes be awarded?

Using the successive events property, there are 3 choices to be made, so that $P(8, 3) = 8 \cdot 7 \cdot 6 = 336$. However, we can also use the formula given above for $P(n, r)$ to get the same result.

$$P(8, 3) = \frac{8!}{5!} = \frac{8 \cdot 7 \cdot 6 \cdot 5 \cdot 4 \cdot 3 \cdot 2 \cdot 1}{5 \cdot 4 \cdot 3 \cdot 2 \cdot 1}$$

$$= 8 \cdot 7 \cdot 6$$

$$= 336 \quad \blacksquare$$

Example 5   In how many ways can 6 students be seated in a row of 6 desks?

Here we have

$$P(6, 6) = 6! = 6 \cdot 5 \cdot 4 \cdot 3 \cdot 2 \cdot 1 = 720. \quad \blacksquare$$

In the work above, we discussed a method for finding the number of ways we can arrange r elements from a set of n elements. Sometimes we are not interested in the arrangement (or order) of the elements.

For example, suppose three people (Ms. Opelka, Mr. Adams, and Ms. Jacobs) apply for 2 identical jobs. Ignoring all other factors, in how many ways can the personnel officer select 2 people from the 3 applicants? Here the arrangement (or order) of the people is unimportant. Selecting Ms. Opelka and Mr.

Adams is the same as selecting Mr. Adams and Ms. Opelka. Therefore, there are only 3 ways to select 2 of the 3 applicants:

Ms. Opelka,   Mr. Adams

Ms. Opelka,   Ms. Jacobs

Mr. Adams,   Ms. Jacobs

These three choices are called the combinations of 3 elements taken 2 at a time. In general, a **combination** of n elements taken r at a time is the number of ways in which we *choose* r elements from n elements.

Each combination of r elements forms $r!$ permutations. Therefore, we can find the number of combinations of n elements taken r at a time by dividing the number of permutations, $P(n, r)$, by $r!$ to get

$$\frac{P(n, r)}{r!}$$

combinations. This expression can be rewritten as

$$\frac{P(n, r)}{r!} = \frac{\dfrac{n!}{(n - r)!}}{r!} = \frac{n!}{(n - r)!r!}$$

The symbol $\binom{n}{r}$ is used to represent the number of combinations of n things taken r at a time. Using this symbol and the results above, we have the following theorem.

Theorem 12.8   If $\binom{n}{r}$ represents the number of combinations of n things taken r at a time, then

$$\binom{n}{r} = \frac{n!}{(n - r)!r!}.$$

This same result was obtained in our work with the binomial theorem in Section 2 of this chapter. There we found that $\binom{n}{r}$ comes up as coefficients in the expansion of a binomial.

In the discussion above, we found that $\binom{3}{2} = 3$. We can get the same result using Theorem 12.8.

$$\binom{3}{2} = \frac{3!}{(3 - 2)!2!} = \frac{3 \cdot 2 \cdot 1}{1 \cdot 2 \cdot 1} = 3$$

Example 6   How many different committees of 3 people can be chosen from a group of 8 people?

We are not interested in the order in which the committee is chosen, so we use combinations.

$$\binom{8}{3} = \frac{8!}{5!3!} = \frac{8 \cdot 7 \cdot 6 \cdot 5 \cdot 4 \cdot 3 \cdot 2 \cdot 1}{5 \cdot 4 \cdot 3 \cdot 2 \cdot 1 \cdot 3 \cdot 2 \cdot 1} = 56 \quad \blacksquare$$

Example 7   From a group of 30 employees, 3 are to be selected to work on a special project.
(a) In how many different ways can the employees be selected?

Here we wish to know the number of 3-element combinations from a set of 30 elements. (We want combinations, not permutations, because we don't care about order within the group of 3.)

$$\binom{30}{3} = \frac{30!}{27!3!} = 4060$$

There are 4060 ways to select the project group.

(b) In how many different ways can the group of 3 be selected if it has already been decided that a certain man must work on the project?

Since one man has already been selected for the project, the problem is reduced to selecting 2 more from the remaining 29 employees.

$$\binom{29}{2} = \frac{29!}{27!2!} = 406$$

In this case, the project group can be selected in 406 different ways. ▌

12.7 Exercises   *Evaluate each of the following.*

1. $P(7, 7)$
2. $P(5, 3)$
3. $P(6, 5)$
4. $P(4, 2)$
5. $P(10, 2)$
6. $P(8, 2)$
7. $P(8, 3)$
8. $P(11, 4)$
9. $P(7, 1)$

10. $P(18, 0)$
11. $P(9, 0)$
12. $P(14, 1)$
13. $\binom{6}{5}$
14. $\binom{4}{2}$
15. $\binom{8}{5}$

16. $\binom{10}{2}$
17. $\binom{15}{4}$
18. $\binom{9}{3}$
19. $\binom{10}{7}$
20. $\binom{10}{3}$

21. $\binom{14}{1}$
22. $\binom{20}{2}$
23. $\binom{18}{0}$
24. $\binom{13}{0}$

25. In how many ways can 6 people be seated in a row of 6 seats?

26. In how many ways can 7 out of 10 people be assigned to 7 seats?

27. In how many ways can 5 bank tellers be assigned to 5 different windows? In how many ways can 10 tellers be assigned to the 5 windows?

28. A couple has narrowed down their choice of names for a new baby to 3 first names and 5 middle names. How many different first- and middle-name arrangements are possible?

29. How many different homes are available if a builder offers a choice of 5 basic plans, 3 roof styles, and 2 types of siding?

30. An automaker produces 7 models, each available in 6 colors, with 4 upholstery fabrics and 5 interior colors. How many varieties of the auto are available?

31. A concert is to consist of 5 works: two modern, two romantic, and one classical. In how many ways can the program be arranged?

32. If the program in Exercise 31 must be shortened to 3 works chosen from the 5, how many arrangements are possible?

33. In Exercise 31, how many different programs are possible if the two modern works are to be played first, then the two romantic, and then the classical?

34. How many 4-letter radio-station call letters can be made if the first letter must be K or W and no letter may be repeated? How many if repeats are allowed?

35. How many of the 4-letter call letters in Exercise 34 with no repeats end in K?

36. A business school gives courses in typing, shorthand, transcription, business English, technical writing, and accounting. How many ways can a student arrange his program if he takes 3 courses?

37. A club has 30 members. If a committee of 4 is to be selected at random, how many different committees are possible?

38. How many different samples of 3 apples can be drawn from a crate of 25 apples?

39. A group of 3 students is to be selected randomly from a group of 12 to participate in an experimental class. In how many ways can this be done? In how many ways can the group which will not participate be selected?

40. Hal's Hamburger Heaven sells hamburgers with cheese, relish, lettuce, tomato, mustard, or ketchup. How many different hamburgers can be made using any 3 of the extras?

41. How many different 2-card hands can be dealt from a deck of 52 cards?

42. How many different 13-card bridge hands can be dealt from a deck of 52 cards?

43. Five cards are marked with the numbers 1, 2, 3, 4, and 5, shuffled, and 2 cards are then drawn. How many different 2-card combinations are possible?

44. If a bag contains 15 marbles, how many samples of 2 marbles can be drawn from it? How many samples of 4 marbles?

45. In Exercise 44, if the bag contains 3 yellow, 4 white, and 8 blue marbles, how many samples of 2 can be drawn in which both marbles are blue?

46. In Exercise 38, if it is known that there are 5 rotten apples in the crate:
    (a) How many samples of 3 could be drawn in which all 3 are rotten?
    (b) How many samples of 3 could be drawn in which there are 1 rotten apple and 2 good apples?

47. Glendale Heights City Council is composed of 5 liberals and 4 conservatives. Three members are to be selected randomly as delegates to a convention.
    (a) How many delegations are possible?
    (b) How many delegations could have all liberals?
    (c) How many delegations could have 2 liberals and 1 conservative?
    (d) If 1 member of the council serves as mayor, how many delegations are possible which include the mayor?

48. Seven factory workers decide to send a delegation of 2 to their supervisor to discuss their grievances.
    (a) How many different delegations are possible?
    (b) If it is decided that a certain employee must be in the delegation, how many different delegations are possible?
    (c) If there are 2 women and 5 men in the group, how many delegations would include a woman?

A poker hand is made up of 5 cards drawn at random from a deck of 52 cards. Any 5 cards in one suit are called a flush. The 5 highest cards, that is, the A, K, Q, J, and 10, of any one suit are called a royal flush. Use combinations to set up each of the following. Do not evaluate.

49. Find the total number of all possible poker hands.

50. How many royal flushes in hearts are possible?

51. How many royal flushes in any of the four suits are possible?

52. How many flushes in hearts are possible?

53. How many flushes in any of the four suits are possible?

54. How many combinations of 3 aces and 2 eights are possible?

Solve the following problems by using either combinations or permutations.

55. In how many ways can the letters of the word TOUGH be arranged?

56. If Matthew has 8 courses to choose from, how many ways can he arrange his schedule if he must pick 4 of them?

57. How many samples of 3 pineapples can be drawn from a crate of 12?

58. Velma specializes in making different vegetable soups with carrots, celery, beans, peas, mushrooms, and potatoes. How many different soups can she make using any 4 ingredients?

Solve each of the following equations for n.

59. $P(n, 3) = 8 \cdot P(n - 1, 2)$

60. $30 \cdot P(n, 2) = P(n + 2, 4)$

61. $\binom{n + 2}{4} = 15 \cdot \binom{n}{4}$

62. $\binom{n}{n - 2} = 66$

Prove each of the following statements for positive integers n and r, with r ≤ n.

63. $P(n, n - 1) = P(n, n)$

64. $P(n, 1) = n$

65. $P(n, 0) = 1$

66. $\binom{n}{n} = 1$

67. $\binom{n}{0} = 1$

68. $\binom{n}{n - 1} = n$

69. $\binom{n}{n - r} = \binom{n}{r}$

70. $\binom{2n}{r} \leq \binom{2n}{n}$ for all r, $0 \leq r \leq 2n$

71. $\binom{n}{r} = \binom{n - 2}{r - 2} + 2 \cdot \binom{n - 2}{r - 1} + \binom{n - 2}{r}$ for $2 \leq r \leq n - 2$.

72. If $n > 1$, then $r \cdot \binom{n}{r} = n \cdot \binom{n - 1}{r - 1}$

73. $\binom{n}{1} + \binom{n}{2} + \cdots + \binom{n}{n} = 2^n - 1$

74. Suppose m and n are any positive integers greater than 1. Decide which is larger, $(mn)!$ or $(m!)(n!)$.

12.8   Basics of Probability

The study of probability theory has become increasingly popular because of the wide range of practical applications. In this section, we introduce the basic ideas of probability.

Consider an experiment which has one or more possible **outcomes,** each of which is equally likely to occur. For example, the experiment of tossing a coin has two possible outcomes, landing heads up (H) or landing tails up (T). The set S of all possible outcomes of a given experiment is called the **sample space** for the experiment. (In this text all sample spaces are finite.) A sample space for the experiment of tossing a coin consists of the outcomes H and T. This sample space can be written in set notation as

$$S = \{H, T\}.$$

Similarly, a sample space for the experiment of rolling a single die is

$$S = \{1, 2, 3, 4, 5, 6\}.$$

(A single die can have either a 1, 2, 3, 4, 5, or 6 showing on top after it is rolled.)

Any subset of the sample space is called an **event.** In the experiment with the die, for example, "the number showing is a three" is an event, say E_1, such that $E_1 = \{3\}$. "The number showing is greater than three" is also an event, say E_2, such that $E_2 = \{4, 5, 6\}$. To represent the number of outcomes which satisfy event E, we use $n(E)$. Then $n(E_1) = 1$ and $n(E_2) = 3$.

The **probability** of an event E, written $P(E)$, is the ratio of *the number of outcomes in sample space S which satisfies event E* compared to *the total number of outcomes in sample space S.* Thus,

$$P(E) = \frac{n(E)}{n(S)} = \frac{\text{number of outcomes satisfying event } E}{\text{number of outcomes in sample space } S}.$$

To use this definition to find the probability of the event E_1, given above, we note that the sample space for the experiment is $S = \{1, 2, 3, 4, 5, 6\}$ and the desired event is $E_1 = \{3\}$. We already know $n(E_1) = 1$ and we can see there are 6 outcomes in the sample space. Thus,

$$P(E_1) = \frac{n(E_1)}{n(S)} = \frac{1}{6}.$$

Example 1   A single die is rolled. Write the following events in set notation and give the probability for each event.

    (a) E_3: the number showing is even.
    (b) E_4: the number showing is greater than 4.
    (c) E_5: the number showing is less than 10.
    (d) E_6: the number showing is 8.

Using the definitions above, we have the following.

    (a) $E_3 = \{2, 4, 6\}$ and $P(E_3) = \frac{3}{6} = \frac{1}{2}$. (Recall that there are six outcomes in the sample space and notice that $n(E_3) = 3$.)

(b) $E_4 = \{5, 6\}$ and $P(E_4) = \dfrac{2}{6} = \dfrac{1}{3}$.

(c) $E_5 = \{1, 2, 3, 4, 5, 6\}$ and $P(E_5) = \dfrac{6}{6} = 1$.

(d) $E_6 = \varnothing$ and $P(E_6) = \dfrac{0}{6} = 0$. ▌

Note that $E_5 = S$. Therefore the event E_5 is certain to occur every time the experiment is performed. We see that an event which is certain to occur, such as E_5, has a probability of 1. On the other hand, $E_6 = \varnothing$ and $P(E_6)$ is 0. The probability of an impossible event, such as E_6, is always 0, since none of the outcomes in the sample space satisfy the event.

The set of all outcomes in the sample space which do *not* satisfy event E is called the **complement** of E, written E'. For example, in the experiment of drawing a single card from a standard deck of 52 cards, let E be the event "the card is an ace." Then E' is the event "the card is not an ace." From the definition of E', we see that for any event E,

$$E \cup E' = S \quad \text{and} \quad E \cap E' = \varnothing.*$$

Example 2   In the experiment of drawing a card from a well-shuffled deck, find the probability of events E, (the card is an ace), and E'.

Since there are four aces in the deck of 52 cards, $n(E) = 4$. Also $n(S) = 52$. Therefore, $P(E) = \dfrac{n(E)}{n(S)} = \dfrac{4}{52} = \dfrac{1}{13}$. Of the 52 cards, 48 are not aces, so that we have $P(E') = \dfrac{n(E')}{n(S)} = \dfrac{48}{52} = \dfrac{12}{13}$. ▌

In Example 2, note that $P(E) + P(E') = (1/13) + (12/13) = 1$. This is always true for any event E and its complement E', so that in general,

$$P(E) + P(E') = 1.$$

This can be restated as

$$P(E) = 1 - P(E') \quad \text{or} \quad P(E') = 1 - P(E).$$

These two equations suggest an alternate way to compute the probability of an event. For example, if it is known that $P(E) = 1/10$, then

$$P(E') = 1 - \dfrac{1}{10} = \dfrac{9}{10}.$$

Sometimes probability statements are expressed in terms of odds, a comparison of $P(E)$ with $P(E')$. The **odds** in favor of an event E are expressed as the ratio of $P(E)$ to $P(E')$ or as the fraction $P(E)/P(E')$. For example, if the probability of rain can be established as 1/3, the odds that it will rain are

---

*The *union* of two sets A and B is the set $A \cup B$ made up of all the elements from either A or B, or both. The *intersection* of sets A and B, written $A \cap B$, is made up of all the elements that belong to both sets at the same time.

$$P(\text{rain}) \text{ to } P(\text{no rain}) = \frac{1}{3} \text{ to } \frac{2}{3}$$

$$= \frac{1/3}{2/3}$$

$$= \frac{1}{2} \quad \text{or} \quad 1 \text{ to } 2.$$

On the other hand, the odds that it will not rain are 2 to 1 (or 2/3 to 1/3). If we know that the odds in favor of an event are, say, 3 to 5, then we can see that the probability of the event is 3/8, while the probability of the complement of the event is 5/8. In general, if the odds favoring event E are m to n, then

$$P(E) = \frac{m}{m + n} \quad \text{and} \quad P(E') = \frac{n}{m + n}.$$

We now consider the probability of a **compound event** which involves an alternative, such as E or F, where E and F are simple events. For example, in the experiment of rolling a die, suppose H is the event "the result is a 3," and K is the event "the result is an even number." What is the probability of "the result is a 3 or an even number"? We have

$$H = \{3\} \qquad\qquad P(H) = \frac{1}{6}$$

$$K = \{2, 4, 6\} \qquad\qquad P(K) = \frac{3}{6} = \frac{1}{2};$$

therefore, $\quad H \text{ or } K = \{2, 3, 4, 6\} \quad P(H \text{ or } K) = \frac{4}{6} = \frac{2}{3}.$

Notice that $P(H) + P(K) = P(H \text{ or } K)$. Before we assume that this relationship is true in general, let us consider another event for this experiment, "the result is a 2," event G. We have

$$G = \{2\} \qquad\qquad P(G) = \frac{1}{6}$$

$$K = \{2, 4, 6\} \qquad\qquad P(K) = \frac{3}{6} = \frac{1}{2};$$

therefore, $\quad K \text{ or } G = \{2, 4, 6\} \quad P(K \text{ or } G) = \frac{3}{6} = \frac{1}{2}.$

In this case $P(K) + P(G) \neq P(K \text{ or } G)$.

The difference in the two examples above comes from the fact that events H and K cannot occur simultaneously. Such events are called **mutually exclusive events**. We see that $H \cap K = \varnothing$, which is true in general for any two mutually exclusive events. Events K and G, however, can occur simultaneously. Both are satisfied if the result of the roll is a 2, the element in their intersection ($K \cap G = \{2\}$). Generalizing the above discussion, we have the following theorem.

Theorem 12.9   For any events E and F,

$$P(E \text{ or } F) = P(E \cup F) = P(E) + P(F) - P(E \cap F).$$

Example 3   For the experiment consisting of one roll of a pair of dice, find the probability that the sum of the points showing is at most 4.

We can rewrite "at most 4" as "2 or 3 or 4." (A sum of 1 is meaningless here.) Then from Theorem 12.10 we have

$$P(\text{at most } 4) = P(2 \text{ or } 3 \text{ or } 4)$$
$$= P(2) + P(3) + P(4), \qquad (1)$$

since the events represented by "2," "3," and "4" are mutually exclusive. By the definition of probability, $P(2) = 1/36$, $P(3) = 2/36$, and $P(4) = 3/36$. Substituting into equation (1) above we have

$$P(\text{at most } 4) = \frac{1}{36} + \frac{2}{36} + \frac{3}{36} = \frac{6}{36} = \frac{1}{6}. \quad \blacksquare$$

Example 4   One card is drawn from a well-shuffled deck of 52 cards. What is the probability that it is an ace or a spade? a three or a king?

The events "drawing an ace" and "drawing a spade" are not mutually exclusive since it is possible to draw the ace of spades, an outcome satisfying both events.

From Theorem 12.10 we have

$$P(\text{ace or spade}) = P(\text{ace}) + P(\text{spade}) - P(\text{ace and spade})$$
$$= \frac{4}{52} + \frac{13}{52} - \frac{1}{52} = \frac{16}{52} = \frac{4}{13}.$$

"Drawing a 3" and "drawing a king" are mutually exclusive events because it is impossible to draw one card which is both a 3 and a king. From Theorem 12.10 we have

$$P(3 \text{ or } K) = P(3) + P(K) - P(3 \text{ and } K) = \frac{4}{52} + \frac{4}{52} - 0 = \frac{8}{52} = \frac{2}{13}. \quad \blacksquare$$

12.8 Exercises   *Write a sample space with equally likely outcomes for each of the following experiments.*

1. A two-headed coin is tossed once.

2. Two ordinary coins are tossed.

3. Three ordinary coins are tossed.

4. Slips of paper marked with the numbers 1, 2, 3, 4, and 5 are placed in a box. After mixing well, two slips are drawn.

5. An unprepared student takes a three-question true/false quiz in which he guesses the answer to all three questions.

6. A die is rolled and then a coin is tossed.

Write the following events in set notation and give the probability of each event.

7. In the experiment of Exercise 2:
   (a) both coins show the same face;
   (b) at least one coin turns up heads.

8. In Exercise 1:
   (a) the result of the toss is heads;
   (b) the result of the toss is tails.

9. In Exercise 4:
   (a) both slips are marked with even numbers;
   (b) both slips are marked with odd numbers;
   (c) both slips are marked with the same number;
   (d) one slip is marked with an odd number, the other with an even number.

10. In Exercise 5:
    (a) the student gets all three answers correct;
    (b) he gets all three answers wrong;
    (c) he gets exactly two answers correct;
    (d) he gets at least one answer correct.

11. A marble is drawn at random from a box containing 3 yellow, 4 white, and 8 blue marbles. Find the following probabilities.
    (a) A yellow marble is drawn;
    (b) a blue marble is drawn;
    (c) a black marble is drawn.
    (d) What are the odds in favor of drawing a yellow marble?
    (e) What are the odds against drawing a blue marble?

12. A baseball player with a batting average of .300 comes to bat. What are the odds in favor of his getting a hit?

13. In Exercise 4, what are the odds that the sum of the numbers on the two slips of paper is 5?

14. If the odds that it will rain are 4 to 5, what is the probability of rain?

15. If the odds that a candidate will win an election are 3 to 2, what is the probability that the candidate will lose?

16. A card is drawn from a well-shuffled deck of 52 cards. Find the probability that the card is
    (a) a 9
    (b) black
    (c) a black 9
    (d) a heart
    (e) the 9 of hearts
    (f) a face card (K, Q, J of any suit)

17. Mrs. Elliott invites 10 relatives to a party: her mother, two uncles, three brothers, and four cousins. If the chances of any one guest arriving first are equally likely, find the following probabilities.
    (a) The first guest is an uncle or a brother.
    (b) The first guest is a brother or cousin.
    (c) The first guest is a brother or her mother.

18. One card is drawn from a standard deck of 52 cards. What is the probability that the card is
    (a) a 9 or a 10?
    (b) red or a 3?
    (c) a heart or black?
    (d) less than a 4? (Consider Aces as 1's.)

19. Two dice are rolled. Find the probability that
    (a) the sum of the points is at least 10;
    (b) the sum of the points is either 7 or at least 10;
    (c) the sum of the points is 2 or the dice both show the same number.

20. A student estimates that his probability of getting an A in a certain course is .4; a B, .3; a C, .2; and a D, .1.
    (a) Assuming that only the grades A, B, C, D, and F are possible, what is the probability that he will fail the course?
    (b) What is the probability that he will receive a grade of C or better?
    (c) What is the probability that he will receive at least a B in the course?
    (d) What is the probability that he will get at most a C in the course?

21. If a marble is drawn from a bag containing 3 yellow, 4 white, and 8 blue marbles, what is the probability that
    (a) the marble is either yellow or white?
    (b) it is either yellow or blue?
    (c) it is either red or white?

Chapter 12   Review Exercises

Use mathematical induction to prove that each of the following is true for every positive integer n.

1. $1 + 3 + 5 + 7 + \cdots + (2n - 1) = n^2$

2. $2 + 6 + 10 + 14 + \cdots + (4n - 2) = 2n^2$

3. $2^2 + 4^2 + 6^2 + \cdots + (2n)^2 = \dfrac{2n(n + 1)(2n + 1)}{3}$

4. $2 + 2^2 + 2^3 + \cdots + 2^n = 2(2^n - 1)$

5. $1 \cdot 4 + 2 \cdot 9 + 3 \cdot 16 + \cdots + n(n + 1)^2 = \dfrac{n(n + 1)(n + 2)(3n + 5)}{12}$

6. $1^3 + 3^3 + 5^3 + \cdots + (2n - 1)^3 = n^2(2n^2 - 1)$

Use the binomial theorem to expand each of the following.

7. $(x + 2y)^4$

8. $(3z - 5w)^3$

9. $\left(3\sqrt{x} - \dfrac{1}{\sqrt{x}}\right)^5$

10. $(m^3 - m^{-2})^4$

Find the indicated term or terms for each of the following expansions.

11. fifth term of $(3x - 2y)^6$

12. eighth term of $(2m + n^2)^{12}$

13. first four terms of $(3 + x)^{16}$

14. last three terms of $(2m - 3n)^{15}$

Write the first five terms for each of the following sequences.

15. $a_n = 2(n + 3)$

16. $a_n = n(n + 1)$

17. $a_1 = 5$, $a_2 = 3$, $a_n = a_{n-1} - a_{n-2}$ for $n \geq 2$

18. $b_1 = -2$, $b_2 = 2$, $b_3 = -4$, $b_n = -2 \cdot b_{n-2}$ if n is even, and $b_n = 2 \cdot b_{n-2}$ if n is odd.

19. arithmetic, $a_1 = 6$, $d = -4$

20. arithmetic, $a_3 = 9$, $a_4 = 7$

21. arithmetic, $a_1 = 3 - \sqrt{5}$, $a_2 = 4$

22. arithmetic, $a_3 = \pi$, $a_4 = 0$

23. geometric, $a_1 = 4$, $r = 2$

24. geometric, $a_4 = 8$, $r = 1/2$

25. geometric, $a_1 = -3$, $a_2 = 4$

26. geometric, $a_3 = 8$, $a_5 = 72$

27. A certain arithmetic sequence has $a_6 = -4$ and $a_{17} = 51$. Find a_1 and a_{20}.

28. For a given geometric sequence, $a_1 = 4$ and $a_5 = 324$. Find a_6.

Find a_8 for each of the following arithmetic sequences.

29. $a_1 = 6$, $d = 2$ **31.** $a_1 = 6x - 9$, $a_2 = 5x + 1$

30. $a_1 = -4$, $d = 3$ **32.** $a_3 = 11m$, $a_5 = 7m - 4$

Find S_{12} for each of the following arithmetic sequences.

33. $a_1 = 2$, $d = 3$ **34.** $a_2 = 6$, $d = 10$ **35.** $a_1 = -4k$, $d = 2k$

Find a_5 for each of the following geometric sequences.

36. $a_1 = 3$, $r = 2$ **39.** $a_1 = 5x$, $a_2 = x^2$

37. $a_2 = 3125$, $r = 1/5$ **40.** $a_2 = \sqrt{6}$, $a_4 = 6\sqrt{6}$

38. $a_1 = 6$, $a_3 = 24$

Find S_4 for each of the following geometric sequences.

41. $a_1 = 1$, $r = 2$ **42.** $a_1 = 3$, $r = 3$ **43.** $a_1 = 2k$, $a_2 = -4k$

Evaluate each of the following sums which exist.

44. $18 + 9 + 9/2 + 9/4 + \cdots$

45. $20 + 15 + 45/4 + 135/16 + \cdots$

46. $-5/6 + 5/9 - 10/27 + \cdots$

47. $1/16 + 1/8 + 1/4 + 1/2 + \cdots$

48. $.9 + .09 + .009 + .0009 + \cdots$

Convert each of the following repeating decimals to rational numbers.

49. $.6666\ldots$ **51.** $.512512512\ldots$

50. $2.1333\ldots$ **52.** $.2499999\ldots$

Evaluate each of the following sums which exist.

53. $\displaystyle\sum_{i=1}^{4} \frac{2}{i}$

54. $\displaystyle\sum_{i=1}^{7} (-1)^{i+1} \cdot 6$

55. $\displaystyle\sum_{i=4}^{8} 3i(2i - 5)$

56. $\displaystyle\sum_{i=1}^{6} i(i + 2)$

57. $\displaystyle\sum_{i=1}^{4} \frac{i + 1}{i}$

58. $\displaystyle\sum_{i=1}^{12} (8i + 2)$

59. $\displaystyle\sum_{i=1}^{10,000} i$

60. $\displaystyle\sum_{i=1}^{6} 4 \cdot 3^i$

61. $\displaystyle\sum_{i=1}^{4} 8 \cdot 2^i$

62. $\displaystyle\sum_{i=1}^{\infty} \left(\frac{5}{8}\right)^i$

63. $\displaystyle\sum_{i=1}^{\infty} -10\left(\frac{5}{2}\right)^i$

64. $\displaystyle\sum_{i=1}^{\infty} 6(2/3)^i$

Find each of the following.

65. $P(9, 2)$

66. $P(8, 3)$

67. $P(6, 0)$

68. $\displaystyle\binom{8}{3}$

69. $\displaystyle\binom{10}{5}$

70. Four students are to be assigned to 4 different summer jobs. Each student is qualified for all 4 jobs. In how many ways can the jobs be assigned?

71. Nine football teams are competing for 1st, 2nd, and 3rd place titles in a statewide tournament. In how many ways can the winners be determined?

72. How many different license-plate numbers can be formed using 3 letters followed by 3 digits if no repeats are allowed? How many if there are no repeats and either letters or numbers come first?

A card is drawn from a standard deck of 52 cards. Find the probability that the card is

73. a black king

74. a face card or an ace

75. an ace or a diamond

76. not a diamond

77. not a diamond or not black

78. a diamond and black.

The following exercises are taken with permission from a standard calculus book.

79. Prove each of the following statements for real numbers a and b.
   (a) $|a| < |b|$ if and only if $a^2 < b^2$
   (b) $|a + b| \le |a| + |b|$
   (c) $|a - b| \ge ||a| - |b||$
   (d) $|a_1 + a_2 + \cdots + a_n| \le |a_1| + |a_2| + \cdots + |a_n|$
   (e) $|a_1 + a_2 + \cdots + a_n| \ge |a_1| - |a_2| - \cdots - |a_n|$

80. Let A_n be the area bounded by a regular n-sided polygon inscribed in a circle of radius r. Show that $A_n = (n/2)r^2 \sin(2\pi/n)$. Let $r = 1$ and find A_1 through A_{10}. Can you decide on a good guess for $\lim_{n \to \infty} A_n$?

Appendix A   Linear Programming

One of the main applications of mathematics to business and social science is called linear programming. Linear programming is used to find such things as minimum cost and maximum profit. We shall explain the basic ideas of this technique with an example.

The Smith Company makes two products, tape decks and amplifiers. Each tape deck gives a profit of $3, while each amplifier earns $7. The company must manufacture at least one tape deck per day to satisfy one of its customers, but no more than five because of production problems. Also, the number of amplifiers produced cannot exceed six per day. As a further requirement, the number of tape decks cannot exceed the number of amplifiers. How many of each should the company manufacture in order to obtain the maximum profit?

To begin, translate the statements of the problem into symbols by assuming

$$x = \text{number of tape decks to be produced daily}$$
$$y = \text{number of amplifiers to be produced daily.}$$

According to the statement of the problem given above, the company must produce at least one tape deck (one or more), so that

$$x \geq 1.$$

No more than 5 tape decks may be produced:

$$x \leq 5.$$

Not more than 6 amplifiers may be made in one day:

$$y \leq 6.$$

The number of tape decks may not exceed the number of amplifiers:

$$x \leq y.$$

The number of tape decks and of amplifiers cannot be negative:

$$x \geq 0 \quad \text{and} \quad y \geq 0.$$

Let us now summarize all the restrictions, or **constraints,** that are placed on production:

$$x \geq 1, \quad x \leq 5, \quad y \leq 6, \quad x \leq y, \quad x \geq 0, \quad y \geq 0.$$

We need to find the maximum possible profit that the company can make, subject to these constraints. To begin, we sketch the graph of each constraint.

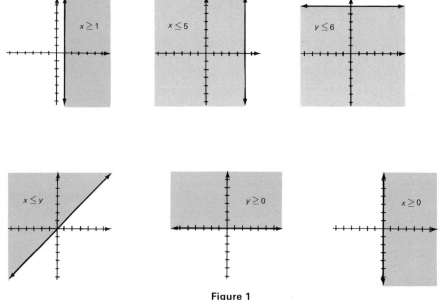

Figure 1

The graphs of the constraints are shown in Figure 1. The only feasible values of x and y are those that satisfy all constraints; that is, the values which lie in the intersection of the graphs of the constraints. The intersection is shown in Figure 2. Any point lying inside the shaded region (boundaries also) of Figure 2 satisfies the restrictions as to the number of tape decks and amplifiers that may be produced.

Since each tape deck gives a profit of $3, the daily profit from the production of x decks is $3x$ dollars. Also, the profit from the production of y amplifiers will be $7y$ dollars per day. The total daily profit is thus

$$\text{profit} = 3x + 7y.$$

The problem of the Smith Company may now be stated as follows: find values of x and y in the shaded region of Figure 2 that will produce the maximum possible value of $3x + 7y$.

A basic idea of linear programming says that in a case such as ours the maximum (or minimum) profit will be found at a corner of the graph. By looking at Figure 2, we see that the corner points are $(1, 1)$, $(1, 6)$, $(5, 5)$, and $(5, 6)$.

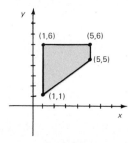

Figure 2

We now check each corner point to find the profit.

Point	Profit = $3x + 7y$
(1, 1)	$3(1) + 7(1) = 10$ ← minimum
(1, 6)	$3(1) + 7(6) = 45$
(5, 5)	$3(5) + 7(5) = 50$
(5, 6)	$3(5) + 7(6) = 57$ ← maximum

Maximum profit of $57 per day will be obtained if five tape decks and six amplifiers are made each day.

Example 1 Robin, who is ill, takes vitamin pills. Each day, she must have at least 16 units of Vitamin A, at least 5 units of Vitamin B_1, and at least 20 units of Vitamin C. She can choose between red pills, costing 10¢ each, which contain 8 units of A, 1 of B_1, and 2 of C; and blue pills, costing 20¢ each, which contain 2 units of A, 1 of B_1, and 7 of C. How many of each pill should she buy in order to minimize her cost and yet fulfill her daily requirements?

Let x represent the number of red pills to buy, and let y represent the number of blue pills to buy. Then the cost in pennies per day is given by

$$cost = 10x + 20y,$$

since Robin buys x of the 10¢ pills and y of the 20¢ pills. Vitamin A comes as follows: 8 units from each red pill and 2 units from each blue pill. Altogether, she gets $8x + 2y$ units of A per day. Since she must get at least 16 units,

$$8x + 2y \geq 16.$$

Each red pill and each blue pill supplies 1 unit of Vitamin B_1. Robin needs at least 5 units per day:

$$x + y \geq 5.$$

For Vitamin C we get the inequality

$$2x + 7y \geq 20.$$

Also, $x \geq 0$ and $y \geq 0$, since Robin cannot buy negative numbers of the pills.

Again, we minimize total cost of the pills by finding the solution of the system of inequalities formed by the constraints. (See Figure 3.)

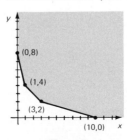

Figure 3

Check the corners to find the lowest cost.

Point	Cost $= 10x + 20y$
(10, 0)	$10(10) + 20(0) = 100$
(3, 2)	$10(3) + 20(2) = 70$ $\leftarrow$ minimum
(1, 4)	$10(1) + 20(4) = 90$
(0, 8)	$10(0) + 20(8) = 160$

Robin's best bet is to buy 3 red pills and 2 blue ones, for a total cost of 70¢ per day. She receives just the minimum amounts of Vitamins B_1 and C, but an excess of Vitamin A. Even though she has an excess of A, this is still the best buy. ▍

Exercises

Exercises 1–4 show regions of feasible solutions. Find the maximum and minimum values of the given expressions.

1. $3x + 5y$

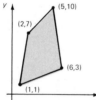

2. $6x + y$

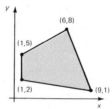

3. $40x + 75y$

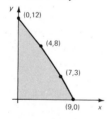

4. $35x + 125y$

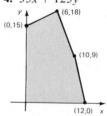

In Exercises 5–10, use graphical methods to find values of x and y satisfying the given conditions. Find the value of the maximum or minimum.

5. Find $x \geq 0$ and $y \geq 0$ such that
$$2x + 3y \leq 6$$
$$4x + y \leq 6$$
and $5x + 2y$ is maximized.

6. Find $x \geq 0$ and $y \geq 0$ such that
$$x + y \leq 10$$
$$5x + 2y \geq 20$$
$$2y \geq x$$
and $x + 3y$ is minimized.

7. Find $x \geq 2$ and $y \geq 5$ such that
$$3x - y \geq 12$$
$$x + y \leq 15$$
and $2x + y$ is minimized.

8. Find $x \geq 10$ and $y \geq 20$ such that
$$2x + 3y \leq 100$$
$$5x + 4y \leq 200$$
and $x + 3y$ is maximized.

9. Find $x \geq 0$ and $y \geq 0$ such that
$$x - y \leq 10$$
$$5x + 3y \leq 75$$
and $4x + 2y$ is maximized.

10. Find $x \geq 0$ and $y \geq 0$ such that
$$10x - 5y \leq 100$$
$$20x + 10y \geq 150$$
and $4x + 5y$ is minimized.

11. Maximize $10x + 12y$ subject separately to each set of constraints.

   (a) $x + \ \ y \leq 20$ (b) $3x + \ \ y \leq 15$ (c) $2x + 5y \geq 22$

       $x + 3y \leq 24$ $x + 2y \leq 18$ $4x + 3y \leq 28$

             $x \geq 0$ $x \geq 0$ $2x + 2y \leq 17$

             $y \geq 0$ $y \geq 0$ $x \geq 0$

                                                           $y \geq 0$

12. Minimize $3x + 2y$ subject separately to each set of constraints.

   (a) $10x + \ \ 7y \leq 42$ (b) $6x + 5y \geq 25$ (c) $\ \ x + 2y \geq 10$

       $4x + 10y \geq 35$ $2x + 6y \geq 15$ $2x + \ \ y \geq 12$

              $x \geq 0$ $x \geq 0$ $\ \ x - \ \ y \leq 8$

              $y \geq 0$ $y \geq 0$ $x \geq 0$

                                                           $y \geq 0$

Solve each of the following linear programming problems.

13. Farmer Jones raises only pigs and geese. He wants to raise no more than 16 animals with no more than 12 geese. He spends $5 to raise a pig and $2 to raise a goose. He has $50 available for this purpose. Find the maximum profit he can make if he makes a profit of $8 per goose and $4 per pig.

14. A wholesaler of party goods wishes to display her products at a convention of social secretaries in such a way that she gets the maximum number of inquiries about her whistles and hats. Her booth at the convention has 12 square meters of floor space to be used for display purposes. A display unit for hats requires 2 square meters; and for whistles, 4 square meters. Experience tells the wholesaler that she should never have more than a total of 5 units of whistles and hats on display at one time. If she receives three inquiries for each unit of hats and two inquiries for each unit of whistles on display, how many of each should she display in order to get the maximum number of inquiries?

15. An office manager wants to buy some filing cabinets. She knows that cabinet #1 costs $10 each, requires 6 square feet of floor space, and holds 8 cubic feet of files. On the other hand, cabinet #2 costs $20 each, requires 8 square feet of floor space, and holds 12 cubic feet. She can spend no more than $140 due to budgetary limitations, while her office has room for no more than 72 square feet of cabinets. She desires the maximum storage capacity within the limitations imposed by funds and space. How many of each type of cabinet should she buy?

16. The manufacture of "Smokey the Bear" ashtrays and "Superman" cufflinks requires two machines, a drill and a saw. Each ashtray needs one minute on the drill and two minutes on the saw; each cufflink set needs two minutes on the drill and one minute on the saw. The drill is available at most for 12 minutes per day, and the saw is available no more than 15 minutes per day. Each product provides a profit of $1. How many of each should be manufactured in order to maximize profit?

Appendix B   **Partial Fractions**

In Section 1.6 we found sums of rational expressions by combining two or more rational expressions into one rational expression. Here we consider the reverse problem. Given one rational expression, we want to express it as the sum of two or more rational expressions, called **partial fractions.**

The methods given below are restricted to quotients of polynomials which are *proper* fractions. The numerator of a proper fraction is of lower degree than the denominator. If the numerator is not of lower degree, we first divide the numerator by the denominator. For example,

$$\frac{x^4 - 3x^3 + x^2 + 5x}{x^2 + 3} = x^2 - 3x - 2 + \frac{14x + 6}{x^2 + 3}.$$

Then we can apply the methods to the remainder, which is a proper fraction.

To write a proper rational expression as the sum of partial fractions, we need to factor the denominator into a product of linear and quadratic factors. Theoretically this can always be done. The possible types of factors fall into four cases.

1. All factors are linear and none is repeated.
2. All factors are linear and some are repeated.
3. Some factors are quadratic but no quadratic factor is repeated.
4. Some factors are quadratic and some quadratic factors are repeated.

We illustrate how to proceed in each case with examples.

Example 1   Express the following as a sum of partial fractions.

$$\frac{5x - 2}{x^3 - 4x}$$

The denominator can be factored as $x^3 - 4x = x(x + 2)(x - 2)$, so write

$$\frac{5x - 2}{x^3 - 4x} = \frac{A}{x} + \frac{B}{x + 2} + \frac{C}{x - 2}, \tag{1}$$

where A, B, and C are constants we must find. There are two methods we can use to find A, B, and C. We can multiply both sides of equation (1) by $x(x + 2)(x - 2)$ to get

$$5x - 2 = A(x + 2)(x - 2) + Bx(x - 2) + Cx(x + 2). \tag{2}$$

Equation (1) is an identity, since both sides represent the same rational expression. Thus, equation (2) is also an identity. Equation (1) holds for all values of x except 0, -2, and 2. However, equation (2) holds for all values of x. If we substitute 0 for x in equation (2), we have

$$-2 = -4A, \quad \text{so that} \quad A = \frac{1}{2}.$$

Now we substitute -2 for x to get

$$-12 = 8B, \quad \text{so that} \quad B = -\frac{3}{2}.$$

Finally we substitute 2 for x to get

$$8 = 8C, \quad \text{so that} \quad C = 1.$$

Thus, the rational expression can be written as a sum of partial fractions

$$\frac{5x - 2}{x^3 - 4x} = \frac{1}{2x} + \frac{-3}{2(x + 2)} + \frac{1}{x - 2}. \quad \blacksquare$$

Another method of finding the constants A, B, and C is demonstrated below.

Example 2   Express the following as a sum of partial fractions.

$$\frac{2x}{(x-1)^3}$$

Here we have a repeated linear factor. The sum may have terms with denominators of $x-1$, $(x-1)^2$, or $(x-1)^3$ since any of these are factors. We begin by writing

$$\frac{2x}{(x-1)^3} = \frac{A}{x-1} + \frac{B}{(x-1)^2} + \frac{C}{(x-1)^3}$$

$$2x = A(x-1)^2 + B(x-1) + C.$$

By substituting 1 for x, we find that $C = 2$, giving

$$2x = A(x-1)^2 + B(x-1) + 2 \tag{3}$$

Clear parentheses on the right in equation (3).

$$2x = A(x^2 - 2x + 1) + B(x-1) + 2$$
$$2x = Ax^2 - 2Ax + A + Bx - B + 2$$

Then collect like terms on the right.

$$2x = Ax^2 + (-2A + B)x + (A - B + 2)$$

Since equation (3) is an identity, the coefficients of the like terms on the two sides of the equation must be equal, so

$$0 = A$$
$$2 = -2A + B$$
$$0 = A - B + 2$$

Solving this system, we find $A = 0$, $B = 2$, and $C = 2$. Thus,

$$\frac{2x}{(x-1)^3} = \frac{2}{(x-1)^2} + \frac{2}{(x-1)^3}.$$ ∎

Example 3   Express the following as a sum of partial fractions.

$$\frac{x^2 + 3x - 1}{(x+1)(x^2 - 2)}$$

Here we have one linear factor and one quadratic factor. (While we could factor $x^2 - 2$ as the product of linear factors $(x - \sqrt{2})(x + \sqrt{2})$, we are usually restricted to rational numbers in the factors.) The quadratic factor may have a numerator which is a linear expression rather than a constant. Start as follows.

$$\frac{x^2 + 3x - 1}{(x+1)(x^2 - 2)} = \frac{A}{x+1} + \frac{Bx + C}{x^2 - 2}$$

$$x^2 + 3x - 1 = A(x^2 - 2) + (Bx + C)(x + 1).$$

We can use a combination of the methods presented earlier to find A, B, and C. Substituting -1 for x, $1 - 3 - 1 = -A$,   so that $A = 3$.
Letting $A = 3$ and combining terms on the right give

$$x^2 + 3x - 1 = 3x^2 - 6 + Bx^2 + (B + C)x + C$$
$$x^2 + 3x - 1 = (3 + B)x^2 + (B + C)x + (C - 6).$$

This leads to the following system of equations.

$$1 = 3 + B$$
$$3 = B + C$$
$$-1 = C - 6$$

The solution of the system is $B = -2$, $C = 5$. Thus, we can write

$$\frac{x^2 + 3x - 1}{(x + 1)(x^2 - 2)} = \frac{3}{x + 1} + \frac{-2x + 5}{x^2 - 2}. \quad \blacksquare$$

Example 4   Express the following as a sum of partial fractions.

$$\frac{2x}{(x^2 + 1)^2(x - 1)}$$

There is a linear factor and a quadratic factor which is squared. Thus we have three partial fractions.

$$\frac{2x}{(x^2 + 1)^2(x - 1)} = \frac{Ax + B}{x^2 + 1} + \frac{Cx + D}{(x^2 + 1)^2} + \frac{E}{x - 1}$$

$$2x = (Ax + B)(x^2 + 1)(x - 1) + (Cx + D)(x - 1) + E(x^2 + 1)^2 \qquad (4)$$

If $x = 1$, then equation (4) becomes $2 = 4E$ and $E = 1/2$. Substituting this value for E into (4) and combining terms on the right gives

$$2x = (A + 1/2)x^4 + (-A + B)x^3 + (A - B + C + 1)x^2$$
$$+ (-A + B + D - C)x + (-B - D + 1/2).$$

By setting the corresponding coefficients equal, a system of equations is determined, which can be solved to give $A = -1/2$, $B = -1/2$, $C = -1$, and $D = 1$. Thus the given rational expression can be written as

$$\frac{2x}{(x^2 + 1)^2(x - 1)} = \frac{-\frac{1}{2}x - \frac{1}{2}}{x^2 + 1} + \frac{-x + 1}{(x^2 + 1)^2} + \frac{1/2}{x - 1}$$

$$\frac{2x}{(x^2 + 1)^2(x - 1)} = \frac{-(x + 1)}{2(x^2 + 1)} + \frac{-x + 1}{(x^2 + 1)^2} + \frac{1}{2(x - 1)}. \quad \blacksquare$$

Exercises   *Write each of the following as the sum of partial fractions.*

1. $\dfrac{3x - 1}{x(x + 1)}$

2. $\dfrac{x + 2}{(x + 1)(x - 1)}$

3. $\dfrac{5}{3x(2x + 1)}$

4. $\dfrac{4x + 2}{(x + 2)(2x - 1)}$

5. $\dfrac{-7}{x(3x - 1)(x + 1)}$

6. $\dfrac{4x^2 - x - 15}{x(x + 1)(x - 1)}$

7. $\dfrac{-2}{x^2(x - 2)}$

8. $\dfrac{2}{x^2(x + 3)}$

9. $\dfrac{2x}{(x + 1)(x + 2)^2}$

10. $\dfrac{2x + 1}{(x + 2)^3}$

11. $\dfrac{5}{x(x^2 + 3)}$

12. $\dfrac{-3}{x^2(x^2 + 5)}$

13. $\dfrac{2x + 1}{(x + 1)(x^2 + 2)}$

14. $\dfrac{3x - 2}{(x + 4)(3x^2 + 1)}$

15. $\dfrac{3}{x(x + 1)(x^2 + 1)}$

16. $\dfrac{1}{x(2x + 1)(3x^2 + 4)}$

17. $\dfrac{x^4 + 1}{x(x^2 + 1)^2}$

18. $\dfrac{3x - 1}{x(2x^2 + 1)^2}$

19. $\dfrac{18x^4 - 12x^2 + x + 1}{(x - 1)(3x^2 - 1)^2}$

20. $\dfrac{3x^4 - x^2 + 2}{(2x^2 - 1)^2(x + 1)}$

21. $\dfrac{11x - 24}{5(x^2 + x - 2)}$

22. $\dfrac{25x - 25}{3(x^2 - 2x - 15)}$

Table 1 Squares and Square Roots

n	n^2	$\sqrt{n}$	$\sqrt{10n}$	n	n^2	$\sqrt{n}$	$\sqrt{10n}$
1	1	1.000	3.162	51	2601	7.141	22.583
2	4	1.414	4.472	52	2704	7.211	22.804
3	9	1.732	5.477	53	2809	7.280	23.022
4	16	2.000	6.325	54	2916	7.348	23.238
5	25	2.236	7.071	55	3025	7.416	23.452
6	36	2.449	7.746	56	3136	7.483	23.664
7	49	2.646	8.367	57	3249	7.550	23.875
8	64	2.828	8.944	58	3364	7.616	24.083
9	81	3.000	9.487	59	3481	7.681	24.290
10	100	3.162	10.000	60	3600	7.746	24.495
11	121	3.317	10.488	61	3721	7.810	24.698
12	144	3.464	10.954	62	3844	7.874	24.900
13	169	3.606	11.402	63	3969	7.937	25.100
14	196	3.742	11.832	64	4096	8.000	25.298
15	225	3.873	12.247	65	4225	8.062	25.495
16	256	4.000	12.649	66	4356	8.124	25.690
17	289	4.123	13.038	67	4489	8.185	25.884
18	324	4.243	13.416	68	4624	8.246	26.077
19	361	4.359	13.784	69	4761	8.307	26.268
20	400	4.472	14.142	70	4900	8.367	26.458
21	441	4.583	14.491	71	5041	8.426	26.646
22	484	4.690	14.832	72	5184	8.485	26.833
23	529	4.796	15.166	73	5329	8.544	27.019
24	576	4.899	15.492	74	5476	8.602	27.203
25	625	5.000	15.811	75	5625	8.660	27.386
26	676	5.099	16.125	76	5776	8.718	27.568
27	729	5.196	16.432	77	5929	8.775	27.749
28	784	5.292	16.733	78	6084	8.832	27.928
29	841	5.385	17.029	79	6241	8.888	28.107
30	900	5.477	17.321	80	6400	8.944	28.284
31	961	5.568	17.607	81	6561	9.000	28.460
32	1024	5.657	17.889	82	6724	9.055	28.636
33	1089	5.745	18.166	83	6889	9.110	28.810
34	1156	5.831	18.439	84	7056	9.165	28.983
35	1225	5.916	18.708	85	7225	9.220	29.155
36	1296	6.000	18.974	86	7396	9.274	29.326
37	1369	6.083	19.235	87	7569	9.327	29.496
38	1444	6.164	19.494	88	7744	9.381	29.665
39	1521	6.245	19.748	89	7921	9.434	29.833
40	1600	6.325	20.000	90	8100	9.487	30.000
41	1681	6.403	20.248	91	8281	9.539	30.166
42	1764	6.481	20.494	92	8464	9.592	30.332
43	1849	6.557	20.736	93	8649	9.644	30.496
44	1936	6.633	20.976	94	8836	9.695	30.659
45	2025	6.708	21.213	95	9025	9.747	30.822
46	2116	6.782	21.448	96	9216	9.798	30.984
47	2209	6.856	21.679	97	9409	9.849	31.145
48	2304	6.928	21.909	98	9604	9.899	31.305
49	2401	7.000	22.136	99	9801	9.950	31.464
50	2500	7.071	22.361	100	10000	10.000	31.623

Table 2 Common Logarithms

n	0	1	2	3	4	5	6	7	8	9
1.0	.0000	.0043	.0086	.0128	.0170	.0212	.0253	.0294	.0334	.0374
1.1	.0414	.0453	.0492	.0531	.0569	.0607	.0645	.0682	.0719	.0755
1.2	.0792	.0828	.0864	.0899	.0934	.0969	.1004	.1038	.1072	.1106
1.3	.1139	.1173	.1206	.1239	.1271	.1303	.1335	.1367	.1399	.1430
1.4	.1461	.1492	.1523	.1553	.1584	.1614	.1644	.1673	.1703	.1732
1.5	.1761	.1790	.1818	.1847	.1875	.1903	.1931	.1959	.1987	.2014
1.6	.2041	.2068	.2095	.2122	.2148	.2175	.2201	.2227	.2253	.2279
1.7	.2304	.2330	.2355	.2380	.2405	.2430	.2455	.2480	.2504	.2529
1.8	.2553	.2577	.2601	.2625	.2648	.2672	.2695	.2718	.2742	.2765
1.9	.2788	.2810	.2833	.2856	.2878	.2900	.2923	.2945	.2967	.2989
2.0	.3010	.3032	.3054	.3075	.3096	.3118	.3139	.3160	.3181	.3201
2.1	.3222	.3243	.3263	.3284	.3304	.3324	.3345	.3365	.3385	.3404
2.2	.3424	.3444	.3464	.3483	.3502	.3522	.3541	.3560	.3579	.3598
2.3	.3617	.3636	.3655	.3674	.3692	.3711	.3729	.3747	.3766	.3784
2.4	.3802	.3820	.3838	.3856	.3874	.3892	.3909	.3927	.3945	.3962
2.5	.3979	.3997	.4014	.4031	.4048	.4065	.4082	.4099	.4116	.4133
2.6	.4150	.4166	.4183	.4200	.4216	.4232	.4249	.4265	.4281	.4298
2.7	.4314	.4330	.4346	.4362	.4378	.4393	.4409	.4425	.4440	.4456
2.8	.4472	.4487	.4502	.4518	.4533	.4548	.4564	.4579	.4594	.4609
2.9	.4624	.4639	.4654	.4669	.4683	.4698	.4713	.4728	.4742	.4757
3.0	.4771	.4786	.4800	.4814	.4829	.4843	.4857	.4871	.4886	.4900
3.1	.4914	.4928	.4942	.4955	.4969	.4983	.4997	.5011	.5024	.5038
3.2	.5051	.5065	.5079	.5092	.5105	.5119	.5132	.5145	.5159	.5172
3.3	.5185	.5198	.5211	.5224	.5237	.5250	.5263	.5276	.5289	.5302
3.4	.5315	.5328	.5340	.5353	.5366	.5378	.5391	.5403	.5416	.5428
3.5	.5441	.5453	.5465	.5478	.5490	.5502	.5514	.5527	.5539	.5551
3.6	.5563	.5575	.5587	.5599	.5611	.5623	.5635	.5647	.5658	.5670
3.7	.5682	.5694	.5705	.5717	.5729	.5740	.5752	.5763	.5775	.5786
3.8	.5798	.5809	.5821	.5832	.5843	.5855	.5866	.5877	.5888	.5899
3.9	.5911	.5922	.5933	.5944	.5955	.5966	.5977	.5988	.5999	.6010
4.0	.6021	.6031	.6042	.6053	.6064	.6075	.6085	.6096	.6107	.6117
4.1	.6128	.6138	.6149	.6160	.6170	.6180	.6191	.6201	.6212	.6222
4.2	.6232	.6243	.6253	.6263	.6274	.6284	.6294	.6304	.6314	.6325
4.3	.6335	.6345	.6355	.6365	.6375	.6385	.6395	.6405	.6415	.6425
4.4	.6435	.6444	.6454	.6464	.6474	.6484	.6493	.6503	.6513	.6522
4.5	.6532	.6542	.6551	.6561	.6571	.6580	.6590	.6599	.6609	.6618
4.6	.6628	.6637	.6646	.6656	.6665	.6675	.6684	.6693	.6702	.6712
4.7	.6721	.6730	.6739	.6749	.6758	.6767	.6776	.6785	.6794	.6803
4.8	.6812	.6821	.6830	.6839	.6848	.6857	.6866	.6875	.6884	.6893
4.9	.6902	.6911	.6920	.6928	.6937	.6946	.6955	.6964	.6972	.6981
5.0	.6990	.6998	.7007	.7016	.7024	.7033	.7042	.7050	.7059	.7067
5.1	.7076	.7084	.7093	.7101	.7110	.7118	.7126	.7135	.7143	.7152
5.2	.7160	.7168	.7177	.7185	.7193	.7202	.7210	.7218	.7226	.7235
5.3	.7243	.7251	.7259	.7267	.7275	.7284	.7292	.7300	.7308	.7316
5.4	.7324	.7332	.7340	.7348	.7356	.7364	.7372	.7380	.7388	.7396
n	0	1	2	3	4	5	6	7	8	9

Table 2 Common Logarithms (cont.)

n	0	1	2	3	4	5	6	7	8	9
5.5	.7404	.7412	.7419	.7427	.7435	.7443	.7451	.7459	.7466	.7474
5.6	.7482	.7490	.7497	.7505	.7513	.7520	.7528	.7536	.7543	.7551
5.7	.7559	.7566	.7574	.7582	.7589	.7597	.7604	.7612	.7619	.7627
5.8	.7634	.7642	.7649	.7657	.7664	.7672	.7679	.7686	.7694	.7701
5.9	.7709	.7716	.7723	.7731	.7738	.7745	.7752	.7760	.7767	.7774
6.0	.7782	.7789	.7796	.7803	.7810	.7818	.7825	.7832	.7839	.7846
6.1	.7853	.7860	.7868	.7875	.7882	.7889	.7896	.7903	.7910	.7917
6.2	.7924	.7931	.7938	.7945	.7952	.7959	.7966	.7973	.7980	.7987
6.3	.7993	.8000	.8007	.8014	.8021	.8028	.8035	.8041	.8048	.8055
6.4	.8062	.8069	.8075	.8082	.8089	.8096	.8102	.8109	.8116	.8122
6.5	.8129	.8136	.8142	.8149	.8156	.8162	.8169	.8176	.8182	.8189
6.6	.8195	.8202	.8209	.8215	.8222	.8228	.8235	.8241	.8248	.8254
6.7	.8261	.8267	.8274	.8280	.8287	.8293	.8299	.8306	.8312	.8319
6.8	.8325	.8331	.8338	.8344	.8351	.8357	.8363	.8370	.8376	.8382
6.9	.8388	.8395	.8401	.8407	.8414	.8420	.8426	.8432	.8439	.8445
7.0	.8451	.8457	.8463	.8470	.8476	.8482	.8488	.8494	.8500	.8506
7.1	.8513	.8519	.8525	.8531	.8537	.8543	.8549	.8555	.8561	.8567
7.2	.8573	.8579	.8585	.8591	.8597	.8603	.8609	.8615	.8621	.8627
7.3	.8633	.8639	.8645	.8651	.8657	.8663	.8669	.8675	.8681	.8686
7.4	.8692	.8698	.8704	.8710	.8716	.8722	.8727	.8733	.8739	.8745
7.5	.8751	.8756	.8762	.8768	.8774	.8779	.8785	.8791	.8797	.8802
7.6	.8808	.8814	.8820	.8825	.8831	.8837	.8842	.8848	.8854	.8859
7.7	.8865	.8871	.8876	.8882	.8887	.8893	.8899	.8904	.8910	.8915
7.8	.8921	.8927	.8932	.8938	.8943	.8949	.8954	.8960	.8965	.8971
7.9	.8976	.8982	.8987	.8993	.8998	.9004	.9009	.9015	.9020	.9025
8.0	.9031	.9036	.9042	.9047	.9053	.9058	.9063	.9069	.9074	.9079
8.1	.9085	.9090	.9096	.9101	.9106	.9112	.9117	.9122	.9128	.9133
8.2	.9138	.9143	.9149	.9154	.9159	.9165	.9170	.9175	.9180	.9186
8.3	.9191	.9196	.9201	.9206	.9212	.9217	.9222	.9227	.9232	.9238
8.4	.9243	.9248	.9253	.9258	.9263	.9269	.9274	.9279	.9284	.9289
8.5	.9294	.9299	.9304	.9309	.9315	.9320	.9325	.9330	.9335	.9340
8.6	.9345	.9350	.9355	.9360	.9365	.9370	.9375	.9380	.9385	.9390
8.7	.9395	.9400	.9405	.9410	.9415	.9420	.9425	.9430	.9435	.9440
8.8	.9445	.9450	.9455	.9460	.9465	.9469	.9474	.9479	.9484	.9489
8.9	.9494	.9499	.9504	.9509	.9513	.9518	.9523	.9528	.9533	.9538
9.0	.9542	.9547	.9552	.9557	.9562	.9566	.9571	.9576	.9581	.9586
9.1	.9590	.9595	.9600	.9605	.9609	.9614	.9619	.9624	.9628	.9633
9.2	.9638	.9643	.9647	.9652	.9657	.9661	.9666	.9671	.9675	.9680
9.3	.9685	.9689	.9694	.9699	.9703	.9708	.9713	.9717	.9722	.9727
9.4	.9731	.9736	.9741	.9745	.9750	.9754	.9759	.9763	.9768	.9773
9.5	.9777	.9782	.9786	.9791	.9795	.9800	.9805	.9809	.9814	.9818
9.6	.9823	.9827	.9832	.9836	.9841	.9845	.9850	.9854	.9859	.9863
9.7	.9868	.9872	.9877	.9881	.9886	.9890	.9894	.9899	.9903	.9908
9.8	.9912	.9917	.9921	.9926	.9930	.9934	.9939	.9943	.9948	.9952
9.9	.9956	.9961	.9965	.9969	.9974	.9978	.9983	.9987	.9991	.9996
n	0	1	2	3	4	5	6	7	8	9

Table 3 Powers of e

x	e^x	e^{-x}	x	e^x	e^{-x}
0.00	1.00000	1.00000			
0.01	1.01005	0.99004	1.60	4.95302	0.20189
0.02	1.02020	0.98019	1.70	5.47394	0.18268
0.03	1.03045	0.97044	1.80	6.04964	0.16529
0.04	1.04081	0.96078	1.90	6.68589	0.14956
0.05	1.05127	0.95122	2.00	7.38905	0.13533
0.06	1.06183	0.94176			
0.07	1.07250	0.93239	2.10	8.16616	0.12245
0.08	1.08328	0.92311	2.20	9.02500	0.11080
0.09	1.09417	0.91393	2.30	9.97417	0.10025
0.10	1.10517	0.90483	2.40	11.02316	0.09071
			2.50	12.18248	0.08208
0.11	1.11628	0.89583	2.60	13.46372	0.07427
0.12	1.12750	0.88692	2.70	14.87971	0.06720
0.13	1.13883	0.87810	2.80	16.44463	0.06081
0.14	1.15027	0.86936	2.90	18.17412	0.05502
0.15	1.16183	0.86071	3.00	20.08551	0.04978
0.16	1.17351	0.85214			
0.17	1.18530	0.84366	3.50	33.11545	0.03020
0.18	1.19722	0.83527	4.00	54.59815	0.01832
0.19	1.20925	0.82696	4.50	90.01713	0.01111
0.20	1.22140	0.81873	5.00	148.41316	0.00674
0.30	1.34985	0.74081	5.50	224.69193	0.00409
0.40	1.49182	0.67032			
0.50	1.64872	0.60653	6.00	403.42879	0.00248
0.60	1.82211	0.54881	6.50	665.14163	0.00150
0.70	2.01375	0.49658			
0.80	2.22554	0.44932	7.00	1096.63316	0.00091
0.90	2.45960	0.40656	7.50	1808.04241	0.00055
1.00	2.71828	0.36787			
			8.00	2980.95799	0.00034
			8.50	4914.76884	0.00020
1.10	3.00416	0.33287			
1.20	3.32011	0.30119	9.00	8103.08393	0.00012
1.30	3.66929	0.27253	9.50	13359.72683	0.00007
1.40	4.05519	0.24659			
1.50	4.48168	0.22313	10.00	22026.46579	0.00005

Table 4   Natural Logarithms

x	$\ln x$	x	$\ln x$	x	$\ln x$
0.0		4.5	1.5041	9.0	2.1972
0.1	-2.3026	4.6	1.5261	9.1	2.2083
0.2	-1.6094	4.7	1.5476	9.2	2.2192
0.3	-1.2040	4.8	1.5686	9.3	2.2300
0.4	-0.9163	4.9	1.5892	9.4	2.2407
0.5	-0.6931	5.0	1.6094	9.5	2.2513
0.6	-0.5108	5.1	1.6292	9.6	2.2618
0.7	-0.3567	5.2	1.6487	9.7	2.2721
0.8	-0.2231	5.3	1.6677	9.8	2.2824
0.9	-0.1054	5.4	1.6864	9.9	2.2925
1.0	0.0000	5.5	1.7047	10	2.3026
1.1	0.0953	5.6	1.7228	11	2.3979
1.2	0.1823	5.7	1.7405	12	2.4849
1.3	0.2624	5.8	1.7579	13	2.5649
1.4	0.3365	5.9	1.7750	14	2.6391
1.5	0.4055	6.0	1.7918	15	2.7081
1.6	0.4700	6.1	1.8083	16	2.7726
1.7	0.5306	6.2	1.8245	17	2.8332
1.8	0.5878	6.3	1.8405	18	2.8904
1.9	0.6419	6.4	1.8563	19	2.9444
2.0	0.6931	6.5	1.8718	20	2.9957
2.1	0.7419	6.6	1.8871		
2.2	0.7885	6.7	1.9021	25	3.2189
2.3	0.8329	6.8	1.9169	30	3.4012
2.4	0.8755	6.9	1.9315	35	3.5553
				40	3.6889
2.5	0.9163	7.0	1.9459		
2.6	0.9555	7.1	1.9601	45	3.8067
2.7	0.9933	7.2	1.9741	50	3.9120
2.8	1.0296	7.3	1.9879		
2.9	1.0647	7.4	2.0015	55	4.0073
				60	4.0943
3.0	1.0986	7.5	2.0149	65	4.1744
3.1	1.1314	7.6	2.0281		
3.2	1.1632	7.7	2.0412	70	4.2485
3.3	1.1939	7.8	2.0541	75	4.3175
3.4	1.2238	7.9	2.0669	80	4.3820
				85	4.4427
3.5	1.2528	8.0	2.0794	90	4.4998
3.6	1.2809	8.1	2.0919		
3.7	1.3350	8.3	2.1163	95	4.5539
3.9	1.3610	8.4	2.1281	100	4.6052
4.0	1.3863	8.5	2.1401		
4.1	1.4110	8.6	2.1518		
4.2	1.4351	8.7	2.1633		
4.3	1.4586	8.8	2.1748		
4.4	1.4816	8.9	2.1861		

Table 5 Trigonometric Functions in Degrees and Radians*

Angle θ		sin θ	csc θ	tan θ	cot θ	sec θ	cos θ		
Degrees	Radians								
0° 00′	.0000	.0000	No value	.0000	No value	1.000	1.0000	1.5708	90° 00′
10	029	029	343.8	029	343.8	000	000	679	50
20	058	058	171.9	058	171.9	000	000	650	40
30	.0087	.0087	114.6	.0087	114.6	1.000	1.0000	1.5621	30
40	116	116	85.95	116	85.94	000	.9999	592	20
50	145	145	68.76	145	68.75	000	999	563	10
1° 00′	.0175	.0175	57.30	.0175	57.29	1.000	.9998	1.5533	89° 00′
10	204	204	49.11	204	49.10	000	998	504	50
20	233	233	42.98	233	42.96	000	997	475	40
30	.0262	.0262	38.20	.0262	38.19	1.000	.9997	1.5446	30
40	291	291	34.38	291	34.37	000	996	417	20
50	320	320	31.26	320	31.24	001	995	388	10
2° 00′	.0349	.0349	28.65	.0349	28.64	1.001	.9994	1.5359	88° 00′
10	378	378	26.45	378	26.43	001	993	330	50
20	407	407	24.56	407	24.54	001	992	301	40
30	.0436	.0436	22.93	.0437	22.90	1.001	.9990	1.5272	30
40	465	465	21.49	466	21.47	001	989	243	20
50	495	494	20.23	495	20.21	001	988	213	10
3° 00′	.0524	.0523	19.11	.0524	19.08	1.001	.9986	1.5184	87° 00′
10	553	552	18.10	553	18.07	002	985	155	50
20	582	581	17.20	582	17.17	002	983	126	40
30	.0611	.0610	16.38	.0612	16.35	1.002	.9981	1.5097	30
40	640	640	15.64	641	15.60	002	980	068	20
50	669	669	14.96	670	14.92	002	978	039	10
4° 00′	.0698	.0698	14.34	.0699	14.30	1.002	.9976	1.5010	86° 00′
10	727	727	13.76	729	13.73	003	974	981	50
20	756	756	13.23	758	13.20	003	971	952	40
30	.0785	.0785	12.75	.0787	12.71	1.003	.9969	1.4923	30
40	814	814	12.29	816	12.25	003	967	893	20
50	844	843	11.87	846	11.83	004	964	864	10
5° 00′	.0873	.0872	11.47	.0875	11.43	1.004	.9962	1.4835	85° 00′
10	902	901	11.10	904	11.06	004	959	806	50
20	931	929	10.76	934	10.71	004	957	777	40
30	.0960	.0958	10.43	.0963	10.39	1.005	.9954	1.4748	30
40	989	987	10.13	992	10.08	005	951	719	20
50	.1018	.1016	9.839	.1022	9.788	005	948	690	10
6° 00′	.1047	.1045	9.567	.1051	9.514	1.006	.9945	1.4661	84° 00′
		cos θ	sec θ	cot θ	tan θ	csc θ	sin θ	Radians	Degrees
								Angle θ	

*Table 1, "Four Place Values of Trigonometric Functions Angle θ in Degrees and Radians," from *Plane Trigonometry*, 3rd ed., Nathan O. Niles. Reprinted by permission of John Wiley & Sons, Inc.

Table 5   (continued)

Angle θ Degrees	Radians	sin θ	csc θ	tan θ	cot θ	sec θ	cos θ		
6° 00′	.1047	.1045	9.567	.1051	9.514	1.006	.9945	1.4661	84° 00′
10	076	074	9.309	080	9.255	006	942	632	50
20	105	103	9.065	110	9.010	006	939	603	40
30	.1134	.1132	8.834	.1139	8.777	1.006	.9936	1.4573	30
40	164	161	8.614	169	8.556	007	932	544	20
50	193	190	8.405	198	8.345	007	929	515	10
7° 00′	.1222	.1219	8.206	.1228	8.144	1.008	.9925	1.4486	83° 00′
10	251	248	8.016	257	7.953	008	922	457	50
20	280	276	7.834	287	7.770	008	918	428	40
30	.1309	.1305	7.661	.1317	7.596	1.009	.9914	1.4399	30
40	338	334	7.496	346	7.429	009	911	370	20
50	367	363	7.337	376	7.269	009	907	341	10
8° 00′	.1396	.1392	7.185	.1405	7.115	1.010	.9903	1.4312	82° 00′
10	425	421	7.040	435	6.968	010	899	283	50
20	454	449	6.900	465	6.827	011	894	254	40
30	.1484	.1478	6.765	.1495	6.691	1.011	.9890	1.4224	30
40	513	507	6.636	524	6.561	012	886	195	20
50	542	536	6.512	554	6.435	012	881	166	10
9° 00′	.1571	.1564	6.392	.1584	6.314	1.012	.9877	1.4137	81° 00′
10	600	593	277	614	197	013	872	108	50
20	629	622	166	644	084	013	868	079	40
30	.1658	.1650	6.059	.1673	5.976	1.014	.9863	1.4050	30
40	687	679	5.955	703	871	014	858	1.4021	20
50	716	708	855	733	769	015	853	992	10
10° 00′	.1745	.1736	5.759	.1763	5.671	1.015	.9848	1.3963	80° 00′
10	774	765	665	793	576	016	843	934	50
20	804	794	575	823	485	016	838	904	40
30	.1833	.1822	5.487	.1853	5.396	1.017	.9833	1.3875	30
40	862	851	403	883	309	018	827	846	20
50	891	880	320	914	226	018	822	817	10
11° 00′	.1920	.1908	5.241	.1944	5.145	1.019	.9816	1.3788	79° 00′
10	949	937	164	974	066	019	811	759	50
20	978	965	089	.2004	4.989	020	805	730	40
30	.2007	.1994	5.016	.2035	4.915	1.020	.9799	1.3701	30
40	036	.2022	4.945	065	843	021	793	672	20
50	065	051	876	095	773	022	787	643	10
12° 00′	.2094	.2079	4.810	.2126	4.705	1.022	.9781	1.3614	78° 00′
10	123	108	745	156	638	023	775	584	50
20	153	136	682	186	574	024	769	555	40
30	.2182	.2164	4.620	.2217	4.511	1.024	.9763	1.3526	30
40	211	193	560	247	449	025	757	497	20
50	240	221	502	278	390	026	750	468	10
13° 00	.2269	.2250	4.445	.2309	4.331	1.026	.9744	1.3439	77° 00′
		cos θ	sec θ	cot θ	tan θ	csc θ	sin θ	Radians	Degrees
								Angle θ	

Table 5 (continued)

Angle θ Degrees	Radians	sin θ	csc θ	tan θ	cot θ	sec θ	cos θ		
13° 00′	.2269	.2250	4.445	.2309	4.331	1.026	.9744	1.3439	77° 00′
10	298	278	390	339	275	027	737	410	50
20	327	306	336	370	219	028	730	381	40
30	.2356	.2334	4.284	.2401	4.165	1.028	.9724	1.3352	30
40	385	363	232	432	113	029	717	323	20
50	414	391	182	462	061	030	710	294	10
14° 00′	.2443	.2419	4.134	.2493	4.011	1.031	.9703	1.3265	76° 00′
10	473	447	086	524	3.962	031	696	235	50
20	502	476	039	555	914	032	689	206	40
30	.2531	.2504	3.994	.2586	3.867	1.033	.9681	1.3177	30
40	560	532	950	617	821	034	674	148	20
50	589	560	906	648	776	034	667	119	10
15° 00′	.2618	.2588	3.864	.2679	3.732	1.035	.9659	1.3090	75° 00′
10	647	616	822	711	689	036	652	061	50
20	676	644	782	742	647	037	644	032	40
30	.2705	.2672	3.742	.2773	3.606	1.038	.9636	1.3003	30
40	734	700	703	805	566	039	628	974	20
50	763	728	665	836	526	039	621	945	10
16° 00′	.2793	.2756	3.628	.2867	3.487	1.040	.9613	1.2915	74° 00′
10	822	784	592	899	450	041	605	886	50
20	851	812	556	931	412	042	596	857	40
30	.2880	.2840	3.521	.2962	3.376	1.043	.9588	1.2828	30
40	909	868	487	994	340	044	580	799	20
50	938	896	453	.3026	305	045	572	770	10
17° 00′	.2967	.2924	3.420	.3057	3.271	1.046	.9563	1.2741	73° 00′
10	996	952	388	089	237	047	555	712	50
20	.3025	979	357	121	204	048	546	683	40
30	.3054	.3007	3.326	.3153	3.172	1.048	.9537	1.2654	30
40	083	035	295	185	140	049	528	625	20
50	113	062	265	217	108	050	520	595	10
18° 00′	.3142	.3090	3.236	.3249	3.078	1.051	.9511	1.2566	72° 00′
10	171	118	207	281	047	052	502	537	50
.20	200	145	179	314	018	053	492	508	40
30	.3229	.3173	3.152	.3346	2.989	1.054	.9483	1.2479	30
40	258	201	124	378	960	056	474	450	20
50	287	228	098	411	932	057	465	421	10
19° 00′	.3316	.3256	3.072	.3443	2.904	1.058	.9455	1.2392	71° 00′
10	345	283	046	476	877	059	446	363	50
20	374	311	021	508	850	060	436	334	40
30	.3403	.3338	2.996	.3541	2.824	1.061	.9426	1.2305	30
40	432	365	971	574	798	062	417	275	20
50	462	393	947	607	773	063	407	246	10
20° 00′	.3491	.3420	2.924	.3640	2.747	1.064	.9397	1.2217	70° 00′
		cos θ	sec θ	cot θ	tan θ	csc θ	sin θ	Radians	Degrees
								Angle θ	

Table 5 (continued)

Angle θ		sin θ	csc θ	tan θ	cot θ	sec θ	cos θ		
Degrees	Radians								
20° 00′	.3491	.3420	2.924	.3640	2.747	1.064	.9397	1.2217	70° 00′
10	520	448	901	673	723	065	387	188	50
20	549	475	878	706	699	066	377	159	40
30	.3578	.3502	2.855	.3739	2.675	1.068	.9367	1.2130	30
40	607	529	833	772	651	069	356	101	20
50	636	557	812	805	628	070	346	072	10
21° 00′	.3665	.3584	2.790	.3839	2.605	1.071	.9336	1.2043	69° 00′
10	694	611	769	872	583	072	325	1.2014	50
20	723	638	749	906	560	074	315	985	40
30	.3752	.3665	2.729	.3939	2.539	1.075	.9304	1.1956	30
40	782	692	709	973	517	076	293	926	20
50	811	719	689	.4006	496	077	283	897	10
22° 00′	.3840	.3746	2.669	.4040	2.475	1.079	.9272	1.1868	68° 00′
10	869	773	650	074	455	080	261	839	50
20	898	800	632	108	434	081	250	810	40
30	.3927	.3827	2.613	.4142	2.414	1.082	.9239	1.1781	30
40	956	854	595	176	394	084	228	752	20
50	985	881	577	210	375	085	216	723	10
23° 00′	.4014	.3907	2.559	.4245	2.356	1.086	.9205	1.1694	67° 00′
10	043	934	542	279	337	088	194	665	50
20	072	961	525	314	318	089	182	636	40
30	.4102	.3987	2.508	.4348	2.300	1.090	.9171	1.1606	30
40	131	.4014	491	383	282	092	159	577	20
50	160	041	475	417	264	093	147	548	10
24° 00′	.4189	.4067	2.459	.4452	2.246	1.095	.9135	1.1519	66° 00′
10	218	094	443	487	229	096	124	490	50
20	247	120	427	522	211	097	112	461	40
30	.4276	.4147	2.411	4557	2.194	1.099	.9100	1.1432	30
40	305	173	396	592	177	100	088	403	20
50	334	200	381	628	161	102	075	374	10
25° 00′	.4363	.4226	2.366	.4663	2.145	1.103	.9063	1.1345	65° 00′
10	392	253	352	699	128	105	051	316	50
20	422	279	337	734	112	106	038	286	40
30	.4451	.4305	2.323	.4770	2.097	1.108	.9026	1.1257	30
40	480	331	309	806	081	109	013	228	20
50	509	358	295	841	066	111	001	199	10
26° 00′	.4538	.4384	2.281	.4877	2.050	1.113	.8988	1.1170	64° 00′
10	567	410	268	913	035	114	975	141	50
20	596	436	254	950	020	116	962	112	40
30	.4625	.4462	2.241	.4986	2.006	1.117	.8949	1.1083	30
40	654	488	228	.5022	1.991	119	936	054	20
50	683	514	215	059	977	121	923	1.1025	10
27° 00′	.4712	.4540	2.203	.5095	1.963	1.122	.8910	1.0996	63° 00′
		cos θ	sec θ	cot θ	tan θ	csc θ	sin θ	Radians	Degrees
								Angle θ	

Table 5 (continued)

Angle θ									
Degrees	Radians	sin θ	csc θ	tan θ	cot θ	sec θ	cos θ		
27 00′	.4712	.4540	2.203	.5095	1.963	1.122	.8910	1.0996	63 00′
10	741	566	190	132	949	124	897	966	50
20	771	592	178	169	935	126	884	937	40
30	.4800	.4617	2.166	.5206	1.921	1.127	.8870	1.0908	30
40	829	643	154	243	907	129	857	879	20
50	858	669	142	280	894	131	843	850	10
28 00′	.4887	.4695	2.130	.5317	1.881	1.133	.8829	1.0821	62 00′
10	916	720	118	354	868	134	816	792	50
20	945	746	107	392	855	136	802	763	40
30	.4974	.4772	2.096	.5430	1.842	1.138	.8788	1.0734	30
40	.5003	797	085	467	829	140	774	705	20
50	032	823	074	505	816	142	760	676	10
29 00′	.5061	.4848	2.063	.5543	1.804	1.143	.8746	1.0647	61 00′
10	091	874	052	581	792	145	732	617	50
20	120	899	041	619	780	147	718	588	40
30	.5149	.4924	2.031	.5658	1.767	1.149	.8704	1.0559	30
40	178	950	020	696	756	151	689	530	20
50	207	975	010	735	744	153	675	501	10
30 00′	.5236	.5000	2.000	.5774	1.732	1.155	.8660	1.0472	60 00′
10	265	025	1.990	812	720	157	646	443	50
20	294	050	980	851	709	159	631	414	40
30	.5323	.5075	1.970	.5890	1.698	1.161	.8616	1.0385	30
40	352	100	961	930	686	163	601	356	20
50	381	125	951	969	675	165	587	327	10
31 00′	.5411	.5150	1.942	.6009	1.664	1.167	.8572	1.0297	59 00′
10	440	175	932	048	653	169	557	268	50
20	469	200	923	088	643	171	542	239	40
30	.5498	.5225	1.914	.6128	1.632	1.173	.8526	1.0210	30
40	527	250	905	168	621	175	511	181	20
50	556	275	896	208	611	177	496	152	10
32 00′	.5585	.5299	1.887	.6249	1.600	1.179	.8480	1.0123	58 00′
10	614	324	878	289	590	181	465	094	50
20	643	348	870	330	580	184	450	065	40
30	.5672	.5373	1.861	.6371	1.570	1.186	.8434	1.0036	30
40	701	398	853	412	560	188	418	1.0007	20
50	730	422	844	453	550	190	403	977	10
33 00′	.5760	.5446	1.836	.6494	1.540	1.192	.8387	.9948	57 00′
10	789	471	828	536	530	195	371	919	50
20	818	495	820	577	520	197	355	890	40
30	.5847	.5519	1.812	.6619	1.511	1.199	.8339	.9861	30
40	876	544	804	661	501	202	323	832	20
50	905	568	796	703	1.492	204	307	803	10
34 00′	.5934	.5592	1.788	.6745	1.483	1.206	.8290	.9774	56 00′
		cos θ	sec θ	cot θ	tan θ	csc θ	sin θ	Radians	Degrees
								Angle θ	

Table 5   (continued)

Degrees	Radians	sin θ	csc θ	tan θ	cot θ	sec θ	cos θ		Degrees
34 00′	.5934	.5592	1.788	.6745	1.483	1.206	.8290	.9774	**56° 00′**
10	963	616	781	787	473	209	274	745	50
20	992	640	773	830	464	211	258	716	40
30	.6021	.5664	1.766	.6873	1.455	1.213	.8241	.9687	30
40	050	688	758	916	446	216	225	657	20
50	080	712	751	959	437	218	208	628	10
35 00′	.6109	.5736	1.743	.7002	1.428	1.221	.8192	.9599	**55° 00′**
10	138	760	736	046	419	223	175	570	50
20	167	783	729	089	411	226	158	541	40
30	.6196	.5807	1.722	.7133	1.402	1.228	.8141	.9512	30
40	225	831	715	177	393	231	124	483	20
50	254	854	708	221	385	233	107	454	10
36 00′	.6283	.5878	1.701	.7265	1.376	1.236	.8090	.9425	**54° 00′**
10	312	901	695	310	368	239	073	396	50
20	341	925	688	355	360	241	056	367	40
30	.6370	.5948	1.681	.7400	1.351	1.244	.8039	.9338	30
40	400	972	675	445	343	247	021	308	20
50	429	995	668	490	335	249	004	279	10
37 00′	.6458	.6018	1.662	.7536	1.327	1.252	.7986	.9250	**53° 00′**
10	487	041	655	581	319	255	969	221	50
20	516	065	649	627	311	258	951	192	40
30	.6545	.6088	1.643	.7673	1.303	1.260	.7934	.9163	30
40	574	111	636	720	295	263	916	134	20
50	603	134	630	766	288	266	898	105	10
38 00′	.6632	.6157	1.624	.7813	1.280	1.269	.7880	.9076	**52° 00′**
10	661	180	618	860	272	272	862	047	50
20	690	202	612	907	265	275	844	.9018	40
30	.6720	.6225	1.606	.7954	1.257	1.278	.7826	.8988	30
40	749	248	601	.8002	250	281	808	959	20
50	778	271	595	050	242	284	790	930	10
39 00′	.6807	.6293	1.589	.8098	1.235	1.287	.7771	.8901	**51° 00′**
10	836	316	583	146	228	290	753	872	50
20	865	338	578	195	220	293	735	843	40
30	.6894	.6361	1.572	.8243	1.213	1.296	.7716	.8814	30
40	923	383	567	292	206	299	698	785	20
50	952	406	561	342	199	302	679	756	10
40 00′	.6981	.6428	1.556	.8391	1.192	1.305	.7660	.8727	**50° 00′**
10	.7010	450	550	441	185	309	642	698	50
20	039	472	545	491	178	312	623	668	40
30	.7069	.6494	1.540	.8541	1.171	1.315	.7604	.8639	30
40	098	517	535	591	164	318	585	610	20
50	127	539	529	642	157	322	566	581	10
41 00′	.7156	.6561	1.524	.8693	1.150	1.325	.7547	.8552	**49° 00′**
		cos θ	sec θ	cot θ	tan θ	csc θ	sin θ	Radians	Degrees

Angle θ

Table 5   (continued)

Angle θ		sin θ	csc θ	tan θ	cot θ	sec θ	cos θ		
Degrees	Radians								
41° 00′	.7156	.6561	1.524	.8693	1.150	1.325	.7547	.8552	49° 00′
10	185	583	519	744	144	328	528	523	50
20	214	604	514	796	137	332	509	494	40
30	.7243	.6626	1.509	.8847	1.130	1.335	.7490	.8465	30
40	272	648	504	899	124	339	470	436	20
50	301	670	499	952	117	342	451	407	10
42° 00′	.7330	.6691	1.494	.9004	1.111	1.346	.7431	.8378	48° 00′
10	359	713	490	057	104	349	412	348	50
20	389	734	485	110	098	353	392	319	40
30	.7418	.6756	1.480	.9163	1.091	1.356	.7373	.8290	30
40	447	777	476	217	085	360	353	261	20
50	476	799	471	271	079	364	333	232	10
43° 00′	.7505	.6820	1.466	.9325	1.072	1.367	.7314	.8203	47° 00′
10	534	841	462	380	066	371	294	174	50
20	563	862	457	435	060	375	274	145	40
30	.7592	.6884	1.453	.9490	1.054	1.379	.7254	.8116	30
40	621	905	448	545	048	382	234	087	20
50	650	926	444	601	042	386	214	058	10
44° 00′	.7679	.6947	1.440	.9657	1.036	1.390	.7193	.8029	46° 00′
10	709	967	435	713	030	394	173	.7999	50
20	738	988	431	770	024	398	153	970	40
30	.7767	.7009	1.427	.9827	1.018	1.402	.7133	.7941	30
40	796	030	423	884	012	406	112	912	20
50	825	050	418	942	006	410	092	883	10
45° 00′	.7854	.7071	1.414	1.000	1.000	1.414	.7071	.7854	45° 00′
		cos θ	sec θ	cot θ	tan θ	csc θ	sin θ	Radians	Degrees
								Angle θ	

Answers to Selected Exercises

Exercises on Calculators   (page x)
1. 4.5 to 5.5   **3.** 9.55 to 9.65   **5.** 8.945 to 8.955   **7.** 19.65 to 19.75   **9.** 253.7405 to 253.7415
11. 28,999.5 to 29,000.5   **13.** 3   **15.** 4   **17.** 4   **19.** 2   **21.** 5   **23.** 769,770
25. 12.5, 13   **27.** 9.00, 9.0   **29.** 76.42   **31.** 8.1   **33.** 28,300,000   **35.** 0.0057489   **37.** 0.0970
39. 0.0557   **41.** 8.6423   **43.** 97   **45.** 0.0808   **47.** -108.1 **49.** $-18,000$ **51.** 6.9

CHAPTER 1

Section 1.1   (page 1)
1. commutative   **3.** commutative   **5.** identity   **7.** associative   **9.** closure   **11.** commutative
property of addition and multiplication   **13.** false (Multiplication Theorem of Zero)   **15.** true   **17.** false
(9/0 is not a rational number)   **19.** false $(0 - 1$ is not in the set)   **21.** true   **23.** yes   **25.** No [$\sqrt{2} +$
$(-\sqrt{2}) = 0$ is not irrational]   **27.** no [$\sqrt{2}(1/\sqrt{2}) = 1$ is not irrational]   **29.** yes   **31.** no $(1 + 1 = 2$ is
not in the set)   **33.** 24   **35.** 17   **37.** -21 **39.** $-6/7$ **41.** not a real number   **43.** 2.22
45. whole, integer, rational, real   **47.** rational, real   **49.** irrational, real   **51.** $(\sqrt{25} = 5)$ whole, integer,
rational, real   **53.** meaningless   **55.** $(0/6 = 0)$ whole, integer, rational, real   **57.** no; for example,
$6 + (5 \cdot 4) \neq (6 + 5)(6 + 4)$ **59.** commutative, distributive, substitution, commutative, substitution

Section 1.2   (page 9)
1. $-9, -4, -2, 3, 8$ **3.** $-|9|, -|-6|, |-8|$ **5.** $-5, -4, -2, -\sqrt{3}, \sqrt{6}, \sqrt{8}, 3$ **7.** 3/4, 7/5, $\sqrt{2}$, 22/15, 8/5
9. 8   **11.** 6   **13.** 4   **15.** 16   **17.** 6   **19.** -6 **21.** $8 - \sqrt{50}$ **23.** $5 - \sqrt{7}$ **25.** $\pi - 3$
27. $x - 4$ **29.** $8 - 2k$ **31.** $56 - 7m$ **33.** $8 + 4m$ or $4m + 8$ **35.** $y - x$ **37.** $3 + x^2$
39. (a) 1; (b) 1; (c) 13; (d) 14; (e) 2   **41.** (a) 2; (b) 7; (c) 2; (d) 0; (e) 9   **43.** if $x = y$ or $x = -y$ **45.** if
$x \geq 0$ and $y < 0$, and $x \geq |y|$ **47.** -1 if $x < 0$ and 1 if $x > 0$

Section 1.3   (page 14)
1. 3375   **3.** 1/8   **5.** 31/108   **7.** $-1/64$ **9.** 8   **11.** .001042   **13.** $-72m^5$ **15.** $1/6^4$
17. $1/5^4$ **19.** 3^7 **21.** $1/d^8$ **23.** $x^2/(2y)$ **25.** $(4 + s)^6$ **27.** $1/(m^8 n^4)$ **29.** $a^3 b^6$
31. $x^6/(4y^4)$ **33.** $9m^5/n^3$ **35.** $1/(r^{10} s^8 t^{12})$ **37.** $k^2/(p + q)^7$ **39.** 6.93×10^4 **41.** 6×10^9
43. 7.92×10^{-3} **45.** 820,000   **47.** 170,000,000   **49.** .00615   **51.** 4.232   **53.** 1.8×10^{-9}
55. 2×10^{-3} **57.** 7×10^4 **59.** 4.86×10^7 **61.** 1.29×10^{-4} **63.** -6.04×10^{11}
65. -2.51×10^5 **67.** $2k$ **69.** x^r **71.** $1/(8b^y)$ **73.** $-2m^{2-n}$

Section 1.4   (page 19)
1. $x^2 - x + 3$ **3.** $3x^3 - 3x^2 + 6x + 2$ **5.** $9y^2 - 4y + 4$ **7.** $p^3 - 7p^2 - p - 7$ **9.** $6a^2 + a - 1$
11. $3b^2 - 8b - 1$ **13.** $-14q^2 + 11q - 14$ **15.** $28r^2 + r - 2$ **17.** $18p^2 - 27pq - 35q^2$ **19.** $15x^2 -$
$\frac{7}{3}x - \frac{2}{9}$ **21.** $\frac{6}{25}y^2 + \frac{11}{40}yz + \frac{1}{16}z^2$ **23.** $25r^2 - 4$ **25.** $16x^2 - 9y^2$ **27.** $36k^2 - 36k + 9$ **29.** $16m^2 +$
$16mn + 4n^2$ **31.** $8z^3 - 12z^2 + 6z - 1$ **33.** $12x^5 + 8x^4 - 20x^3 + 4x^2$ **35.** $15m^4 - 10m^3 + 5m^2 - 5m$
37. $-2z^3 + 7z^2 - 11z + 4$ **39.** $27p^3 - 1$ **41.** $8m^3 + 1$ **43.** $m^2 + mn - 2n^2 - 2km + 5kn - 3k^2$
45. $a^2 - 2ab + b^2 + 4ac - 4bc + 4c^2$ **47.** $2m^2 - 4m + 8$ **49.** $5x^3 + 10x^2 + 4x - \frac{3}{x}$ **51.** $5y^2 - 3xy + 8x^2$
53. $k^{2m} - 4$ **55.** $b^{2r} + b^r - 6$ **57.** $3p^{2x} - 5p^x - 2$ **59.** $m^{2x} - 4m^x + 4$ **61.** $27k^{3a} - 54k^{2a} + 36k^a - 8$

Section 1.5   (page 23)
1. $4m(3n - 2)$ **3.** $3r(4r^2 + 2r - 1)$ **5.** $2px(3x - 4x^2 - 6)$ **7.** $2(a + b)(1 + 2m)$ **9.** $(x - 3)(x - 8)$
11. $(4p - 1)(p + 1)$ **13.** $(2z - 5)(z + 6)$ **15.** $3(2r - 1)(2r + 5)$ **17.** $(6r - 5s)(3r + 2s)$
19. $(3x - 4y)(5x + 2y)$ **21.** $x^2(3 - x)^2$ **23.** $z(2r - 3)(r + 1)$ **25.** $(2m + 5)(2m - 5)$ **27.** $(9 - x)(9 + x)$
29. $9(4r + 3s)(4r - 3s)$ **31.** $(11p^2 - 3q^2)(11p^2 + 3q^2)$ **33.** $(a + b)(a^2 - ab + b^2)$ **35.** $(2m - 3n) \times$
$(4m^2 + 6mn + 9n^2)$ **37.** $(2 - x)(2 + x)(4 + 2x + x^2)(4 - 2x + x^2)$ **39.** $(4 + m)(x + y)$ **41.** $(q + 3 + p) \times$
$(q + 3 - p)$ **43.** $(a + b + x + y)(a + b - x - y)$ **45.** $(2x - y)y$ **47.** $(3x - y)(19y^2 - 24xy + 9x^2)$
49. $(x + y + 5z)(x + y - 3z)$ **51.** $(3a + 3b + 8c)(2a + 2b - 5c)$ **53.** $4pq$ **55.** $(m^n + 4)(m^n - 4)$
57. $(x^n - y^{2n})(x^{2n} + x^n y^{2n} + y^{4n})$ **59.** $(2x^n + 3y^n)(x^n - 13y^n)$ **61.** $9.44(x^3 + 5.1x^2 - 3.2x + 4)$
63. $7.88(8.2z^4 - 3z^2 + z + 14.5)$

Section 1.6   (page 27)

1. $x \neq 3/5$ **3.** all real numbers   **5.** $3/5$ **7.** $(y + 2)/2$ **9.** $5x/y$ **11.** $a + 2$ **13.** 1
15. $(x^2 - 1)/x^2$ **17.** $(x + y)/(x - y)$ **19.** $(x^2 - xy + y^2)/(x^2 + xy + y^2)$ **21.** 1   **23.** $(2y + 1)/[y(y + 1)]$
25. $3/[2(a + b)]$ **27.** $(2m^2 + 2)/[(m - 1)(m + 1)]$ **29.** $4/(a - 2)$ **31.** $(3x + y)/(2x - y)$
33. $(6r^2 + 9r)/[(r + 2)(r + 3)(r - 1)]$ **35.** $5/[(a - 2)(a - 3)(a + 2)]$ **37.** $(p + 5)/[p(p + 1)]$
39. $a(a + 5)/[(a + 6)(a + 1)(a - 1)]$ **41.** $(6x^2 - 6x - 5)/[(x + 5)(x - 2)(x - 1)]$ **43.** $-1/[x(x + h)]$
45. $a + b$ **47.** -1 **49.** $1/(ab)$ **51.** $y(xy - 9)/(x^2y^2 - 9)$ **53.** $(x + 1)/(x - 1)$
55. $(2 - b)(1 + b)/[b(1 - b)]$ **57.** $(2x + 1)/(x + 1)$

Section 1.7   (page 33)

1. $5\sqrt{2}$ **3.** $3\sqrt[3]{3}$ **5.** $5\sqrt[3]{2}$ **7.** $-3\sqrt{5}/5$ **9.** $\sqrt{15}/6$ **11.** $3\sqrt{5}$ **13.** $9\sqrt{3}$ **15.** $-\sqrt[3]{12}/2$
17. $\sqrt[4]{24}/2$ **19.** $2\sqrt[3]{2}$ **21.** $2\sqrt{3}$ **23.** $xyz^2\sqrt{2x}$ **25.** $2x^2yz\sqrt[3]{2z^2x^2y}$ **27.** $np^2\sqrt[4]{m^2n^2}$
29. $ab\sqrt{ab}(b - 2a^2 + b^3)$ **31.** -7 **33.** 10   **35.** $11 + 4\sqrt{6}$ **37.** $5\sqrt{6}$ **39.** $2\sqrt[3]{9} - 7\sqrt[3]{3} - 4$
41. $\sqrt{6x}/(3x)$ **43.** $x^2y\sqrt{xy}/z$ **45.** $2\sqrt[3]{x}/x$ **47.** $-km\sqrt[3]{k^2}/r^2$ **49.** $h\sqrt[4]{9g^3hr^2}/(3r^2)$ **51.** $m\sqrt[3]{n^2}/n$
53. $2\sqrt[4]{x^3y^3}$ **55.** $\sqrt[6]{4}$ **57.** $\sqrt[18]{x}$ **59.** $-3(1 + \sqrt{2})$ **61.** $(4\sqrt{3} - 3)/13$ **63.** $-2x - 2\sqrt{x(x + 1)} - 1$
65. $5(\sqrt[3]{a^2} - \sqrt[3]{ab} + \sqrt[3]{b^2})/(a + b)$ **67.** $3/(2\sqrt{3})$ **69.** $-1/[2(1 - \sqrt{2})]$ **71.** $x/(\sqrt{x} + x)$
73. $-1/(2x - 2\sqrt{x(x + 1)} + 1)$ **75.** 5.36×10^3 **77.** 1.40×10^{-1} **79.** 2.64×10^{-1}
81. 9.93 or 9.93×10^0 **87.** approx. 3.146

Section 1.8   Exercises (page 37)

1. 2   **3.** 4   **5.** $1/9$ **7.** $27/8$ **9.** $4p^2$ **11.** $9x^4$ **13.** $x^{2/3}$ **15.** $z^{5/3}$ **17.** $y^{9/2}$
19. $m^{5/6}$ **21.** $m^{7/3}$ **23.** $(1 + n)^{5/4}$ **25.** $6yz^{2/3}$ **27.** $r^{3/14}s^{7/20}$ **29.** $a^{2/3}b^2$ **31.** $h^{1/3}t^{1/5}/k^{2/5}$
33. 1   **35.** $x^{11/12}$ **37.** $16/y^{11/12}$ **39.** $4z^2/(x^5y)$ **41.** r^{6+p} **43.** $m^{3/2}$ **45.** $p^{(m+n+m^2)/(mn)}$
47. $(r^2 - 2r + 1)/r$ **49.** $(x + 1)/x^{1/2}$ **51.** $r\sqrt[6]{r^5}$ **53.** $p\sqrt[10]{p^3}$ **55.** $p^2q^2\sqrt[6]{p}$ **57.** $m^2n\sqrt[6]{m^2n}$
59. $mn^2\sqrt[15]{m^{14}n^{13}}$ **61.** 64   **63.** \$64,000,000   **65.** about \$10,000,000   **67.** about 86.3 mi
69. about 211 mi   **71.** 29   **73.** 177

Chapter 1   Review Exercises   (page 41)

1. commutative   **3.** inverse   **5.** distributive   **7.** no   **9.** $20/3$ **11.** $9/4$ **13.** false
15. $-|3 - (-2)|, -|-2|, |6 - 4|, |8 + 1|$ **17.** $3 - \sqrt{7}$ **19.** $m - 3$ **21.** (a)1; (b) 12   **23.** if $x \geq 0$
25. if $x = 0$ and $y = 0$ **27.** if A and B are the same   **29.** $-8x^2 - 15x + 16$ **31.** $24k^2 - 5k - 14$
33. $x^6/2$ **35.** $r^{2z} - 64$ **37.** $(x + 1)(x - 3)$ **39.** $3x(x - 2)(1 + 4x)(1 - x)$ **41.** $(z^{3n} + 10)(z^{3n} - 10)$
43. $x/(2y)$ **45.** $2m/(m - 4)$ **47.** $(x + 9)/[(x - 3)(x - 1)(x + 1)]$ **49.** $(q + p)/(pq - 1)$
51. $(3 + 2x)/(2 + x)$ **53.** $y^6/(36x^4z^4)$ **55.** $m^{13}/(81n^7)$ **57.** $2n - m$ **59.** $\sqrt{21r}/(3r)$
61. $-r^2m\sqrt[3]{m^2z}/z$ **63.** $2q$ **65.** $z\sqrt{z} - 1/(z - 1)$ **67.** $\sqrt{5} - 2$ **69.** $1/216$ **71.** $16r^{9/4}s^{7/3}$
73. $4xz^3/y^3$ **75.** $x - 2 + 1/x$ **77.** $2|a|^5$ **83.** >1 **85.** $b^2 < a^2 < b < a < \sqrt{b} <$
$\sqrt{a} < 1 < 1/a < 1/b$

CHAPTER 2

Section 2.1   (page 45)

1. not equivalent   **3.** not equivalent   **5.** not equivalent   **7.** not equivalent   **9.** identity
11. conditional   **13.** identity   **15.** identity   **17.** 4   **19.** 12   **21.** $-2/7$ **23.** -1 **25.** 3
27. 4   **29.** $3/4$ **31.** $-12/5$ **33.** no solution   **35.** $27/7$ **37.** $-59/6$ **39.** $-9/4$ **41.** -4
43. $-3a + b$ **45.** $(3a + b)/(3 - a)$ **47.** $(3 - 3a)/(a^2 - a - 1)$ **49.** $(2a^2)/(a^2 + 3)$ **53.** 6
55. -2 **57.** .72   **59.** 6.53   **61.** -13.26

Section 2.2   (page 49)

1. $V = k/P$ **3.** $l = V/(wh)$ **5.** $g = (V - V_0)/t$ **7.** $g = 2s/t^2$ **9.** $B = 2A/h - b)$
11. $r_1 = S/(2\pi h) - r_2$ **13.** $l = gt^2/(4\pi^2)$ **15.** $h = (S - 2\pi r^2)/(2\pi r)$ **17.** $f = AB(p + 1)/24$
19. $R = r_1r_2/(r_2 + r_1)$ **21.** 26 years   **23.** 8 folk, 24 electric, and 21 classical   **25.** 6 cm   **27.** \$57.65
29. \$12,000 at 6 1/2%; \$8000 at 8%   **31.** \$54,000 at 8 1/2%; \$6000 at 16%   **33.** \$70,000 for land that
made a profit; \$50,000 for land that produced a loss   **35.** \$267.57   **37.** 2 liters   **39.** $12^2/_3$ kg

41. about 840 mi   **43.** 15 min   **45.** 35 kph   **47.** $3^3/5$ hr   **49.** 78 hr   **51.** $13^1/3$ hr   **53.** 2 hr
55. $m(b - c)/(a - b)$ **57.** $(100I - nB)/(m - n)$ at $m\%$; $(Bm - 100I)/(m - n)$ at $n\%$

Section 2.3 (page 58)

1. $4, -4$ **3.** $\pm 3\sqrt{3}$ **5.** $3 \pm \sqrt{5}$ **7.** $(1 \pm 2\sqrt{3})/3$ **9.** $2, -3$ **11.** $2, 3$ **13.** $10/3, -5/2$
15. $(1 \pm \sqrt{5})/2$ **17.** $(-7 \pm \sqrt{73})/6$ **19.** $3 \pm \sqrt{2}$ **21.** $(-7 \pm \sqrt{41})/4$ **23.** $(2 \pm \sqrt{17})/3$
25. $0, 8$ **27.** $3, -1/4$ **29.** $3/2, 1$ **31.** $1.243, -.643$ **33.** $3.562, -.562$ **35.** $.839, -.239$
37. $a = 1$, $b = 8$, $c = 16$; 0; exactly one rational   **39.** $a = 4$, $b = -6$, $c = -3$; 84; two irrational
41. $a = 9$, $b = 11$, $c = 4$; -23; no real solutions   **43.** $t = \pm\sqrt{2s/g}$ **45.** $h = \pm\sqrt{d^4kL/L}$ or $\pm d^2\sqrt{kL/L}$
47. $t = \pm\sqrt{(s - s_0 - k)/g}$ **49.** $R = (E^2 - 2Pr \pm \sqrt{(2Pr - E^2)^2 - 4P^2r^2})/(2P)$ **51.** 16, 18, or $-18, -16$
53. $12, -2$ **55.** 50 m by 100 m   **57.** 9 ft by 12 ft   **59.** $9^1/3$ hrs   **61.** 50 mph   **63.** 16.95 cm,
20.95 cm, 26.95 cm   **65.** ± 12 **67.** $121/4$ **69.** $1, 9$ **75.** $x = (y \pm \sqrt{8 - 11y^2})/4$;
$y = (x \pm \sqrt{6 - 11x^2})/3$

Section 2.4 (page 65)

1. $3, -3, 2, -2$ **3.** $\pm\sqrt{10}/2, 1, -1$ **5.** $4, 6$ **7.** $(-6 \pm 2\sqrt{3})/3$, $(-4 + \sqrt{2})/2$ **9.** $7/2, -1/3$
11. $-63, 28$ **13.** 1   **15.** -4 **17.** $1/2$ **19.** -1 **21.** 5   **23.** 9   **25.** 9   **27.** $5/4$
29. $2, -2$ **31.** -2 **33.** 2   **35.** $3/2$ **37.** 31   **39.** $1, -3$ **41.** $1/4, 1$ **43.** $0, 8$
45. $\pm 2.121, \pm 1.528$ **47.** $\pm.917$ **49.** $h = (d/k)^2$ **51.** $L = P^2g/4$ **53.** $y = (a^{2/3} - x^{2/3})^{3/2}$

Section 2.5 (page 68)

1. $(-\infty, 4]$ ⟵———┤———   **3.** $[-1, \infty)$ ———├———⟶   **5.** $(-\infty, 6]$ ⟵———┤———   **7.** $(-\infty, 4)$ ⟵———├———

9. $[1, 4]$ ———├—┤———   **11.** $(-6, -4)$ ———├—├———   **13.** $[3, 6]$ ———├—┤———   **15.** $(1, 2)$ ———├—├———

17. $(-\infty, 2)$ or $(8, \infty)$ ⟵—├———├—⟶   **19.** $(9, \infty)$ ———├———⟶   **21.** $(3, \infty)$ ———├———⟶

23. $[-3, 3]$ **25.** $(0, 10)$ **27.** $[-2, 3]$ **29.** $(-\infty, 1/2)$ or $(4, \infty)$ **31.** $((-5 - \sqrt{33})/2, (-5 + \sqrt{33})/2)$
33. $(-\infty, -2]$ or $[0, 2]$ **35.** $(-2, 0)$ or $(1/4, \infty)$ **37.** $(-\infty, -1)$ or $(0, \infty)$ **39.** $(-\infty, 6)$ or $(15/2, \infty)$
41. $(-\infty, 1)$ or $(9/5, \infty)$ **43.** $(-\infty, -3/2)$ or $[-1/2, \infty)$ **45.** $(-2, \infty)$ **47.** $(0, 4/11)$ or $(1/2, \infty)$
49. $(-\infty, -2]$ or $(1, 2)$ **51.** $[3/2, \infty)$ **53.** $(-\infty, 4)$ **55.** $(5/2, \infty)$ **57.** $[-8/3, 3/2]$ or $(6, \infty)$
59. 140   **61.** $[500, \infty)$ **63.** $[45, \infty)$ **65.** $R < C$ for all positive x. This product will never
break-even.   **67.** $(0, 5/4), (6, \infty)$ **69.** $[0, 5/3)$ or $(10, \infty)$ **71.** 32°F to 86°F   **77.** $(-\infty, 1]$ or
$[2, 3)$ or $(4, \infty)$

Section 2.6 (page 76)

1. $-1/3, 1$ **3.** $2/3, 8/3$ **5.** $-6, 14$ **7.** $7/2, 5/2$ **9.** $-7/3, -1/7$ **11.** $-3/5, 11$ **13.** $-1/2$
15. $[-3, 3]$ **17.** $(-\infty, -1)$ or $(1, \infty)$ **19.** $[-10, 10]$ **21.** $(-\infty, -2/3)$ or $(2, \infty)$ **23.** $(-\infty, -13/4]$ or $[1/4, \infty)$
25. $(-\infty, 2)$ or $(3, \infty)$ **27.** $(-3/2, 13/10)$ **29.** $(-3, -1)$ **31.** $(1, 5)$ or $(5, \infty)$ **33.** $(-\infty, 3/2]$ or
$[5/2, \infty)$ **35.** $[7/4, 2)$ or $(2, 5/2]$ **37.** $(-\infty, -4)$ or $(-2, \infty)$ **39.** $(-\infty, 3/8)$ or $(7/16, \infty)$ **41.** $[-3, 1/5]$
43. $|x - 2| \leq 4$ **45.** $|z - 12| \geq 2$ **47.** $|k - 1| = 6$ **49.** if $|x - 2| \leq .0004$, then $|y - 7| \leq .00001$
51. $m = 2$, $n = 20$

Chapter 2   Review Exercises   (page 82)

1. $-11/3$ **3.** $-96/7$ **5.** 13   **7.** $-7 \pm \sqrt{5}$ **9.** $5/2, -3$ **11.** $-1/2, 3$ **13.** no real number
solutions   **15.** $-2, 3$ **17.** $5/2, -15$ **19.** 3   **21.** $-2, -1$ **23.** $1, -4$ **25.** $3, -2$
27. $3/5, -1/11$ **29.** $x = [-m \pm \sqrt{m^2 - 4(3m - 2m^2)}]/2$ **31.** $P = A/(1 + i)$ **33.** $f = [Ab(p + 1)]/24$
35. $I = (Ft + m\sqrt{2})^2/m^2$ **37.** $E = \pm (r + R)\sqrt{P/R}$ **39.** $b = \pm\sqrt{c^2 - a^2}$ **41.** $[4, 5]$ **43.** $(-\infty, \infty)$
45. $(-\infty, -1)$ or $(5/2, \infty)$ **47.** $(-\infty, -5)$ or $(2, \infty)$ **49.** $(-2, 0)$ **51.** $[-1/3, 3]$ **53.** $500
55. 12 hrs   **57.** 50 m by 225 m or 112.5 m by 100 m   **59.** for $x \leq 2$, $x = y - 2$; for $x > 2$, $x = (y + 2)/3$

528 Answers to Selected Exercises

CHAPTER 3

Section 3.1 (page 85)

1–5. 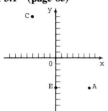   7. 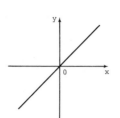   9. 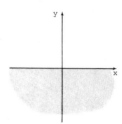   11.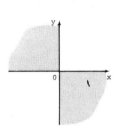

13. 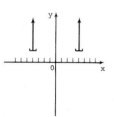   15. 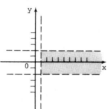   17.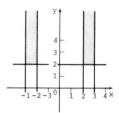

19. $8\sqrt{2}$; $(9, 3)$ 21. $\sqrt{34}$; $(-11/2, -7/2)$ 23. $\sqrt{133}$; $(2\sqrt{2}, 3\sqrt{5}/2)$ 25. 7.616   27. 27. 203
29. $(13, 10)$ 31. $(-10, 11)$ 33. yes   35. no   37. no   39. $5, -1$ 41. $9 + \sqrt{119}$,
$9 - \sqrt{119}$ 43. $2\sqrt{2}, -2\sqrt{2}$

47. $x^2 + y^2 = 25$

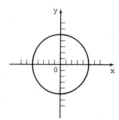

49. $(2 + \sqrt{7}, 2 + \sqrt{7}), (2 - \sqrt{7}, 2 - \sqrt{7})$ 51. $7x^2 + 16y^2 = 112$

Section 3.2 (page 91)

1. 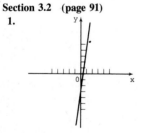   3. 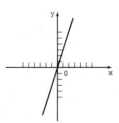   5. 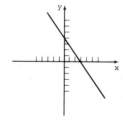   7.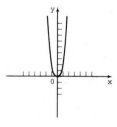

9. 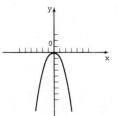   11. 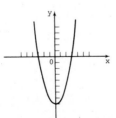   13. 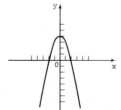   15.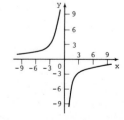

17.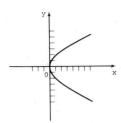

19.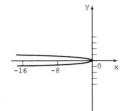

21.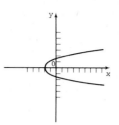

23.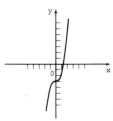

25.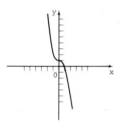

27.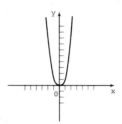

29.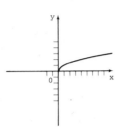

31.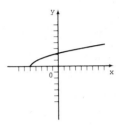

33.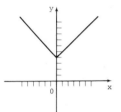

35.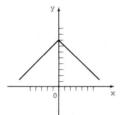

37.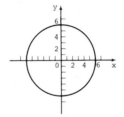

39.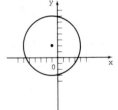

41.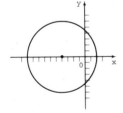

43. $(x-1)^2 + (y-4)^2 = 9$ **45.** $(x+8)^2 + (y-6)^2 = 25$ **47.** $(x+1)^2 + (y-2)^2 = 25$
49. $(x+3)^2 + (y+2)^2 = 4$

Section 3.3   (page 95)

1.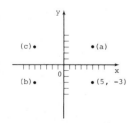

3.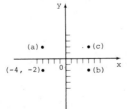

5.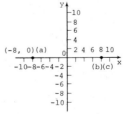

7.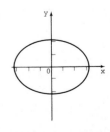

9. 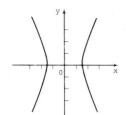   **11.** 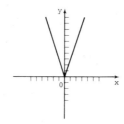   **13.** 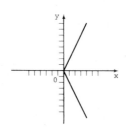   **15.**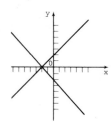

17. 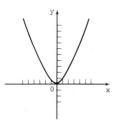   **19.** 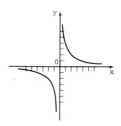   **21.** 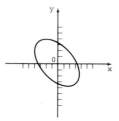   **23.**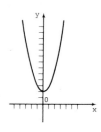

25. 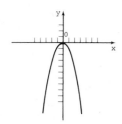   **27.** 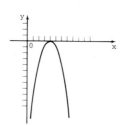   **29.** 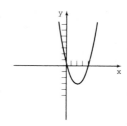   **31.**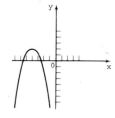

33. reflected about the x-axis   **35.** symmetric   **37.** symmetric   **39.** not symmetric   **41.** symmetric
43. not symmetric

Section 3.4 (page 103)

1. all reals   **3.** all reals   **5.** $\{x| -4 \le x \le 4\}$ **7.** $\{x|x \ge 3\}$ **9.** $\{x|x \ne 2, x \ne -2\}$
11. all real numbers   **13.** all real numbers   **15.** $\{x|x \le -1 \text{ or } x \ge 5\}$ **17.** $\{x|x \le -5/3 \text{ or } x \ge 1/2\}$
19. -1 **21.** 4   **23.** $3a - 1$ **25.** 5   **27.** $15a - 7$ **29.** $25p^2 - 20p + 4$ **31.** $3m^2 - 1$
33. -66.8 **35.** -42.464 **37.** 2   **39.** $\frac{1}{4}$ **41.** 2^m **43.** approx. 1.414   **45.** (a) $x^2 + 2xh + h^2 - 4$;
(b) $2xh + h^2$; (c) $2x + h$ **47.** (a) $6x + 6h + 2$; (b) $6h$; (c) 6   **49.** (a) $2x^3 + 6x^2h + 6xh^2 + 2h^3 + x^2 +$
$2xh + h^2$; (b) $6x^2h + 6xh^2 + 2h^3 + 2xh + h^2$; (c) $6x^2 + 6xh + 2h^2 + 2x + h$ **51.** increasing on $(-\infty, -3]$ and
$[3, \infty)$; decreasing on $[-3, 3]$ **53.** increasing on $(-\infty, -1]$; decreasing on $[-1, \infty)$ **55.** increasing on $(-\infty, \infty)$;
decreasing nowhere   **57.** always decreasing   **59.** decreasing on $(-\infty, 0]$; increasing on $[0, \infty)$
61. increasing on $(-\infty, -2]$; decreasing on $[-2, \infty)$ **63.** increasing on $[0, \infty)$ **65.** even   **67.** even
69. neither   **71.** neither   **73.** even   **77.** 0, 0, 0, 1, 1, 2   **79.** domain: all real numbers; range: all
integers   **81.** no

Section 3.5 (page 111)

1. $10x + 2; -2x - 4; 24x^2 + 6x - 3; (4x - 1)/(6x + 3)$; all domains are the set of all real numbers, except for $(f/g)(x)$,
which is $\{x|x \ne -1/2\}$ **3.** $4x^2 - 4x + 1; 2x^2 - 1; (3x^2 + 2x)(x^2 - 2x + 1); (3x^2 - 2x)/(x^2 - 2x + 1)$; all domains

are the set of all real numbers, except for $(f/g)(x)$, which is $\{x|x \neq 1\}$ **5.** $\sqrt{2x + 5} + \sqrt{4x - 9}; \sqrt{2x + 5} - \sqrt{4x - 9}; \sqrt{(2x + 5)(4x - 9)}; \sqrt{(2x + 5)/(4x - 9)}$; domain is $\{x|x \geq 9/4\}$ except for $(f/g)(x)$, which is $\{x|x > 9/4\}$
7. $5x^2 - 11x + 7; 3x^2 - 11x - 3; (4x^2 - 11x + 2)(x^2 + 5); (4x^2 - 11x + 2)/(x^2 + 5)$; all domains are the set of all real numbers   **9.** 55   **11.** 1848   **13.** $-6/7$ **15.** $4m^2 + 6m + 1$ **17.** 1122   **19.** 97
21. $256k^2 + 48k + 2$ **23.** $24x + 4; 24x + 35$ **25.** $-5x^2 + 20x + 18; -25x^2 - 10x + 6$ **27.** $-64x^3 + 2;$
$-4x^3 + 8$ **29.** $1/x^2; 1/x^2$ **31.** $\sqrt{8x^2 - 4}; 8x + 10$ **33.** $x/(2 - 5x); 2(x - 5)$ **35.** $\sqrt{(-1 + x)/x};$
$-1/\sqrt{x + 1}$ **49.** $18a^2 + 24a + 9$ **51.** $16\pi t^2$

Section 3.6   (page 115)
1. yes   **3.** yes   **5.** yes   **7.** no   **9.** no   **11.** no   **13.** yes   **15.** yes   **17.** no
19. yes   **21.** no   **23.** yes   **25.** yes   **27.** yes   **29.** yes   **31.** no

33. $f^{-1}(x) = (x + 4)/3$

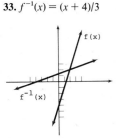

35. $f^{-1}(x) = \sqrt[3]{x - 1}$

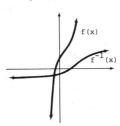

37. $f^{-1}(x) = 12 - 4x$

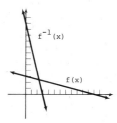

39. not one-to-one

41. $f^{-1}(x) = 1/x$

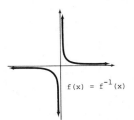

43. $f^{-1}(x) = (x + 3)/(4x - 8)$

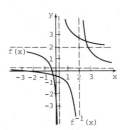

45. $f^{-1}(x) = -\sqrt{4 - x};$
domain: $(-\infty, 4]$

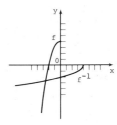

47. Choose any nonzero number for a. Then $c = 1/a$. Choose any number for d. Then $b = -ad$.

Section 3.7   (page 122)
1. $a = kb$ **3.** $x = k/y$ **5.** $r = kst$ **7.** $w = kx^2/y$ **9.** 220/7   **11.** 32/15   **13.** 18/125
15. 1075   **17.** 2304 ft   **19.** .0444 ohms   **21.** 140 kg per cm^2 **23.** \$1375   **25.** 8/9 metric tons
27. 7500 lbs   **29.** 150 kg per m^2 **31.** 4,000,000   **33.** 1600

Chapter 3   Review Exercises   (page 126)

1.

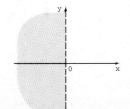

3.

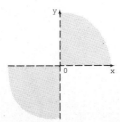

5. $d(P, Q) = \sqrt{85}$; $(-1/2, 2)$ **7.** $(7, -13)$ **9.** $-7, -1, 8, 23$

11. no such points exist   **15.** domain: real numbers   **17.** domain: real numbers

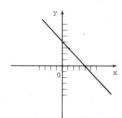

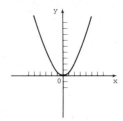

19. domain: $\{x|x \neq 0\}$ **21.** domain: $\{x|x \geq 7\}$

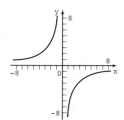

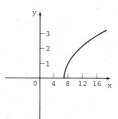

23. $(x + 2)^2 + (y - 3)^2 = 25$ **25.** $(x + 8)^2 + (y - 1)^2 = 289$ **27.** yes, yes, yes, no   **29.** no, no, no, no
31. yes, no, no, no   **33.** yes, yes, yes, yes
35.

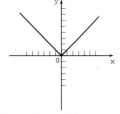

39. move 1 unit to left, reflect about x-axis, translate 3 units up   **41.** all real numbers   **43.** all real numbers
45. $\{x|x \neq 8\}$ **47.** $-4x - 2h + 4$ **49.** (a) $3x^2 + 4x - 1$; (b) $12x^3 - 3x^2$; (c) $(4x - 1)/(3x^2)$; (d) 720; (e) $-13/27$
51. $34 + 54x$; $54x - 8$ **53.** $1/(\sqrt{3 + x})$; $\sqrt{3 + (1/x)}$ **55.** even   **57.** one-to-one   **59.** not one-to-one
61. increasing on $(-\infty, -1]$, decreasing on $[-1, \infty)$ **63.** never increasing or decreasing
65. $f^{-1}(x) = (x - 3)/12$ **67.** $f^{-1}(x) = \sqrt[3]{x + 3}$ **69.** $f^{-1}(x) = \sqrt{25 - x^2}$;
domain: $[0, 5]$

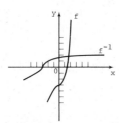

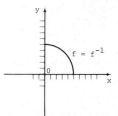

71. $m = kz^2$ **73.** $Y = (kMN^2)/X^3$ **75.** 847   **77.** 36cm   **79.** (a) yes; (b) yes; (c) yes, on intervals
where $f(x) \geq 0$, but not on any interval where $f(x) \leq 0$ (for example, $f(x) = x$); (d) yes   **81.** (a) 0; (d) 2; (e) 1/2
83. $(-2, 4)$, $2\sqrt{5}$

CHAPTER 4

Section 4.1 (page 130)
1. 3/5   **3.** 2   **5.** no slope   **7.** 2   **9.** .5785   **11.** decreasing   **13.** increasing
15. $2x + y = 5$ **17.** $y = 1$ **19.** $x + 3y = 10$ **21.** $3x + 4y = 12$ **23.** $2x - 3y = 6$ **25.** $x = -6$
27. $5.081x + y = -4.69$
29.

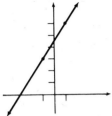

31.

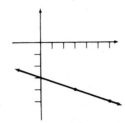

33. $x + 3y = 11$ **35.** $x - y = 7$ **37.** $-2x + y = 4$ **39.** no   **41.** (a) $-1/2$; (b) $-7/2$
47.

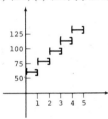

49.

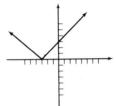

51.

53.

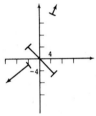

55. (a) \$58; (b) \$58; (c) \$58; (d) \$76; (e) \$94   (g) yes; (h) no
(f)

Section 4.2 (page 139)
1.

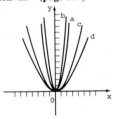

3.

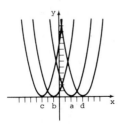

5.

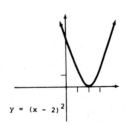
$$y = (x - 2)^2$$

7.

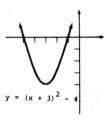
$$y = (x + 3)^2 - 4$$

9.

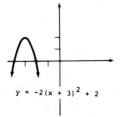
$$y = -2(x + 3)^2 + 2$$

11.

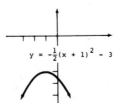
$$y = -\tfrac{1}{2}(x + 1)^2 - 3$$

13.

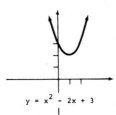
$$y = x^2 - 2x + 3$$

15.

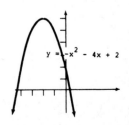
$$y = -x^2 - 4x + 2$$

17.

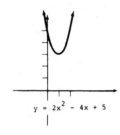

$y = 2x^2 - 4x + 5$

19.

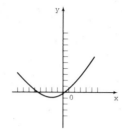

21.

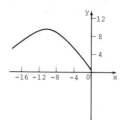

23. $[2, \infty)$ **25.** $(-\infty, 0]$ **27.** $(-\infty, -5/4]$ **29.** 80 by 160   **31.** 300 sandwiches; 100   **33.** 5 in
35. 10, 10 feet   **37.** (a) $x(500 - x) = 500x - x^2$ (b)   (c) 250   (d) \$62,500

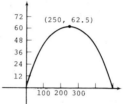

39.

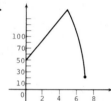

41. $6\sqrt{3}$ cm

Section 4.3 (page 146)
1. (a)   (b) y-axis   **3.** (a)   (b) origin

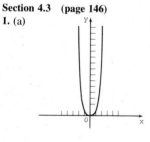

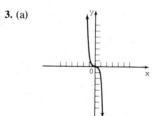

5. (a)   (b) (0, 1)   **7.** (a)   (b) $(-1, 0)$

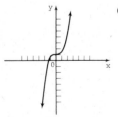

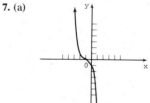

9. (a) 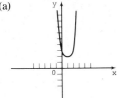   (b) $x = 1$ **11.** 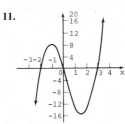   **13.** 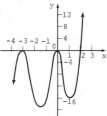   **15.**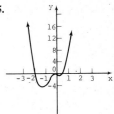

17. 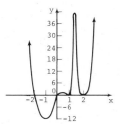   **19.** 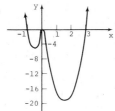   **21.** (a)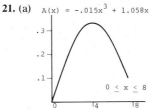

$A(x) = -.015x^3 + 1.058x$

(b) between 4 and 5 hours, closer to 5 hours
(c) from about 1 hour to about 8 hours

23. in $[-1, 0]$ maximum is 1.048 at $x = -.1$, minimum is -5 when $x = -1$; in $[1.4, 2]$, maximum is -4.712 when $x = 1.4$, minimum is -5.336 when $x = 1.8$

Section 4.4   (page 152)

1. 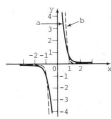   **3.** (a) 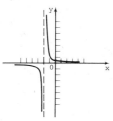   **3.** (b) 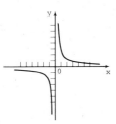   **3.** (c)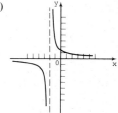

3. (d) 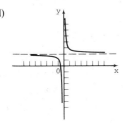   **5.** 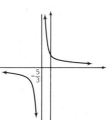   **7.** 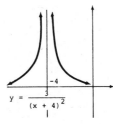   **9.**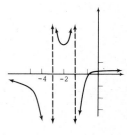

$y = \dfrac{3}{(x + 4)^2}$

11. 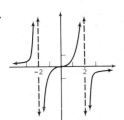   **13.** 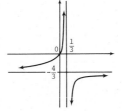   **15.** 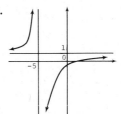   **17.**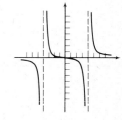

19. (a) 12.5, 10, 6.25, 4.76, 3.85

21.

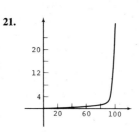

Section 4.5 (page 158)
1. center $(-3, -4)$; radius 4   **3.** center $(6, -5)$; radius 6   **5.** center $(0, 1)$; radius 7   **7.** center $(1.42, -.7)$,
$r = .8$ **9.** $y = (5/3)x$, $y = (-5/3)x$ **11.** $y = (2/3)x$, $y = (-2/3)x$

13.
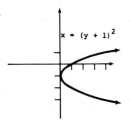

15.
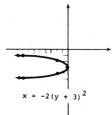

17.
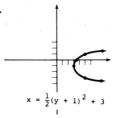

19.
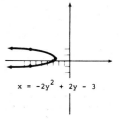

21.
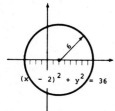

23.
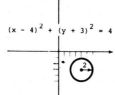

25.
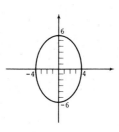

27.
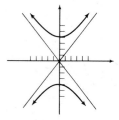

29.
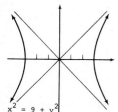

31.
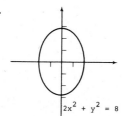

33.
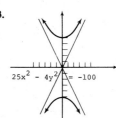

35.
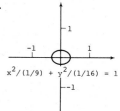

37.
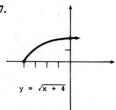

39.
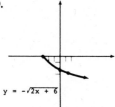

41.
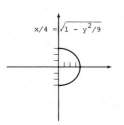

43.
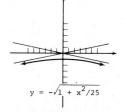

47. about 141.6 million miles

Section 4.6   (page 170)

1.

3.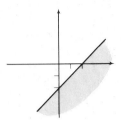

5.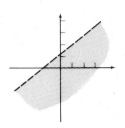

7.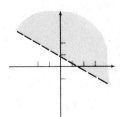

9.

11.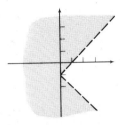

13.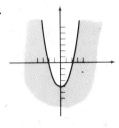

15.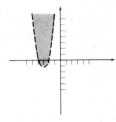

17.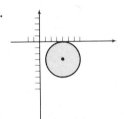

19.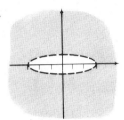

21.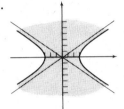

23.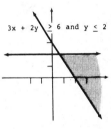

$3x + 2y \geq 6$ and $y \leq 2$

25.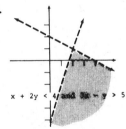

$x + 2y < 4$ and $3x - y > 5$

27.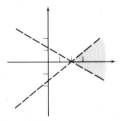

29.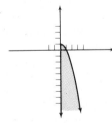

31.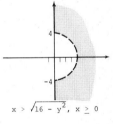

$x > \sqrt{16 - y^2}$, $x \geq 0$

33.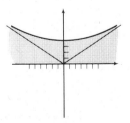

35.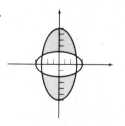

Chapter 4   Review Exercises   (page 175)

1. 0   **3.** 1   **5.** 9/4   **7.** $6x - 5y = 13$ **9.** $x = 1$ **11.** $5x - 8y = -40$

13.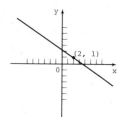

15.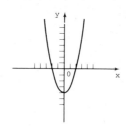

17.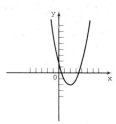

19. 11/2, 11/2   **21.** a square, 45 m on a side

23.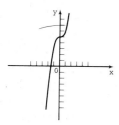

25.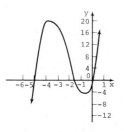

27.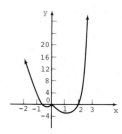

29.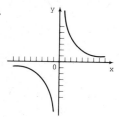

31.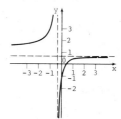

33.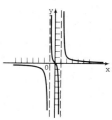

35.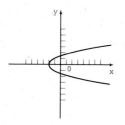

37.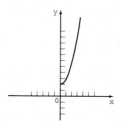

39.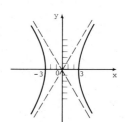

41.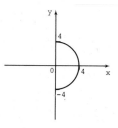

43. $(2, -3)$; 1   **45.** $(-7/2, -3/2)$, $(3\sqrt{6})/2$

47.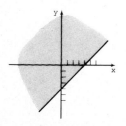

49.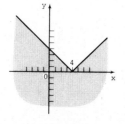

51.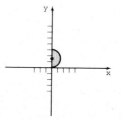

53.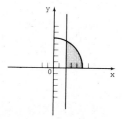

55. (a) $7   (b) $10   (c) $9

(d)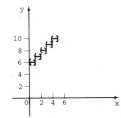

(e) yes

57. $2x - 3y = 14$ **59.** -7 **61.** $(\sqrt{3}/4, 3/4)$ and $(-\sqrt{3}/4, 3/4)$ **65.** $(x - 6)^2 + (y - 7)^2 = 49$, $(x - 6)^2 + (y - 7)^2 = 169$

CHAPTER 5

Section 5.1   (page 178)

1. (a) 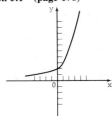   (b) 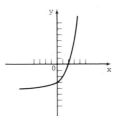   (c) 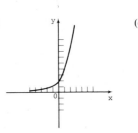   (d)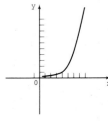

3. 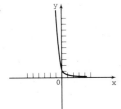   **5.** 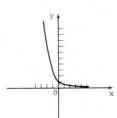   **7.** 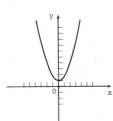   **9.**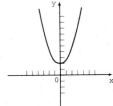

11. 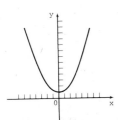   **13.**

15. 3   **17.** 1/2   **19.** -1 **21.** 0   **23.** 8   **25.** 5   **27.** 10, -10 **29.** 3   **31.** 8
33. a series of points, one for each rational number on the number line   **35.** 1,000,000   **37.** about 1,080,000
39.

41. 409 g **43.** 184 g **45.** \$21,665.74 **47.** \$7686.32 **49.** \$22,779.72 **51.** \$102,813.91
53. about 2,690,000 **55.** about 9,600,000 **57.** 40 **59.** 6 **61.** neither **63.** 2.717

Section 5.2 (page 184)
1. $\log_3 81 = 4$ **3.** $\log_{1/2} 16 = -4$ **5.** $\log_{10} .0001 = -4$ **7.** $6^2 = 36$ **9.** $(\sqrt{3})^8 = 81$ **11.** $m^n = k$
13. 1/5 **15.** 6 **17.** 3/2 **19.** 16 **21.** $\log_3 2 - \log_3 5$ **23.** $\log_2 6 + \log_2 x - \log_2 y$
25. $1 + (1/2)\log_5 7 - \log_5 3$ **27.** no change possible **29.** $\log_a (xy/m)$ **31.** $\log_m (a^2/b^6)$
33. $\log_x a^{3/2} b^{-4}$ **35.** 2.9957 **37.** 6.6846 **39.** 7.2724 **41.** -2.5258 **43.** -1.6095
45. -4.9619

47. (a) 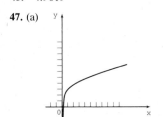 **(b)** 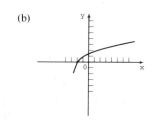 **(c)**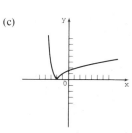

49. 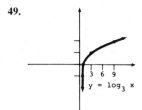 **51.** 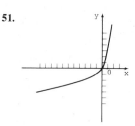 **53.** 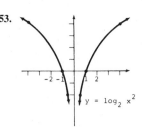 **55.**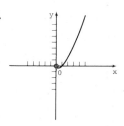

57. .7781 **59.** .9542 **61.** 1.4771
63. (a) about 350 **(b)** about 1040 **(c)** about 1400
(d) about 1700 **(e)**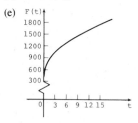

Section 5.3 (page 190)
1. 6 **3.** -4 **5.** -5 **7.** 2.9420 **9.** 4.1072 **11.** $6.9509 - 10$ **13.** 4.8338
15. $6.5821 - 10$ **17.** 4.6331 **19.** -2.091820 **21.** 34.4 **23.** .0747 **25.** .000373
27. 81.6 **29.** 713 **31.** 2.01 **33.** 10.6 **35.** 21.5 **37.** 16.0 **39.** 31.2 lbs per cubic ft
41. (a) 350 years; **(b)** 3990 years; **(c)** 2300 years **43.** 3.2 **45.** 1.8 **47.** 2.0×10^{-3} **49.** 1.6×10^{-5}

Section 5.4 (page 196)
1. 1.63 **3.** $\log 8/\log 7 \approx 1.07$ **5.** 2.26 **7.** 1.08 **9.** 1.104 **11.** 11 **13.** 5 **15.** 8
17. no solution **19.** $10\sqrt{5}, -10\sqrt{5}$ **21.** 1, 10 **23.** 2.65 **25.** -0.204 **27.** $x = -\ln y$
29. $x = \ln(y \pm \sqrt{y^2 - 1})$ **31.** $t = (1000/k) \cdot \ln(P/P_0)$ **33.** $t = (-1/k) \log [(T - T_0)/(T_1 - T_0)]$
35. 15 seconds **37.** 46 days

Section 5.5 (page 200)
1. 4.83 **3.** $-.02$ **5.** 1.43 **7.** .59 **9.** -1.59 **11.** .96 **13.** 1 **15.** 2 **17.** 2
19. 2.59×10^{10} **21.** about 3 months **23.** about 7 years **25.** 5600 years **29.** about 3280 years
31. 1810, 7,298,000; 1900, 77,330,000; 1970, 168,200,000

Chapter 5   Appendix   (page 205)
1. 3.3701   **3.** 1.6836   **5.** 8.7975 − 10   **7.** 1.4322   **9.** 62.26   **11.** .004534   **13.** 493,200
15. .0001667   **17.** 1.396   **19.** 1.550   **21.** .9308   **23.** 15.57   **25.** .1405

Chapter 5   Review Exercises   (page 208)
1. 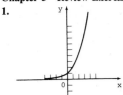   **3.**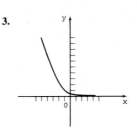

5. 5/3   **7.** 3/2   **9.** 800 g   **11.** $1790.19   **13.** about 12 years   **15.** $\log_2 32 = 5$
17. $10^{-3} = .001$ **19.** $\log_3 m + \log_3 n - \log_3 p$ **21.** $2 \log_5 x + 4 \log_5 y + (1/5)(3 \log_5 m + \log_5 p)$
23. −3 + .6243   **25.** 5,300,000,000   **27.** 5.97   **29.** 1.44   **31.** ½ (log 17/log 5 + 3) ≈ 2.38
33. 29   **35.** 3   **37.** $x = \log_5 [(1 \pm \sqrt{1 + 16y^2})/(4y)]$ **39.** −9.8856   **41.** 2.2553   **43.** 6.0486
45. 1.2 m   **47.** 1.8 m   **49.** $7182.87   **51.** $1241.99   **53.** $10,000 now   **55.** $109,658.91
57. $141,246.23   **59.** $287,199.45   **61.** .6779   **63.** 84.24   **65.** .0001965   **67.** 9189
69. $\log_{10} N = (\ln N)/(\ln 10)$; 0.30103   **71.** 1/(ln 10)

CHAPTER 6

Section 6.1   (page 211)
1. $(-\sqrt{2}/2, -\sqrt{2}/2)$ **3.** (−1, 0)   **5.** (1, 0)   **7.** (1, 0)   **9.** (0, 1)   **11.** $(-\sqrt{2}/2, -\sqrt{2}/2)$
13. $(\sqrt{2}/2, \sqrt{2}/2)$ **15.** $(-\sqrt{2}/2, \sqrt{2}/2)$ **17.** (a) $(2/3, -\sqrt{5}/3)$; (b) $(2/3, \sqrt{5}/3)$; (c) $(-2/3, -\sqrt{5}/3)$;
(d) $(-2/3, \sqrt{5}/3)$ **19.** (a) (4/5, −3/5); (b) (4/5, 3/5); (c) (−4/5, −3/5); (d) (−4/5, 3/5)   **21.** (a) $(-1/2, -\sqrt{3}/2)$;
(b) $(-1/2, \sqrt{3}/2)$; (c) $(1/2, -\sqrt{3}/2)$; (d) $(1/2, \sqrt{3}/2)$ **23.** (a) $(-2/5, \sqrt{21}/5)$; (b) $(-2/5, -\sqrt{21}/5)$;
(c) $(2/5, \sqrt{21}/5)$; (d) $(2/5, -\sqrt{21}/5)$ **25.** 0; 1   **27.** $\sqrt{2}/2$; $\sqrt{2}/2$ **29.** −1; 0   **31.** 0; −1
33. $-\sqrt{2}/2$; $\sqrt{2}/2$ **35.** $-\sqrt{2}/2$; $-\sqrt{2}/2$ **37.** III   **39.** III   **41.** II   **45.** (b) $(1/2, \sqrt{3}/2)$
(c) $(1/2, -\sqrt{3}/2)$; $(-1/2, \sqrt{3}/2)$; $(-1/2, -\sqrt{3}/2)$ **47.** $\sqrt{3}/2$ **49.** −1/2   **51.** $-\sqrt{3}/2$ **53.** 1/2

Section 6.2   Exercises   (page 217)
1. $\tan s = \sqrt{3}/3$; $\cot s = \sqrt{3}$; $\sec s = 2\sqrt{3}/3$; $\csc s = 2$ **3.** $\tan s = -4/3$; $\cot s = -3/4$; $\sec s = -5/3$;
$\csc s = 5/4$ **5.** $\tan s = -\sqrt{3}$; $\cot s = -\sqrt{3}/3$; $\sec s = 2$; $\csc s = -2\sqrt{3}/3$

In Exercises 7–17 and 31–37 answers are given in the order sine, cosine, tangent, cotangent, secant, cosecant.
7. 0; −1; 0; undefined; −1; undefined   **9.** $\sqrt{2}/2$; $-\sqrt{2}/2$; −1; −1; $-\sqrt{2}$; $\sqrt{2}$ **11.** $-\sqrt{2}/2$; $\sqrt{2}/2$; −1; −1;
$\sqrt{2}$; $-\sqrt{2}$ **13.** 1/2; $\sqrt{3}/2$; $\sqrt{3}/3$; $\sqrt{3}$; $2\sqrt{3}/3$; 2   **15.** $\sqrt{3}/2$; −1/2; $-\sqrt{3}$; $-\sqrt{3}/3$; −2; $-2\sqrt{3}/3$
17. −1/2; $-\sqrt{3}/2$; $\sqrt{3}/3$; $\sqrt{3}$; $-2\sqrt{3}/3$; −2   **19.** +, +   **21.** −, −, +, +, −, −   **23.** II   **25.** III
27. II or III   **29.** III or IV   **31.** $\sin s = \sqrt{65}/9$; $\tan s = -\sqrt{65}/4$; $\cot s = -4\sqrt{65}/65$; $\sec s = -9/4$;
$\csc s = 9\sqrt{65}/65$ **33.** $3\sqrt{13}/13$, $2\sqrt{13}/13$, 3/2, 2/3, $\sqrt{13}/2$, $\sqrt{13}/3$ **35.** $\cos t = -2\sqrt{5}/5$; $\tan t = -1/2$;
$\cot t = -2$; $\sec t = -\sqrt{5}/2$; $\csc t = \sqrt{5}$ **37.** a, $\sqrt{1 - a^2}$, $a\sqrt{1 - a^2}/(1 - a^2)$, $\sqrt{1 - a^2}/a$, $1/\sqrt{1 - a^2}$, $1/a$

In Exercises 39–42, your answers may differ slightly in the last digits, depending on the method you use to get the
number.
39. sin s = .903687, tan s = −2.11047, cot s = −.473829, sec s = 2.33540, csc s = 1.10658
41. sin t = −.095832, cos t = .995397, tan t = −.096275, cot t = −10.3869, sec t = 1.00462

Section 6.3 Exercises   (page 223)
1. 320°   **3.** 235°   **5.** 90°   **7.** 179°   **9.** π/3   **11.** π/2   **13.** 3π/4   **15.** 5π/3
17. 9π/4   **19.** 7π/9   **21.** 60°   **23.** 315°   **25.** 330°   **27.** −30°   **29.** 900°   **31.** 63°
33. .9847   **35.** 42° 07′ 08″   **37.** π/2   **39.** π   **41.** 1800°   **43.** 3/2   **45.** 1.23   **47.** 3.09309
49. 980 mi   **51.** 2200 mi   **53.** 3700 mi   **55.** 477 ft   **57.** π/6 radians per hr   **59.** 200π/3
radians per min   **61.** π/18 radians per second   **63.** 7800 mi

Section 6.4   (page 232)

In Exercises 1–15, answers are given in the order sine, cosine, tangent, cotangent, secant, and cosecant.
1. $\sqrt{3}/2, -1/2, -\sqrt{3}, -\sqrt{3}/3, -2, 2\sqrt{3}/3$ **3.** $1/2, -\sqrt{3}/2, -\sqrt{3}/3, -\sqrt{3}, -2\sqrt{3}/3, 2$
5. $-\sqrt{3}/2, -1/2, \sqrt{3}, \sqrt{3}/3, -2, -2\sqrt{3}/3$ **7.** $-1/2, \sqrt{3}/2, -\sqrt{3}/3, -\sqrt{3}, 2\sqrt{3}/3, -2$
9. $\sqrt{3}/2, 1/2, \sqrt{3}, \sqrt{3}/3, 2, 2\sqrt{3}/3$ **11.** $1/2, -\sqrt{3}/2, -\sqrt{3}/3, -\sqrt{3}, -2\sqrt{3}/3, 2$ **13.** $0, -1, 0$, undefined,
-1, undefined   **15.** $-1, 0$, undefined, 0, undefined, -1 **17.** $\sqrt{3}/3, \sqrt{3}$ **19.** $\sqrt{3}/2, \sqrt{3}/3, 2\sqrt{3}/3$
21. $-1, -1$ **23.** $-\sqrt{3}/2, -2\sqrt{3}/3$ **25.** $4/5, -3/5, -4/3, -3/4, -5/3, 5/4$ **27.** $7/25, 24/25, 7/24, 24/7$,
$25/24, 25/7$ **29.** $-5/13, -12/13, 5/12, 12/5, -13/12, -13/5$ **31.** $-4/5, -3/5, 4/3, 3/4, -5/3, -5/4$

In Exercises 33–37, answers are given in the order sine, cosine, tangent, contangent, secant, and cosecant.
33. $3/5, 4/5, 3/4, 4/3, 5/4, 5/3$ **35.** $21/29, 20/29, 21/20, 20/21, 29/20, 29/21$ **37.** $n/p, m/p, n/m, m/n$,
$p/m, p/n$ **39.** $.759260, .650787, 1.16668$ **41.** $.87166, .49011, 1.7785$ **43.** true   **45.** false
47. false   **49.** true

Section 6.5   (page 238)

1. $35°$ **3.** $37°$ **5.** $69°50'$ **7.** $.0684$ **9.** $.3142$ **11.** $.8814$ **13.** $.6338$ **15.** $-.6248$
17. $-.5712$ **19.** -3.072 **21.** $.9636$ **23.** $-.6361$ **25.** $.5704$ **27.** 1.162 **29.** $.1628$
31. $-.3131$ **33.** $58°00'$ **35.** $68°45'$ **37.** 1.4573 **39.** $.001$ **41.** $.01$ **43.** $.01$ **45.** $.10$
47. 1   **49.** 1   **51.** $.8417$ **53.** $.0100$ **55.** 1.0000 **57.** $c = 68.4$ km, $b = 58.2$ km
59. $b = 3330.68$ m, $a = 1311.04$ m   **61.** 2.00 m

Section 6.6   (page 245)

1. $2\pi, 2$

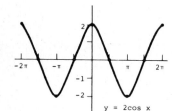

3. $2\pi, 3$

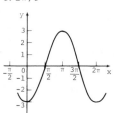

5. $16\pi, 1$

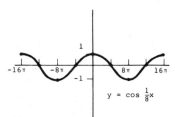

$y = \cos \frac{1}{8}x$

7. $2\pi/3, 1$

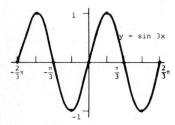

$y = \sin 3x$

9. $\pi/3, 1$

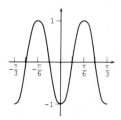

11. $8\pi, 2$

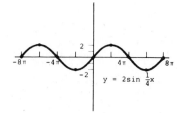

$y = 2\sin \frac{1}{4}x$

13.

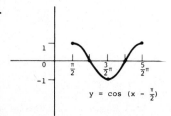

$y = \cos (x - \frac{\pi}{2})$

15.

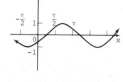

17.

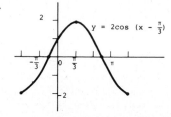

$y = 2\cos (x - \frac{\pi}{3})$

19.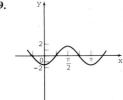

21.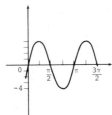

23.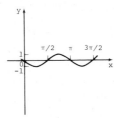

25. odd   **27.** $y = \cos x$ has same graph (see Figure 6.38)   **29.** 1, 240°   **31.** 65°   **33.** getting cooler
35. 20

37. 2π, 1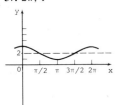

39. 2π, 2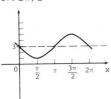

47.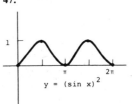

$y = (\sin x)^2$

49.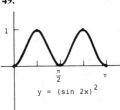

$y = (\sin 2x)^2$

Section 6.7   (page 252)

1.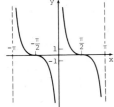

3.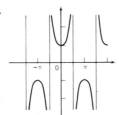

5.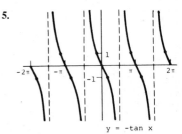

$y = -\tan x$

7.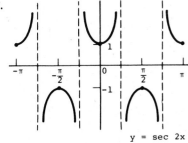

$y = \sec 2x$

9.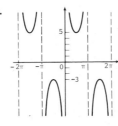

11.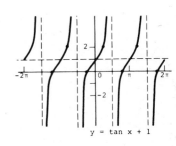

$y = \tan x + 1$

13.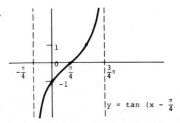

$y = \tan (x - \frac{\pi}{4})$

15.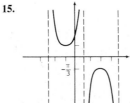

17.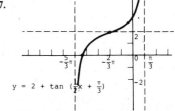

$y = 2 + \tan (\frac{1}{2}x + \frac{\pi}{3})$

19.

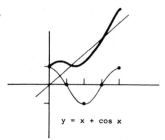

$y = x + \cos x$

21.

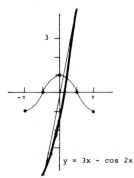

$y = 3x - \cos 2x$

23.

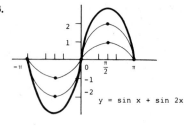

$y = \sin x + \sin 2x$

25.

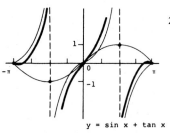

$y = \sin x + \tan x$

27.

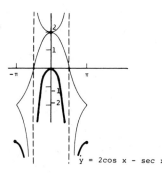

$y = 2\cos x - \sec x$

29.

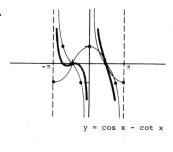

$y = \cos x - \cot x$

31.

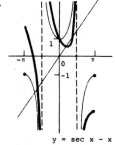

$y = \sec x - x$

Section 6.8   (page 257)

1. $-\pi/3$ **3.** $\pi/4$ **5.** $-\pi/2$ **7.** $\pi/3$ **9.** $3\pi/4$ **11.** $-\pi/3$ **13.** $-7°40'$ **15.** $113°30'$
17. $22°00'$ **19.** $48°00'$ **21.** $-42°40'$ **23.** $.8058$ **25.** -1.332 **29.** $-26°21'29''$
31. $23°52'41''$ **33.** $\sqrt{5}/2$ **35.** $\sqrt{5}/5$ **37.** $-\sqrt{21}/2$ **39.** $-3\sqrt{10}/10$ **41.** $x = \sin(y/4)$
43. $x = \frac{1}{2}\tan 2y$ **45.** $x = -2 + \sin y$ **47.** $\sqrt{1 - x^2}$ **49.** $1/x$ **51.** $\sqrt{1 - x^2}/x$

53. domain: $-1 \le x \le 1$; range: $0 \le y \le 2\pi$

55. domain: $-1 \le x \le 1$; range: $(-\pi/2) + 2 \le y \le (\pi/2) + 2$

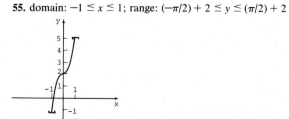

61. false   **63.** false   **65.** false   **67.** false

Chapter 6   Review Exercises   (page 261)
1. $(\sqrt{2}/2, -\sqrt{2}/2)$ **3.** $(-1, 0)$ **5.** $-\sqrt{3}/2, 1/2, -\sqrt{3}$ **7.** $(-2/3, -\sqrt{5}/3)$ **9.** $(2/3, \sqrt{5}/3)$
11. IV   **13.** IV   **15.** $\sin s = -3/5$, $\tan s = -3/4$, $\cot s = -4/3$, $\sec s = 5/4$, $\csc s = -5/3$
17. $\sin s = 4/5$, $\cos s = -3/5$, $\cot s = -3/4$, $\csc s = 5/4$ **19.** $144°$ **21.** $3\pi/2$ **23.** $\sqrt{3}/2$ **25.** $\sqrt{3}$
27. -1 **29.** $-4/5, -3/5, 4/3, 3/4, -5/3, -5/4$ **31.** 1.428 **33.** $-.9216$ **35.** 0.5289 **37.** $79°10'$
39. $62°31'$ **41.** 1.2857 **43.** $2, 2\pi, \pi$ to the right   **45.** $1, \pi/2$, none

47. 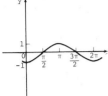   **49.** 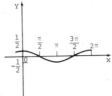   **51.**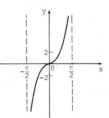

53. 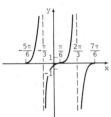   **55.**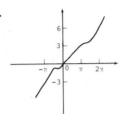

57. $y = \frac{1}{3} \sin 4\pi t/3$ **59.** $\pi/4$ **61.** $-\pi/3$ **63.** -0.7214

65. 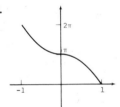   **67.**

69. $\sqrt{2}/4$

CHAPTER 7

Section 7.1   Exercises   (page 265)
1. $\sqrt{7}/4$ **3.** $-2\sqrt{5}/5$ **5.** $\sqrt{21}/2$ **7.** $\cos \theta = -\sqrt{5}/3$, $\tan \theta = -2\sqrt{5}/5$, $\cot \theta = -\sqrt{5}/2$,
$\sec \theta = -3\sqrt{5}/5$, $\csc \theta = 3/2$ **9.** $\sin \theta = 2\sqrt{2}/3$, $\cos \theta = -1/3$, $\tan \theta = -2\sqrt{2}$, $\cot \theta = -\sqrt{2}/4$, $\csc \theta = 3\sqrt{2}/4$
11. $\sin s = 3/5$, $\cos s = 4/5$, $\tan s = 3/4$, $\sec s = 5/4$, $\csc s = 5/3$ **13.** $\sin s = -\sqrt{7}/4$, $\cos s = 3/4$,
$\tan s = -\sqrt{7}/3$, $\cot s = -3\sqrt{7}/7$, $\csc s = -4\sqrt{7}/7$
15. b   **17.** e   **19.** a   **21.** a   **23.** b or d   **25.** 1   **27.** $-\sin \alpha$ **29.** 0
31. $(1 + \sin \theta)/\cos \theta$ **33.** $1/\sin^2 \alpha$ **35.** $\sin^2 t \cos^2 t$ **37.** $(1 + \cos^4 x)/\cos^2 x$
39. $(\cos^2 \theta - \sin^2 \theta)/\cos^4 \theta$ **41.** $\cos x = \pm\sqrt{1 - \sin^2 x}$; $\tan x = \pm \sin x\sqrt{1 - \sin^2 x}/(1 - \sin^2 x)$;
$\cot x = \pm \sqrt{1 - \sin^2 x}/\sin x$; $\sec x = \pm \sqrt{1 - \sin^2 x}/(1 - \sin^2 x)$; $\csc x = 1/\sin x$
43. $\tan x = \pm\sqrt{\csc^2 x - 1}/(\csc^2 x - 1)$ **45.** $\cot s = \pm\sqrt{\sec^2 s - 1}/(\sec^2 s - 1)$
49. $(25\sqrt{6} - 60)/12; - (25\sqrt{6} + 60)/12$

Section 7.2   (page 270)
1. $1/(\sin \theta \cos \theta)$ **3.** $1 + \cos s$ **5.** $-2/\cos^2 \alpha$ or $-2 \sec^2 \alpha$ **7.** $2 + 2 \sin t$
9. $(\sin \gamma + 1)(\sin \gamma - 1)$ **11.** $4 \sin x$ **13.** $(2 \sin x + 1)(\sin x + 1)$ **15.** $(\cos^2 x + 1)^2$ **17.** $\sin \theta$

19. $\tan^2 \beta$ **21.** $\tan^2 x$ **23.** $\sec^2 x$ **65.** identity   **67.** not an identity   **69.** not an identity
71. not an identity

Section 7.3   (page 274)

1. $\cot 3°$ **3.** $\sin 5\pi/12$ **5.** $\sec 104°24'$ **7.** $\cos -\pi/8$ **9.** $\csc(-56°42')$ **11.** true
13. false   **15.** true   **17.** 15°   **19.** 140/3°   **21.** 20°   **23.** $(\sqrt{6} - \sqrt{2})/4$ **25.** $(\sqrt{6} - \sqrt{2})/4$
27. $\sqrt{2}/2$ **29.** $\sqrt{2}/2$ **31.** $(\sqrt{3} \cos \theta - \sin \theta)/2$ **33.** $(\cos \theta - \sqrt{3} \sin \theta)/2$ **35.** $-\sin x$
37. 16/65; 56/65   **39.** $(-2\sqrt{10} + 2)/9$; $(-2\sqrt{10} - 2)/9$ **41.** −36/85; 84/85   **51.** $\cos t$; $\sin t$; $-\cos t$;
$-\sin t$; $\cos t$; $-\sin t$; $-\cos t$; $\sin t$ **55.** −0.77791   **57.** 0.98132   **61.** 36/85

Section 7.4   (page 280)

1. $(\sqrt{6} - \sqrt{2})/4$ **3.** $(-\sqrt{6} - \sqrt{2})/4$ **5.** $(\sqrt{6} + \sqrt{2})/4$ **7.** $\sqrt{2}/2$ **9.** −1   **11.** $\sqrt{2}/2$
13. $\sqrt{2}(\sin t + \cos t)/2$ **15.** $(\sqrt{3} - \tan t)/(1 + \sqrt{3} \tan t)$ **17.** $\tan t$ **19.** $-\sin t$ **21.** 63/65; 33/65;
63/16; 33/56   **23.** $(4\sqrt{2} + \sqrt{5})/9$; $(4\sqrt{2} - \sqrt{5})/9$; $(-8\sqrt{5} - 5\sqrt{2})/(20 - 2\sqrt{10})$;
$(-8\sqrt{5} + 5\sqrt{2})/(20 + 2\sqrt{10})$ **25.** 77/85; 13/85; −77/36; 13/84   **39.** 18°   **41.** 15°
43. $\sqrt{2} \sin(x + 135°)$ **45.** $13 \sin(\theta + 293°)$ or $13 \sin (\theta - 67°)$ **47.** $17 \sin (\beta + 332°)$
49. $25 \sin(s + 106°)$
51. $2 \sin(x + 30°)$

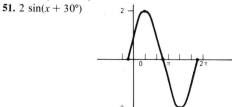

$y = \sqrt{3} \sin x + \cos x$

53. $\sqrt{2} \sin(x + 135°)$

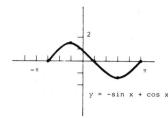

$y = -\sin x + \cos x$

57. −0.996728   **59.** −0.959882   **61.** $(8\sqrt{17} + \sqrt{85})/51$ **63.** 23/80

Section 7.5   (page 287)

1. $2\pi/5$ **3.** $\cos 2x$ **5.** 160°, 160°   **7.** $\cos^2, \sin^2$ **9.** 9°   **11.** $\tan 170°$ **13.** −   **15.** +
17. $-\sqrt{42}/12$ **19.** $-\sqrt{10}/4$ **21.** $\sin 22\frac{1}{2}° = \sqrt{2 - \sqrt{2}}/2$, $\cos 22\frac{1}{2}° = \sqrt{2 + \sqrt{2}}/2$, $\tan 22\frac{1}{2}° = \sqrt{3 - 2\sqrt{2}}$
23. $\sin 195° = -\sqrt{2 - \sqrt{3}}/2$, $\cos 195° = -\sqrt{2 + \sqrt{3}}/2$, $\tan 195° = \sqrt{7 - 4\sqrt{3}}$ **25.** $\sin 5\pi/2 = 1$, $\cos 5\pi/2 = 0$,
$\tan 5\pi/2$ does not exist   **27.** $\cos x = -\sqrt{42}/12$, $\sin x = \sqrt{102}/12$, $\tan x = -\sqrt{119}/7$, $\sec x = -2\sqrt{42}/7$,
$\csc x = 2\sqrt{102}/17$, $\cot x = -\sqrt{119}/17$ **29.** $\cos 2\theta = 17/25$, $\sin 2\theta = -4\sqrt{21}/25$, $\tan 2\theta = -4\sqrt{21}/17$,
$\sec 2\theta = 25/17$, $\csc 2\theta = -25\sqrt{21}/84$, $\cot 2\theta = -17\sqrt{21}/84$ **31.** $\tan 2x = -4/3$, $\sec 2x = -5/3$,
$\cos 2x = -3/5$, $\cot 2x = -3/4$, $\sin 2x = 4/5$, $\csc 2x = 5/4$ **33.** $\sin \alpha/2 = \sqrt{3}/3$, $\cos \alpha/2 = -\sqrt{6}/3$,
$\tan \alpha/2 = -\sqrt{2}/2$, $\cot \alpha/2 = -\sqrt{2}$, $\sec \alpha/2 = -\sqrt{6}/2$, $\csc \alpha/2 = \sqrt{3}$ **49.** $4 \tan^2 x/(1 - 2 \tan^2 x + \tan^4 x)$
51. $3 \sin x \cos^2 x - \sin^3 x$ **53.** $1 - 8 \sin^2 x \cos^2 x$ or $\cos^4 x - 6 \sin^2 x \cos^2 x + \sin^4 x$ **55.** 84°
57. 60°   **59.** 3.9   **61.** −.843580   **63.** 0.537003   **65.** −1.570905   **67.** 1   **69.** $\sec^2 4x$

Section 7.6   (page 293)

1. $(1/2)[\sin 60° - \sin 10°] = (1/2)[\sqrt{3}/2 - \sin 10°]$ **3.** $(3/2)[\cos 8x + \cos 2x]$ **5.** $(1/2)[\cos 2\theta - \cos(-4\theta)] =$
$(1/2)[\cos 2\theta - \cos 4\theta]$ **7.** $-4[\cos 9y + \cos(-y)] = -4(\cos 9y + \cos y)$ **9.** $2 \cos 45° \sin 15°$
11. $2 \cos 95° \cos (-53°) = 2 \cos 95° \cos 53°$ **13.** $2 \cos 15\beta/2 \sin 9\beta/2$ **15.** $-6 \cos (7x/2) \sin(-3x/2) =$
$6 \cos (7x/2) \sin (3x/2)$

Section 7.7   (page 297)

1. $3\pi/4, 7\pi/4$ **3.** $\pi/3, 5\pi/3$ **5.** $\pi/6, 7\pi/6, 4\pi/3, 5\pi/3$ **7.** $\pi/3, 5\pi/3, \pi/6, 11\pi/6$ **9.** π
11. $3\pi/2, 7\pi/6, 11\pi/6$ **13.** $\pi/4, 3\pi/4, 5\pi/4, 7\pi/4$ **15.** $0, \pi/2, \pi, 3\pi/2$ **17.** $\pi/12, 7\pi/12, 13\pi/12,$
$19\pi/12$ **19.** $3\pi/8, 5\pi/8, 11\pi/8, 13\pi/8$ **21.** $\pi/2, 3\pi/2$ **23.** 71°30′, 251°30′, 63°30′, 243°30′
25. 135°, 315°, 71°30′, 251°30′   **27.** 33°30′, 326°30′   **29.** 45°, 225°   **31.** 0°, 90°, 180°, 270°
33. 30°, 60°, 210°, 240°   **35.** 0°   **37.** 120°, 240°   **39.** 270°, 30°, 150°   **41.** 90°, 270°, 45°, 315°
43. 70°30′, 289°30′   **45.** 90°, 270°, 30°, 150°, 210°, 330°   **47.** 90° + 360° · n, 180° + 360° · n
49. 30° + 360° · n, 150° + 360° · n, 90 ° + 360° · n, 270° + 360° · n **51.** 45° + 180° · n, 108°30′ + 180° · n
53. 22½° + 180° · n, 112½° + 180° · n **55.** 53° 40′, 126° 20′, 188° 00′, 352° 00′   **57.** 149° 40′, 329° 40′,

106° 20′, 286° 20′   **59.** no solution   **61.** $\pi/12, \pi/2, 5\pi/12, 3\pi/2, 13\pi/12, 17\pi/12$ **63.** $0, \pi/4, 3\pi/4, \pi,$
$5\pi/4, 7\pi/4$ **65.** $\pi/6, \pi/2, 3\pi/2, 5\pi/6$ **67.** $\pi/4$ seconds   **69.** 3/5   **71.** 4/5   **73.** 0   **75.** 1/2
77. −1/2   **79.** 0

Chapter 7   Review Exercises   (page 303)
1. $\sin x = -4/5, \tan x = -4/3, \sec x = 5/3, \csc x = -5/4, \cot x = -3/4$ **3.** $\sin (x + y) = (4 + 3\sqrt{15})/20,$
$\cos (x - y) = (4\sqrt{15} + 3)/20$ **5.** $\sin x = \sqrt{2 - \sqrt{2}}/2, \cos x = \sqrt{2 + \sqrt{2}}/2, \tan x = \sqrt{3 - 2\sqrt{2}}$ **7.** j
9. c   **11.** d   **13.** a   **15.** f   **17.** e   **19.** 1   **21.** $1/\cos^2 \theta$ or $\sec^2 \theta$ **23.** $1/\sin^2 \theta \cos^2 \theta$
53. $\pi/2, 3\pi/2$ **55.** $\pi/6, 5\pi/6$ **57.** $\pi/8, 3\pi/8, 5\pi/8, 7\pi/8, 9\pi/8, 11\pi/8, 13\pi/8, 15\pi/8$ **59.** $\pi/2$
61. $\pi/3, 5\pi/3, \pi$ **63.** 60°, 300°   **65.** 270°   **67.** 0°, 45°, 180°, 225°   **77.** $2 - \sqrt{3}$

CHAPTER 8

Section 8.1   (page 306)
1. $B = 62°, C = 90°, a = 8.17$ m, $b = 15.4$ m   **3.** $A = 17°, C = 90°, a = 39.1$ in, $c = 134$ in
5. $c = 85.9$ yd, $A = 62°50′, B = 27°10′, C = 90°$ **7.** $b = 42.3$ cm, $A = 24°10′, B = 65°50′, C = 90°$
9. $A = 50°50′, C = 90°, a = .483$ m, $b = .393$ m   **11.** $B = 30°16′, a = 16.19$ feet, $b = 9.445$ feet, $C = 90°$
13. $B = 42.38°, b = 36.01$ cm, $c = 53.42$ cm, $C = 90°$ **15.** $c = 581.9$ cm, $A = 34.24°$ or 34°14′,
$B = 55.76°$ or 55°46′, $C = 90°$ **17.** 26.6 m   **19.** 52°30′   **21.** 11 ft   **23.** 35°50′   **25.** 1581 ft
27. 51.4 m   **29.** 8200 ft   **31.** 446 ft   **33.** 114 ft   **35.** 5.18 m   **37.** $h = k(\tan B - \tan A)/\tan A$
39. 156 mi   **41.** 120 mi   **43.** 38°   **45.** $m(1 - \cos \alpha)$ **47.** $\sqrt{15}/4$ **49.** $\sqrt{5}/3$

Section 8.2   (page 314)
1. $C = 83°, a = 11$ m, $b = 10$ m   **3.** $C = 80°40′, a = 79.5$ mm, $c = 108$ mm   **5.** no such triangle
7. $A = 56°00′, c = 361$ ft, $a = 308$ ft   **9.** $C = 125°01′, b = 576.7$ m, $c = 1224$ m   **11.** $B = 6.50°,$
$A = 148.36°, a = 1171$ cm   **13.** $A_1 = 43°40′, C_1 = 106°40′, A_2 = 136°20′, C_2 = 14°00′$ **15.** no such triangle
17. $B = 27°10′, C = 10°40′$ **19.** $C = 21.61°, B = 99.97°, b = 65.64$ m   **21.** $B = 20°40′, C = 116°50′,$
$c = 20.6$ m   **23.** no such triangle   **25.** $A_1 = 52°10′, C_1 = 95°00′, c_1 = 9520$ cm, $A_2 = 127°50′,$
$C_2 = 19°20′, c_2 = 3160$ cm   **27.** $A_1 = 53°20′, C_1 = 87°00′, c_1 = 37.1$ m, $A_2 = 126°40′, C_2 = 13°40′, c_2 = 8.77$ m
29. $B_1 = 30°08′, C_1 = 120°05′, c_1 = 504.5$ cm, $B_2 = 149°52′, C_2 = 0°21′, c_2 = 3.561$ cm   **31.** 118 m
33. 1.93 mi   **35.** 929 ft   **37.** 41.0 sq ft   **39.** 356 sq cm   **41.** 722.3 sq m

Section 8.3   (page 323)
1. $a = 4.38$ in, $B = 80°20′, C = 60°00′$ **3.** $c = 6.47$ m, $A = 53°00′, B = 81°10′$ **5.** $b = 13.7$ in, $A = 32°00′,$
$C = 22°30′$ **7.** $c = 138.6$ m, $B = 105°46′, A = 49°29′$ **9.** $A = 29°00′, B = 46°30′, C = 104°30′$
11. $A = 81°50′, B = 37°20′, C = 60°50′$ **13.** $A = 88°01′, B = 44°36′, C = 47°23′$ **15.** 257 m
17. 281 km   **19.** 1130 ft   **21.** 1472 m   **23.** 6.01 km   **25.** 25.24983 mi   **27.** 34 sq ft
29. 450 sq m   **31.** 228 sq m   **33.** 1922 sq ft   **35.** 33 cans

Section 8.4   (page 329)
1. m and p, n and r **3.** m and p equal $2t$, or t is one half m or p

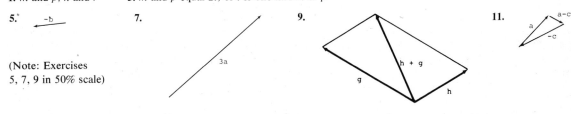

5.   **7.**   **9.**   **11.**

(Note: Exercises
5, 7, 9 in 50% scale)

13. $\langle 1, 3 \rangle$ **15.** $\langle 22, -22 \rangle$ **17.** 14, 14   **19.** 14.2, 24.8   **21.** −123, 155   **23.** −22.3, −65.4
25. $\sqrt{2}, 45°$ **27.** 16, 315°   **29.** 17, 332°   **31.** 6, 180°   **33.** $-5i + 8j$ **35.** $2i$
37. $4\sqrt{2}i + 4\sqrt{2}j$ **39.** $-.2536i + .5438j$ **47.** −22   **49.** −50   **53.** 151° 00′

Section 8.5   (page 337)
1. 94° 00′   **3.** 17 g   **5.** 18°   **7.** 225 kg   **9.** 283, 190   **11.** 126° 40′ between 760 and 1220;
88° 10′ between 760 and 980; 141° 30′ between 980 and 1220   **13.** 173°   **15.** 470 mph, 237° 10′

Chapter 8   Review Exercises   (page 341)
1. $B = 42° \ 40'$, $c = 58.4$ cm   **3.** $A = 56° \ 00'$, $B = 34° \ 00'$ **5.** $a = 11.7$ ft, $c = 402$ ft   **7.** 535 ft
9. 70.8 m   **11.** triangle does not exist   **13.** $17° \ 10'$ **15.** 52.9 ft   **17.** other angles can be $36° \ 10'$,
$115° \ 40'$, third side 40.4; or $8° \ 00'$, $143° \ 50'$, and 6.25   **19.** $25° \ 00'$ **21.** $19° \ 50'$ **23.** 185 sq cm

25. 4950 sq yd   **27.**

29. 2, 2   **31.** 13.2, −21.2   **33.** 12, 135°   **35.** π, 0°   **37.** $-6i + 3j$ **39.** $-4.76i + 1.55j$
41. −13   **43.** 20   **45.** $63° \ 30'$ **47.** 90°   **49.** 270, $56° \ 20'$ **51.** 105 kg
53. 306°, 524 mph

CHAPTER 9

Section 9.1   (page 345)
1. (3, 6)   **3.** (−2, 0)   **5.** (3, 1)   **7.** no solution   **9.** (1, 3)   **11.** (4, −2)   **13.** (2, −2)
15. (12, 6)   **17.** (4, 3)   **19.** (−4, −1)   **21.** (.38, −.47)   **23.** no solution   **25.** (2, 2)
27. (1/5, 1)   **29.** (1/5, 14/3)   **31.** (1, 4), (1, −4), (−1, 4), (−1, −4)   **33.** $a = −3$, $b = −1$
35. goats cost $30, sheep cost $25   **37.** 32 days at $14   **39.** 18 liters of 70%, 12 liters of 20%
41. $10,000 at 8%, $15,000 at 10%   **43.** $5,000 at 8%, $15,000 at 7%   **45.** 200 gallons
47. 72 kph, 92 kph

Section 9.2   (page 352)
1. (1, 2, −1)   **3.** (2, 0, 3)   **5.** no solution   **7.** (1, 2, 3)   **9.** (−1, 2, 1)   **11.** (4, 1, 2)
13. (3, −1, −2)   **15.** (2, 2, 0)   **17.** (4, 6, 1)   **19.** (.4, −.8, .7)   **21.** no solution
23. $(x, 2x − 5, (3x − 4)/3)$ **25.** $(x, −x, −9x)$ **27.** $(x, 2x, 6 − 6x)$ **29.** (1, 1, 1, 1)

More than one equivalent system is possible in Exercises 31–36.

31. (−1, 4, 6), $x + + 7z = 41$ or $x − \frac{3}{2}y + z = −1$ **33.** (2, 1, 3, −1), $x − y + z − w = 5$

$$y + 4z = 28 \qquad\qquad y − \frac{8}{11}z = \frac{−4}{11} \qquad\qquad y − \frac{2}{3}z = −1$$

$$z = 6 \qquad\qquad\qquad z = 6 \qquad\qquad\qquad z − 6w = 9$$

$$w = −1$$

35. (0, 0, 0), $x + 2y − z = 0$ **37.** $a = 3/4$, $b = 1/4$, $c = −1/2$ **39.** $C = −4$, $D = 4$, $F = −8$

$$y − \frac{3}{5}z = 0$$

$$z = 0$$

41. $8, $6, $5   **43.** $10,000 at 9%, $12,000 at 10%, $8,000 at 5%   **45.** 18, −3, 0   **47.** 60 liters of $1,
120 liters of $1.50, 120 liters of $3

Section 9.3   (page 359)
1. (−32, −8)   **3.** (1, 3)   **5.** (1, 0, 2)   **7.** (1, 1), (−2, 4)   **9.** (2, 1), (1/3, 4/9)   **11.** (−3/5, 7/5), (−1, 1)
13. (2, 2), (2, −2), (−2, 2), (−2, −2)   **15.** (0, 0)   **17.** (1, −1), (−1, 1), (1, 1), (−1, −1)
19. (6, 2), (−6, 2), (6, −2), (−6, −2)   **21.** (3, 6), (−3, 6), (3, −6), (−3, −6)   **23.** same circles
25. (2, 3), (3, 2)   **27.** (−3, 5), (15/4, −4)   **29.** (4, −1/8), (−2, 1/4)   **31.** (3, 2), (−3, −2), (4, 3/2),
(−4, −3/2)   **33.** (3, 5), (−3, −5)   **35.** $(\sqrt{5}, 0)$, $(−\sqrt{5}, 0)$, $(\sqrt{5}, \sqrt{5})$, $(−\sqrt{5}, −\sqrt{5})$ **37.** (1, 3),
(31/14, −9/14)   **39.** (0, 1)   **41.** (12, 1)   **43.** 5 m and 12 m   **45.** yes   **47.** $a \neq 5$

Section 9.4   (page 365)
1. $x = 2$, $y = 4$, $z = 8$ **3.** $x = −15$, $y = 5$, $k = 3$ **5.** $z = 18$, $r = 3$, $s = 3$, $p = 3$, $a = 3/4$
7. $\begin{bmatrix} 14 & −11 & −3 \\ −2 & 4 & −1 \end{bmatrix}$ **9.** $\begin{bmatrix} −6 & 8 \\ 4 & 2 \end{bmatrix}$ **11.** can't be done   **13.** $\begin{bmatrix} −12x + 8y & −x + y \\ x & 8x − y \end{bmatrix}$

15. $\begin{bmatrix} 7 & 2 \\ 9 & 0 \\ 8 & 6 \end{bmatrix}$; $\begin{bmatrix} 7 & 9 & 8 \\ 2 & 0 & 6 \end{bmatrix}$ **17.** $\begin{bmatrix} −4 & 8 \\ 0 & 6 \end{bmatrix}$ **19.** $\begin{bmatrix} 2 & 6 \\ −4 & 6 \end{bmatrix}$ **21.** $\begin{bmatrix} −1 & −3 \\ 2 & −3 \end{bmatrix}$ **23.** $\begin{bmatrix} 13 \\ 25 \end{bmatrix}$

25. $\begin{bmatrix} -2 & 5 & 0 \\ 6 & 6 & 1 \\ 12 & 2 & -3 \end{bmatrix}$ **27.** $\begin{bmatrix} 20 & 0 & 8 \\ 8 & 0 & 4 \end{bmatrix}$ **29.** can't be multiplied   **31.** $[-8]$ **33.** $\begin{bmatrix} -6 & 12 & 18 \\ 4 & -8 & -12 \\ -2 & 4 & 6 \end{bmatrix}$

35. (a) $\begin{bmatrix} 17\frac{3}{4} & 23\frac{3}{4} \\ 9 & 12\frac{3}{4} \\ 33 & 42 \\ 6 & 8 \end{bmatrix}$; (b) [220 890 105 125 70]; (c) [4165 5605]   **37.** $\begin{bmatrix} .018 & -.984 \\ 1.002 & -.056 \end{bmatrix}$

39. $\begin{bmatrix} -7.88 & .7 & -.068 \\ -4.87 & -.324 & .259 \\ -1.54 & -.803 & -.192 \end{bmatrix}$ **41.** yes, always true   **43.** yes, always true   **45.** yes, always true

47. always true   **49.** always true   **51.** yes, always true   **53.** Not true. $(A + B)(A - B) = A^2 + BA - AB - B^2$. Since multiplication is not commutative, $BA - AB$ is not always 0.

Section 9.5 (page 374)

1. $\begin{bmatrix} 2 & 3 & | & 11 \\ 1 & 2 & | & 8 \end{bmatrix}$ **3.** $\begin{bmatrix} 1 & 5 & | & 6 \\ 0 & 1 & | & 1 \end{bmatrix}$ **5.** $\begin{bmatrix} 2 & 1 & 1 & | & 3 \\ 3 & -4 & 2 & | & -7 \\ 1 & 1 & 1 & | & 2 \end{bmatrix}$ **7.** $\begin{bmatrix} 1 & 1 & 0 & | & 2 \\ 0 & 2 & 1 & | & -4 \\ 0 & 0 & 1 & | & 2 \end{bmatrix}$

9. $2x + y = 1, 3x - 2y = -9$ **11.** $x = 2, y = 3, z = -2$ **13.** $3x + 2y + z = 1, 2y + 4z = 22,$ $-x - 2y + 3z = 15$ **15.** (2, 3)   **17.** (−3, 0)   **19.** (7/2, −1)   **21.** (5, 0)   **23.** (−2, 1, 3)
25. (−1, 23, 16)   **27.** (3, 2, −4)   **29.** (2, 1, −1)   **31.** no solution   **33.** (3, 3 − z, z)
35. $\left(\frac{-12}{23} - \frac{15}{23}z, \frac{1}{23}z - \frac{13}{23}, z \right)$ **37.** $\left(-6 - \frac{1}{2}z, \frac{1}{2}z + 2, z \right)$ **39.** (−1, 2, 5, 1)   **41.** $(1 - 4w, 1 - w, 2 + w, w)$
43. (1.7, 2.4)   **45.** (.5, −.7, 6)   **47.** wife 40 days, husband 32 days   **49.** 5 model 201, 8 model 301
51. \$10,000 at 8%, \$7000 at 10%, \$8000 at 9%   **53.** $\begin{bmatrix} 1 & 0 & 0 & 1 & | & 1000 \\ 1 & 1 & 0 & 0 & | & 1100 \\ 0 & 1 & 1 & 0 & | & 700 \\ 0 & 0 & 1 & 1 & | & 600 \end{bmatrix} ; \begin{bmatrix} 1 & 0 & 0 & 1 & | & 1000 \\ 0 & 1 & 0 & -1 & | & 100 \\ 0 & 0 & 1 & 1 & | & 600 \\ 0 & 0 & 0 & 0 & | & 0 \end{bmatrix}$
55. 1000, 1000   **57.** 600, 600   **59.** inconsistent system, no solution   **61.** (−15 + z, 5 − 2z, z)

Section 9.6 (page 382)

1. yes   **3.** no   **5.** $\begin{bmatrix} 0 & 1/2 \\ 1/5 & -1/10 \end{bmatrix}$ **7.** does not exist   **9.** does not exist

11. $\begin{bmatrix} -1/12 & 1/6 & -7/12 \\ 7/24 & -1/12 & 25/24 \\ 7/24 & -1/12 & 1/24 \end{bmatrix}$ **13.** $\begin{bmatrix} 1/2 & 0 & 1/2 & -1 \\ 1/10 & -2/5 & 3/10 & -1/5 \\ -7/10 & 4/5 & -11/10 & 12/5 \\ 1/5 & 1/5 & -2/5 & 3/5 \end{bmatrix}$ **15.** $\begin{bmatrix} -2.5 & 5 \\ 12.5 & -15 \end{bmatrix}$

17. $\begin{bmatrix} -.4762 & .7937 & 2.6984 \\ .9524 & .0794 & 1.2698 \\ -.7143 & 1.190 & -.9524 \end{bmatrix}$ **19.** $\begin{bmatrix} 2 \\ -1 \\ 1 \end{bmatrix}$ **21.** (2, 3)   **23.** (−2, 4)   **25.** (1, 1, 2)

27. (0, 1, 4)   **29.** (1, 0, 2, 1)   **31.** $\begin{bmatrix} 10 \\ 4 \\ 12 \end{bmatrix}$

35. $\dfrac{1}{ad - bc} \begin{bmatrix} d & -b \\ -c & a \end{bmatrix}$

Section 9.7 (page 388)

1. −36   **3.** 7   **5.** 0   **7.** −26   **9.** −16   **11.** $y^2 - 16$ **13.** $x^2 - y^2$ **15.** 0, −5, 0
17. −10, −1, −6   **19.** −1   **21.** 8   **23.** 0   **25.** 0   **27.** $4x$ **29.** $10i + 17j - 6k$ **31.** −88
33. −5.5   **43.** 5/2   **45.** 7   **47.** 8

Section 9.8 (page 394)

1. Theorem 9.7   **3.** Theorem 9.3   **5.** By Theorem 9.6, multiply each element in the second row by −1/4. The determinant of the resulting matrix is 0, by Theorem 9.7.   **7.** Use Theorem 9.7 after multiplying each element in the third column by 1/2.   **9.** Theorem 9.4   **11.** Theorem 9.5   **13.** Theorem 9.6
15. Theorem 9.8 (first row added to second row)   **17.** Theorem 9.6   **19.** 0   **21.** 0   **23.** 5   **25.** 32   **27.** −32

Section 9.9   (page 400)

1. (2, 2)   **3.** (2, −5)   **5.** (2, 3)   **7.** (9/7, 2/7)   **9.** no solution, since $D = 0$ **11.** (−1, 2, 1)
13. (−3, 4, 2)   **15.** (0, 0, −1)   **17.** no solution, since $D = 0$ **19.** (197/91, −118/91, −23/91)
21. (2, 3, 1)   **23.** (0, 4, 2)   **25.** (31/5, 19/10, −29/10)   **27.** (1, 0, −1, 2)   **29.** (−.2, −.8)
31. (.2, .5, −.2)   **33.** 4 years   **35.** 17.5 g of 12-carat, 7.5 g of 22-carat   **37.** 52/3 lbs
39. 164 fives, 86 tens, 40 twenties

Section 9.10   (page 405)

1.
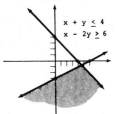

3.
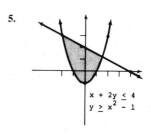

5.
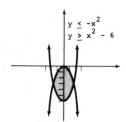

7.
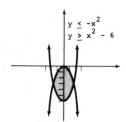

9.
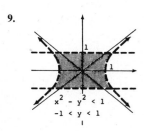

11.
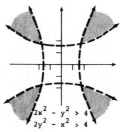

13.
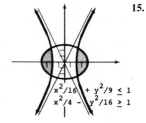

15.
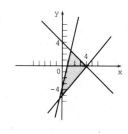

17.
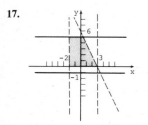

19.
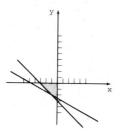

21.
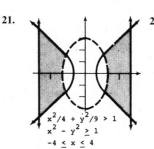

23.
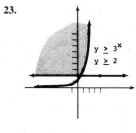

25.
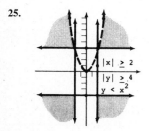

27.
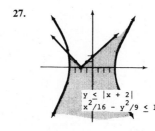

29.
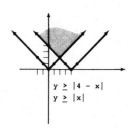

31. Let x = number of units of basic, y = number of units of plain; $x \geq 3$, $y \geq 2$, $5x + 4y \leq 50$, $2x + y \leq 16$.

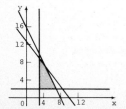

33. Let x = number of red pills, y = number of green pills; $8x + 2y \geq 16$, $x + y \geq 5$, $2x + 7y \geq 20$, $x \geq 0$, $y \geq 0$.

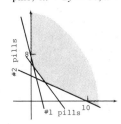

35. Let x = number shipped to warehouse A and y = number shipped to B; $0 \leq x \leq 75$, $0 \leq y \leq 80$, $x + y \geq 100$, $12x + 10y \leq 1200$.

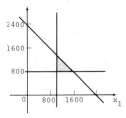

Chapter 9   Review Exercises   (page 409)

1. $(-1, 3)$ **3.** $(6, -12)$ **5.** $(2, 5)$ **7.** $(-1, 2, 3)$ **9.** 10 at 25¢, 12 at 50¢   **11.** $10,000 at 6%, $20,000 at 7%, $20,000 at 9%   **13.** $x = \frac{15}{11}z + \frac{6}{11}$; $y = \frac{14}{11}z - \frac{1}{11}$ **15.** $(3\sqrt{3}, \sqrt{2}), (-3\sqrt{3}, \sqrt{2}), (3\sqrt{3}, -\sqrt{2}), (-3\sqrt{3}, -\sqrt{2})$ **17.** $(-2, 0), (1, 1)$ **19.** $((8 - 8\sqrt{41})/5, (16 + 4\sqrt{41})/5), ((8 + 8\sqrt{41})/5, (16 - 4\sqrt{41})/5)$ **21.** $a = 5, x = 3/2, y = 0, z = 9$ **23.** $\begin{bmatrix} 0 & -2 & 7 \\ 6 & -1 & 10 \end{bmatrix}$ **25.** cannot be done   **27.** $\begin{bmatrix} -9 & 3 \\ 10 & 6 \end{bmatrix}$ **29.** $(-4, 6)$ **31.** $(0, 1, 0)$ **33.** $\begin{bmatrix} 3 & -1 \\ -5 & 2 \end{bmatrix}$ **35.** $\begin{bmatrix} 2/3 & 0 & -1/3 \\ 1/3 & 0 & -2/3 \\ -2/3 & 1 & 1/3 \end{bmatrix}$ **37.** $(2, 1)$ **39.** $(-3, 5, 1)$ **41.** -25 **43.** -44 **45.** 138 **47.** rows and columns interchanged   **49.** two identical rows   **51.** exchange columns 2 and 3   **53.** $(-4, 2)$ **55.** dependent system   **57.**

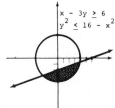

59. Let x = number of batches of cakes, let y = number of batches of cookies; $2x + \frac{3}{2}y \leq 16$; $3x + \frac{2}{3}y \leq 12$; $x \geq 0$; $y \geq 0$

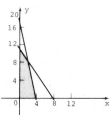

CHAPTER 10

Section 10.1   (page 412)

1. $7 - i$ **3.** $3 - 6i$ **5.** $1 - 10i$ **7.** $-10 + 5i$ **9.** $8 - i$ **11.** $31 - 5i$ **13.** $5 - 12i$ **15.** $-8 - 6i$ **17.** 13   **19.** 29   **21.** 7   **23.** $25i$ **25.** $-198 + 10i$ **27.** $161 + 240i$ **29.** $3i$ **31.** $-20i$ **33.** $\sqrt{7}i$ **35.** -5 **37.** -4 **39.** 2   **41.** -2 **43.** i **45.** 1   **47.** $-i$ **49.** 1   **51.** $-i$ **53.** $-i$ **55.** $a = 23, b = 5$ **57.** $a = 18, b = -3$ **59.** $a = -5, b = 1$ **61.** $a = -3/4, b = 3$ **71.** 25   **73.** $a = 0$ or $b = 0$

Section 10.2   (page 417)

1. $-i$ **3.** $(1/4)i$ **5.** $1/2 - (1/2)i$ **7.** $5/169 + (12/169)i$ **9.** i **11.** $7/25 - (24/25)i$

13. $13/20 - (1/20)i$ **15.** $32/37 - (7/37)i$ **17.** $5/2 + i$ **19.** $-\dfrac{16}{65} - \dfrac{37}{65}i$ **21.** $\dfrac{27}{10} + \dfrac{11}{10}i$

23. $\dfrac{17}{10} - \dfrac{11}{10}i$ **25.** $\dfrac{37}{34} + \dfrac{165}{34}i$ **27.** $\sqrt{29}$ **29.** $4\sqrt{5}$ **31.** 4   **33.** 23

35.    **37.** 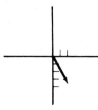   **39.**    **41.**

43. $1 + i$ **45.** $-2 + 2i$ **47.** $2 + 4i$ **49.** $7 + 9i$

59. 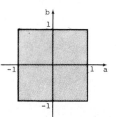   **61.** 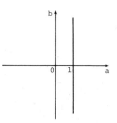   **63.**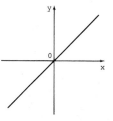

Section 10.3   (page 422)
1. $3 \pm 4i$ **3.** $(-1 \pm i\sqrt{11})/3$ **5.** $(\sqrt{2} \pm i\sqrt{2})/2$ **7.** $(3\sqrt{2} \pm i\sqrt{14})/4$ **9.** $(-i \pm i\sqrt{5})/2$
11. $-i \pm i\sqrt{2}$ or $(-1 \pm \sqrt{2})i$ **13.** $[1 - i \pm (i\sqrt{7} + \sqrt{7})]/4$ **15.** $i, -3i$ **17.** $(-3i \pm \sqrt{23})/4$
19. $1, (-1 \pm i\sqrt{3})/2$ **21.** $-4, 2 \pm 2i\sqrt{3}$ **23.** $-3, (3 \pm 3i\sqrt{3})/2$ **25.** $x^2 - 4x + 5 = 0$
27. $x^2 - 2x + 5 = 0$ **29.** $x^3 + (i - 1)x^2 + (-2 - i)x - 2i = 0$

Section 10.4   (page 424)
1. $(2\sqrt{2}, 315°)$ **3.** $(3, 90°)$ **5.** $(2, 30°)$ **7.** $(2, 60°)$ **9.** $\sqrt{2} + i\sqrt{2}$ **11.** $-\sqrt{2}/2 + i\sqrt{2}/2$
13. $3i$ **15.** $\sqrt{3}/2 - i/2$ **17.** $\sqrt{2} + i\sqrt{2}$ **19.** $10i$ **21.** $-2 - 2i\sqrt{3}$ **23.** $\sqrt{3}/2 + i/2$
25. $3\sqrt{2}(\cos 315° + i \sin 315°)$ **27.** $2(\cos 330° + i \sin 330°)$ **29.** $5\sqrt{2}(\cos 225° + i \sin 225°)$
31. $5(\cos 270° + i \sin 270°)$ **33.** $6i$ **35.** 4   **37.** $12\sqrt{3} + 12i$ **39.** $-15\sqrt{2}/2 + 15i\sqrt{2}/2$
41. $3\sqrt{3}/2 + 3i/2$ **43.** $-1 - i\sqrt{3}$ **45.** $2\sqrt{3} - 2i$ **47.** $-1/2 - i/2$

Section 10.5   (page 430)
1. -8 **3.** 1   **5.** $-16\sqrt{3} + 16i$ **7.** $-128 + 128i\sqrt{3}$ **9.** $128 + 128i$ **11.** $-.1892 + .0745i$
13. $(\cos 120° + i \sin 120°)$
$(\cos 240° + i \sin 240°)$
$(\cos 0° + i \sin 0°)$

15. $2(\cos 90° + i \sin 90°)$
$2(\cos 210° + i \sin 210°)$
$2(\cos 330° + i \sin 330°)$

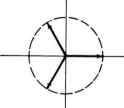   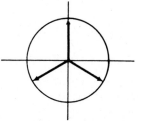

17. $4(\cos 60° + i \sin 60°)$
$4(\cos 180° + i \sin 180°)$
$4(\cos 300° + i \sin 300°)$

19. $\sqrt[3]{4}(\cos 50° + i \sin 50°)$
$\sqrt[3]{4}(\cos 170° + i \sin 170°)$
$\sqrt[3]{4}(\cos 290° + i \sin 290°)$

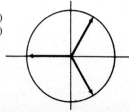   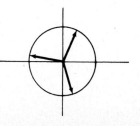

21. $1.585 + .6722i, -1.375 + 1.036i, -.2103 - 1.709i$ **23.** $4.0150, -4.0150, 4.0150i, -4.0150i$

25. $(\cos 0° + i \sin 0°)$
$(\cos 180° + i \sin 180°)$

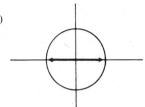

27. $(\cos 0° + i \sin 0°)$
$(\cos 60° + i \sin 60°)$
$(\cos 120° + i \sin 120°)$
$(\cos 180° + i \sin 180°)$
$(\cos 240° + i \sin 240°)$
$(\cos 300° + i \sin 300°)$

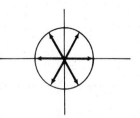

29. $(\cos 45° + i \sin 45°)$
$(\cos 225° + i \sin 225°)$

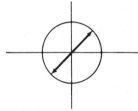

31. $(\cos 0° + i \sin 0°), (\cos 120° + i \sin 120°), (\cos 240° + i \sin 240°)$ **33.** $2(\cos 0° + i \sin 0°),$
$2(\cos 120° + i \sin 120°), 2(\cos 240° + i \sin 240°)$ **35.** $(\cos 45° + i \sin 45°), (\cos 135° + i \sin 135°),$
$(\cos 225° + i \sin 225°), (\cos 315° + i \sin 315°)$ **37.** $1.97, -.983 + 1.70i, -.983 - 1.70i$
39. $\sqrt[4]{2}(\cos 22\frac{1}{2}° + i \sin 22\frac{1}{2}°), \sqrt[4]{2}(\cos 202\frac{1}{2}° + i \sin 202\frac{1}{2}°)$
41. $\sqrt[4]{18}(\cos 157\frac{1}{2}° + i \sin 157\frac{1}{2}°); \sqrt[4]{18}(\cos 337\frac{1}{2}° + i \sin 337\frac{1}{2}°)$

Chapter 10   Review Exercises   (page 434)

1. $-2 - 3i$ **3.** $5 + 4i$ **5.** $29 + 37i$ **7.** $-32 + 24i$ **9.** $-2 - 2i$ **11.** i **13.** $\frac{8}{5} + \frac{6}{5}i$
15. $\frac{-5}{26} + \frac{1}{26}i$ **17.** $\frac{7}{2} - \frac{11}{4}i$ **19.** $2i\sqrt{3}$ **21.** $3\sqrt{5}$ **23.** 2 **25.** $a = -1, b = 7$
27. $a = 3/2, b = 5$ **29.** $1 - 6i$ **31.**

33. $\frac{2 \pm i\sqrt{2}}{2}$ **35.** $\frac{-\sqrt{3} \pm i\sqrt{5}}{4}$ **37.** $2, -1 \pm i\sqrt{3}$ **39.** $x^2 - 4x + 5 = 0$ **41.** $x^3 - 3x^2 + 16x - 48 = 0$
43. $(2\sqrt{2}, 135°), 2\sqrt{2}(\cos 135° + i \sin 135°)$ **45.** $\sqrt{2} - i\sqrt{2}, (2, 315°)$ **47.** $-30i$ **49.** $\frac{-1}{8} + \frac{i\sqrt{3}}{8}$
51. $8i$ **53.** $-\frac{1}{2} - i\frac{\sqrt{3}}{2}$ **55.** $8^{1/10} (\cos 27° + i \sin 27°), 8^{1/10} (\cos 99° + i \sin 99°), 8^{1/10} (\cos 171° + i \sin 171°),$
$8^{1/10} (\cos 243° + i \sin 243°), 8^{1/10} (\cos 315° + i \sin 315°)$ **57.** $x = -7/3, y = -24$ **59.** $x = -1, y = 0$
65. all points $(t, 0)$

CHAPTER 11

Section 11.1   (page 436)

1. $x^2 - 3x + 2$ **3.** $x^2 + 2x + 3$ **5.** $2z^3 - z^2 - (1/2)z - 5/4 + \dfrac{(-13/4)z + 17/4}{2z^2 + z + 1}$ **7.** $p^3 - 5p^2 + 5p - 8$
9. $4m^2 - 4m + 1 + [-3/(m + 1)]$ **11.** $x^4 + x^3 + 2x - 1 + 3/(x + 2)$ **13.** yes   **15.** yes   **17.** yes
19. no   **21.** yes   **23.** no   **25.** -8 **27.** 2 **29.** $-6 - i$ **31.** $-2 - 3i$ **33.** 42
35. -20 **37.** 4 **39.** $x^3 + 4x^2 - 7x - 10 = 0$ **41.** $x^3 - 3x^2 - 2x + 6 = 0$ **43.** $2x^4 - 4x^3 - 15x^2 +$
$17x + 30 = 0$ **45.** -9 **47.** -5.19 **55.** 1.51

Section 11.2   (page 443)

1. $P(x) = -\frac{1}{6}x^3 + \frac{13}{6}x + 2$ 3. $P(x) = \frac{1}{9}x^3 + \frac{7}{9}x^2 + \frac{16}{9}x + \frac{4}{3}$ 5. $P(x) = -10x^3 + 30x^2 - 10x + 30$

7. $x^2 - 10x + 26$ 9. $x^3 - 4x^2 + 6x - 4$ 11. $x^3 - 3x^2 + x + 1$ 13. $x^4 - 6x^3 + 10x^2 + 2x - 15$
15. $x^3 - 8x^2 + 22x - 20$ 17. $x^4 - 4x^3 + 5x^2 - 2x - 2$ 19. $x^4 - 10x^3 + 42x^2 - 82x + 65$
21. $-1 + i, -1 - i$ 23. $3, -2 - 2i$ 25. $(-1 + i\sqrt{5})/2, (-1 - i\sqrt{5})/2$ 27. $3, -2, 1 - 3i$
29. $2 - i, 1 + i, 1 - i$ 31. other zeros are $i, -i$; $P(x) = (x - 2)^3(x - i)(x + i)$

Section 11.3   (page 448)

1. $-1, -2, 5$ 3. $2, -3, -5$ 5. no rational solutions   7. $1, -2, -3, -5$ 9. $3/2, -1/3, -4$
11. $1/2, -2/3, -3/2$ 13. $1/2$ 15. no rational solutions   17. $-1, -2, -3, 4$ 19. $-2, 2/3$
21. 1 23. $3, -1, -2/3$ 25. $1, -5/4$ 27. 1

Section 11.4   (page 450)

17. (a) positive, 1; negative, 2 or 0; (b) $-3, -1.4, 1.4$ 19. (a) positive, 2 or 0; negative, 1; (b) $-2, 1.6, 4.4$
21. (a) positive, 1; negative, 0; (b) 1.6   23. (a) positive, 3 or 1; negative, 1; (b) $-.7, 1.6, 2.7, 4.4$
25. $3.24, -1.24$ 27. $-3.65, -.32, 1.65, 6.32$

Chapter 11   Review Exercises   (page 453)

1. $Q(x) = 2x^2 + \frac{3}{2}$; $R(x) = \frac{13}{2}$ 3. $Q(x) = x^2 - 5$; $R(x) = 5x + 9$ 5. $Q(x) = 2x^2 + 5x + 1$; $r = 2$

7. $Q(x) = 2x^2 + 4x + 4$; $r = 14$ 9. 11   11. 28   13. $P(x) = x^3 - 10x^2 + 17x + 28$
15. $P(x) = x^4 - x^3 - 9x^2 + 7x + 14$ 17. no   19. no   21. $P(x) = -2x^3 + 6x^2 + 12x - 16$
23. $P(x) = x^4 - 3x^2 - 4$ 25. $P(x) = x^3 + x^2 - 4x + 6$ 27. $3 + i, 3 - i, 2i, -2i$ 29. $1/2, -1, 5$
31. $4, -1/2, -2/3$ 33. none   43. $-2.3, 4.6$

CHAPTER 12

Section 12.1   (page 455)
1. S_1: $2 = 1(1 + 1)$
   S_2: $2 + 4 = 2(2 + 1)$
   S_3: $2 + 4 + 6 = 3(3 + 1)$
   S_4: $2 + 4 + 6 + 8 = 4(4 + 1)$
   S_5: $2 + 4 + 6 + 8 + 10 = 5(5 + 1)$
35. $3 \cdot 4^{n-1}$

Section 12.2   (page 461)

1. $x^6 + 6x^5y + 15x^4y^2 + 20x^3y^3 + 15x^2y^4 + 6xy^5 + y^6$ 3. $p^5 - 5p^4q + 10p^3q^2 - 10p^2q^3 + 5pq^4 - q^5$
5. $r^{10} + 5r^8s + 10r^6s^2 + 10r^4s^3 + 5r^2s^4 + s^5$ 7. $p^4 + 8p^3q + 24p^2q^2 + 32pq^3 + 16q^4$
9. $m^6/64 - 3m^5/16 + 15m^4/16 - 5m^3/2 + 15m^2/4 - 3m + 1$ 11. $16p^4 + 32p^3q/3 + 8p^2q^2/3 + 8pq^3/27 + q^4/81$
13. $m^{-8} + 4m^{-4} + 6 + 4m^4 + m^8$ 15. $p^{10/3} - 25p^4 + 250p^{14/3} - 1250p^{16/3} + 3125p^6 - 3125p^{20/3}$
17. $x^{21} + 126x^{20} + 7560x^{19} + 287{,}280x^{18}$ 19. $3^9m^{-18} + 45 \cdot 3^8m^{-20} + 900 \cdot 3^7m^{-22} + 10{,}500 \cdot 3^6m^{-24}$
21. $7920m^8p^4$ 23. $180m^2n^8$ 25. $4845p^8q^{16}$ 27. $439{,}296x^{21}y^7$ 29. $90{,}720x^{28}y^{12}$ 31. 1.105
33. 245.937   35. 758.650   37. 1.002; 5.010   39. .942   41. $1 - x + x^2 - x^3 + \ldots$ 47. 6

Section 12.3   (page 468)

1. $10, 16, 22, 28, 34$ 3. $1, 1/2, 1/4, 1/8, 1/16$ 5. $1, -1, 1, -1, 1$ 7. $1/2, 4/5, 1, 8/7, 5/4$
9. $4/3, 12/5, 20/7, 28/9, 36/11$ 11. $-2, 8, -24, 64, -160$ 13. $2/3, 5/6, 10/11, 17/18, 26/27$
15. x, x^2, x^3, x^4, x^5 17. $2, 3, 5, 7, 11$ 19. $1, 3, 6, 10, 15$ 21. $4, 9, 14, 19, 24, 29, 34, 39, 44, 49$
23. $-9, -5, -5, -1, -1, 3, 3, 7, 7, 11$ 25. $2, 4, 8, 16, 32, 64, 128, 256, 512, 1024$ 27. $1, -2, 3, -4, 5, -6,$
$7, -8, 9, -10$ 29. 2584   31. 35   33. 87/60   35. 139/108   37. 3   39. 25/2
41. 89   43. 31   45. .123456   47. $x + 2x^2 + 3x^3 + 4x^4 + 5x^5$ 49. $.6667, .8889, .9630, .9877,$
$.9959, .9986, .9995, .9998, .9999, 1.000$; approaching 1   51. $1.6667, 4.4444, 9.0741, 16.7901,$
$29.6502, 51.0837, 86.8061, 146.3435, 245.5726, 410.9543$; doesn't approach any number   59. 3

61. 2, 2.25, 2.3704, 2.4414, 2.4883, 2.5216, 2.5465, 2,5658, 2.5812, 2.5937, 2.6042, 2.6130; $a_{50} = 2.6916$, $a_{100} = 2.7048$, $a_{1000} = 2.7169$

Section 12.4 (page 473)

1. 4, 6, 8, 10, 12   **3.** 11, 9, 7, 5   **5.** $4 - \sqrt{5}$, 4, $4 + \sqrt{5}$, $4 + 2\sqrt{5}$, $4 + 3\sqrt{5}$ **7.** $d = 5$, $a_n = 7 + 5n$
9. $d = -3$, $a_n = 21 - 3n$ **11.** $d = \sqrt{2}$, $a_n = -6 + n\sqrt{2}$ **13.** $d = m$, $a_n = x + nm - m$
15. $d = -m$, $a_n = 2z + 2m - mn$ **17.** $a_8 = 19$, $a_n = 3 + 2n$ **19.** $a_8 = 7$, $a_n = n - 1$
21. $a_8 = -6$, $a_n = 10 - 2n$ **23.** $a_8 = -9$, $a_n = 15 - 3n$ **25.** $a_8 = 5.1$, $a_n = 2.7 + .3n$ **27.** $a_8 = x + 21$,
$a_n = x + 3n - 3$ **29.** $a_8 = 4m$, $a_n = mn - 4m$ **31.** 215   **33.** 125   **35.** 230   **37.** 16.745
39. 32.28   **41.** 18   **43.** 140   **45.** −684   **47.** 500,500   **49.** 400   **51.** −78   **53.** $a_1 = 7$

55. $a_1 = 0$ **57.** $a_1 = 7$ **59.** 1281   **61.** $\dfrac{n(n + 1)}{2}$ **63.** 4680   **65.** 100 m, 550 m   **67.** 240 ft,

1024 ft   **69.** 9, 14, 19, 24   **71.** 170 m   **73.** All terms are 0 or all terms are 1.

Section 12.5 (page 480)

1. 2, 6, 18, 54   **3.** 1/2, 2, 8, 32   **5.** −2, 6, −18, 54   **7.** 3/2, 3, 6, 12, 24   **9.** $a_5 = 324$, $a_n = 4 \cdot 3^{n-1}$
11. $a_5 = -1875$, $a_n = -3(-5)^{n-1}$ **13.** $a_5 = 24$, $a_n = (3/2)2^{n-1}$ **15.** $a_5 = -256$, $a_n = -1 \cdot (-4)^{n-1}$
17. $r = 2$, $a_n = 6 \cdot 2^{n-1}$ **19.** $r = 2$, $a_n = (3/4)2^{n-1}$ **21.** Not geometric   **23.** $a_n = (9/4)2^{n-1}$
25. $a_n = (-2/9)3^{n-1}$ **27.** 93   **29.** 33/4   **31.** 860.95   **33.** −6.27   **35.** 30   **37.** 255/4
39. 406/625   **41.** 585/8   **43.** 120   **45.** 272/25   **47.** $\$2^{30}$ or \$1,073,741,824; $\$2^{31} - 1$

or \$2,147,483,647   **49.** .00002%   **51.** $80\left(\dfrac{4}{5}\right)^8 \%$ **53.** \$26,214.40   **55.** $.016 \times 2^{11}$ inches, or about

33 inches   **57.** any sequence of the form a, a, a **59.** $a_1 = 2$ or -2, $r = 3$ or -3 **61.** $a_1 = 128$ or -128,
$r = 1/2$ or $-1/2$

Section 12.6 (page 485)

1. $r = 2$ **3.** $r = 10$ **5.** $r = 1/2$, sum would exist   **7.** $r = 1.1$ **9.** $r = -.9$, sum would exist
11. 64/3   **13.** 1000/9   **15.** 135   **17.** 512/3   **19.** 3/2   **21.** 1/5   **23.** can't be found
25. 1/3   **27.** can't be found   **29.** −1/5   **31.** 1/4   **33.** 1/9   **35.** 5/9   **37.** 4/33
39. 31/99   **41.** 508/999   **43.** 311/900   **45.** 70 m   **47.** 1600   **49.** 12 m

Section 12.7 (page 489)

1. 5040   **3.** 720   **5.** 90   **7.** 336   **9.** 7   **11.** 1   **13.** 6   **15.** 56   **17.** 1365
19. 120   **21.** 14   **23.** 1   **25.** 720   **27.** 120, 30,240   **29.** 30   **31.** 120   **33.** 4
35. 552   **37.** 27,405   **39.** 220,220   **41.** 1326   **43.** 10   **45.** 28   **47.** (a) 84; (b) 10;

(c) 40; (d) 28   **49.** $\binom{52}{5} = 2{,}598{,}960$ **51.** 4   **53.** $4 \cdot \binom{13}{5} = 5148$ **55.** $P(5, 5) = 120$

57. $\binom{12}{3} = 220$ **59.** 8   **61.** 4

Section 12.8 (page 496)

1. $S = \{H\}$ **3.** $S = \{HHH, HHT, HTH, THH, HTT, THT, TTH, TTT\}$ **5.** Let c = correct,
w = wrong $S = \{ccc, ccw, cwc, wcc, wwc, wcw, cww, www\}$ **7.** (a) $\{HH,TT\}$, 1/2; (b) $\{HH, HT, TH\}$, 3/4
9. (a) {2 and 4}, 1/10; (b) {1 and 3, 1 and 5, 3 and 5}, 3/10; (c) $\varnothing$, 0; (d) {1 and 2, 1 and 4, 2 and 3, 2 and 5, 3
and 4, 4 and 5}, 3/5   **11.** (a) 1/5; (b) 8/15; (c) 0; (d) 1 to 4; (e) 7 to 8   **13.** 1 to 4   **15.** 2/5
17. (a) 1/2; (b) 7/10; (c) 2/5   **19.** (a) 1/6; (b) 1/3; (c) 1/6   **21.** (a) 7/15; (b) 11/15; (c) 4/15

Chapter 12   Review Exercises   (page 501)

7. $x^4 + 8x^3y + 24x^2y^2 + 32xy^3 + 16y^4$ **9.** $243x^{5/2} - 405x^{3/2} + 270x^{1/2} - 90x^{-1/2} + 15x^{-3/2} - x^{-5/2}$
11. $2160x^2y^4$ **13.** $3^{16} + 16 \cdot 3^{15}x + 120 \cdot 3^{13}x^2 + 560 \cdot 3^{12}x^3$ **15.** 8, 10, 12, 14, 16   **17.** 5, 3, −2, −5, −3
19. 6, 2, −2, −6, −10   **21.** $3 - \sqrt{5}$, 4, $5 + \sqrt{5}$, $6 + 2\sqrt{5}$, $7 + 3\sqrt{5}$ **23.** 4, 8, 16, 32, 64
25. −3, 4, −16/3, 64/9, −256/27   **27.** $a_1 = -29$, $a_{20} = 66$ **29.** 20   **31.** $-x + 61$ **33.** 222
35. $84k$ **37.** 25   **39.** $x^5/125$ **41.** 15   **43.** $-10k$ **45.** 80   **47.** can't be found
49. 2/3   **51.** 512/999   **53.** 25/6   **55.** 690   **57.** 73/12   **59.** 50,005,000   **61.** 240
63. $r > 1$, so sum does not exist   **65.** 72   **67.** 1   **69.** 252   **71.** 504   **73.** 1/26   **75.** 4/13
77. 4/13

Appendix A (page 505)
1. maximum of 65 at (5, 10); minimum of 8 at (1, 1)   **3.** maximum of 900 at (0, 12); minimum of 0 at (0, 0)
5. ($^6/_5$, $^6/_5$)   **7.** ($^{17}/_3$, 5)   **9.** ($^{105}/_8$, $^{25}/_8$)   **11.** (a) maximum of 204 at (18, 2); (b) 117$^3/_5$ at ($^{12}/_5$, $^{39}/_5$);
(c) 102 at (0, $^{17}/_2$)   **13.** $112, with 4 pigs, 12 geese   **15.** 8 of #1, 3 of #2

Appendix B   (page 509)
1. $-1/x + 4/(x + 1)$ **3.** $5/3x - 10/3(2x + 1)$ **5.** $7/x - 63/4(3x - 1) - 7/4(x + 1)$
7. $1/(2x) + 1/x^2 - 1/[2(x - 2)]$ **9.** $-2/(x + 1) + 2/(x + 2) + 4/(x + 2)^2$ **11.** $5/3x - 5x/3(x^2 + 3)$
13. $-1/3(x + 1) + (x + 5)/3(x^2 + 2)$ **15.** $3/x - 3/2(x + 1) - 3(x + 1)/2(x^2 + 1)$ **17.** $1/x - 2x/(x^2 + 1)^2$
19. $2/(x - 1) + 1/(3x^2 - 1)^2$ **21.** $-13/[15(x - 1)] + 46/[15(x + 2)]$

Index

What do you think of *Algebra and Trigonometry,* Second Edition?

We would appreciate it if you would take a few minutes to answer these questions. Then cut the page out, fold it, seal it, and mail it. No postage is required.

Which chapters did you cover?
(circle)   1   2   3   4   5   6   7   8   9   10   11   12   All _____

Which helped most?
Explanations _____   Examples _____   Exercises _____   All three _____

Does the book have enough worked-out examples? Yes _____   No _____

Does the book have enough exercises? Yes _____   No _____

Were the answers in the back of the book helpful? Yes _____   No _____

How was your course taught? Regular class _____   Self-paced _____

For you, was the course elective _____   required by _____

Do you plan to take more mathematics courses? Yes _____   No _____

If yes, which ones?
Finite mathematics _____   Statistics _____
Analytic geometry _____
Calculus (for engineering and physics) _____
Calculus (for business and social science) _____
Other _____

How much algebra did you have before this course?
Years in high school   (circle   0   ½   1   1½   2   more
Courses in college   0   1   2   3

If you had algebra before, how long ago?
Last 2 years _____   3–5 years _____   5 years or more _____

Have you had trigonometry before? Yes _____   No _____

If yes, was it in high school or college? _____

What is your major or your career goal? _____   Your age? _____

We would appreciate knowing of any errors you found in the book.

What did you like most about the book?

What did you like least about the book?

College _____ State _____

BUSINESS REPLY MAIL

FIRST CLASS   PERMIT NO. 31   GLENVIEW, IL

Postage will be paid by

SCOTT, FORESMAN AND COMPANY

College Division   Attn: Lial/Miller

1900 East Lake Avenue   LM-1

Glenview, Illinois   60025